VERTEBRATES: THEIR STRUCTURE AND LIFE

VERTEBRATES

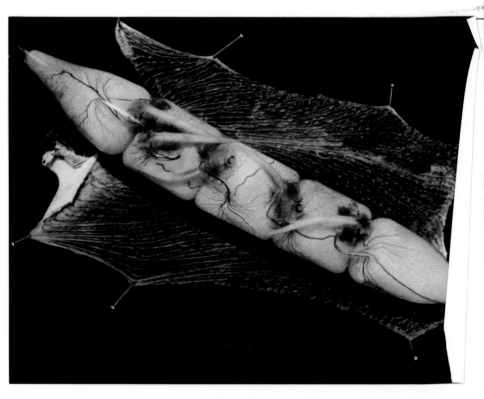

Embryos of a viviparous dogfish in the oviduct of the mother.

Their Structure and Life

W. B. YAPP

DEPARTMENT OF ZOOLOGY AND COMPARATIVE PHYSIOLOGY

UNIVERSITY OF BIRMINGHAM, ENGLAND

Illustrated by KATHLEEN M. LYONS

NEW YORK

OXFORD UNIVERSITY PRESS \ 1965

PRINTED IN THE UNITED STATES OF AMERICA

Preface

THERE ARE MANY good books on vertebrate zoology, but in teaching the subject on both sides of the Atlantic I have been unable to find one that is really suitable for my courses of some twenty to sixty lectures. So, like many before me, I have written my own.

There has been much discussion recently of the content of biology courses, and some enthusiasts would have all the traditional zoology and botany relegated to a very minor role, and its place taken by the study of genes, proteins, and phosphatic nucleotides. The trouble with this sort of approach is that, interesting though the new knowledge about the synthesis of proteins is, it cannot yet be related to such problems as the interaction between predator and prey, the conquest of the land, or the extinction of the dinosaurs. The time may come when it will explain all these things (just as atomic physics is now beginning to explain the 'properties of matter' of classical teaching), but meanwhile it remains something apart, and is in many ways closer to the chemistry in which its exponents have often been trained than to the study of living animals and plants with which biologists are chiefly concerned.

From an educational point of view what is more important than the content of a course is the way in which it is taught. Only too often zoology has been taught as a string of facts explained by dogmatic concepts, such as recapitulation and the germ layer theory, which would not stand, and were seldom given, close scrutiny, and this approach can be seen also in some of the recent syllabuses based on the new knowledge. But the mark of a good scientist (and indeed of a good citizen) is that he does not believe anything if he can help it; as Professor H. J. Muller said in a recent seminar on the Reform of Biology Teaching arranged by the Organization for Economic Co-operation and Development, we must teach in such a way as to rouse the student to think, to criticise, to inquire for himself.' This is what I have tried to do in this book. It is not a textbook of histology, of embryology, of physiology, of ecology, or of ethology, but it contains more of all these than is common in books on the vertebrates. I have tried to display the pageant of vertebrate life in terms of structure, and to explain the structure by the use to which it is put in life, making assumption of no principles except that of natural selection, which, given the facts of variation, heredity, and death, is a logical necessity.

v

Any honest author of a textbook must realize, as he writes it, how little he knows. When I wrote my first I thought that this could be remedied by an assiduous reading of original papers; I now know that even in my own special field I cannot read everything that is published, or even everything that is important. I have often relied on the best secondary sources available to me, and no doubt I have made mistakes and copied other people's errors, but in everything controversial I have tried to read enough of the original work to be able to assess the strength of the arguments. As a result I have sometimes questioned current interpretations. I have, moreover, tried to give the evidence for the orthodox view as fairly as possible, and while making clear where I think the truth most probably lies, to leave the reader to make his own decision.

My debt to my predecessors is obvious, and, like everyone else, I have repeatedly gone to Goodrich's *Studies on the Structure and Development of Vertebrates* for instruction. I have received advice and information on particular points from many people, and to name all those to whom I am indebted would be to make an almost complete list of my zoological friends. I hope they will accept this blanket expression of my gratitude. I must, however, thank especially my colleague Dr. Jack Cohen, who read the whole typescript, who taught me much embryology, and who stood up with equanimity to a continual barrage of questions. My colleagues Messrs. Desmond Costa and John Wilkes gave me the benefit of their knowledge of Latin and Greek in reading the glossary.

All the illustrations have been prepared especially for this book, the majority having been drawn by Miss Kathleen M. Lyons. Where they are adaptations of previously published figures acknowledgment is given in the captions. Most of them are original, having been drawn by Miss Lyons either direct from specimens or from my sketches. Many of the drawings of fossils differ from those usually published in that they show the bones as they are, and not restored to a more or less hypothetical perfection. While this has some disadvantages, it allows the student to see the sort of evidence, often very fragmentary, on which the evolutionary story is based. I am grateful to the museum curators, both in the United States and in England, who have allowed me to study specimens. The drawings are as correct as Miss Lyons and I have been able to make them, but they must not be taken to have the detailed accuracy of a photograph. All magnifications are approximate. Some of the dissections were made for me by Miss Barbara M. Clarke.

Church End   W.B.Y.
June 1965

Contents

Color plates between pages 214 and 215.

VERTEBRATES: THEIR STRUCTURE AND LIFE

1

Chordates

ALL ANIMALS, with very few exceptions, start life from a structure known as an egg, or more strictly a fertilized egg, which is itself the product of the fusion of an unfertilized egg or female gamete produced by the female parent, and a very much smaller sperm or male gamete produced by the male parent. Even in those animals such as the tunicates (p. 20), where a new individual grows as a bud from the old, one has to go back only a few generations to come to an egg. A few animals, such as worker bees, are derived from unfertilized eggs, but such parthenogenesis occurs in vertebrates only under rare experimental conditions. An egg, whether fertilized or not, has the general structure which biologists have long associated with the word 'cell': some sort of membrane enclosing a mass of protoplasm, in the middle of which is a specialized part, the nucleus.

By contrast, the adult animal consists of many millions of cells, of several different sorts, arranged in characteristic ways to form the organs of the body, the whole having a shape by which the species can usually be recognized. There must therefore be a process of development or ontogeny by which the single egg becomes the complex individual. Study of this process (the science of embryology) shows that it has three parts: cell division; cell movements; and specialization of cells; and it is indeed inconceivable that development should go on without any one of these. The early divisions are often synchronous, so that a mass of cells is formed equal in number to the powers of two (2, 4, 8, 16 . . .), but from about the 128- or 256-cell stage some of the cells lag behind the others in division so that regularity is lost. In some chordates the cells early pull apart from one another, perhaps because of their surface tension, and form a hollow ball or blastula (Fig. 1.1A), the cavity of which is the blastocele (Fig. 1.1B). In a few, such as the mammals, the cells stick together to form a solid mass or morula.

After the blastula (or morula) has been formed, changes in shape and structure begin, leading to the filling up of the blastocele and the first signs of an animal which obviously has the head and tail ends, and the right and left sides, of the adult. The cells slide past each other in various directions, carrying out what are called morphogenetic movements, which are much more complicated than the simple pushing of one side of a hollow

3

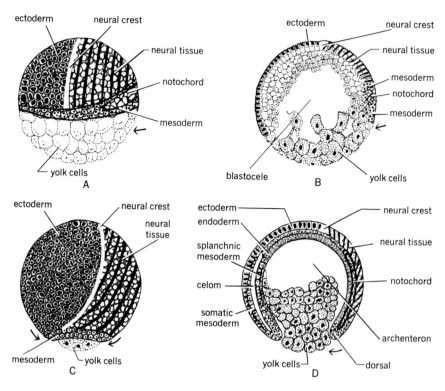

FIG. 1.1   (A) Blastula of a frog, lateral. The presumptive areas are shown. (B) Sagittal section of the blastula shown in A. (C) Gastrula of a frog, lateral. The presumptive areas are shown. (D) Sagittal section of the gastrula shown in C. Arrows show the direction of movement of the cells, x 10.

sphere into the other, described in the older books. The complexity of pattern of their movements was not appreciated until Vogt in 1928 applied spots of stain to developing blastulae and watched them change in form and position. These movements are gastrulation, and the embryo they produce is a gastrula. (Fig. 1.1C). The blastocele has virtually disappeared, but there is a new cavity, the enteron or archenteron (Fig. 1.1D).

It is customary to describe the gastrula as having 'layers' of cells, an outer or epiblast in contact with the external world, an inner or hypoblast making the wall of the archenteron, and a third or mesoblast between them, but these distinctions are theoretical rather than practical. There is necessarily an outer layer, and the archenteron necessarily has a wall, but everything between them is not mesoblast, since the epiblast and hypoblast may be more than one cell thick. Sometimes, as in most Amphibia, a distinction can be made on the way in which the layers originate; the epiblast is part of the surface of the blastula which is always in contact with the outside world, while the hypoblast moves in from the surface and as it goes forms a bag, the hollow of which is the archenteron, which is at first open to the surroundings by a wide blastopore. The mesoblast consists of those cells which move independently between the epiblast and hypoblast. In other animals the distinction is not so clear. In *Branchiostoma* (p. 16), for example, what is called mesoblast arises from the hypoblast after the gastrula is formed, so that its homology (p. 13) with the mesoblast of vertebrates is doubtful. In eggs with much yolk, such as those of birds, the early cell division gives rise to a plate of cells, and this becomes several cells thick, partly by further division and partly by inward movement along a line, the primitive streak (Fig. 1.2). In all chordates the nervous tissue, although usually called epiblast, early becomes so distinct

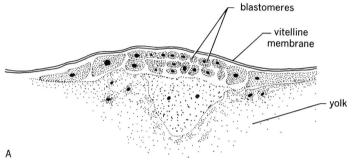

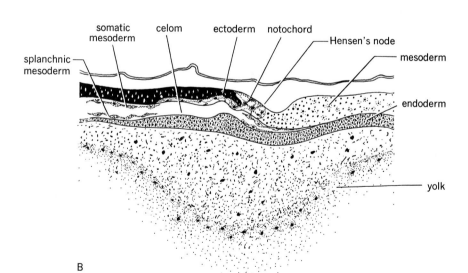

FIG. 1.2 (A) Semi-diagrammatic sagittal section through an early blastoderm of a chick, x 12. (B) A later stage, x 12. The posterior part of the ectoderm shown in the section (near the guide line) will later roll up to form the neural tube.

that it is best regarded as something of its own. It is formed as a neural tube by the sinking in and rolling up, in one way or another, of a plate of cells running the length of the body on the dorsal surface. The sides of this plate, which do not form part of the neural tube, are called the neural crest, whose cells later give rise to many important parts of the body. Tissues derived from epiblast are called ectoderm, those from mesoblast are mesoderm, and those from hypoblast, endoderm.

Specialization may begin very early—in tunicates (p. 20) it is present even within the egg, so that the first division produces two cells that are unlike—but it always becomes more marked as development proceeds.

Segmentation and Symmetry

The animals with which we are concerned in this book are vertebrates, but they are usually placed in the wider classificatory group or phylum Chordata, which contains some animals which are not vertebrates.

The chordates are metazoan, because like most other animals they are made of many cells, and triploblastic because, with the qualifications already mentioned, they have three layers of cells. They are also celomate, because soon after the gastrula is formed a hollow or celom appears in the mesoblast. These features they share with the majority of invertebrates. They further resemble some of these, especially the annelids and arthropods, in being segmented. This means that there is some repetition of parts down the body, but while in the invertebrates segmentation, if it is present, is nearly complete, applying to almost everything except the gut, in chordates it is very limited. It is expressed chiefly in the mesoblast and structures derived from this—the muscles, skeleton, blood vessels, and kidneys. It is found also in the nerves, though not in the central nervous system, and perhaps for this reason it is usual to say that the segmentation of the nerves is secondary. There seems no justification for this distinction, since segmentation means nothing more than repetition of parts, which is shown by the nerves from their first appearance, which is more than can be said for the mesoblast of most vertebrates. Chordate segmentation is never well marked in the head; in the vertebrates it is best shown in the muscles of fish (Fig. 1.3).

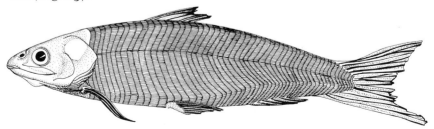

FIG. 1.3 A skinned bony fish, the char (*Salvelinus alpinus*), to show the muscle segments, x 1/2.

FIG. 1.4 'Leisure' by Heywood Hardie (1843–1933), in the possession of the author, which shows the relationships between the surface of the body. (The dog is facing the wrong way!)

Another characteristic that chordates share with most invertebrates is bilateral symmetry. This means that there are anterior and posterior (or cephalic and caudal) ends, right and left sides, and ventral and dorsal surfaces, the lines joining the opposite ends of a pair being axes. While 'anterior' may be distinguished from 'posterior' as that which is in front when the animal moves normally, and 'ventral' from 'dorsal' as that which is usually nearer the ground, there seems to be no way of distinguishing 'right' from 'left' except by reference to an example, unless one says that it is that side which, in North America or Europe, is toward the sunset when the animal is facing the sun at mid-day. Unfortunately many animals cheat by adopting attitudes other than the normal: the little fish *Hippocampus* (Fig. 4.33) stands on its tail, while a flatfish lies on its side (Fig. 4.32). Man himself moves with his ventral surface forward and his anterior end in the air. In these cases the word 'normally' in the definition must be taken to apply to the whole phylum and not to the exceptional particular species. Human anatomists have a vocabulary of their own, which the student is advised to learn to recognize but never to use. Since 'ventral' comes from the Latin word *venter*, meaning the belly or abdomen, and 'dorsal' from the Latin *dorsum*, meaning the back, they are clearly and indeed primarily applicable to man, but anatomists cause needless confusion by using instead the words anterior and posterior. Less confusing, though equally unnecessary, are the terms superior and inferior for the zoologist's anterior and posterior. The relationships between these axes are shown in Fig. 1.4.

Much can be learned of the structure of animals by cutting them across and examining the surface so exposed. Usually two cuts are made so close together that the resulting slice or section is thin enough to be transparent, so that it can be looked at under the microscope by transmitted light. Ideally, a section should be one cell thick, and should be the same from whichever side it is seen. If this is not so, the slice is known as a thick section.

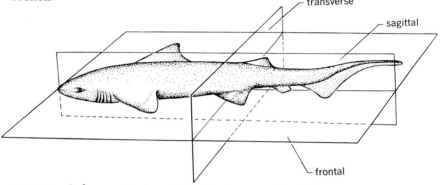

FIG. 1.5   A diagram to show the chief planes in which the animal body can be sectioned.

The axes of symmetry determine the kinds of sections that can be cut (Fig. 1.5). A transverse section is at right angles to the anterior-posterior axis. Since bilateral symmetry is seldom perfect there are often differences between right and left sides, and all transverse sections illustrated in this book, unless noted otherwise, are drawn from the anterior surface, so that the right side of the animal is on the reader's left. A longitudinal section is cut parallel to the anterior-posterior axis. If it is also parallel to the dorsal-ventral axis it is vertical. The commonest sort of vertical longitudinal section goes through the anterior-posterior axis and is unique; it is called median or sagittal. It is sometimes useful to have sections cut a little to one side of the anteroposterior axis. These may be described as lateral, though the term is seldom used. A longitudinal section taken parallel to the ventral surface is called frontal. All the longitudinal sections in this book have their anterior ends to the left.

Where a structure such as a limb sticks out from the body it is spoken of as having its own axis, and its longitudinal axis runs from the base, or proximal end, to the tip, or distal end. Transverse sections cut across this.

Diagnostic Features

All the above-mentioned features are shared by several groups of animals, but the chordates are marked out from the rest of the animal kingdom by the possession of five distinctive characteristics, or at least of some of these. A feature that is possessed by all members of a group, and by none which are not members of the group, is called diagnostic. Since there are a few chordates which do not possess all these features, none is strictly diagnostic, but they are nearly so. They are:

1. a notochord
2. a hollow dorsal central nervous system
3. gill slits
4. a tail
5. blood which circulates forward in the main ventral vessel, backward in the dorsal

The notochord, from which the phylum gets its name, is usually described as a skeletal structure, but as it is well developed only in small animals its supporting functions must be small. It is best seen in a transverse section of a tadpole (Fig. 1.6) or of *Branchiostoma* (Fig. 1.7) or in a sagittal section of the latter (Fig. 1.8). It consists of large vacuolated cells containing a fluid under pressure, so that it possesses considerable rigidity and elasticity, just as does the stem of a herbaceous plant. In *Branchiostoma* it is formed by the pinching off of a band of cells in the

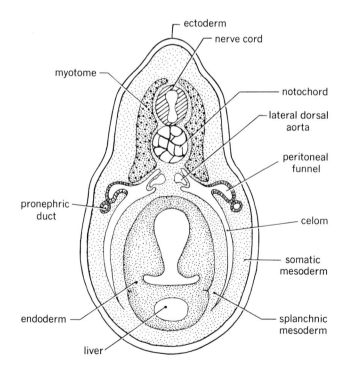

FIG. 1.6   A diagram of a transverse section of a tadpole at hatching, x 30.

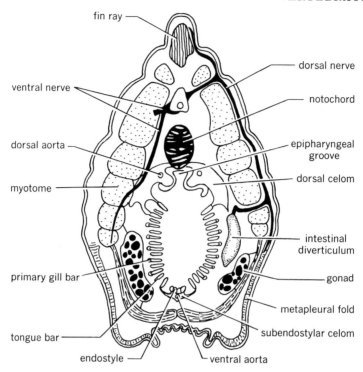

FIG. 1.7 *Branchiostoma*. A transverse section through the region of the pharynx, x 20.

roof of the archenteron, and so is formed from hypoblast. In the Amphibia
it is formed directly, at the same time as the mesoblast, by the morphogenetic movements of gastrulation, so that the mass of cells which are
moving together is called chordamesoderm, those in the middle line forming the notochord and those to each side forming mesoblast. The notochord disappears, partially or completely, in most adult chordates.

All Metazoa, that is, all animals except the sponges and Protozoa, possess cells that are specialized for conducting impulses, that is, a nervous
system; and all except the coelenterates have some of these cells concentrated into tracts which are in effect junction-boxes, where an impulse
originating in one nerve cell can be relayed to several others. Such a tract
is called a central nervous system, and usually consists of a series of knots
or ganglia connected by cords, the whole being more or less in the ventral
part of the animal. The central nervous system of chordates is quite different, being formed as a tube, as described on p. 6. At the same time the
cells of the epiblast to each side of the neural plate have moved across to
meet each other, and the arrangement shown in section in Figs. 1.6 and
1.7 is formed. By later growth the hollow is very much reduced, but it is
always visible.

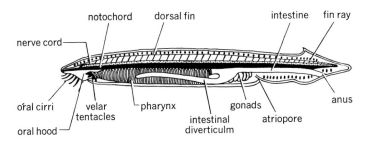

notochord dorsal fin intestine fin ray

nerve cord

oral cirri velar tentacles pharynx gonads atriopore anus

oral hood intestinal diverticulm

FIG. 1.8 *Branchiostoma*. A dissection, semi-diagrammatic; the notochord, and parts dorsal to it, are shown in sagittal section; x 2.

Gill slits, which are known also as branchial or pharyngeal slits or clefts, have no counterpart in other animals. They are simply paired openings from the anterior part of the gut, or pharynx, arranged segmentally. They are absent from the adults of all terrestrial chordates, but where they remain and are functional a current of water, taken in at the mouth, passes continuously or intermittently out through them. Though they often have gills on their walls—hence their name—they were probably in origin concerned with feeding rather than breathing. An external view of them in a fish is shown in Fig. 1.9. *Branchiostoma* has more than 100 gill slits, and as they are tall and narrow, and are not placed vertically but slope backward from top to bottom, a transverse section shows many of them cut at different levels (Fig. 1.7). In land vertebrates the gill slits have only a brief existence in the embryo and may never pierce the wall of the pharynx (Fig. 1.10).

A tail is such a simple and common thing that students are sometimes surprised when it is spoken of as a characteristic feature of the chordates. But in all other bilaterally symmetrical Metazoa the anus, at least in the embryo, is at the extreme posterior end of the body; and where this is not so in the adult, as in snails, its forward position is seen to be the result of a bending of the body during development. In chordates the anus, at its first appearance, is some distance from the posterior end, and in almost all of them, men and frogs being notable exceptions, an extension of the body behind the anus persists throughout life.

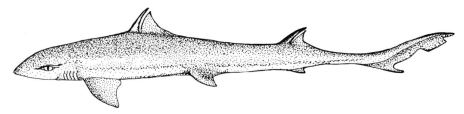

FIG. 1.9 The spiny dogfish, *Squalus acanthias*, x 1/10.

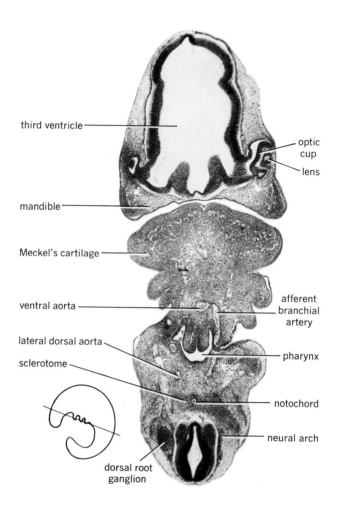

third ventricle

optic
cup

lens

mandible

Meckel's cartilage

ventral aorta

afferent
branchial
artery

lateral dorsal aorta

sclerotome

pharynx

notochord

neural arch

dorsal root
ganglion

FIG. 1.10   A transverse section of a 7mm. human embryo in the fifth week to
show the gill clefts, x 24. Owing to the curvature of the head the central nervous system is cut twice. The inset shows the approximate line of section.

Not all non-chordates have a blood vascular system, but in those that
do the blood never flows forward in the main ventral vessel, nor is this
vessel ever the pumping organ. Instead the blood flows forward in the
dorsal vessel, and is pumped either by this, as in insects, or by lateral connectives, as in annelids. In chordates the ventral vessel drives the blood
forward and is usually developed at one point into the heart.

Some of the features in which a chordate contrasts with a non-chordate,
such as an annelid, are shown diagrammatically in Plates I.1 and I.2.

Homology

The plan on which this book is based assumes that one can fruitfully consider structures in different animals as being in some sense the same thing. Just as an elegant piece of eighteenth-century mahogany, a crude structure nailed together from old broken boxes, and a modern aluminum piece for the patio are all included in the word 'table,' so the structures which pump the blood round the body are all called hearts. But the zoologist makes a distinction between structures that do the same job, and those that he considers to be the same thing whether or not they have the same function. All hearts pump blood, but the heart of a crab and the heart of a vertebrate are very different in make-up; they are said to be analogous but not homologous. The wing of a bird and the wing of a bat are very different in detail (Figs. 6.6 and 17.18) but their basic plan is the same, so they are both analogous and homologous; an insect's wing is merely analogous to them, since its structure is quite different. The bird's wing or bat's wing has a skeleton of the same general pattern as that of the limbs of frogs or mammals, and more doubtfully as that of the paired fins of fish, so that these also are homologous with it.

Theoretically, structures are homologous if one evolved from the other or if they had a common ancestor, but in fact we can never know the course of evolution for certain except in very short runs where the fossil evidence is exceptionally good, so that our judgment of the course of evolution is based mostly on similarities in structure. Hence it is better to say that two structures are homologous if they are so similar in structure that it is reasonable to believe that one has evolved from the other or that they have both evolved from a common ancestral pattern. Two glosses must be added to this; fossils may enable us to see similarity between apparently unlike structures by demonstrating how they may have diverged from each other by small steps; and in a similar way embryos, which can be seen to change in form as they develop, may show that apparently dissimilar structures develop in the individuals possessing them from structures that are alike. We shall continually refer in this book to the results of paleontological and embryological studies.

There is sometimes difficulty in naming structures. The common English words for the parts of the human body and the obvious features of the vertebrates with which primitive man was familiar, such as head, heart, kidneys, wings, gills, were applied to structures in other animals that had a similar appearance, or were thought to have the same function, long before the theory of organic evolution and the concept of homology were formulated, and most of these applications are so well established that they cannot be disturbed. Further, it is convenient to have a single word for all structures that carry out a single obvious function; if 'wing,' for example, were not used for the things by means of which insects (and air-

craft) fly, one would have to invent another word, and no one is likely to
be misled into thinking that there is any homology. The case is different
with names which are the inventions of zoologists and with structures
whose functions are complex and doubtful. 'Nephridium,' though it is simply a Latin word for a little kidney, was invented for a particular type of
small structure found in worms, which was believed, without any experimental evidence, to have the same function as the kidney of man. It is now
used for all structures of a particular type and origin (p. 34), irrespective
of whether their functions are excretory, of some other sort, or quite unknown, but it should not be used for an excretory organ of a different type.
The word 'liver' was transferred to certain offshoots of the gut in invertebrates, such as molluscs, which were assumed to have the same functions
as the vertebrate liver. This turned out not to be so, and it is now best to
give these invertebrate organs other names. The rule then is that the same
name should be used for a series of structures in different animals only if
they have the same parts (i.e. are homologous) or have the same function
(i.e. are analogous). Where neither of these is true, or where there is any
doubt, different words should be used.

The determination of analogy—similarity of function—is a matter for observation and experiment, but decisions about homology and ancestry
must be a matter of speculation. Similarly, decisions on the functions of
the organs of extinct animals must also be largely speculative. But biological speculation must be reasonable. Intermediate stages that may be
postulated to link up two not very similar structures, so as to make them
homologous, must be such as might conceivably have existed; where a
changing function is part of the picture, as in the transformation of the
fish's fin into the amphibian limb (p. 399), there must be an intermediate
stage capable of carrying out both functions; one need not expect that the
intermediate structure will carry out either the old or the new function as
efficiently as they are carried out by the old and the new organs respectively.
This restriction is sometimes forgotten, and many of the phylogenetic specu-
lations of the past have been more enthusiastic than wise. We shall try, in
the following chapters, to give a reasonable account of the evolution of the
vertebrate body, but no one can ever be sure that it is true.

Where animals are generally similar in structure in all or most of their
parts there is seldom much doubt about homology, but difficulties occur
when what appears superficially to be the same organ arises in ontogeny
in more than one way. Thus what is called the liver is always in much the
same position in all vertebrates, and it always has a duct (or there may be
two or three) which opens into the gut about the level of the heart. Its
function, that of carrying out many complex chemical processes of intermediate metabolism, is much the same in all animals that have been thoroughly investigated. It begins, however, in two distinct ways. In most
vertebrates it is formed from hypoblast cells and is 'solid' from the start,

and in many animals mesoblast cells also contribute to it; a hollow is later formed in it and grows out to open into the gut as the bile duct. (In the Amphibia it is possibly formed from the yolky cells that have never formed part of the wall of the gut). In other animals, such as birds, two out-pushings develop from the wall of the gut; one, as it expands and branches, loses most of its hollow so that its walls come to form the solid tissue of the liver. The other expands into the hollow gall bladder, in which the bile formed by the liver is stored. The two outpushings join each other, so that the bile duct may be formed from either or both.

If structures with such diverse origins occurred in totally different ani-mals they would certainly not be regarded as homologous, but since it is easier to suppose that the mode of origin has changed than that one organ has disappeared and another taken its place, most zoologists would regard the livers of all vertebrates as homologous. Since we cannot imagine a vertebrate existing without a liver we should have to suppose, if there are two analogous structures called by the same name, that while one was degenerating the other was developing alongside it. This is not impossible, but there is no evidence for it.

Another difficulty sometimes arises with what is known as serial homol-ogy; this is the repetition of parts down the length of the body. No one doubts that in this sense all the spinal nerves or all the vertebrae are homologous with one another, for they repeat each other's parts almost exactly. Structures made of more than one segment, such as the fore- and hind-limbs, are more difficult. The skeleton of one is much the same as that of the other, but the nerves may be very different. Thus the fore-limb of the frog has a brachial plexus formed from only three spinal nerves, while the hind-limb has four, suggesting that they are formed from differ-ent numbers of segments, and the numbers of nerves going to the limbs in other animals are quite different and usually much larger (p. 260). It is simplest to assume that such organs are all homologous, but that it does not matter how many segments take part in their formation. In other cases, such as the nerves of the head (p. 262), the assignment to particular seg-ments is important in the argument of what may be called their hypoho-mology. This happens because, so far as can be seen, a particular segment, say the third, usually produces parts which are recognizably similar.

Protochordates

We have already referred to creatures which are not vertebrates but yet, in a humble way, seem to be related to them by possession of some or all of the fundamental characters discussed on p. 9. There are three groups or subphyla of these, not very much like each other, and we will now describe some examples.

Branchiostoma lanceolatum, also called *Amphioxus lanceolatus* and in English the amphioxus or lancelet, is common in shallow seas of the North Atlantic. Other species, and the related genus *Asymmetron,* are found in other parts of the world. It possesses all five of the typical chordate characters, and the notochord, hollow central nervous system, and gill slits are well shown in a transverse section (Fig. 1.7). The notochord extends to the extreme anterior end of the body, from which is derived the name of the subphylum, Cephalochordata. The nerve cord is slightly expanded at the anterior end, but does not form a proper brain, and there are no marked sense organs. There are, as we have seen, many gill slits; a peculiar feature is that each is, after its formation, divided into two by the down growth of a piece of body wall called a tongue bar; further subdivision by horizontal bars or synapticulae, two or three in each slit, makes the wall of the pharynx into a network. The anus is about one-eighth of the length of the body from the posterior end, so that the tail is conspicuous in lateral view.

There are main dorsal and ventral blood vessels or aortae, and the direction of flow is of the chordate type, but there is no heart.

The body is segmented, and much of its bulk consists of about 62 pairs of muscle blocks or myomeres, each of which is shaped like a V lying on its side with the point forward (Fig. 1.11). Since the V's fit into each other, several are cut in one transverse section. They are separated by sheets of connective tissue or myocommata, and the myomeres of the two sides alternate, the myocomma of one side coming against the muscle of the other. The nerves have a segmental arrangement. On each side a dorsal nerve passes outside the myomere and goes to the skin, the non-segmented ventral muscles, and the gut; it is both motor and sensory in function (p. 257), and the cell bodies of the sensory fibers are at the peripheral ends, as they are in invertebrates generally, and not, as in vertebrates, in ganglia just outside the central nervous system (p. 236). A ventral nerve, which is motor, goes direct to the myomere.

The gonads, twenty-six in number on each side, are segmentally arranged in the middle part of the body. The sexes are separate and there

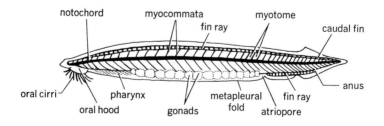

FIG. 1.11 *Branchiostoma.* External, x 2.

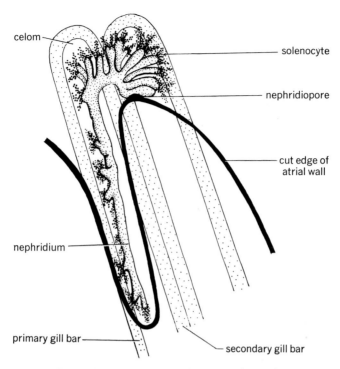

celom

solenocyte

nephridiopore

cut edge of
atrial wall

nephridium

primary gill bar

secondary gill bar

FIG. 1.12   A single nephridium of *Branchiostoma lanceolatum*, x 160. (Redrawn from Goodrich, *Quart. J. Micr. Sci.* 75, 1933)

are no genital ducts. Also segmental are the nephridia, which are found in the 14 segments of the pharynx where the first gill slits occur. They are bent tubes, ending dorsally in a number of hollow flame cells or solenocytes, each with an internal flagellum (Fig. 1.12). They are almost certainly formed from ectoderm—certainly not from mesoderm—and so agree in development, as well as in general appearance, with the nephridia of Platyhelminthes and the protonephridia of some polychaetes. Their function is unknown, but as the lancelet lives in the sea, where osmoregulation is unimportant, they are likely to be excretory.

The first gill slits, fourteen in number, are segmental, but many others are added behind these without relation to the myomeres until there are about ninety; and as each is divided into two the total number is about 180. Since the blood vessels joining the aortae are in the gill bars, they too lose their segmental arrangement.

The celom is well developed, but in the pharyngeal region is much divided up by the gill slits, so that it appears as spaces in the gill bars.

A peculiarity of the lancelet is that during its development a fold called metapleural grows down from the dorsolateral body wall above the gill slits on each side. The two folds meet and fuse, so that they enclose a cavity, the atrium, into which the gill slits open. It is closed in front, but has a ventral opening, the atriopore, about one-third of the length of the body from the posterior end. Its cavity extends some distance behind this on the right side.

Two of the most interesting things about the lancelet are its method of moving and its method of feeding. It spends most of its time with its tail end buried in the sand at depths to about 300 feet, but it occasionally swims vigorously. A continuous median fin runs from the anterior end along the back, around the tail, where it is expanded as a caudal fin, and forward along the ventral surface as far as the atriopore. Alternate contractions of the myomeres, the fibers of which run longitudinally from myocomma to myocomma, bend the body in opposite directions, so that the tail exerts on the water a force which has a backward component, and the animal swims much as does a fish (p. 469). Since the notochord is stiff, much of the energy in the contraction of the muscles is exerted in bending it, and its elasticity causes a quick flick back to make the propulsive force. This is probably the primary function of the notochord, which, as has been said above, cannot be needed to support such a small body. The incompressibility of the notochord also helps in confining the shortening of the body, produced by the unilateral contraction of the muscles, to one side of the body. It is surrounded by a fibrous sheath, which presumably prevents displacement of the vacuolated cells, and then again by more fibers, the function of which is not clear. They extend round the nerve cord and also into the fin, where there are also rods of an organic material of unknown nature. They are sometimes called 'cartilage,' but there is no evidence that they have any relationship to the skeletal tissues of vertebrates.

The mouth is on the ventral surface and not quite at the anterior end. It is surrounded by an oral hood, the edge of which is produced into tentacles or cirri and whose roof bears the notochord, which may here have a supporting function in spreading the hood open. The mouth leads into a short buccal cavity or vestibule, which is nearly closed behind by a partition or velum. Round the posterior part of the buccal cavity runs a lobed structure, the wheel organ, and in the roof in front of this is a depression, called Hatschek's pit. The opening in the velum leads into the pharynx, and projecting into this are about 12 velar tentacles. The pharynx runs nearly to the atriopore, and is, as we have seen, pierced by the gill slits. On its floor is the endostyle, consisting of four rows of ciliated cells alternating with four rows of cells that secrete mucus, and in its roof is an epipharyngeal groove.

The oral cirri, the wheel organ, and the anterior and posterior surfaces of the gill bars all bear cilia, and the beating of these produces a current which goes in at the mouth, down the pharynx, and out by the gill slits and atriopore. The oral cirri, bent inward when the animal is feeding, act as a crude filter to keep out sand particles. Smaller particles of food are entangled in the mucus secreted by the endostyle, carried upward in a current produced by the beating of cilia on the inner surface of the gill bars, and backward by cilia in the epipharyngeal groove, and so into the midgut. The food, still embedded in mucus, continues to be carried by cilia in this, and is digested there, probably by enzymes secreted mostly in the large diverticulum. Most absorption takes place in the short hind-gut, but there is some intracellular digestion.

Balanoglossus, a worm-like marine animal of the subphylum Hemichordata, is a very different creature (Fig. 1.13). Different species and closely related genera range from 2 cm. to 2 m. in length and are found in all parts of the world. The body is divided externally into an anterior proboscis, a collar surrounding the mouth, and a trunk. Projecting into the base of the collar is a diverticulum of the pharynx; since the cells that make the walls of this diverticulum are vacuolated, it has been called, without much justification, a notochord. The nervous system consists chiefly of a felt of fibers just beneath the ectoderm, and bears no resemblance to that of vertebrates. It is, however, thickened in the mid-line both dorsally and ventrally, and the dorsal tract in the collar is rolled up to form a short tube open at both ends. The pharynx has several gill slits opening to the exterior, usually toward the dorsal surface, and new ones are formed as the animal grows. The total number varies in different

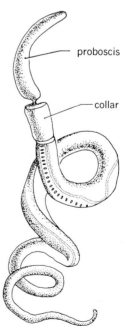

species and related genera from 10 to 700. They are divided by tongue bars, but these do not reach the ventral edge. There is no tail, and the blood travels forward in the dorsal vessel, which is slightly contracile. There is no trace of segmentation. The celom is divided into three parts, an unpaired hollow in the proboscis, a pair of cavities in the collar, and a pair in the trunk.

The animal moves chiefly by cilia which cover the surface of the body, but it is said also to burrow by thrusting the proboscis into mud, expanding it by pressing fluid into the diverticulum of the pharynx, and then drawing the trunk forward on the grip so obtained. It feeds by passing a current of water and food particles into the pharynx and out at the gill slits, but the currents start on the external surface of the

proboscis

collar

FIG. 1.13   The acorn worm, *Balanoglossus* sp., x 1.

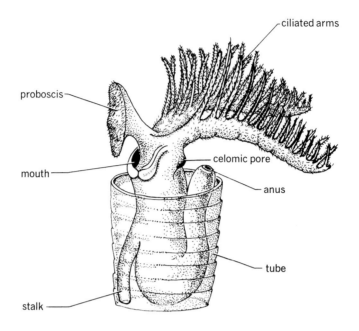

FIG. 1.14   A single zooid of the colonial hemichordate *Rhabdopleura*, x 12.

proboscis, not, as in the lancelet, at the mouth. The egg develops into a
pelagic larva called a tornaria. It swims by two bands of cilia and an apical
tuft, and somewhat resembles the larvae of echinoderms. These also swim
by a band or bands of cilia in various patterns, which are obtained by the
reduction of the uniform ciliation of the blastula.

Also placed in the Hemichordata is *Rhabdopleura* (Fig. 1.14), another
marine organism of nearly world-wide distribution. It is sessile and colonial, and each zooid is about half a centimeter long. There is an anterior
diverticulum of the buccal cavity, resembling the 'notochord' of *Balanoglossus;* such nervous system as there may be is not hollow. There are no
gill slits and no tail; nothing seems to be known of the circulation of the
blood.

The Urochordata or tunicates are a little more convincing as chordates,
though the adults, which are mostly sessile, have lost most of their characters. *Ciona intestinalis* (Fig. 1.15) is common in the North Atlantic, and
occurs in many other seas. After gastrulation, the embryo develops into a
tadpole-like creature (Fig. 1.17), in which can be seen a notochord of
vacuolated cells (which is present in the posterior portion or tail only),
a hollow nerve cord, with a slight swelling in the head, and a single pair
of gill slits. The tadpole does not feed and there is no anus; but the tail
contains no gut cavity, the endoderm having become solid. At this stage

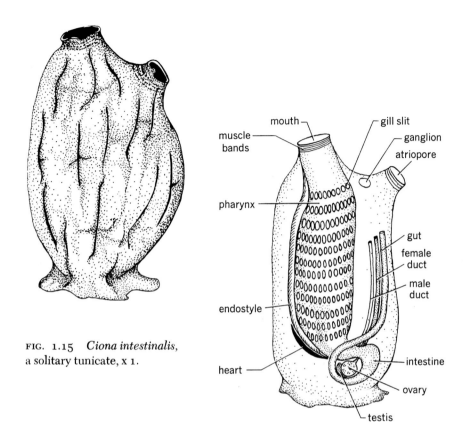

FIG. 1.15 *Ciona intestinalis*,
a solitary tunicate, x 1.

FIG. 1.16 *Ciona intestinalis* withdrawn from its case, x 1.

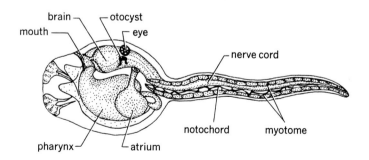

FIG. 1.17 A diagram of a tunicate tadpole, after various authors.

there are no blood vessels, and the nerve cord has no nerve cells and is apparently functionless. Since the tadpole swims in a corkscrew manner, 'dorsal' and 'ventral' are meaningless, and all that can be said of the position of the nerve cord is that it is superficial to the notochord.

The tunicates never show any trace of segmentation, and it is not certain that they possess a celom. Some authors have claimed that it is represented by the pericardium, which develops at the same time as the heart which it surrounds, or by the epicardium, blind sacs which grow back from the pharynx beside the heart. Both these claims seem speculative.

After a day or two swimming at the surface, the tadpole goes to the floor of the sea, attaches itself by the mouth region, and metamorphoses into the adult. It loses its tail, and so its notochord. The pharynx enlarges greatly, two more pairs of gill slits are formed, and then all three are greatly subdivided by tongue bars and synapticulae to form a complex basketwork (Fig. 1.16). An anus forms, and the intestine elongates and bends dorsally and upward to open in the same direction as the mouth. From the ventral surface a mantle grows out to form an atrium, into which the gill slits open. The atrium opens by a funnel and atriopore a little below and dorsal to the mouth. The mantle secretes a case that almost completely surrounds the animal; it is made of tunicin, which is cellulose associated with protein. There is a well-developed heart at the base of the animal, which beats in each direction for about a minute at a time alternately.

Feeding is by cilia maintaining a current from mouth to gill slits to atriopore, but muscles also help, and quite large contractions of the mantle occasionally produce the jets that give the animal its common name of sea squirt. There is a mucus-secreting endostyle on the ventral surface of the pharynx.

Many tunicates reproduce by budding, and they form quite complicated colonies. Some are free-living, and move by jet propulsion; presumably they are descended from sessile ancestors of the normal type. A few planktonic species retain the tail and notochord.

We must now consider the relationships of the protochordates to the Vertebrata, and why they are considered to give us important information about the origin of that group.

The usual story, which was established in its main outlines by the English zoologist Bateson (better known as the man who demonstrated that Mendel's genetical principles applied to animals as well as plants) at the end of the last century, is as follows.

A sedentary animal, related to the early echinoderm stock, lived by collecting small particles of food in currents produced by cilia on the outside of the body. Its descendants grew cilia in the pharynx, and opened gaps, the gill slits, through which the water could escape, so improving the collection of food that these features were established by natural selection.

The central nervous system, at first a feltwork of fibers just beneath the surface, rolled up into a tube for some unknown reason. Meanwhile, since sedentary animals are at a disadvantage unless they have means of dispersal, a free-swimming larva was produced; this in time developed a locomotory tail, and a notochord to stiffen it. This is the condition reached by the tunicates; later, the gonads became prematurely functional before the tadpole metamorphosed, a condition known as neoteny, and the sessile stage was abandoned. Further development led to a segmented lancelet-like creature and so on to the vertebrates.

There are several difficulties in this view of things. In the first place, it is based on the assumption that similar structures can never arise more than once in evolution. The distinction between homology and analogy discussed above should warn us against this assumption. Examples of very similar structures which no morphologist would regard as having the same origin are the tails of ichthyosaurs (p. 93) and fish, the eyes of cephalopods and vertebrates, and the tracheae of insects, crustaceans, and arachnids; some authors would add the compound eyes of insects and crustaceans. It is indeed clear that, faced by the same problem, different animals may produce what is in effect the same solution. In all the cases cited, part of the argument is that the details of the structure differ. This appears to be true, so far as the published descriptions go, of notochord, gill slits, and nervous system of the protochordates and vertebrates. There is certainly no functional resemblance between the hollow 'notochord' of *Balanoglossus*, used for transmitting fluid pressure to the proboscis, and the elastic rod in the tail of the tunicate tadpole. The slightly rolled nerve cord of *Balanoglossus* (which is a very variable character) is much different from that of the others. The gill slits have more resemblance in the three subphyla (though *Rhabdopleura* is without them), but they are in fact a simple solution to a common problem, and no different in principle from the lattice-work of the gills of bivalve molluscs, which are used for the same type of feeding with currents produced by cilia very similarly situated.

The supposed close connection between the chordates and the echinoderms rests almost entirely on the similarity of the tornaria larva of the hemichordates to the auricularia larva of starfish and holothurians. The alleged biochemical connection—the use of creatine phosphate instead of arginine phosphate in muscular contraction—has been shown to be erroneous; if it meant anything it would connect the vertebrates just as closely to the annelids, many members of which also possess creatine phosphate. A recent review of the embryology of echinoderms has pointed out that if they are classified on the basis of their larvae the result is completely different from a classification based on comparative anatomy and paleontology. Hence it seems clear that the different types of larvae have been evolved independently, with considerable convergence, a conclusion that agrees with the general rule that free-living embryos are subject to pressures of natural selection independent of those acting on the adults. But if the resemblance of the bipinnaria of starfish to the auricularia of the holothurians does not indicate close relationship, the argument for relating either of them to the tornaria of *Balanoglossus* disappears. This is indeed in accordance with common sense, for the hemichordate *Dolichoglossus otagoensis* does not have a tornaria, and if one starts with a ciliated free-living embryo—as many organisms from the coelenterates to the vertebrates do—the particular pattern of reduction of the cilia to give efficient swimming will be the result partly of chance and partly of natural selection, and of no phylogenetic significance. Similarities in cell division of the egg, which is by radial cleavage, and of the gastrulation, may be little more than a common geometrical solution to the problem of transforming a single cell into a multicellular organism (p. 3). There are certainly differences as well as similarities, for while the early embryos of vertebrates and echinoderms are indeterminate—that is, separated cells can develop into complete animals—those of *Branchiostoma* and the tunicates are highly determinate, with much specialization of cytoplasm even within the unfertilized egg. If *Balanoglossus* is the link with the echinoderms, there is no explanation of why the first chordate was sessile, like a tunicate. Berrill, who has recently restated and strongly advocated the descent of vertebrates from tunicates, dismisses the hemichordates as of no importance in the story.

The biggest difficulty comes with the lancelet. The segmentation is explained as making the swimming more efficient, since the division of the muscles into separate short lengths means that they need not all contract at once, so that the tail can take on a wave-form instead of a simple side-to-side motion. This does not account for the segmental arrangement of the gonads or of the nephridia. The nature of the nephridia is the biggest stumbling block; if their similarity to the fiame-cell system of invertebrates means anything, it relates *Branchiostoma* not to the echinoderms but to the platyhelminth-annelid-mollusc complex. If the resemblance is fortuitous we are back at the position stated at the beginning of this discussion, and no reliance can be placed on the similarities of notochord, nerve cord, gill slits, and tail in the vertebrates and three protochordate groups. While the celom of the lancelet, the hemichordates, and most echinoderms arises as a pouch from the archenteron, so that the mesoblast has once been hypoblast, that of the vertebrates is formed by the splitting of mesoblast which is directly formed by the morphogenetic movements of gastrulation. The anus of echinoderms was the blastopore, that of vertebrates and the lancelet is a new formation.

The origin of the vertebrates, their connection with the invertebrates, and the whole position of the protochordates are problems which are by no means solved. While the great groups of the animal kingdom, the phyla, are clear enough, and the members of each all built on a consistent plan, any connection between them remains, as Darwin said, based on argument from analogy. There are in addition some species which combine the characters of two phyla in such a way that they can justly be placed in neither—though zoologists with a passion for tidiness have usually forced them into one or the other. Thus *Peripatus*, with its cilia, nephridia, tracheae, and antennae, is neither annelid nor arthropod, though usually listed as the latter. *Branchiostoma*, with nephridia and notochord, is neither annelid nor vertebrate, though somewhat unhappily yoked with the vertebrates as a chordate. *Balanoglossus* has slight resemblances to both echinoderms and chordates, but in locomotion and habits is more like a worm. *Rhabdopleura* has the same sort of doubtful notochord as *Balanoglossus*. The tunicates resemble no other animals except that their larva is somewhat like the lancelet, from which they might be descended, as was once generally held, by becoming sessile and degenerate. If the student is helped by believing the standard story of the origin of the vertebrates given above, no harm is done, provided that he realizes that the evidence is slender and that those who are capable of suspending belief may be justified in doing so. In this book we shall regard the Protochordata and the Vertebrata as separate but possibly related phyla.

Unlike the vertebrates and the echinoderms, the protochordates have no hard parts and so have left no fossil record, unless, as seems possible, *Ainiktozoon loganense*, a problematical creature from the upper Silurian with a large head-like structure and a jointed tail, was some sort of relative of the tunicates.

For the rest of our history we shall make frequent use of paleontology. The basic principles of this science are that the surface of the earth is covered by rocks which, though much folded and distorted, lie in recognizable layers or strata; that in general the lower a layer may be the older it is; and that, other things being equal, layers in different parts of the world are of the same age if they contain the same sorts of fossils. The last is a somewhat dangerous assumption, since there are many cases of animals persisting through several layers while others round them change or disappear. In the last few years it has become possible to date the rocks by physical means, mainly depending on the known rate of decay of radioactive material contained in them, and the results show that the equations made by paleontologists on purely fossil evidence are generally true. Figure 1.18 shows the main periods in proportion to their probable duration, with sketches of the vertebrates that first appeared in each of them.

The existence of any fossils in Precambrian rocks is doubtful. Many of the objects that have been described as such are more easily explained as of inorganic origin, but there remain as probables, traces of coelenterates, perhaps of sponges, and of holes apparently made by some burrowing creatures.

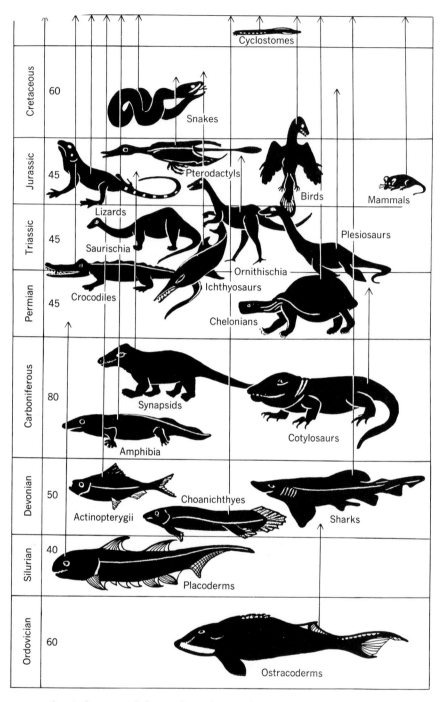

FIG. 1.18 A diagram of the geological periods, with their approximate lengths in millions of years. Drawings are placed in the first period in which the animal is known to occur, and vertical lines show the extension of the group in time; they do not show evolutionary relationships.

2

Vertebrates

THE MEMBERS of the taxon Vertebrata have all the chordate characteristics, and in addition they have a group of diagnostic characters of their own. Chief among these is a skeleton, made either of a material called cartilage, or partly of this and partly of bone. The most important features of this skeleton are two that we sometimes take for granted—that it is almost wholly internal and that it is arranged in separate pieces which move or rotate on each other in articulations or joints, so that they can be pulled by the muscles that are attached to them and act as levers. These levers are best seen in the bones of an animal such as a man, but occur even in those fish whose only skeleton is of cartilage. Some parts of the skeleton appear to have as their chief function the protection of delicate parts of the body; the skull in particular more or less surrounds the brain.

Connected with the internal position is the origin of the skeleton, which is usually said to be from mesoblast, but this statement must be accepted with some caution. Many cartilage cells come from cells of the neural crest (p. 6), which have migrated and mixed with mesoblastic cells that have moved in round the blastopore in the normal way. The molluscs and the arthropods, the best known invertebrates with a skeleton, have theirs on the outside, where it is secreted by the ectoderm. Only occasionally, as in the endophragmal skeleton of Crustacea and the pen of cuttlefishes, does it grow inward and becomes secondarily internal. The echinoderms are the only invertebrates with a mesoblastic skeleton, and in them it comes to lie mostly very near the surface, so that it is effectively external; it consists of secreted spicules or plates of calcium carbonate, which bear no resemblance either to cartilage or to bone. Except for its origin, it resembles the shell of some Protozoa or the exoskeleton of corals more than anything in vertebrates. As cells of the neural crest form also the dorsal spinal nerves, which are usually described as ectodermal, the importance of the similarity between the skeleton of vertebrates and that of echinoderms, or of the distinction between the skeleton of vertebrates and that of other invertebrates, must be doubted.

Cartilage has a very uniform and striking structure, and is one of the easiest of all tissues to recognize under the microscope (Fig. 2.1). It consists of large oval cells, each with a large nucleus. Around each is a cloudy halo or capsule, and this fades into the general background of a material

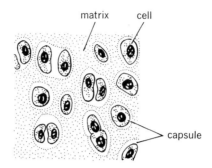

FIG. 2.1   A stained preparation of cartilage, x 150.

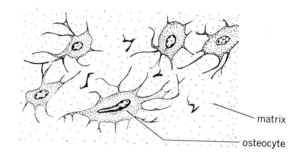

FIG. 2.2   A stained preparation of bone, x 550.

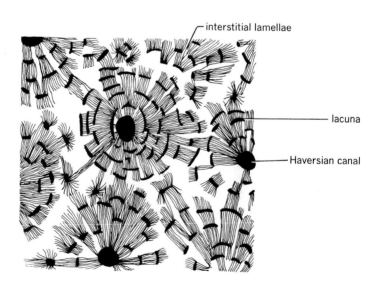

FIG. 2.3   A diagram of a transverse section of compact bone, x 150.

that does not take up any of the stains ordinarily used. Each cell has in fact secreted round itself throughout its life a material called chondrin, so that adjacent cells are gradually pushed apart from each other. Chondrin, which is a mixture of proteins with a high proportion of collagen, at first takes up a little stain, hence the cloudy appearance of the capsule, but later does not. Sometimes the cells divide, and then two, or occasionally four, may be seen inside a common capsule. Most of the cell division takes place near the surface, where there is consequently a concentration of cells. Since cartilage is never penetrated by blood vessels the rate at which oxygen can be supplied to the cells must be small, and the tissue is in fact capable of living completely anaerobically. Some cartilage, called hyaline, is, except for the cells, completely clear, but other types contain one or other of the two sorts of protein fibers widely found in vertebrates—yellow fibers of elastin and white fibers of collagen. All cartilage is tough and to some degree flexible and elastic, but white fibrocartilage is presumably stronger and yellow fibrocartilage is certainly more springy; it is found, for instance, in the pinna or external ear. Calcium carbonate is occasionally deposited in cartilage, which then loses many of its properties. The only invertebrate material that in the least resembles cartilage is that of the box surrounding the brain in cuttlefish. This consists largely of collagen. It must have arisen entirely independently.

Bone cells and cartilage cells develop from very similar mechanocytes in the embryo, but there the resemblance ends. Bone cells are branched (Fig. 2.2), and not only secrete round themselves a material rich in collagen but liberate at the same time a phosphatase enzyme which precipitates calcium phosphate from a soluble calcium hexose phosphate supplied by the blood. Some of the phosphate is in the form of a complex salt with calcium fluoride, called apatite. The result is a series of plates or lamellae, which are tough and hard, with the cells in small spaces between them. These spaces communicate with each other, and in the larger ones there are arteries, veins, and nerves, so that bone is very different from cartilage. In hard or compact bone the lamellae are arranged in concentric cylinders, the Haversian systems (Fig. 2.3), with the blood vessels and nerves running down the central canal. In the spaces between the cylinders, and in some softer or cancellated bones, the lamellae and the spaces are irregular.

The arrangement of the skeleton, whether of bone or cartilage, follows a uniform plan. An axial skeleton runs the length of the body near the dorsal surface. In the trunk and tail this consists of separate pieces or vertebrae, sometimes few, as in the frog—where there are ten bones, of which the last is given the special name of urostyle and is not usually called a vertebra—sometimes more than a hundred, as in many fish, usually something in between. In the head it is a skull which more or less surrounds the brain. Attached to the axial skeleton and usually considered as forming part of it, but not present in all vertebrates, are, in the trunk and tail, ribs, and in the head, jaws, and various supports for the region of the gill slits making the branchial or pharyngeal skeleton. In land vertebrates, but not in fish, there is a ventral axial skeleton or sternum, which is usually attached to the ribs.

The rest of the skeleton, called appendicular, makes the support for the limbs. These are not present in the simplest vertebrates, and there are others, such as whales and snakes, which have lost limbs which their ancestors possessed, so that the appendicular skeleton is not diagnostic. When present, it consists of two parts, a girdle for each pair of limbs, which is more or less internal, and the supports for the projecting limbs themselves. The bones of the limbs of a land vertebrate exemplify particularly well the principles of the lever. The parts of the skeleton of a fish and a man are shown in Figs. 2.4 and 2.5.

The notochord, its function having been taken over by the vertebral column, is of little importance in vertebrates. It is always present in the embryo, but disappears wholly or partly in the adult. Even where, as in the sharks, much of it persists throughout life, it is surrounded by the vertebrae and is probably functionless. Even in the embryo it never extends to the extreme anterior end of the body.

Where there is a strong exoskeleton, as in turtles and many extinct fish, it is usually formed largely from pieces of ordinary bone or cartilage which have come very near the surface. Nearly all vertebrates have also an exoskeleton of the protein keratin. This is secreted by the cells of nearly all epithelia, and at its simplest is a thin, partly waterproof layer, but it is sometimes specialized in such things as hair and horns, and may be closely applied to the outer surface of the bony exoskeleton in such armored creatures as the tortoises.

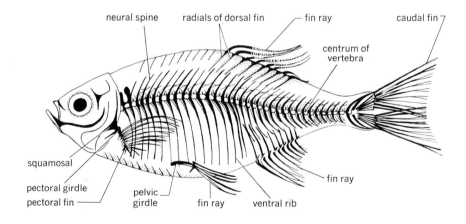

FIG. 2.4 A diagram of the skeleton of a bony fish.

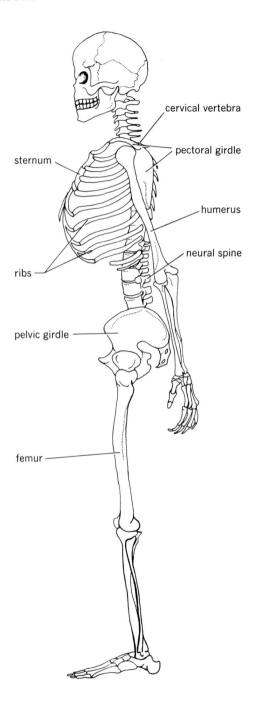

cervical vertebra

pectoral girdle

sternum

humerus

ribs

neural spine

pelvic girdle

femur

FIG. 2.5   A diagram of the skeleton of a man, x 1/10.

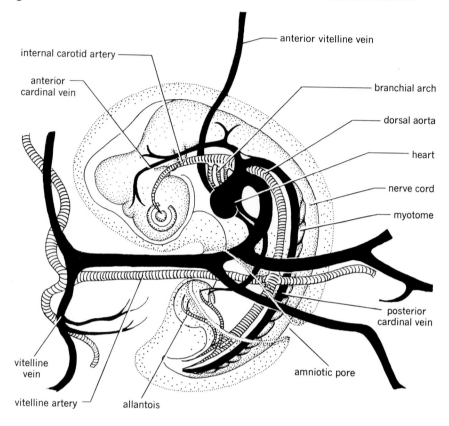

internal carotid artery

anterior vitelline vein

anterior cardinal vein

branchial arch

dorsal aorta

heart

nerve cord

myotome

posterior cardinal vein

vitelline vein

vitelline artery

allantois

amniotic pore

FIG. 2.6   The heart and blood vessels of an embryo chick, at about three days' incubation, x 16.

The central nervous system begins in a similar position to that of the lancelet, but the portion in the head is always expanded to form a brain. Associated with the brain are special sense organs; the nose, the eyes, and the labyrinths, or ears.

Gill slits are present and functional in fish and in the larvae of amphibians; but in reptiles, birds, and mammals they are seen, if at all, only as transient features of the embryo.

The tail is usually a conspicuous feature, but is lost in a few adults.

Both the main ventral blood vessel, in which the blood flows forward, and the main dorsal vessel, in which it flows backward, are formed in many vertebrate embryos by the fusion of two lateral vessels, and this may be taken as a sign that they were thus evolved in the early vertebrate ancestors. Much of this doubling still persists in fish, but the only traces of it in terrestrial animals are in the part of the body in front of the heart. This organ (Fig. 2.6), always formed by the fusion of two ventral precursors, is characteristic of vertebrates. It is always divided into chambers, typically a passive posterior one that merely receives the blood, a muscular middle one that drives the blood forward, and an anterior one, with valves, that regulates the flow. In land animals and some fish it is secondarily divided, more or less completely, into right and left halves.

Most animals with a blood system possess a blood pigment, which carries oxygen to the tissues by combining with it at regions of high concentration near the surface of the animal, and giving it up in the tissues where its concentration is low. One of the commonest of these is the red pigment hemoglobin, although this name applies to a series of compounds with the same active group but very varying sizes of molecule. Those of chordates are generally small—their molecular weight is 68,000 or less. Perhaps for this reason (see p. 203) the hemoglobin of vertebrates is always contained in special cells, the red blood corpuscles or erythrocytes, instead of being free in the blood plasma as in non-chordates (Fig. 2.7).

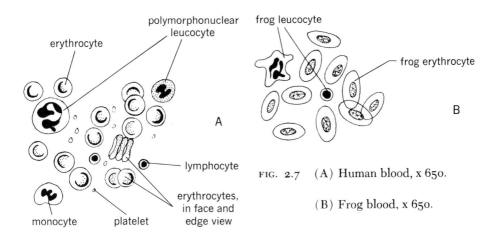

FIG. 2.7   (A) Human blood, x 650.

(B) Frog blood, x 650.

The condition of the blood of the protochordates is neither consistent nor well known. That of *Branchiostoma* contains neither pigment nor cells; that of the hemichordates contains a few cells and in some species is red or pink. The pigment, whether hemoglobin or not, seems to be dissolved in the plasma. The blood of tunicates has no hemoglobin, but has many cells, some of which contain peculiar organic pigments containing vanadium. These are of unknown function, and in some individuals of some species the vanadium is replaced by niobium or tantalum, adjacent metals in the periodic system. The method by which the animals concentrate these very rare elements, which were for long undetectable in sea water, would, if it were known, be of considerable interest.

Many celomate animals have paired passages opening from the celom to the exterior. If they are formed by a secondary outgrowth of the mesoderm they are called celomoducts. Such occur in all vertebrates, but their arrangement is obscured by the fact that ducts from many segments fuse together and have a common opening to the exterior, instead of there being, as in the annelids, a separate pair of ducts in each segment. Celomoducts resemble nephridia in position, often in function, and to some extent in appearance, but can always be formally distinguished (Plates I.3 and I.4). The chief differences are as follows:

CELOMODUCT	NEPHRIDIUM
Formed of mesoderm	Formed of ectoderm
Grows outward or centrifugally	Grows inward or centripetally
The lumen is intercellular	The lumen is intracellular
The cilia if present are extracellular	Cilia, always present in the terminal flame cell, are intracellular
Always open to the celom	Opening to the celom, if present, is secondary

The skin of vertebrates is characteristic, and is well seen in a section of that of a mammal (Fig. 2.8). Outside is an epidermis, derived from ecto-

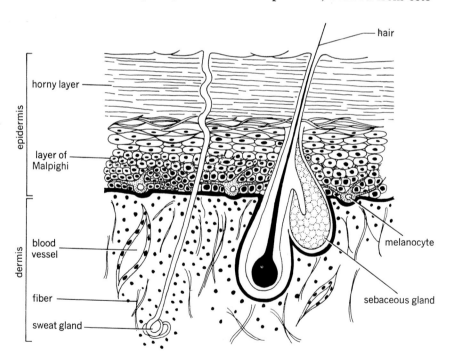

FIG. 2.8   A diagram of a transverse section of mammalian skin, x 150.

derm, of several layers of cells. These secrete the hard protein keratin inside themselves, so that their living cytoplasm gradually becomes less and less. Eventually there may be a thick layer of dead material, as on the soles of the feet and on the tips of the fingers of man, through which it is possible to push a pin tangentially without causing any sensation. The surface of the keratin is continually worn away, but as the cells at the base of the epidermis are actively dividing its thickness is maintained.

Beneath the epidermis is a mixed tissue, the dermis, mesodermal in origin, consisting largely of fibers and the few cells which secrete them. Most of the fibers are white or collagenous but a few are yellow or elastic, so that when the skin is cut they contract and the wound gapes. In the dermis run blood vessels and nerves, and in places it contains muscle fibers. At the base of the epidermis is a layer of peculiar branched cells, the dendritic cells or melanocytes, which may be able to make the black pigment melanin. They are derived from the neural crest.

The celom of vertebrates is well developed, but the segmentation is always more or less obscured. At most it is represented in the adult by some muscles with their attendant nerves and blood vessels, by the gill slits and associated structures, and in a modified way by the vertebrae. The external surface, the ventral musculature, and the central nervous system are never segmented; and in the adult all trace of segmentation is lost from the celomoducts, the gonads, and the dorsal portion of the head.

The development of the anterior part of the body into a specialized region or head, a process known as cephalization, is characteristic of active animals, such as the arthropods and to a lesser extent the polychaetes, as well as the vertebrates. In the vertebrates the head includes not only brain, sense organs, and structures for feeding but special parts of the skeleton and blood system as well.

The Classification of Vertebrates

If a man had set out, in the second half of the nineteenth century, to test the theory of organic evolution by using it to make predictions, he would probably have said that in the future, with increased knowledge and the discovery of more fossils, it would be possible to associate animals in fewer and fewer major groups. In fact, the reverse has happened. Charles Darwin knew of four or five phyla; modern textbooks have sixteen or twenty. In the first half of the nineteenth century there were four vertebrate classes, but in 1864 T. H. Huxley raised the number to five by separating the Amphibia and Reptilia. This division was not immediately accepted; Rymer Jones's textbook of 1871, for example, still retained the old arrangement. Cope associated the cyclostomes and the extinct ostracoderms as a sixth class, the Agnatha, in 1889, but their separation from the fish was not agreed by other zoologists. The old five divisions persist, for example, in Sedgwick's textbook of 1905, though by this time *Branchiostoma* has been removed from the Pisces to a phylum of its own. In the 1920's the extensive researches of Stensiö into fossil vertebrates led to the almost universal recognition of the cyclostomes and many extinct forms as a separate subphylum, or, according to some authors, a superclass, of jawless vertebrates, for which Cope's name of Agnatha was used, leaving the rest as Gnathostomata. In the 1950's Romer and others proposed the division of the fish into two or more classes, and the discovery of further fossils has led to the division of the Agnatha. Hence the second edition of J. Z. Young's *The Life of Vertebrates*, published in 1962, has two superclasses and thirteen classes, while the second edition of A. S. Romer's *The Vertebrate Body*, published in the same year, divides the vertebrates into only eight classes, and has no superclasses.

Some authors separate the earliest Amphibia as a distinct class, the Stegocephalia or Labyrinthodontia. Thus the four classes recognized when *The Origin of Species* was published have been multiplied more than three times. In this book we shall use the following scheme:

PHYLUM VERTEBRATA
    SUBPHYLUM AGNATHA   EXAMPLES

Class	1.	Cyclostomata	*Petromyzon, Myxine, Bdellostoma*
	2.	Osteostraci	*Cephalaspis*
	3.	Anaspida	*Birkenia, Jamoytius*
	4.	Heterostraci	*Pteraspis*
	5.	Coelolepida	*Lanarkia*

    SUBPHYLUM GNATHOSTOMATA

Class	6.	Placodermi	*Climatius*
	7.	Elasmobranchii	*Squalus, Scyliorhinus*
	8.	Crossopterygii	*Coelacanthus, Latimeria, Epiceratodus*
	9.	Actinopterygii	*Gadus, Salmo*
	10.	Amphibia	*Eogyrinus, Necturus, Rana*
	11.	Reptilia	*Dimetrodon, Alligator, Lacerta*
	12.	Aves	*Passer, Falco, Archaeopteryx*
	13.	Mammalia	*Ornithorhynchus, Macropus, Homo*

3

The Agnatha

APART FROM some unidentifiable bone scales from the Ordovician of Colorado, the earliest known fossil vertebrates are found in the Silurian, and similar animals extend into the Devonian. Vertebrate fossils of this date, all fish-like and not differing much from each other, have been found in various parts of North America, in the United Kingdom, and in Spitzbergen, and they agree in being without jaws. The mouth appears to have been ventral, and as there are no signs of any teeth the animals presumably either sucked mud like a sturgeon or maintained a current of water from which they extracted food like *Branchiostoma*. The best known of them are the Osteostraci, such as *Cephalaspis* (Fig. 3.1), which had an upturned or heterocercal tail (p. 348) and a large shield over the

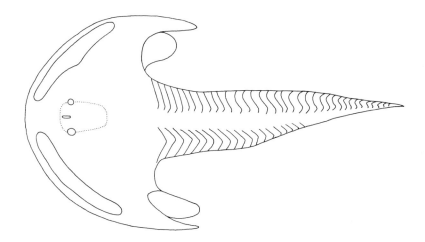

FIG. 3.1 *Cephalaspis* sp. (Osteostraci), lower Devonian, dorsal, x 2/3.

head. Both this and the scales that covered the rest of the body are of bone, so that so far as the fossil evidence goes this is a much older material than cartilage. There was a thin plate of internal bone, and this may have been preceded, as internal bone usually is in existing vertebrates, by cartilage, but there is no direct evidence that this was so. In the head shield are impressions of many of the soft parts, so that quite a lot is known about the

37

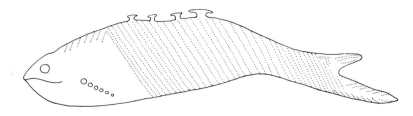

<small>FIG. 3.2</small> *Birkenia elegans* (Anaspida), Silurian, x 2/3.

anatomy of these animals. The most striking thing is that the nerves, blood vessels, and hollows which appear to be gill pouches, were regularly and clearly segmented, the number of segments being ten. There were a pair of eyes, a single external nostril, and two pairs of semicircular canals. In the last two points, as well as in the general form of the brain, these animals resembled the modern lampreys. There were no hind-limbs, but a pair of lateral projections just behind the head may have been pectoral fins. They did not, however, contain any recognizable internal skeleton.

The Anaspida, such as *Birkenia* (Fig. 3.2), are less well known, partly because they lacked the large head shield, so that the nerves and blood vessels cannot be reconstructed. They had bony scales, a down-turned or hypocercal tail (which, since tails of this sort are unknown in living fish, led to their being for long pictured upside down in books), large eyes, dorsal spines, and a ventral fin. *Lasanius problematicus* had a row of lateral spines behind the head which perhaps supported a short fin fold. *Jamoytius*, a problematical Silurian fossil, is usually placed here. It may have been an unarmored form with a notochord, on the way to becoming something like a modern cyclostome, but its interpretation is difficult. What one paleontologist thinks are myotomes others say are scales; the lateral fin fold of one is the ventral edge of the scales for another; the last author finds lateral fin folds in what the former thought was torn skin. Clearly until its interpretation is better agreed upon no argument can be based on it.

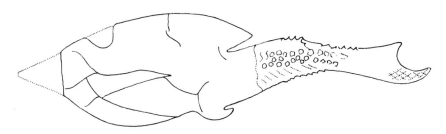

<small>FIG. 3.3</small> *Pteraspis rostrata* (Heterostraci), lower Devonian, x 2/3. The carapace is in dorsal view, the tail in lateral.

The Heterostraci, for example *Pteraspis* (Figs. 3.3 and 3.4), had a hypo-cercal tail and a head covered with both dorsal and ventral shields. These and the scales that covered the rest of the body were of a modified form of bone similar to the dentine of which teeth are largely made. There were paird eyes, two semicircular canals on each side, but no visible nostril. The fish scales found in the Ordovician appear to belong to these crea-tures; if so, they are the oldest known vertebrates.

The Coelolepida are little-known forms, some of which have been pro-posed as larval Osteostraci.

It is difficult for one who is not a paleontologist to disentangle what can be really seen in these early fossils from what is 'conjectural emendation,' but at least it appears certain that (1) they were all vertebrates with a bony skeleton, which was largely very near the surface, and well-developed eyes and ears; (2) none had jaws; (3) the tail was either heterocercal or hypocercal; and (4) there was at most one pair of laterally projecting limbs. The four groups, which are called collectively ostracoderms, do not seem to be very closely related, and they are all more or less contempo-raneous, so that although in a general way they can be associated with each other and with the modern cyclostomes no serious discussion of lines of descent is possible.

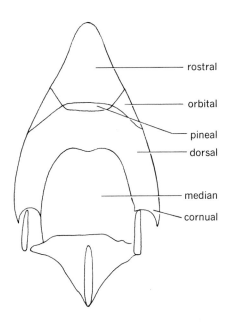

rostral

orbital

pineal

dorsal

median

cornual

FIG. 3.4   *Pteraspis rostrata*, a reconstruction of the carapace in dorsal view showing the plates.

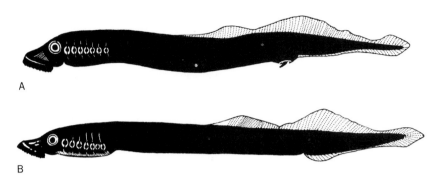

A

B

FIG. 3.5   A lamprey, *Lampetra planeri*, (A) male, x 1/3; (B) female, x 1/3.

A group of modern animals, the lampreys, represented by *Petromyzon* and Lampetra (Fig. 3.5), and the hagfishes, by *Myxine* and *Bdellostoma* (Fig. 3.6), are called Cyclostomata, or round mouths, and are also placed in the Agnatha. Stensiö, who first worked out the detailed anatomy of the fossil forms, thought that lampreys could be assigned to the Osteostraci, and the hagfishes to the Heterostraci, but as the extinct forms vanished 350 million years ago and no fossil cyclostomes are known, the association seems dubious. Lampreys are found all over the temperate parts of the world, mainly in the sea, while the hagfishes are found in the Atlantic and Pacific.

Whatever the relationship of lampreys and hagfishes, both are specialized toward a parasitic way of living, and so are likely to be very different from any free-living ancestors. The mouth of lampreys is circular and muscular, forming a sucker. Inside it are epidermal teeth, and a tongue with similar teeth. The animal attaches itself to the body of a fish, works a bare patch with its teeth, and sucks blood. The hagfishes attach chiefly to dying fish, or even dead ones, and suck the body dry, often entering by the mouth of the prey to do so.

Lampreys have all the chordate characters. The notochord is present throughout life, and extends from the middle of the head to the tail as a rod of large vacuolated cells surrounded by a fibrous sheath. It presumably has the same function as the notochord in *Branchiostoma*, since the vertebrae, which are lumps of cartilage that lie above the notochord on each side of the nerve cord, are not in contact with one another and so seem to have no function in swimming. Some species have one piece of cartilage on each side in each segment, others have two. There is a skull of several

FIG. 3.6   A hagfish, *Bdellostoma* sp., x 1/3.

pieces of cartilage, and a cartilaginous basketwork in the region of the gills and heart. The nervous system is typically vertebrate, expanded into a brain at the anterior end, and there are eyes and labyrinths, but the latter have only two semicircular canals, both vertical. On the top of the head is a single nasal opening. The dorsal and ventral nerve roots remain separate, as in the lancelet. There are seven pairs of gill slits, but these are of a peculiar form. The external openings are small and circular, and lead into expanded spaces, the gill pouches, whose walls are folded and presumably respiratory. The pouches open internally by small holes into a part of the pharynx separated from the food passage by a horizontal plate and protected at its anterior end by a ring of velar tentacles. This specialized arrangement appears to be connected with the feeding habits of the lamprey, for while the animal is attached to its prey it breathes by sucking water in and out of the external gill slits. The velar tentacles presumably fit together to prevent the blood that is taken as food from passing into the gill pouches.

The tail is surrounded by a caudal fin, and in the female there is a small ventral anal fin. There are no signs of paired limbs.

The blood circulates forward ventrally, being pumped by a three-chambered heart. There are cells containing hemoglobin, but this is peculiar in having a molecular weight of only 17,000, instead of the usual 68,000, and each molecule takes up only one molecule of oxygen. It makes an efficient transport system.

There is a series of celomoducts making the kidney. The skin consists of many layers of cells and is divided into dermis and epidermis. The celom is well developed. Segmentation is clearly shown by the muscles of the trunk and tail, which are shaped like a series of W's with the points forward, and by the nerves that supply them. The early segmental arrangement of the celomoducts is later obscured.

The hagfishes resemble the lamprey in their basic characters, but differ in many important ways. There is only one semicircular canal in the labyrinth, and the nasal passage opens internally on the roof of the mouth. Water is pumped in by this and out through six to fourteen gill pouches which have ducts leading back to a single branchial aperture on each side. This arrangement, functionally similar to but morphologically different from that of lampreys, suggests that it has been evolved independently.

One of the more interesting features of the lamprey is the type of larva. This, known as the ammocoete (Fig. 3.7), was at first described as a

FIG. 3.7   The ammocoete larva of a lamprey, *Lampetra planeri*, x 1.

separate genus of fishes. It begins as a transparent thread only a few milli-meters long, but at metamorphosis has much the shape of the adult and may be 17 cm. in length. It lives in the mud at the bottom of streams, for the adults are, like salmon, anadromous; that is, they leave the sea and swim up rivers to spawn. They have been known as a delicacy in Europe since the Middle Ages, and Henry I of England is said to have died in 1135 by eating too many of them at a meal. The fish make a depression by dragging stones by the suckers, and the male then clings to the female and twines round her, shedding sperms over the eggs as she lays them. After spawning both sexes die.

The ammocoete has no sucker, and feeds by using muscles to lead a cur-rent of water in at the mouth and out at the gill slits. On the floor of the pharynx is a complicated endostyle, which stands up as a ridge. Internally are cells secreting mucus which escapes by a single slit, and running along the top of the ridge is a shallow groove with cilia. The details are not clear but, as in the lancelet, cilia and mucus between them extract food particles from the mud and take them back to the esophagus. At meta-morphosis all this is lost, and as the sucker, teeth, eyes, and other fea-tures of the adult develop, the endostyle changes to a series of closed vessels resembling the thyroid gland (p. 452). The animal then migrates to the sea.

It has been generally assumed that because the simplest existing verte-brates have larvae which feed, in part, by ciliary currents, and because the protochordates feed in a similar fashion, the earliest vertebrates must have fed in the same way. This may be so, but it cannot be accepted as certain. Ciliary feeding is known in many animals—ciliate Protozoa, coel-enterates, polychaetes, bivalve and gastropod molluscs, and the tadpoles of frogs and toads, to name some of them. The details of the method are so different that it must have been evolved several times over. This need not surprise us; ciliated surfaces are almost universal in the animal kingdom, being found in all phyla except the Nematoda and Arthropoda, and all that the animal has to do to make use of the currents so produced is to find some means of extracting the food particles from them. This may be done in a purely mechanical way, as in the bivalves, but is more often as-sisted by the secretion of mucus, another common product of epithelia. The ciliary feeding of tadpoles, which is dependent on the use of the rasp-like tongue, a peculiar larval feature, to scrape particles off the surface, must be a new invention. There is no reason why the larvae of cyclostomes should not also have invented such a convenient method. That the extinct Agnatha, without jaws, fed on small particles, seems obvious; that they used cilia for the purpose is possible but unproven.

It has also been argued, from the fact that the blood of most vertebrates has a much lower osmotic pressure than sea water, that the vertebrates must have evolved in fresh water, and this view has been generally accepted. It is supported by the fact that the kidney seems to be designed primarily to get rid of water rather than to excrete waste products, a function which would make sense only if the animal's blood were hyperosmotic to the surrounding medium. The fossil evidence suggests otherwise. The very earliest remains, the mid-Silurian fish scales from Colorado, come from a deposit which, from its nature and the associated invertebrate fossils, is accepted as undoubtedly formed under the sea. More and more evidence is tending to show that the earliest recognizable fish were marine; the nature of the fossil beds suggests it, and the occurrence of almost identical species at widely separated parts of the world shows that migration must have been easy; this could only have happened in the sea. Further, the reliance on the kidney as a fresh-water organ is unsound. Celomoducts occur in other phyla, and may have been in origin no more than means of escape for the eggs and sperms, a function that, in a modified form, they retain in most vertebrates. The glomerulus (p. 202), which makes them into organs for filtering off water and crystalloids, depends on the blood pressure for its working, so that without a heart it could not have evolved; but it has no connection with osmotic pressure except that that of the proteins in the plasma must be less than the blood pressure. It could serve just as well for eliminating urea as for expelling water. Its mechanism is, in fact, the same as that of the excretory organ of decapod Crustacea (which also is developed from the celomoduct), and no one suggests that they have ever been anything but marine. A glomerulus, once formed, would be a mechanism that could easily be used to eliminate water, and so would enable its possessor to invade estuaries and eventually rivers. Some of the fossil ostracoderms seem to have been estuarine, so that this may well have happened. The lampreys repeat the story when they come to breed. Not only the lampreys, but the hagfishes, which remain in the sea throughout their life and have blood whose osmotic pressure is about that of the sea water, have well-developed glomeruli, showing that these are not incompatible with marine existence. There is, in fact, no reason for thinking that the ancestors of the hagfishes ever lived in fresh water or ever had blood of lower osmotic pressure.

Two other points about the first vertebrates are worth attention. It is extremely unlikely that they sprang into existence fully armored, as are most of the fossils, and those forms with a complete and continuous head shield must have been capable of little or no growth once it was complete. Hence the ostracoderms, as we see them as fossils, must have had both unarmored ancestors and unarmored young stages or larvae. With one possible exception no fossils corresponding to these are known. But were the internal skeleton cartilaginous their preservation would be difficult and their absence from the rocks not surprising. The exception is *Jamoytius*. There is no general agreement on the interpretation of this fossil, but some paleontologists consider that it is a truly primitive form, surviving

4

Fishes

THE REST of the vertebrates, the Gnathostomata, possess jaws supported by bone or cartilage to which are attached muscles, so that the mouth can open and shut. In almost all of them the backbone consists of vertebrae which articulate with one another, or at least are in contact so that there is some sliding movement when the body bends, and in most there are two pairs of lateral limbs with an endoskeleton of bone or cartilage. Generally, where the vertebrae or limbs are not present or are incomplete, they may reasonably be considered to have been lost. The gnathostomes divide fairly easily by habit into the fish, which live in water, swim by the tail, and breathe by gills, and the tetrapods which live on land, walk or crawl on four legs, and breathe by lungs, but this is not a classificatory division and there are many examples of animals that do not fulfill all three conditions of either group. Thus both the whales and the Dipnoi swim by their tails like fish and breathe by lungs like tetrapods; in such cases the assignment of the animals to the best place in any taxonomic scheme must depend on other things, and in the end is a matter for the judgment of the systematists. The whales are regarded as tetrapods and the Dipnoi as fish, for reasons that will appear later.

The term 'fish' is now taken to imply only the grade of organization and the sort of animal just described, and the old class name Pisces is seldom used. Whether the Agnatha are regarded as fish or not is a matter for personal choice. Since 1889, when Cope excluded them from the Pisces, general zoological sense would say no, but there is no other English word that can conveniently describe all such swimming creatures as salmon, sharks, lampreys, and ostracoderms. The usual habit is probably to use 'fish' to mean sometimes all these, sometimes the gnathostomatous ones only, according to the needs of the context, and in any case to distinguish the Agnatha as jawless fishes; the common but little-used English name round-mouths might well be revived for the same purpose.

The Dogfish: A Typical Vertebrate

The small sharks known as dogfish which are commonly dissected in courses on vertebrate anatomy are very convenient creatures, since they display most of the vertebrate characteristics in a fairly simple form and are large enough for the student to see these for himself without special aids. We will therefore consider one of them from this point of view. Most of the following description will apply both to *Squalus acanthias* (= *Acanthias vulgaris*) (Fig. 1.9), the species commonly dissected in America, and to the smaller *Scyliorhinus caniculus* (= *Scyllium canicula*), which is more often dissected in England. In addition to the spines in front of the dorsal fins, which distinguish *Squalus* and give it its name, there are some differences of detail in the internal structure, but none of importance for the present purpose.

The first and most obvious thing about the dogfish is that it is a fish and swims. It has a large upturned or heterocercal tail, and the vertebral column can be felt running upward in this to its tip. The membranous part which makes the fin is much larger below the backbone than above. There are two other unpaired fins, both dorsal. All three are supported by stiff compound rays; proximally, there is a cartilaginous piece or basal (which in the tail is a projection from the vertebrae), then another cartilage called radial, and, distally, a double series of dermotrichia made of elastin. These rays are almost diagnostic of fish, but are not found in the tetrapods, even though their unpaired fins, as in whales, look externally very much like those of fish.

Pressure on a stationary point under water acts equally in all directions at once, but when the point is moving it is greater in some directions than in others. The forces acting on a swimming fish are, by Newton's Second Law of Motion, equal and opposite to those exerted by the fish on the water, and are conventionally represented in three directions at right angles (Fig. 4.1). The weight of the fish is acting downward, and is counteracted by the lift of the water; the bending of the trunk and tail produces a variable force which can be resolved into a lateral component and a forward component, which are counteracted by lateral resistance and

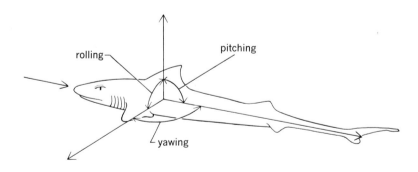

FIG. 4.1   A diagram to show the way in which a swimming dogfish may oscillate. Arrow on the left shows the direction of the force of the resistance of the water acting on the fish.

drag respectively. When a fish swims it inevitably turns its head from side to side, i.e. it yaws. It may also rotate on its long axis, or roll, and dip up and down, or pitch. (All these motions are familiar to travelers in boats, where they are produced by the action of the waves on the hull.) A simple long body tends to be unstable; that is, if it once begins to pitch or yaw the forces tending to make it do so increase, and the pitching and yawing increase too, with the result that the long axis sets approximately across the line of motion. This is well seen if a light stick is dropped from a height. Experiments with models in the shape of a dogfish have shown that one function of the unpaired fins is to reduce the yawing instability to zero. They must also reduce roll, acting like the stabilizers on an ocean liner, though this is probably less important.

The question of pitching is more difficult. The dogfish is heavier than water, so that in the absence of a lifting force greater than its weight it will sink to the bottom, and this accords with its habits of feeding on crabs and such creatures and with the ventral position of the mouth; but it must be capable also of swimming upward. The explanation that is generally given is that the pectoral fins, in their normal position, tend to lift the head; this lift is compensated partly by the weight of the fish and partly by a lifting component produced by the movement of the tail (since the animal tends to turn about its center of gravity, lifting the tail must force the head down). This matter is discussed further on p. 348 ff.

The forward motion of swimming is produced by the movement of the trunk or tail as an inclined plane across the line of travel. (Fig. 4.2). The force produced on the water is at right angles to the plane, and the force produced by the water on the fish is equal and opposite to this. It can, as usual, be resolved into two directions at right angles, one across the fish tending to produce yawing, and one driving it forward. The latter is at a maximum when the tail sweeps across the middle line (Fig. 4.2B), zero when the fin, at its extreme outward movement, is parallel to the fish's long axis (Fig. 4.2A). The segmental arrangement of the muscles enables contraction to proceed as a wave down the body, so that some part of the trunk or trail is always exerting a backward force.

The angle of the pectoral fins can be altered to enable the fish to rise in the water. The pelvic fins have no known function in swimming.

All the more highly developed groups of animals, annelids, arthropods, molluscs, as well as vertebrates, have developed a greater or lesser degree of cephalization, that is, a concentration of central nervous system and sense organs, together with apparatus for feeding, in a specialized anterior end of the body or head. The dogfish has a distinct head, although it is not marked off from the trunk by any neck or constriction. We shall consider in Chapter 19 how the limits of the vertebrate head may be defined. In the dogfish there is a ventral mouth, which is not completely separated from two external nostrils; five gill slits on each side, and in

FIG. 4.2   A swimming dogfish, seen from above. (Redrawn from Gray, *J. Exp. Biol.* 10, 1933).

front of the first of these is a small hole or spiracle; and on the sides of the head two large eyes. Internally, there is a brain, two labyrinths or balancing organs each with three semicircular canals, and a characteristic skeleton of skull and jaws.

The endoskeleton is entirely cartilaginous. The notochord is surrounded by vertebrae, each made of a number of pieces of cartilage (Plate VI.2). The largest of these, the centrum, grows into the notochord, almost obliterating it in the middle but leaving parts of it fore and aft; the final shape of the centrum is therefore that of a biconcave disc with a hole in the middle, and the notochord is said to be constricted. As described in Chapter 15, the centra are intersegmental and alternate with the myotomes so that the lateral bending of the body is facilitated. Dorsal processes make a neural arch over the nerve cord, and in the tail a similar ventral hemal arch surrounds the caudal artery and vein. Spines from the bottom of the hemal arches extend into the lower lobe of the caudal fin. There is a great variation in the number of pieces of cartilage making the neural arches in different species of dogfish, and in some the centra are hardened with calcium salts. In others the separate centra cannot be distinguished, and there is a more or less continuous cover of fibrocartilage around the notochord.

The skull (Fig. 4.3), although it is developed from separate pieces of cartilage, is, in effect, in the adult a single box, with floor, sides, and an incomplete roof. Several parts can be distinguished in it. The main part is the brain box or cranium, and contains the brain. Its sides are hollowed into orbits, which hold the eyes, above and below which there are supra-orbital and suborbital ridges. In the front part of the roof is a large gap, the anterior fontanelle. Such spaces, in various positions, are common in the cartilaginous skulls of other vertebrates. Several holes, chiefly in the orbits, are known as foramina (singular, foramen) and allow blood vessels or nerves to reach the brain. Behind each orbit is an auditory capsule, almost completely enclosing the labyrinth, the semi-circular canals of which

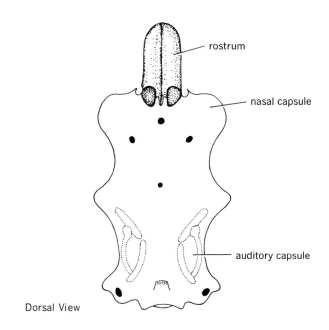

Dorsal View

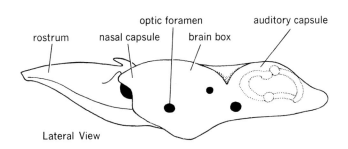

Lateral View

FIG. 4.3   *Squalus acanthias*. The skull, x 2/3.

may be seen as ridges on the surface of the capsule. Between the auditory capsules posteriorly the cranium has two knobs, or occipital condyles, which fit into hollows on the first vertebra, and between these is a large hole, the foramen magnum, through which the nerve cord runs to the brain. It is obvious that two condyles alongside each other will allow very little side-to-side movement of the head on the trunk, but more in an up and down direction. (The same is true of man; moving the head from side to side always involves bending the neck.) No fish, in fact, can move its head from side to side like a mammal or bird, but the dogfish probably makes some use of its ability to move the head up and down in altering its level in the water, the flattened head acting as an elevator in the same way as the pectoral fins.

Attached to the cranium in front are two nasal capsules, which are roughly incomplete hollow spheres with the open parts downward. They

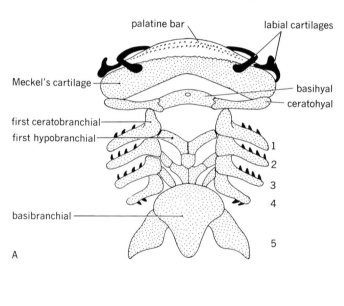

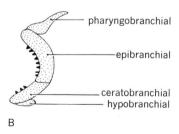

FIG. 4.4 *Squalus acanthias.* (A) The visceral skeleton, ventral, x 2/3. 1-5, the branchial arches. The pharyngobranchials and epibranchials and the hyomandibular are not shown. (B) One branchial arch in lateral view.

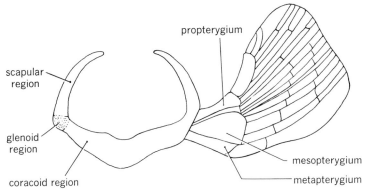

FIG. 4.5 *Squalus acanthias*. The pectoral girdle and skeleton of the left fin, anterior, x 2/3.

cover the olfactory organ. Between them a rostrum projects forward. In *Squalus* it is large and long; in *Scyliorhinus* it consists of three slender rods.

Below the cranium is a series of cartilages sometimes known as the ventral skull or visceral skeleton, because in tetrapods and some fish, portions of it are firmly attached to the brain box. In dogfish, however, the only junctions are by ligament, so that in a preserved skeleton its pieces appear quite separate. The chief parts of the ventral skull are the cartilages of the jaws. (Fig. 4.4).

On each side there is one curved bar, the palatoquadrate, making the upper jaw, and another, Meckel's cartilage, making the lower. The palatoquadrates are joined to each other in front by ligament, and each is slung from the skull by two more ligaments. The two Meckel's cartilages also are joined in front by ligament, and each has a hollow behind in which the palatoquadrate bar rests, so that there is an articulation or joint and the mouth can open and shut.

Behind the jaws is the skeleton of the gill region, or branchial basket (Fig. 4.4A). Basically, there is a hoop of cartilages, incomplete dorsally, behind the spiracle and behind each gill slit. Each is made of several pieces; the number varies, but the full set is four on each side and one median ventral piece. From above downward they are known as pharyngo-, epi-, cerato-, hypo-, and basibranchials. The hoop behind the spiracle, known as the hyoid arch, has two pieces on each side, of which the upper or epihyal, usually known as the hyomandibular cartilage, is attached by ligament to the jaw cartilages and to the auditory capsule, so that it forms the chief jointure of jaws and cranium. The ceratohyal reaches forward into the floor of the mouth, in which the median basihyal lies.

The paired fins have a skeleton to the general pattern of which nearly all

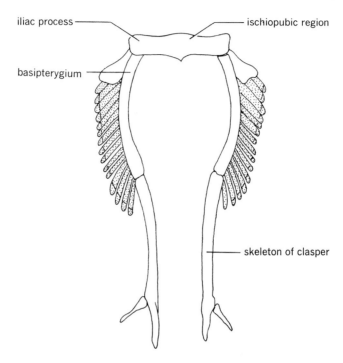

iliac process ———
——— ischiopubic region

basipterygium ———

——— skeleton of clasper

FIG. 4.6 *Squalus acanthias.* The pelvic girdle and skeleton of the fins of a male, ventral, x 2/3.

the limbs of fish can be assimilated. (Figs. 4.5, 4.6). Inside the body is a bar or hoop of cartilage, the girdle, which bears an articular surface on which the fin can move. The fin itself is supported by several rows of cartilages, the proximal ones being known as basals, the middle ones as rays, and the distal ones as polygonal plates. Beyond these are dermotrichia of elastin. (The old name for these was horny rays, but they have nothing to do with horn, which is made of the quite different protein keratin.)

The detailed pattern of the cartilages differs between the pectoral and pelvic fins and in different species of dogfish. In general the pectoral girdle is an incomplete hoop with dorsal points, and the pelvic girdle is a horizontal bar. The articular surface of the former is called the glenoid cavity, that of the pelvic girdle the acetabulum. There are usually three basals in the pectoral fin, all articulating with the girdle, and one large one in the pelvic. In males a long extra cartilage supports the clasper (p. 61).

The skin has the usual thick structure of vertebrates, but in it are embedded scales of a type called placoid, large in *Scyliorhinus*—so that when it is stroked from tail to head it justifies its English name of rough hound— and small in *Squalus*. These are described more fully in Chapter 18. Their interest here is that they have not only a tip of enamel but also a core of dentine, which is in effect bone without blood vessels. They are generally regarded as descended from the large bony scales or continuous head shields of the early vertebrates. On the lips of the dogfish they form a continuous series with the teeth, from which they cannot be distinguished in structure.

The dogfish can change in color by the movement of pigment in the chromatophores. In the rough hound, control is entirely by hormones, but this is not normal in fishes and there is generally a complementary control by both hormones and nerves.

The mouth opens into the buccal cavity, which is indistinguishable from the next portion of the gut, or pharynx. At the sides of the latter are five pairs of gill slits (some species of shark have more) which slope backward but open independently to the exterior. There is a slight vertical extension of the passage to make a gill pouch, but this is not expanded like those of the lamprey. On each wall of the first four slits, and on the front wall of the fifth, is a highly vascular expansion called a hemibranch or gill. A small similar structure on the anterior wall of the spiracle supports the view, derived from its position and relationship to the branchial skeleton, that this a modified gill slit.

The mechanism of breathing is quite different from that in lampreys. Muscles attached to the basihyal contract and lower the floor of the mouth; the external edges of the gill slits act as valves, so that water cannot enter by them, but it flows in through the open mouth and spiracles. These are then shut, muscles draw the epi- and cerato-branchials closer together, and the increased pressure in the pharynx forces water through the gills and out by the slits. The flow of water may be aided by expansion and contraction of the outer part of the gill pouch, which sucks water through the gills and then ejects it to the outside. This mechanism also works independently of the other, so that the fish can breathe with its mouth open, as when it is feeding.

The mouth of gnathostomes is a very versatile structure, as can be seen by its use in mammals and birds for carrying, building, preening, and holding the mate in copulation, in fact in almost everything for which man uses his hands. The invention of jaws, which make in effect a pair of tongs, probably led to the great development of the fish and to their great superiority over the Agnatha. We cannot be certain, but may guess that jaws were first used for handling food, and so enabled their possessors to feed on other animals and so to become active in pursuit of their prey. High speed demands good sense organs and complex co-ordination, and so for success a large brain and good eyes and balancing organs had to be developed.

The rest of the gut is relatively simple (Fig. 4.7). There is a large stomach (Fig. 4.8A), with highly acid contents, as in man. Lampreys and pro-

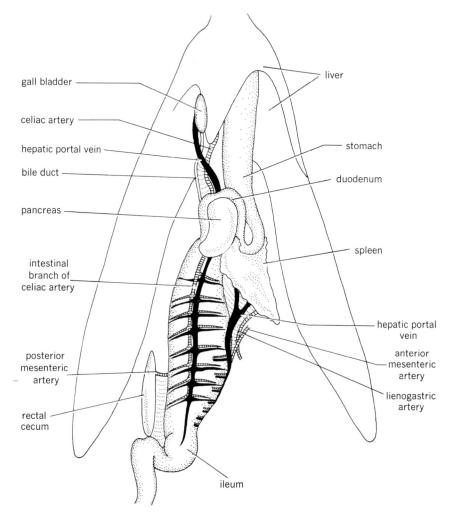

FIG. 4.7 *Squalus acanthias*. A dissection to show the gut in ventral view, x 1/2. The ileum has been displaced slightly to the animal's right.

tochordates do not have a stomach, and neither they nor any other inverte-brates possess the type of enzyme known as pepsin, which splits protein in an acid medium. It looks as if the stomach and pepsin were both gnatho-stome inventions, developed to deal with the animal food made possible by the presence of jaws. The stomach could have originated as a mere stor-age organ, very necessary if the food comes in large lumps, and pepsin could have been added to speed up digestion.

The intestine is divided into three portions, the duodenum, ileum, and rectum, of which the ileum, the longest and widest, has its internal sur-

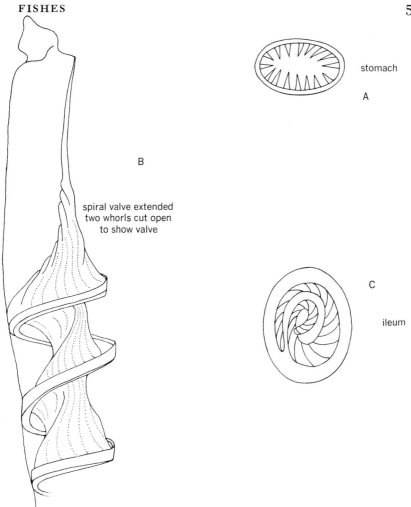

stomach

A

B

spiral valve extended
two whorls cut open
to show valve

C

ileum

FIG. 4.8 *Squalus acanthias*. (A) Transverse section of the cardiac portion of the stomach, x 1. (B) Ileum cut open and pulled
out longitudinally. (C) Transverse section of the ileum, x 1.

face increased by a twisted fold called the spiral valve (Figs. 4.8B, C).
There is a pancreas and a large liver, both opening into the duodenum.

The blood circulates in a system that in its general lay-out is typical of
vertebrates. The heart, lying above the ventral part of the pectoral girdle,
drives the blood forward into a ventral aorta. This gives off five pairs of
afferent branchial arteries, the first running in front of the first gill slits,
and each of the others in the branchial arch between two slits. The aorta
divides to make the first two pairs of afferent branchials, and does not continue beyond them. The blood passes through the gills by capillaries; it is

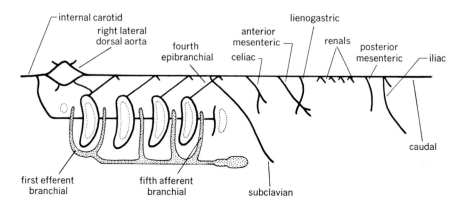

FIG. 4.9   A diagram of the arterial system of an elasmobranch.

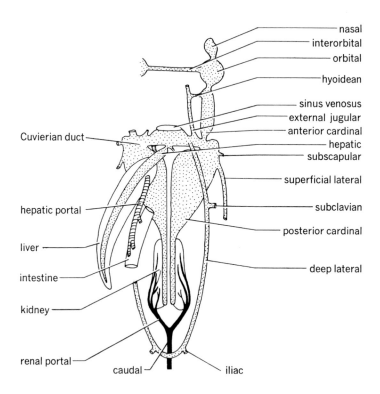

FIG. 4.10   A diagram of the venous system of an elasmobranch. The sinuses are labeled on the right.

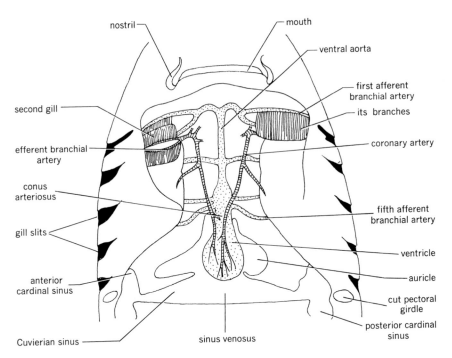

nostril

mouth

ventral aorta

first afferent
branchial artery

its branches

second gill

coronary artery

efferent branchial
artery

conus
arteriosus

fifth afferent
branchial artery

gill slits

ventricle

auricle

anterior
cardinal sinus

cut pectoral
girdle

posterior cardinal
sinus

Cuvierian sinus

sinus venosus

FIG. 4.11 *Squalus acanthias*. The heart and afferent branchial arteries, ventral,
x 3/4. The second gill pouch of the right side has been cut open to show the
efferent branchial arteries and the origin of the coronary arteries; the first gill
of the left side is pressed back to show the branches of the first afferent branchial
artery.

collected from them by efferent branchial arteries which open into four
pairs of epibranchial arteries. These run inward and join to make the dorsal aorta on the roof of the pharynx. From this, small vessels run forward
to the head, but most of the blood runs backward. Some blood also goes to
the head in small branches from the first efferent branchials. The ventral
aorta gives off several arteries, some paired, others not, which break up
into smaller and smaller vessels, so that eventually the blood is flowing in
capillaries, with walls so thin that oxygen and dissolved food materials can
diffuse rapidly out to the tissues.

The capillaries gradually condense, and the blood is returned to the
heart by a system of veins or sinuses. There is no strict difference between
these two, but a large ill-defined space in which the blood travels to the
heart is called a sinus, a more constricted one is a vein.

The general plan of the blood system is shown in Figs. 4.9 and 4.10.
The details of the system differ slightly in different dogfishes, but some are
shown for *Squalus* in Figs. 4.11 and 4.12.

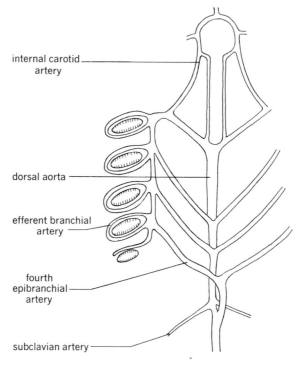

internal carotid
artery

dorsal aorta

efferent branchial
artery

fourth
epibranchial
artery

subclavian artery

FIG. 4.12   *Squalus acanthias,* the efferent branchial arteries, x 4/5.

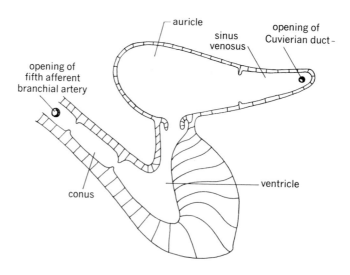

auricle

sinus
venosus

opening of
Cuvierian duct –

opening of
fifth afferent
branchial artery

conus

ventricle

FIG. 4.13   *Squalus acanthias.* The heart in sagittal section,
semi-diagrammatic, x 2.

The heart (Figs. 4.11, 4.13) has four chambers, and has developed from a tube that has grown into an S-shaped bend in the vertical plane, so that the morphologically middle part comes to lie above and slightly in front of the morphologically anterior part. Blood is received into a thin-walled sinus venosus, and then goes into the rather thicker-walled auricle, which is the middle part of the heart that has come to lie forward. From it the blood flows downward and slightly backward into the ventricle, which has thick muscular walls and is the working part of the heart. When the muscle of the ventricle contracts the blood is driven forward into the last chamber of the heart, the conus arteriosus, which merges into the ventral aorta. The direction of the flow of blood is determined by valves at the openings of sinus into auricle and auricle into ventricle, and by two rings of valves in the conus.

A small caudal vein from the tail divides into two renal portal veins. A portal vein is one that carries venous blood from one set of capillaries to another; a renal portal vein conveys it to the kidneys. The blood that has passed through the portal circulation of the kidneys, as well as that which has gone direct to them in the renal arteries, leaves them by two large posterior cardinal sinuses. These open into a transverse Cuvierian sinus, which opens into the sinus venosus.

Blood from the gut is taken by a hepatic portal vein to the liver, and then by two hepatic veins to the Cuvierian sinus. Blood from the rest of the posterior part of the body drains by two deep lateral sinuses to the Cuvierian sinus, and by two superficial lateral sinuses to the posterior cardinal sinuses. Blood from the head flows through a series of sinuses into a small jugular sinus and a larger anterior cardinal sinus on each side, both opening into the Cuvierian sinus.

The blood has red cells with hemoglobin, and is noteworthy both because it is isosmotic with sea water and because a large part of its osmotic pressure is provided by the nitrogenous compounds urea and trimethylamine oxide, which most animals treat as excretory substances to be eliminated as quickly as possible.

A thick section through the trunk of a dogfish shows many of the characteristic features. Skin, central nervous system, notochord, vertebral column, and aorta are obvious. Most of the dorsal part of the section is occupied by myotomic muscles on each side, and there is unsegmented lateral plate muscle below. A relatively large space, the celom, has the gut slung from its roof, and in appropriate places liver or pancreas can be seen joined to this. Also hanging from the roof, on each side of the gut, are the kidneys and gonads. A section through the region of the pectoral girdle shows that the celom is reduced to a pericardium surrounding the heart. This is separated from the abdominal cavity by a vertical wall, which is not, however, quite complete, the two cavities communicating by a small pericardio-peritoneal canal (Fig. 8.3A).

The kidneys are slightly different in the two sexes (Fig. 4.14). In both they are made of a series of celomoducts, and in both they run almost the full length of the abdomen, but in the female the anterior portion is much narrowed. This portion in the male, though present and large, is concerned chiefly in carrying the spermatozoa. In both sexes a duct opens into a cloaca, a common passage for excretory products, feces, and ova or sperms. The differences between the sexes are shown in the diagrams.

The testes are a pair of large soft bodies. The sperms that they produce pass by several small efferent ducts, which are derived from the anterior

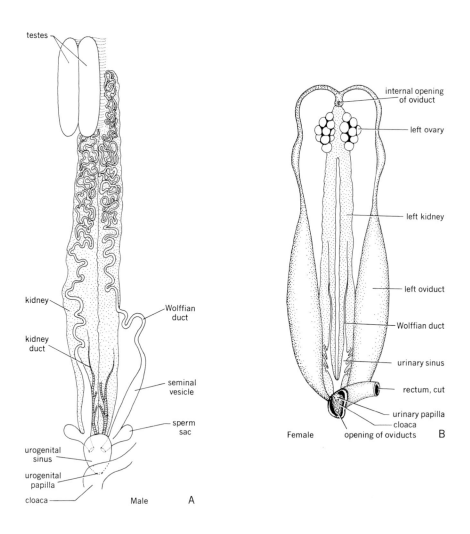

FIG. 4.14 *Squalus acanthias.* (A) The male urogenital system, x 1/2. (B) The female urogenital system, x 1/2.

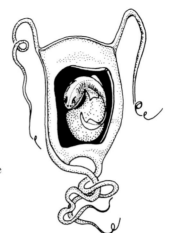

FIG. 4.15 *Sycliorhinus caniculus.* An egg case
cut open to show the embryo, x 2/3.

celomoducts of the kidneys, into a long Wolffian duct on each side. This
swells out into a seminal vesicle which opens into a urogenital sinus, which
receives also the kidney ducts, and has opening out of it two sperm sacs, in
which semen is stored. It opens by a single papilla into the cloaca.

The ovaries are large, and consist of little but a collection of eggs. In
Scyliorhinus there is only one. Two large oviducts convey the eggs to the
cloaca.

In nearly all species of dogfish, fertilization is internal. Two fish twist
their bodies round each other, their heads being back to back, and the
claspers of the male, dilated under the influence of adrenaline (p. 463) are
thrust into the cloaca of the female. In this position semen passes into the
female. The fertilized eggs are large and yolky, and only a few are present
at any one time. In *Scyliorhinus* and most others they are covered with a
shell, which is not calcareous but horny. It is much larger than the egg,
which fits loosely into it, and is shaped like a rectangular pocket with a
long filament at each corner (Fig. 4.15). The filaments twine around sea-
weed, and the egg develops inside the case. Dried egg shells are often
picked up on the seashore, where they are known as 'mermaids' purses.'
In *Squalus* and others the egg has no shell, but develops inside the parent,
so that a young active dogfish is produced and the animal is viviparous
(Fig. 4.16).

The nervous system of the dogfish is on the typical vertebrate plan, and
as, owing to the absence of bone, the brain and cranial nerves are exceptionally easy to dissect, it is well worth while to pay special attention to
them.

The brain (Fig. 13.11) has all the typical parts, and will be left for consideration until the chapter dealing with the brain in general. It is usually

said to give off ten pairs of nerves within the skull but there are in fact fourteen pairs, nos. XI and XII of the list on p. 263 being absent. Although, as we shall see in Chapter 19, most of these can be arranged in a segmental pattern, it is still advisable to learn them in dissection as a simple series, numbered in order from the front (Fig. 4.17).

Some of these clearly accept messages from the main sense organs and so are sensory nerves. The optic nerve runs from the eyes, which are relatively large, with lens and retina. The auditory comes from the labyrinth, which is concerned chiefly with balance but does enable the fish to respond to sounds, though discrimination is not good. The lateral line organs, structures peculiar to fish and some amphibians, use chiefly nerve X. It is doubtful how far smell can be said to exist in fish, or whether smell and taste can be distinguished.

The dogfishes and sharks are placed in the class Elasmobranchii, which includes also the skates or rays, which are essentially sharks that have been flattened from top to bottom (a state known technically as depressed) and some other forms, all being known collectively as cartilaginous fishes. Some sharks are very large, up to seventy feet long, and some

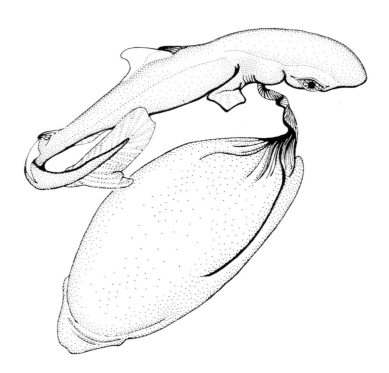

FIG. 4.16 *Squalus acanthias.* An embryo, x 2. Compare also the frontispiece.

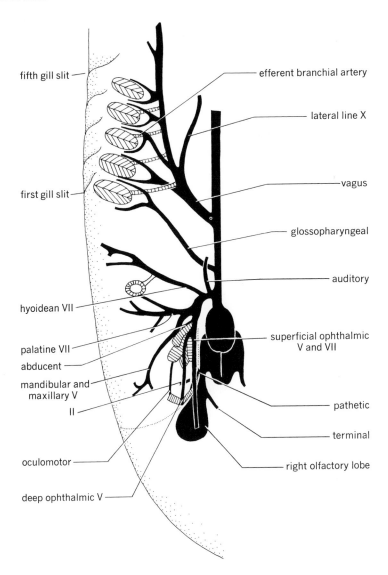

FIG. 4.17 *Squalus acanthias*. A dissection of the cranial nerves, dorsal, x 2/3.

have developed peculiar features such as the transversely extended anterior end of the hammerhead (*Sphyrna zygaena*, Fig. 4.18). Many are
without spiracles, and some have six or seven pairs of gill slits. *Cetorhinus*,
the basking shark, has given up the predaceous habits of the group and
feeds on plankton, which it strains from the water by processes developed
on the gills, much as the toothless whales use their whalebone.

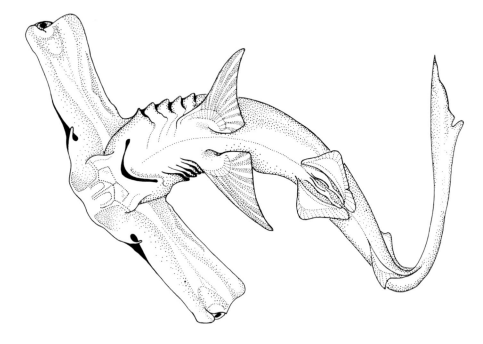

FIG. 4.18   A hammerhead shark, *Sphyrna zygaena*, ventral, x 1/8.

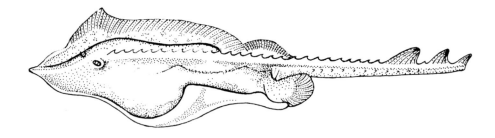

FIG. 4.19   A skate, *Raia batis*, swimming, x 1/6.

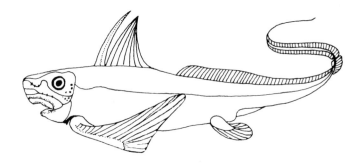

FIG. 4.20   A holocephalan, *Chimaera monstrosa*, x 1/5. The lateral lines are very conspicuous.

The rays (Fig. 4.19) have a small tail, but the pectoral fins are greatly expanded, and the fish swims by a wave-like motion of these. Internally, they are very similar to the dogfish, but the fin is supplied by many more spinal nerves, suggesting that more segments have gone into its making.

The Holocephali are a separate subclass, notable for peculiarities in the skull, which are dealt with in Chapter 16. *Chimaera monstrosa* (Fig. 4.20) is an example.

The only thing that is diagnostic of elasmobranchs is that they are fish with no trace of bone except for the dentine in the scales and teeth, the placoid structure of which is characteristic. In all modern forms the egg is large and yolky, and fertilization is internal, copulation being assisted by the male's claspers, structures not found in any other fish. They share several characteristic points with various other fish. The tail is heterocercal. The gills, although wrinkled, remain as plates on the wall of the gill slits, and do not stretch out from them as filaments. There is no trace of any diverticulum from the alimentary canal containing air. The intestine has a large spiral valve. The conus of the heart is muscular and has several rows of valves. Beside the anus are two small openings into the celom, the abdominal pores.

Early Fish

When we try to apply these characteristics to fossils it is obvious that the absence of bone, the placoid scales, the heterocercal tail, and the claspers are the only ones that are likely to be of much use, and we have seen the heterocercal tail in the Osteostraci, which on other grounds cannot be closely related to the sharks. By the test of the scales and the absence of bone several fossil elasmobranchs have been recognized. The

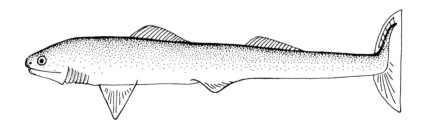

FIG. 4.21   A fossil shark, *Cladoselache*, restored, x 1/12.

earliest traces of them are isolated scales and teeth from the middle Devonian. *Cladoselache* (Fig. 4.21), one of the best-known forms, comes
from the lower Carboniferous. It had a very shark-like form, with five gill
slits and a large and markedly heterocercal but probably outwardly symmetrical tail. The paired fins (Fig. 17.2) were peculiar in that their cartilages stood out from the trunk more or less parallel to each other, so that
the fins would have been capable of an up and down motion but of very
little of the tilting which is so important in the swimming of the dogfish.
This could have been associated with the development of the symmetrical tail. Some of the fossils show that muscle extended out into the base of
the fin, as in modern sharks. *Pleuracanthus*, from the Permian, had a completely symmetrical or diphycercal tail, and the basal cartilages of the
paired fins were arranged as an axis, which has many more rays in front
of it than behind. Claspers were present. In many of the extinct forms the
vertebrae were simple rings, not constricting the notochord, and in some
there was much calcification in the cartilage.

Most interesting of these extinct jawed fishes are a group called the
Placodermi, which were formerly considered to be elasmobranchs but are
now raised to a distinct class. They are found almost as early as the earliest
Agnatha, in the upper Silurian, and were living alongside the best known
of these, continuing into the Permian. The best known of them, the Acanthodii, were small, only a few inches long, and had heterocercal tails, but
there the resemblance to the dogfish ends (Fig. 17.1). The hyoid arch was
completely separate from the skull, so that presumably the spiracle was a
functional gill slit. Down the side of the body was a row of up to seven
spines made of dentine. Since similar spines on the back of a dogfish are always placed in front of fins, it is assumed that this was so with the placo-
derm spines and the fish are usually said to have had several pairs of lateral
fins, as well as two large dorsal fins and a large median anal fin indicated by
spines in those positions. This does not, however, seem to be necessary. The
first and last spines of the lateral series are larger than the others, and might

have supported pectoral and pelvic fins, while the intermediate ones might have had some other function. The whole body was covered with flat scales of layers of dentine, and on the head these were enlarged or fused. There was therefore a general tendency toward armor plating, which could account for the extra spines. There seems to have been no endoskeleton in the paired fins except in the shoulder girdle, but there was some ossification in the skull. Other placoderms, such as the Antiarchi, including *Bothriolepis* (Fig. 4.22), were heavily armored.

We are left with the surprising result that not only the earliest Agnatha but the earliest gnathostomes possessed bone, and that in both groups armoring was common. Such a strong external covering, which is found also in many molluscs, crustaceans, and reptiles, is generally said to be a defense against attack, but it is difficult to see against whom these fish were defending themselves. If there were any invertebrates large enough to be important enemies, the speed implied by the fishes' tails would have been adequate protection. Equally difficult is the mode of origin of the modern elasmobranchs from the others. Much bone must clearly have been lost and the rest reduced to the dentine of the scales, though the detailed structure of these, with a hollow pulp cavity, is something not possessed by the placoderms, so that there was specialization and not mere degeneration. The modern elasmobranchs are, with very few exceptions, all marine, and so, probably, were most of the extinct forms, including the Silurian placoderms. It looks as if both Agnatha and gnathostomes originated in the sea, but soon invaded the rivers. The glomerular kidney, by which

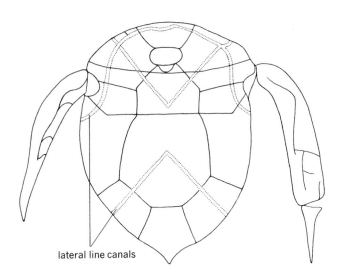

lateral line canals

FIG. 4.22 *Bothriolepis canadensis* (Antriarchi), Devonian, dorsal, x 2/5.

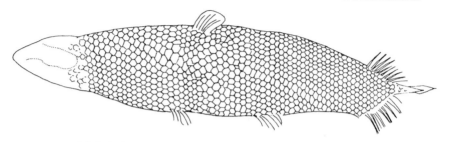

FIG. 4.23　*Rhabdoderma elegans* (Rhipidistia), Carboniferous, x 2/3.

they could regulate the composition of the blood, enabled them to do this. It was, therefore, a 'pre-adaptation,' that is to say, a feature which was evolved in one environment but proved especially useful in another.

Bony Fish

All the 'bony fish,' that is, those which have a bony endoskeleton but no placoid scales, are sometimes included in one class, but it is probably commoner for them to be divided into two, an arrangement that is adopted here.

In some ways the more primitive of the two classes is the Crossopterygii. They first appeared in the middle Devonian, and were characterized by a heterocercal or diphycercal tail, paired fins with an endoskeletal axis comparable to what we have described in *Pleuracanthus*, and—if the structure

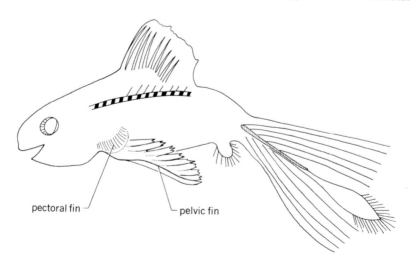

pectoral fin　　　　　　　　　　pelvic fin

FIG. 4.24　*Coccoderma suecicum* (Rhipidistia), Jurassic, x 1/3. In this late crossopterygian the pelvic fins have moved forward to a position just below the pectoral fins.

FIG. 4.25 *Latimeria chalumnae*, the contemporary coelacanth, x 1/12. (Photograph by courtesy of the Trustees of the British Museum (Natural History))

of the skull is correctly interpreted—internal nares. The scales are of a peculiar type called cosmoid (p. 428), which are quite different from placoid scales but could conceivably have been derived from them.

One group of crossopterygians, the Rhipidistia, represented by *Rhabdoderma* (Fig 4.23) and *Coccoderma* (Fig. 4.24), was long unknown later than the Cretaceous, but in 1938 a fish, now called *Latimeria chalumnae* (Fig. 4.25), which was very similar to the restorations of the Carboniferous *Coelacanthus*, was found in the Pacific near Madagascar. A few more specimens have since been caught, and dissection of them has given us insight into what these early crossopterygians were like. There is a long air bladder opening from the intestine, but its lumen is narrow, and although there are two pairs of nares, both open on the top of the head. The heart is unbent, with the ventricle in front of the auricle, and the conus is long, with four rows of valves. The notochord is unconstricted, and spiracles are present.

Also present in the Devonian were members of another subdivision, the Dipnoi (Fig. 4.26). These resemble the others in their main features, but differ in the structure of the skull, and in the possession of peculiar, large, teeth. As with the coelacanths the fossils gradually become fewer, and

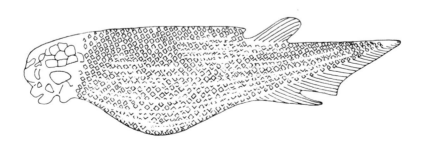

FIG. 4.26 *Dipterus valenciennsis* (Dipnoi), Devonian, x 1/4.

none is known later than the Jurassic, so that it looks as if the group became extinct. Some dipnoans must have survived, however, because three
living genera are known. *Epiceratodus* (Fig. 4.27) lives in rivers in
Queensland (it was formerly placed in the genus *Ceratodus*, which was
based on teeth collected from Jurassic rocks); *Lepidosiren,* in rivers of
South America; and *Protopterus,* in rivers and lakes of Africa. All three
are tropical, and *Lepidosiren* and *Protopterus* survive in the mud when
their habitat dries up for half the year. Most of the skeleton is cartilaginous and the notochord is unconstricted. There are internal nares and an
air bladder or lung is used for respiration. The intestine is ciliated. There
are several features, which will be mentioned in later chapters, in which
the Dipnoi resemble the Amphibia, but their gut and habits are somewhat
specialized.

The remaining bony fishes are the Osteichthyes or Actinopterygii. Their
characters are for the most part the opposite of those of elasmobranchs.
The endoskeleton is almost entirely bony, and the vertebrae are complex,
completely constricting the notochord, of which only small remnants are
left in the hollows between them. The skull and pectoral girdle also are
complex, with more bones than are found in any other animal. The tail is
usually symmetrical, but goes through a heterocercal stage in the embryo, a condition known as homocercal (Fig. 15.18). The scales are not
placoid. The bones of the fin are small and largely sunk into the body, almost the whole of the fin being supported by the dermotrichia only. There
are no internal nares and no spiracle. There are usually five gill slits, sometimes four, with long filamentar gills which stretch into the outer world
and are covered by a flap or operculum grown back from the first gill arch.
An air bladder opens out of the pharynx, but it is not used as a lung. The
intestine has no spiral valve.

The heart has a short conus, generally called a bulbus arteriosus, and
urea and trimethylamine oxide are not retained in the blood. The kidneys
and reproductive systems are relatively simple and have much less connection with each other than is usual in vertebrates. There is no cloaca, a feature not found elsewhere except in the mammals. The eggs, though small
and often produced in millions, are yolky.

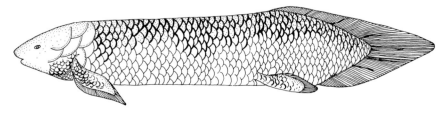

FIG. 4.27   *Epiceratodus forsteri,* the contemporary dipnoan of Australia, x 1/6.

FIG. 4.28   The bichir, *Polypterus bichir*, x 1/4.

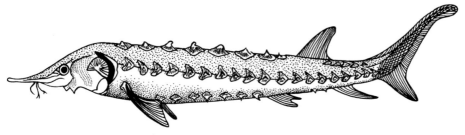

FIG. 4.29   A sturgeon, *Acipenser sturio*, x 1/12.

It is now customary to put in the Actinopterygii some extinct orders and a few modern forms which do not have all the above characters, and which were formerly associated with the Crossopterygii. The living examples of these possibly primitive forms include the bichir (*Polypterus*, Fig. 4.28), sturgeons (*Acipenser*, Fig. 4.29), and the bow fin (*Amia*, Fig. 4.30).

The bichir lives in African rivers and is very similar to some Carboniferous forms. The cranium is largely cartilaginous, though covered with dermal bones (p. 355). The skeleton of the paired fins is much like that of the dogfish, with basals partly ossified, supporting a fleshy base. There is a spiral valve and a long conus with three rows of valves. The air bladder is double and is perhaps used as a lung, though this is not certain.

The sturgeons are anadromous, breeding in the rivers of the Northern Hemisphere, especially Pacific North America and Russia. They look extremely like dogfish, swimming along the bottom with a heterocercal tail,

FIG. 4.30   The bowfin, *Amia calva*, x 1/3.

FIG. 4.31   A typical teleost, the herring, *Clupea harengus*, x 1/2.

and this resemblance extends to many of the internal organs. The skeleton is mostly cartilaginous, spiracles are present, and the heart has a long valvular conus. The bow fin is a peculiar creature found in fresh waters of central and southern North America, including Lake Huron and Lake Erie, which gets its name from a long vibratile dorsal fin. It has few bones in the skull, a spiral valve in the intestine, and a long conus with three rows of valves. The air bladder is used as a lung.

The typical bony fish, or Teleostei, are a relatively recent group, their first-known members being found in the Jurassic. They have the charac-ters given above, have radiated into many different shapes, and have ex-ploited all the aquatic habitats there are. A few have even become more or less terrestrial, getting their oxygen, however, not by lungs but usually through the skin. The herring (*Clupea*) (Fig. 4.31) and salmon (*Salmo*) have a typical fishy shape and are fast swimmers. Herrings live in the sea in vast shoals which undergo regular migrations, following the plankton on which they feed. The salmon is more solitary, and two individuals associate together in fresh water for spawning. The male is distinguished from the female by the large hook on the end of the lower jaw (Fig. 4.34).

The propulsion of these fishes is basically similar to that of the dogfish, but there are some differences. The body is generally shorter in proportion to its thickness, so that fewer waves are passing down the body at any one time. The tail is externally symmetrical, so that it has no pitching com-ponent. The fish can alter its level in the water by secreting gas into the air bladder or absorbing it through a special glandular surface well sup-plied with blood vessels. This means that the pectoral fins are no longer needed as elevators. They tend to project from the body in a vertical plane and are used as brakes or, by moving backward and forward with some bending, for swimming slowly in either direction. The pelvic fins help to steady the fish when it stops dead, and to assist in this they have in many teleosts moved forward to a position below the pectorals, or even in front of them.

There is much variation both in form and in habit in teleosts. Some, especially those that live in the depths of the oceans, have become more or less globular. Others are flattened, and lie in sand in relatively shallow seas. Whereas the flat skates are depressed, the flat bony fish, such as turbots (*Scophthalmus*) (Fig. 4.32) and plaice (*Pleuronectes*) are compressed or flattened from side to side. They start life with a normal shape, and after they have lain down on one side the eye that was below moves around to the upper surface and the mouth becomes asymmetrical. The flatfish can change their pattern to match the background, control of the chromatophores being by nerves and hormones as in sharks.

The sea horse (*Hippocampus*, Fig. 4.33) stands with its head up in the water, swimming by means of its dorsal fin, which it uses much as does a bow fin, except that the axis of the body is vertical not horizontal. The tail is prehensile, and twines around sea weed or the tails of other sea horses. In many fish the pectoral fin is specially developed. In flying fish, which are found in shoals in all warm seas, they are greatly expanded, and are vibrated to keep the fish in the air after it has leaped out of the water by

FIG. 4.32   A flatfish, the turbot, *Scophthalmus maximus*, x 1/4.

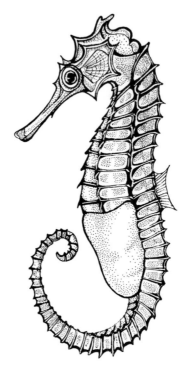

FIG. 4.33   The sea horse, *Hippocampus antiquorum*, x 1.

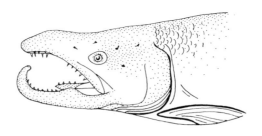

FIG. 4.34   The head of a male salmon, *Salmo salar*, to show the hook on the lower jaw, which is developed in the breeding season only, x 1/3.

powerful tail strokes. In the gurnards the pectoral fins are used for walking along the bottom of the sea, and in the mud skipper (*Periophthalmus*) of the East Indies, for hopping about on the land.

The air bladder is not always connected with the pharynx, and in many species, especially the flatfishes, it is not present. The eel (*Anguilla*) migrates partly over land through wet grass, breathing through its tail as it does so, the mud skipper breathes through its tail, and the climbing perch (*Anabas scandens*) uses special sacs which diverge from the pharynx just above the gill slits. Even in well-oxygenated water it cannot get enough oxygen if it is prevented from coming to the surface and compelled to use its gills only.

We may now recapitulate something of the history of fishes. In the Ordovician, marine jawless forms, the ostracoderms, were in existence, and during the Silurian and Devonian they became much more numerous and lived also in fresh water. Before the end of the Devonian they disappeared from the record, but presumably a few must have survived to give rise to their remote present-day descendants, the lampreys and hagfishes. Before the end of the Silurian, shark-like gnathostomes, the Placodermi, were living alongside the Agnatha. They, too, flourished throughout the Devonian in both salt water and fresh water, but were extinct by the Permian. Meanwhile, in the middle Devonian the first true elasmobranchs or sharks appeared. A few, such as *Pleuracanthus*, in the Carboniferous and Permian, lived in fresh water, but on the whole the elasmobranchs, though still fairly successful in the seas, have never been able to invade rivers or lakes.

The first fish with a bony endoskeleton appear in the Devonian. The early forms are difficult to disentangle and there has been much disagreement about the placing of many of them, but most paleontologists now believe that, from the first, two types of body structure existed. One, based on the existence of internal nares and the use of the lung, includes the coelecanths and Dipnoi and later led on to the Amphibia (p. 77), while the other, without internal nares, remained as fish. The line leading to *Polypterus* and the sturgeons early split off, and that leading to *Amia* became distinct in the Triassic. The rest, the teleosts, expanded greatly in the Cretaceous, and are now the dominant vertebrates in all waters.

It is easy to forget, when we are dealing with periods as remote as the Devonian, Silurian, and Ordovician, that they lasted for many millions of years—the three of them together longer than the time back from the present day to the beginning of the Cretaceous, when the placental mammals had only just come into existence—but even when allowance is made for this it seems impossible to connect these lines of evolution, at least five in number, earlier than the Cambrian. This raises the important question of why no Cambrian vertebrate fossils are known. Even if the original vertebrate had a body as soft and unfossilizable as that of *Branchiostoma*, it must have had many descendants with bony scales before the fish of the Silurian were produced. One is almost driven to believe, for want of any better explanation, that the vertebrates arose relatively suddenly and several times over from whatever prochordate ancestors they had. A similar outburst of evolution seems to have happened in the Mesozoic, when several groups of animals that are called mammals apparently arose more or less at the same time (p. 113).

5

Land Vertebrates

THE EXAMPLES of the eel, the mud skipper, and the climbing perch, as well as of many invertebrates, such as the leeches and crabs that climb trees and the hermit crabs that feed in trash cans on tropical islands, show that it is not particularly difficult for an aquatic animal to live on land. There is more oxygen than in the streams or seas, and the chief difficulty is to prevent loss of water by evaporation. This should be easy for the fish, with their thick scaly skin, but, as we shall see later, it was long before the vertebrates became able to live in really dry situations. Much more difficult for the fish is locomotion. Swimming in the water by means of the segmented tail is something quite inappropriate to movement on land, and fish cannot, therefore, like crabs, simply walk out of the water. Since the vast majority of land vertebrates walk on four paired limbs, we should expect their ancestors to be fish which had already begun to use their fins in this way. As we have seen, there are a few teleosts which do use the pectoral fins for pushing themselves along, and *Epiceratodus* uses both pectoral and pelvic fins to walk backward, the pectorals alone to walk forwards. The possibility of fish giving rise to terrestrial descendants is clearly there. Since the air sacs of Crossopterygii are very similar to the lungs of tetrapods (Chapter 9), it is among these that we can most hopefully look for our ancestors.

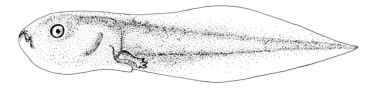

FIG. 5.1   A tadpole of a frog, *Rana temporaria*, x 10.

The tetrapods that most resemble fish are the Amphibia; they are characterized by having a larva which is in effect a fish (Fig. 5.1). It swims by a tail, and has open gill slits, although the functional respiratory organs are external gills that project into the surrounding water and are not dependent on the presence of the slits. (Similar structures are found in a few fish such as *Polypterus*.)

77

Apart from their larvae, the Amphibia are difficult to characterize. In comparison with the teleosts or Chondrichthyes their skull is simple; there is much cartilage and there are far fewer bones. The notochord is often completely obliterated and the vertebrae are well formed; in the frogs they are greatly reduced in number, most genera having nine, and one genus, *Hymenochirus*, only seven, the same number as there are in the neck of mammals. The limbs have the standard pattern to which those of all land vertebrates can be referred—one proximal bone, then two, next a wrist or ankle of several little bones, and distally a hand or foot of fingers or toes, each with several bones. Scales are small or absent.

Internally, amphibians have much resemblance to fish, especially to the Dipnoi. The gill slits are closed in the adult but the lungs are very similar to crossopterygian air sacs. The heart also has some similarity, with two auricles in parallel instead of the single auricle partly divided by a partition which is present in the Dipnoi. From the ventricle there leads a conus with valves, and from this a short single vessel called the truncus arteriosus, which is clearly the ventral aorta. The urogenital system is very similar in general to that of a dogfish. As befits land animals, the eyes are often well developed and the labyrinth has some extra parts not found in fishes; but the lateral line system, though present in the larvae, is generally lost in the adults.

FIG. 5.2 A swimming frog, *Rana temporaria*, with its head just breaking the surface of the water, x 2/3. (Photograph by Miss P. Hunt)

FIG. 5.3   The mud puppy, *Necturus maculosus*, x 1/3.

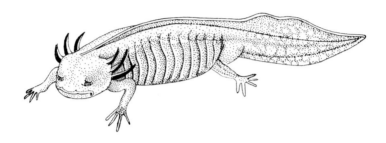

FIG. 5.4   An axolotl, *Amblystoma*, sp., x 1/2.

The living Amphibia are divided into three groups. The Anura, tail-less when adult, are the frogs and toads (Fig. 5.2); they include the most terrestrial of Amphibia, for while some, such as the bull frog (*Rana catesbiana*) and the edible frog of Europe (*R. esculenta*), spend much of their time in water, the tree frogs (*Hyla*) live, as their name implies, in trees, and *Chiroleptes* of Australia lives in deserts. The most obvious characteristic of the Anura is their method of movement by leaping, and many of the peculiarities in the skeleton can be referred to this. The hind-limbs and pelvic girdle are so modified for this peculiar mode of progression that they cannot be said to resemble the fins of fish in any way whatsoever.

The Urodela spend most of their life in the water, even though they have 'walking limbs,' and they retain the tail, metamorphosis consisting chiefly of the loss of the larval gills. *Necturus*, the mud puppy (Fig. 5.3), which is the type commonly dissected in America, does not even do this, and remains in what is in effect a larval condition throughout its life. It is an example of neoteny, or sexual maturity reached by a larva. That this is the most probable explanation of what has happened is shown by another genus, *Amblystoma* (Fig. 5.4). One species, *A. tigrinum*, normally metamorphoses, but sometimes—especially in cold conditions at high altitudes—does not; while another, *A. mexicanum*, never, so far as it is known, metamorphoses in nature but can be induced to do so by feeding it with extract of thyroid gland. Attempts to make *Necturus* and similar forms metamorphose have been unsuccessful.

Only a few urodeles, such as the salamanders (*Salamandra*) of Europe and Asia, use the legs in a properly terrestrial way, but although they can move quite fast they do not lift the body off the ground and there is much side-to-side bending of the whole trunk reminiscent of the swimming of a fish.

In spite of their generally more aquatic life the urodeles differ from the frogs and toads in having internal fertilization. This has enabled viviparity to develop in several of them, including the salamanders. The young are born fully developed, but if they are removed alive from the uterus they can swim and complete their development in water.

The last group, the Apoda (or Gymnophiona or cecelians), are obviously specialized creatures, living in burrows in the tropics (Fig. 5.5). They are blind and limbless, and there is no larva, but the structure of the heart, brain, and urogenital organs and the usual presence of external gills in the embryos rank them as Amphibia. They differ from both Anura and Urodela in the presence of small scales in the skin.

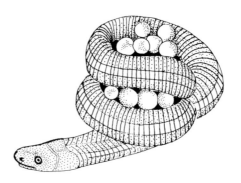

FIG. 5.5   An apodan, *Ichthyophis*, x 1/2.

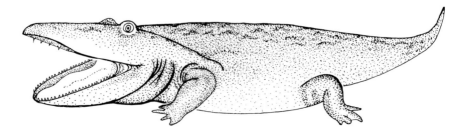

FIG. 5.6   A Triassic amphibian, *Paracyclotosaurus*, sp., x 1/30. (Drawn from a restoration by M. Wilson in *Fossil Amphibians and Reptiles*, British Museum (Natural History), 1962)

No fossils that can be ascribed to any of these groups are known earlier than the Cretaceous, where there are skeletons referable to the Urodela, and the Trias, where *Protobatrachus* may be a primitive anuran, and these are much too late to mark the origin of land animals. The modern Amphibia do not therefore help us much in understanding the change from water to land, especially in view of their many specializations and frequent neoteny. It is in fact almost certain that most newts and probably most frogs are more aquatic than their ancestors. Many zoologists believe that the Anura and Urodela are descended from different groups of early Amphibia, and so are not closely related; the Apoda are probably more closely related to the newts than to the frogs.

The first skeletons with limbs of the same general type as those of the Amphibia are found in the late Devonian. They, and similar forms extending to the Trias, are called Stegocephalia, but this name may include several not very closely related lines.

The skeleton of the early stegocephalians, such as *Eogyrinus* from the lower Carboniferous, was very similar to that of a crossopterygian. The skull had much the same bones, but the face, the portion in front of the orbits, was relatively longer, and that behind the orbits shorter. This is a change that continued in later tetrapods. The pectoral girdle too was very similar, and still attached to the skull. No sternum is known, although some anatomists have argued that one must have been present, presumably made of cartilage. The pelvic girdle did not articulate with the backbone. All these features suggest that the creature was unable to turn its head from side to side and that its legs were unable to support its body. Since *Eogyrinus* was about fifteen feet long, this is not surprising. Later Stegocephalia, such as *Eryops* from the Permian, had the pectoral girdle free from the skull and an articulation between ilium and backbone, but in *Paracyclotosaurus* (Fig. 5.6) from the Triassic, which had presumably returned to an aquatic life, the ilium merely touched the sacral ribs. *Diplovertebron*, of the Carboniferous and lower Permian, seems to have had a neck, and had longer limbs with five toes, so that the body must have been distinctly lizard-like. In all these ancient amphibians the skeleton of the limbs was of the same pattern as that of the modern ones, though the wrist and hand (and ankle and foot) were often much shortened.

The vertebrae were bony, but of a type more closely related to that of some reptiles than to the modern amphibians.

The geological environment of most of the early amphibian fossils suggests that they lived in fresh-water lakes or marshes, and their weak limbs suggest that at best they were amphibious, or even that they never came out of the water. The modern animals nearest to them in an ecological sense would perhaps be the crocodiles. The skeleton shows that they had internal nostrils and there is no trace of any support for gill slits, so that they were presumably air-breathing. Swamps, where the water is often poor in oxygen, might clearly encourage air-breathing, as occurs in the modern Dipnoi, but do not seem to provide very promising conditions for an active exploration of the land. Further, large animals seem to be always an end product of an evolutionary line, and the early Stegocephalia were all large. Many of the later ones are even more aquatic than *Eogyrinus*, having elongated bodies and small limbs that must have been nearly or totally useless. All this suggests that the Stegocephalia are not very near

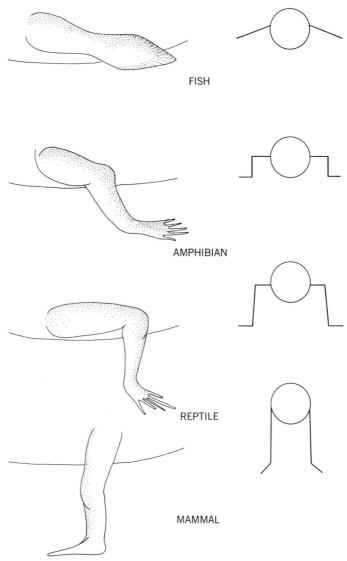

FIG. 5.7   Diagrams of the positions of the limbs in four types of vertebrate.

the base of the tetrapod line. They may indeed be, like *Necturus*, creatures which were on their way back to the water, and descended from more fully terrestrial ancestors. Since the Stegocephalia were in existence before the end of the Devonian and were well developed and thriving in the Carboniferous, the first land vertebrates must have evolved at the beginning of the Devonian or even in the Silurian. This would make them as old as any known fish except the ostracoderms and the placoderms, and means that they could not have evolved from any known Crossopterygii.

We do not strictly know that the Stegocephalia were Amphibia, since no certain fossil larvae have been found, and they are placed with them rather because it has always been assumed that the first tetrapods would have laid their eggs in water than for any other reason.

Active terrestrial life requires limbs that lift the body off the ground, so that it can be moved without waste of energy in overcoming friction. The alterations that must take place in the limbs for this to occur are shown in Fig. 5.7; they can be demonstrated by the human arm, thanks to the fact that it has great facility of movement. If one lies prone, with the arms stretched out at right angles to the side of the body, one is in much the same position as an early Stegocephalian, as *Necturus,* or even as a dog-fish. The ventral surface of the limb (the palm of the hand) is downward, and the pre-axial border (the thumb) is in front. Movement of the limb backward and forward on the shoulder joint will tend to push the body forward, provided that friction is less as the limb swings forward than it is when it moves back. Such differentiation could be produced either by lifting the limb in the forward swing or by the development of scales or claws that projected backward. A newt taken out of water and placed on a table can be seen to move in this way, the oscillation of the limbs being produced by a wave contraction of the trunk very similar to that in the swimming of fish. Amphibia have no scales or claws, so that presumably there must be some lifting of the limb. Alternate but independent movements of the limbs, such as can be made by man, can occur only when the segmental arrangement of the muscles has been lost.

Such independence is followed or accompanied by the body being lifted off the ground by two right-angled bends in the limbs, in opposite directions; the forearm is bent down on the elbow and the hand up on the wrist, to give the gymnastic position known as 'press-up.' Useless friction is now eliminated, and the limbs can easily be brought forward clear of the ground; when the muscles that would otherwise pull them back are contracted, the weight of the body pressing on the hand produces enough friction to pull the body forward instead.

A further stage, reached much later in evolution, allows much faster movement. The elbow joint is straightened again, the limb twists so that the fingers point forward, and the limb is swung backward and forward

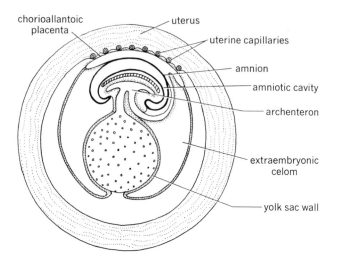

FIG. 5.8   Diagrammatic sagittal section of the embryo of a viviparous lizard.

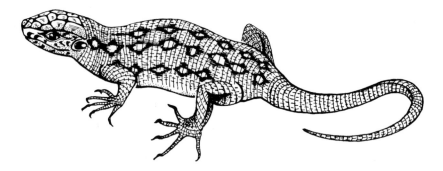

FIG. 5.9   A lizard, *Lacerta agilis*, x 1.

more or less underneath the body. In a few animals the bend at the wrist is also eliminated, and they walk on the tips of their fingers.

Similar changes take place in the hind-limb, but cannot be demonstrated in the human leg.

The first tetrapods to lift their bodies off the ground were the reptiles, and some of them reached the stage of back-and-forward motion beneath the body. Existing reptiles are easy to recognize but difficult to characterize except in a negative way. They do not have aquatic larvae, and so are not Amphibia, and they have neither hair nor feathers, and so are neither mammals nor birds.

Some reptiles are viviparous, but the majority have large yolky eggs, which are laid on land, even when the adults are aquatic. The embryo has two peculiar sacs or membranes (Fig. 5.8). One, the amnion, completely surrounds it and takes no part in the make-up of the body; it is presumably protective. The outer parts of the folds from which it is formed make the chorion. The other, which is an outgrowth from the gut, is called the allantois and is concerned in both nutrition and respiration. It is later absorbed. The reptiles, together with the birds and mammals, are known through the possession of the first of these as the amniotes. A membrane which surrounds the yolk, and shrinks as this is absorbed, is called the yolk sac. A similar, though probably not homologous, membrane is present in teleosts.

Internally, the reptiles show a very wide range of structure. The skeleton is almost completely bony, with limb bones and girdles well developed in accordance with the function of the legs. The skin is thick and scaly and respiration is almost entirely by lungs. There are always two auricles, and the ventricle sometimes has a partition, which may be nearly complete. There is no ventral aorta, separate aortic arches coming off from the ventricle and bending right and left. The former of these is often very much larger than the other. The kidneys have lost all trace of segmental arrangement, a condition called metanephric; and there is a new kidney duct, the ureter. Though they often have large heads the brain remains small.

The existing reptiles are lizards (Fig. 5.9), some of which are limbless (Fig. 5.10); snakes (Fig. 5.11); a peculiar species called *Sphenodon*

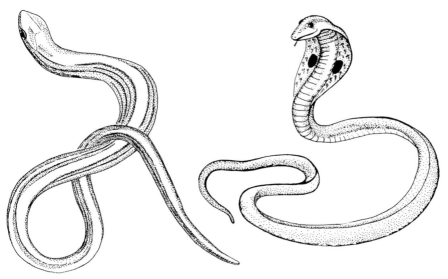

FIG. 5.10　A legless lizard, the European slow-worm, *Anguis fragilis*, dorsal, x 1/2.

FIG. 5.11　A snake, the king cobra, *Naia bungarus*, x 1/2.

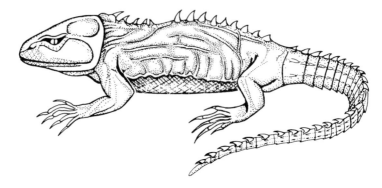

FIG. 5.12   *Sphenodon punctatus*, x 1/3.

punctatus (Fig. 5.12), confined to New Zealand, which was formerly put in a subclass of its own but is now closely associated with the lizards; the crocodiles and alligators (Fig. 5.13); and the turtles (Fig. 5.14).

The lizards and snakes are placed together in the order Squamata. There is a wide range of size in the order, and most of its members are active. Snakes cannot be very sharply distinguished from lizards, but the main characters, apart from the absence of limbs, lie in the skull. This is highly mobile, so that the upper jaw and part of the face can move forward and upward on the cranium. This makes the gape very wide, and since at the same time the two sides of the lower jaw are not sutured but merely joined by an elastic ligament, snakes can sometimes swallow prey much larger than themselves. A few, such as pythons, have vestiges of hind-limbs and pelvis, but none has any trace of fore-limb or shoulder girdle, whereas both girdles are present in limbless lizards.

Sphenodon, of the order Rhynchocephalia, a rare reptile, is very similar to fossils that have been found in the Permian. It looks like a lizard but differs in a number of points, especially in the form of the skull, which will be discussed in Chapter 16.

Crocodiles, Crocodilia, are all large and aquatic. Their feet are partly webbed, and they swim slowly by these and move rapidly by the laterally

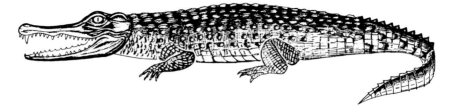

FIG. 5.13   An alligator, *Alligator* sp., x 1/20.

FIG. 5.14 A marine turtle, *Chelone midas*, x 1/12.

flattened tail. The skull is of the same basic pattern as that of *Sphenodon*, but it is elongated, and has the external nares high on the anterior end, and the internal nares carried far back by the presence of a secondary bony palate, so that the animal can breathe while its mouth is open under water. The condition of the circulatory system approaches that of birds, with an almost completely divided ventricle and the right systemic arch much larger than the left.

The turtles and tortoises, or Chelonia, have a wide range of habitat, terrestrial, fresh water, and marine, and are characterized by a thick box-like shell, made of shields of keratin ('tortoise shell') covering a series of flattened bones, from holes in which head and limbs protrude (Figs. 18.14, 18.15). Only in a few aquatic forms is the shell reduced, but the skin is always thick. The skull has some similarity to that of the earliest known reptiles, but it is specialized in having the teeth replaced by a horny beak and in having far fewer bones in the temporal region. There is also reduction in the number of vertebrae, which is smaller than in any other vertebrates except the frogs.

A bewildering variety of extinct reptiles is now known. The most important from a phylogenetic point of view are the earliest of all, the Cotylosauria. Bones ascribed to this group have been found in the Carboniferous, but the earliest reasonably complete skeleton is that of *Seymouria*, of the lower Permian. The structure of the vertebrae, limbs, and girdles suggests that, though the body was not raised above the ground, the genus was distinctly terrestrial. Further, the lacrimal bone on the front of the orbit is pierced, presumably for a tear duct, and tears are not of much use in water. Hence most zoologists regard it as a reptile. On the other hand, the rest of the skull is little different from that of the Stegocephalia, some specimens even showing traces of lateral-line canals, so that there is some

FIG. 5.15   A restoration of *Limnoscelis*, a Permian cotylosaur, x 1/40.

reason for thinking that *Seymouria* was still an amphibian. Since the distinction between Amphibia and Reptilia depends on the embryo and larva, the question is likely to remain unresolved.

Many other skeletons with the same completely roofed skull but distinctively reptilian in vertebrae, girdles, and limbs are found later in the Permian and in the Triassic (Fig. 5.15). Their type of skull, with an arch of dermal bones completely covering the jaw muscles in the temporal region, is called anapsid, and the name Anapsida is commonly used for a subclass to include the Cotylosauria and the Chelonia.

Living at the same time as the cotylosaurs, from the Carboniferous to the Triassic, was another group of reptiles, the Synapsida. The temporal region of the skull is pierced by a single large opening, known as a vacuity, which is below the postorbital, which, as its name implies, is the bone immediately behind the orbit, making its posterior border. On account of this condition, which is very different from anything found in the Stegocephalia, the synapsids are generally considered to have descended from the cotylosaurs, but, as is so often the case, no actual fossil ancestors are known, all the cotylosaurs so far discovered being much too late. We have already seen a similar frustrating situation in the evolution of the fish, and other examples of the same thing will be seen later.

The best known of the synapsids are the Therapsida, or mammal-like

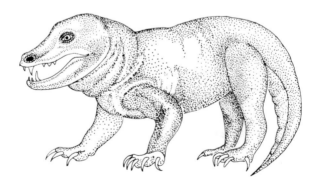

FIG. 5.16   A restoration of a therapsid, *Cynognathus* sp., x 1/24.

reptiles (Fig. 5.16), of which a very large number of skeletons of some four hundred species have been found in South Africa. They had achieved the state in which the limbs fully support the body, and were clearly very active animals. To judge from the teeth, some were herbivorous and others carnivorous, the latter presumably pursuing and eating the former. All four limbs were of equal length, so that the animals were terrestrial in a normally quadrupedal way. They became extinct in the Jurassic, but to judge from changes that had taken place in the skull before that time their descendants became the mammals.

The therapsids were the dominant land vertebrates of the Permian and the Triassic, but during the latter period they were replaced by other forms, apparently descended independently from the cotylosaurs. These are characterized by two vacuities in the temporal region of the skull, one below and one above the postorbital, hence their description as diapsid. The name Diapsida is not, however, generally used as a classificatory term. The dominant diapsids from the Triassic to the Cretaceous were the Saurischia and the Ornithischia, commonly known together as dinosaurs. Both groups contain many giant forms, though there are small ones as well, and both have a general tendency to have the hind-limbs much larger than the fore-limbs, even to the extent of being completely bipedal. This tendency is also present in the earlier diapsids, the Pseudosuchia. The Saurischia include both the largest known terrestrial carnivores (*Tyrannosaurus*, 50 feet long, Fig. 5.17) and the largest herbivores (*Diplodocus*, 80 feet long, Fig. 5.18). Their large size suggests that they must have lived in water, since their bones could not otherwise have supported their weight, and the presence of external nostrils on the top of the head in the herbivores confirms this. The carnivores presumably lived on the herbivores, and both became extinct together before the end of the Cretaceous. Their large size suggests also that they must have had some cooling mechanism, and perhaps temperature control. Since the velocity of conduction of the nervous impulse in cold-blooded animals is only about one meter per second, their co-ordination, unless they had warm blood, must have been slow and imperfect, for the passage of an impulse from a toe to the brain and back again would take anything up to 40 seconds, and during this time conditions might have changed so that the response would be inappropriate. It is presumably because of this difficulty that, as suggested by the hollowing of the vertebrae, there was an expansion of the central nervous system in the sacral region. This would mean that the hind-limbs could be moved without impulses having to go to the cerebellum, but does not get over the difficulty of the co-ordination of fore-and-hind-limbs, or of the fact that, so far as is known, the only balancing organ was, as in all vertebrates, in the head.

The Ornithischia (Fig 5.19) had a beak which replaced teeth at the front of the jaws, and their skeleton had some resemblances to that of a

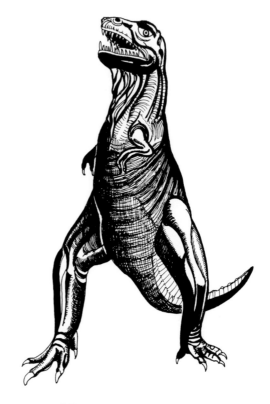

FIG. 5.17   A restoration of *Tyrannosaurus,* a carnivorous dinosaur from the Cretaceous, x 1/100. (Based on the restoration by Neave Parker, in *Dinosaurs,* British Museum (Natural History), 1962)

FIG. 5.18   A restoration of *Diplodocus,* a vegetarian dinosaur of the Jurassic, x 1/200. The animal almost certainly lived in water. (Based on a restoration by Neave Parker, in *Dinosaurs,* British Museum (Natural History), 1962)

bird. They seem all to have been herbivorous, and include both bipedal and quadrupedal forms. Some of the latter were heavily armored, with horns on the skull or huge vertebral spines.

The dinosaurs are included with some other diapsid reptiles in the sub-class Archosauria. Other orders in this are the crocodiles, the Pseudosuchia, and the Phytosauria. All three of these are first found in the Triassic. While the Phytosauria were aquatic and very similar to crocodiles, the pseudo-suchians were like bipedal lizards.

Also placed in the Archosauria are the Pterosauria or pterodactyls (Fig. 5.20), flying forms first found in the Jurassic. Their skeleton shows that they had a large wing supported mainly by the elongated fourth finger but also probably by the hind-limbs. It seems unlikely that they could have walked, and their life was presumably more like that of bats than birds. Many are found near what are thought to have been sea cliffs, where

FIG. 5.19 *Iguanodon*, a beaked dinosaur from the Cretaceous, x 1/24. (Based on restorations by various authors)

FIG. 5.20   An early pterodactyl, *Dimorphodon* sp., x 1/10. (Drawn from the restoration by M. Wilson in *Fossil Amphibians and Reptiles*, British Museum (Natural History), 1962)

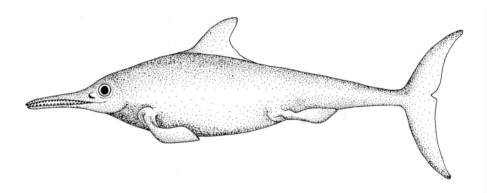

FIG. 5.21   A restoration of a later ichthyosaur, *Ichthyosaurus* sp., x 1/20.

soaring flight and slow stalling speed are important. An aircraft was designed in the 1920's on the basis of a pterodactyl, and could fly at speeds
as low as twenty five miles per hour. It seems likely that the pterodactyls
must have picked fish off the surface of the sea like a skimmer
(*Rhyncops*), for they could probably not rise from the surface once they
ceased to be air-borne. Pterodactyls are not found after the Cretaceous.

Two other subclasses with no living members are the Ichthyosauria
(= Ichthyopterygia) and Synaptosauria. Of all secondarily aquatic vertebrates, the former (Fig. 5.21) are the most completely adapted to the
water, their only rivals in this respect being the whales. They had a dorsal
fin and a laterally flattened tail, into the lower lobe of which the vertebral
column extended, so that they were hypocercal. The paired limbs show
both more digits and more joints than usual—hyperdactyly and hyperphalangy—and the whole skeleton of the limb consisted of a large number
of small bones fitting closely but not articulated together, so that the general effect was very similar to the fin of a dogfish. The limbs were presumably used in a similar way. Since small skeletons have been found
inside large ones some species at least were presumably viviparous. The
skull had one temporal vacuity, above the postorbital, a type called
parapsid.

Most of the Synaptosauria were also aquatic, and are put in the order
Plesiosauria or Sauropterygia (Fig. 5.22). They were more awkward creatures than the ichthyosaurs, with enlarged girdles with big surfaces for
muscle attachment, and large paddles, with hyperphalangy but no hyperdactyly, with which they presumably swam. The neck and tail were usually long and the skull was parapsid. Placed in the same subclass are a few
terrestrial fossils with the same type of skull, including *Araeoscelis* from
the Permian, which was at one time thought to be a possible ancestor of
the lizards.

The last subclass, the Lepidosauria, includes only the Rhynchocephalia
and Squamata, with which we have already dealt, and some rather doubtful fossils such as the Permian *Youngina* and the Triassic *Prolacerta*. These

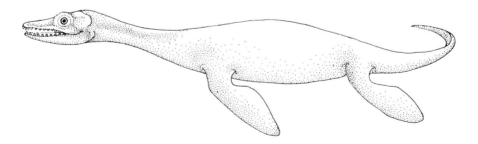

FIG. 5.22   A restoration of an early plesiosaur, *Macroplata* sp., x 1/30.

are diapsid, but in *Prolacerta* the quadratojugal making the bar below the lower vacuity was only one mm. thick, showing how the condition of the lizards, in which the lower vacuity is open below (p. 374), might have been produced. *Prolacerta* is, however, much too late to be an ancestor, and has already lost the pineal eye, which lizards retain.

Classification of the Reptiles

Although the orders of reptiles are mostly obvious and natural, their association into subclasses and arrangement in a phylogenetic tree are difficult, constantly changing, and not generally agreed. It is almost impertinent for one who is not an expert in the group to write on the subject and the following discussion is offered to help the student to find his way through a cloud of opinions by the help of a few facts. It should be read again after Chapters 10 and 16 have been studied.

Order began to appear when Goodrich in 1916 showed that there were four basic types of reptilian skull: anapsid, with the jaw muscles completely covered by a series of bones in the temporal region, behind the orbit; diapsid, with two gaps in this region, separated by the postorbital and squamosal bones; synapsid, with a single gap in the position of the lower one of the diapsid skull; and parapsid, with a single upper gap. Reptiles of the first type, the Anapsida, included the Cotylosauria and, a little doubtfully, the Chelonia; the diapsids included the crocodiles, dinosaurs, pterodactyls, and *Sphenodon;* the Synapsida only the Therapsida and Pelycosauria; and the Parapsida were rather a waste-paper basket for a few fossils not easily placed elsewhere, and perhaps the Squamata and some extinct groups. Some zoologists, however, thought that these were really diapsids which had lost the bar below the lower temporal gap.

Since the structure of the skeleton points positively to the dinosaurs as being very near the ancestors of birds, and even more strongly to the therapsids as the ancestors of mammals, Goodrich further suggested that the structure of the heart and great vessels in these groups could be projected back into their reptilian forebears; and since the crocodiles and, as he erroneously thought, the lizards, have a heart which could easily give rise to that of birds, he distinguished two main lines of descent from the cotylosaurs: the theropsidan (note the spelling) leading through the Therapsida to the mammals and the sauropsidan, leading by radiation to all other reptiles and the birds.

Such a simple scheme can no longer be sustained, for while the theropsidan line still seems clear, the other reptilian orders are too diverse to be associated in one subclass. The heart of crocodiles, though similar to that of birds, is divided on a different principle from that of lizards, so that the Squamata and crocodilia must have separated very early, perhaps being independent evolutions from the cotylosaurs. There are also important, though smaller, differences between the hearts of lizards and turtles, suggesting that they too are not closely related. This can only mean that the cotylosaurs had a much simpler heart, from which all three reptilian types, as well as that of the mammals, could be derived. This was, indeed, nearly the conclusion that Goodrich came to, and it is a strong reason for not including the Chelonia in the Anapsida. We cannot know the condition of the heart in those extinct reptiles that cannot be associated with any living descendants, so that they must be placed by the characters of their skeletons and especially their skulls.

Much unnecessary difficulty has been caused by slight changes of name in recent classifications, so that 'Pterodactyla' have become 'Pterosauria,' and so on; unfortunately the student has to learn to recognize both the old name and the new, whichever he chooses to use.

The following table shows the subclasses and chief orders of reptiles as they have appeared in recent books—doubtful assignments are indicated by square brackets.

SUBCLASS	ORDER	TIME	NOTES
Anapsida	Cotylosauria	Carboniferous to Trias	Anapsid
	[Chelonia]	Permian to present	Doubtfully anapsid
	Millerosauria	Permian	Synapsid
Synaptosauria = Euryapsida	Protorosauria	Permian to Trias	Parapsid
	Sauropterygia = Plesiosauria	Trias to Cretaceous	Parapsid
Ichthyopterygia	Ichthyosauria	Trias to Cretaceous	Parapsid
Lepidosauria	Eosuchia	Permian to Eocene	Diapsid
	Rhynchocephalia	Trias to present	Diapsid
	[Squamata]	Trias to present	Doubtfully diapsid
Archosauria	Pseudosuchia = Thecodontia	Trias	Diapsid
	Phytosauria	Trias	Diapsid
	Crocodilia	Trias to present	Diapsid
'Dinosaurs'	{ Saurischia	Trias to Cretaceous	Diapsid
	{ Ornithischia	Trias to Cretaceous	Diapsid
	Pterosauria = Pterodactyla	Jurassic to Cretaceous	Diapsid
Synapsida	Pelycosauria = Theromorpha	Carboniferous to Permian	Synapsid
	[Mesosauria = Proganosauria]	Permian	Synapsid
	Therapsida	Permian to Jurassic	Synapsid

The evolutionary relationship of these groups appears to be something like this:

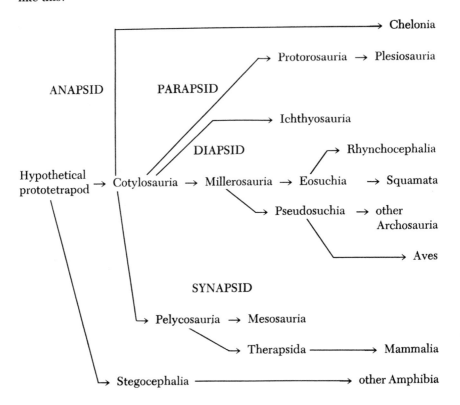

6

Birds

IN THE Permian and Jurassic the reptiles were extremely successful.
They dominated the land, and had sent at least three branches back into
the water and one into the air, all of which were numerous enough to leave
plenty of fossils. Afterwards their decline was rapid, and none of the
dominant groups of reptiles of the past has any members alive at the
present day. There are about two hundred species of tortoise, five thousand of lizards and snakes, and only twenty-five of crocodiles, whereas
there are some hundreds of described species of therapsid, and the total
number lying in the sands of the Karoo desert in South Africa must be
hundreds or thousands or millions. The lizards and snakes are the most
successful existing reptiles, occupying many different terrestrial habitats
and a few in water, but nowhere present in very large numbers. The decline of the reptiles may be due in part to their replacement by descendants distinct enough to be placed in separate classes—the Mammalia (discussed in the next chapter), and the Aves, or birds.

Birds illustrate how much more we can know of living creatures than
we can ever learn from fossils, and show how our judgment may be influenced accordingly. If we knew no modern birds, and could study the
group only in fossil skeletons, there is little doubt that we should regard
them as merely another subclass of reptiles, or perhaps even as an order
to be placed in the Archosauria. There are many peculiarities in the skeleton, but it is doubtful if they are any greater than those in, for example,
the pterodactyls, and many can in fact, as we shall see shortly, be paralleled in various reptilian groups. In spite of this the whole mode of life of
the birds is so different from that of the reptiles, and their radiation into
different habitats is so distinct, that no one has ever seriously doubted the
propriety, if not the wisdom, of putting them in a separate class.

The diagnostic feature of birds is not that they fly, for some do not, but
that the body is covered with feathers. These are discussed in Chapter 18,
and they are well enough known not to need further description here. All
birds have them, and they cover almost the whole body, though the lower
portions of the legs are often without them and are covered instead with
quite reptilian scales.

What may be called an ordinary bird may be illustrated by a song bird,
or passerine (Fig. 6.1). The animal flies, walks, or hops on its legs, and is
completely terrestrial and largely arboreal. Other birds, such as the kiwi

FIG. 6.1   A passerine bird, the magpie, *Pica pica*, x 1/4.

FIG. 6.2   A flightless bird, the kiwi, *Apteryx* sp., x 1/2.

(*Apteryx*) (Fig. 6.2) and ostrich (*Struthio*), cannot fly, but have wings similar in structure to the song bird's. Many birds have some degree of adaptation to swimming in or under the water, for example, the cormorants (Fig. 6.3), using their wings and feet for the purpose but still able to walk and fly quite actively. The penguins (Fig. 6.4) have a fore-limb which is a flattened paddle, excellent for swimming but useless for flight.

FIG. 6.4 A penguin, *Pygoscelis adeliae*, a flightless swimming bird, ventral, x 1/5.

FIG. 6.3 The shag, *Phalacrocorax aristotelis*, a bird which can fly, dive, and swim, x 1/5. Various species of *Phalacrocorax* (cormorants) are found throughout the world, including the Pacific and the Atlantic coasts of North America.

The wing of a bird, whether used for flight or not, has a quite distinctive skeleton (Figs. 6.5, 6.6). The embryo has a set of bones which might be purely reptilian, but as the animal grows some of them fuse, and instead of separate carpal and metacarpal bones a compound carpometacarpus is formed. It is difficult to see how this arrangement helps in flight; the mystery is made greater by the formation of a similar tarsometatarsus in the hind-limb (Fig. 6.7, 6.8). If either of these was produced by natural selection it looks as if the same gene produced both and as if the advantage of one of them was so great as to carry the other along with it. Since something similar to the tarsometatarsus was possibly present in some of the

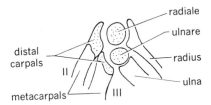

FIG. 6.5   The right wrist of a young house martin (*Delichon urbica*) ventral, x3. The distal carpals are not yet completely fused to the metacarpals. Compare Fig. 6.6.

FIG. 6.6   The skeleton of the wing of a pigeon, *Columba livia*, x 1.

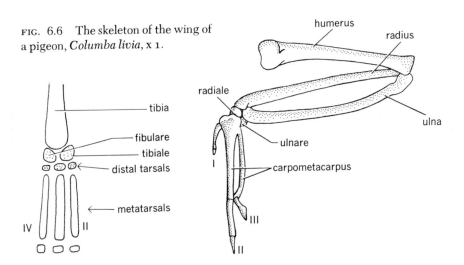

FIG. 6.7   The right ankle of a young house martin (*Delichon urbica*) dorsal, x 3. The tibiale and fibulare are separate from the tibia, and the distal tarsals are separate from the metatarsals. Compare Fig. 6.8.

this, being stiff yet flexible, easily replaced when damaged, and being versatile enough to be modified for the soaring of the eagle, in which the separation of the distal feathers to make a slotted wing is probably important, and for the rapid vibratory flight of the hummingbird. But a bat can fly quite as well as most birds though it has no feathers, and their use for flight would not seem to necessitate their growth all over the body. Here, however, they have another function, that of preventing loss of heat. Temperature control, in an animal the size of most birds, would probably be impossible in the absence of an insulating layer, and this is perhaps the first function of feathers, since the birds, like the mammals, which use hair for the same purpose, are warm-blooded. If this is so we have an example, of which there are many more, of the birds having taken over and used for flight a structure already present in non-flying ancestors. Preadaptation of this sort has probably been of great importance in evolution.

The movement of the wing necessitates large muscles, and the pectoral muscles of birds are proportionately much bigger than those of any other animal. Big muscles need a big surface of bone for their attachment, and the sternum of birds is marked by a deep vertical plate, or keel. A similar but smaller keel is found in the other flying vertebrates, the pterodactyls and bats.

The other chief feature of the skeleton, the complete fusion of pelvic girdle and vertebrae to form a synsacrum (Fig. 6.8), is connected with bipedal gait rather than directly with flight. The same is true of the heterocelous vertebrae (Fig. 15.4) in the neck, which make this part of the body very flexible, so that the bird can reach almost any part of its body to preen the feathers with its beak, but have no direct connection with flight. How careful one must be in deciding on the adaptation of an animal is shown by the uncinate processes on the ribs. These, which project backwards from the ribs, each passing outside the rib behind it, have been often said to be an adaptation to flight because they make the thorax more rigid. They are found also in Eryops, in Sphenodon, and in crocodiles, some of the most sluggish of animals. Again they may be a preadaptation in birds, but what their first function was remains a mystery.

The skull of birds is diapsid but much modified, and in the adult one can seldom make out the limits of separate bones.

The internal organs of birds show three features that are found in no reptiles. The lungs have a unique structure and are associated with a system of air sacs which are placed in the thorax and the abdomen, and extend into some of the bones. Air is taken in through bronchi to the air sacs, and is then forcibly expelled from them through the many fine divisions of the lungs. There is thus no stagnant air in the lungs, that which comes in contact with the respiratory surface having the full oxygen concentration of the atmosphere. That the air sacs are never quite emptied does not matter, since the oxygen concentration in them does not fall to any extent nor does the carbon dioxide concentration rise. Not even the mammals have so efficient a system.

The ventricles are completely separated and there is no left systemic arch, a condition that is foreshadowed in the crocodiles. This means that deoxygenated blood brought back from the tissues to the right auricle goes only to the lungs, for by a spiral twist down to the base of the aorta the right systemic arch comes from the left ventricle, and the left from the right.

The brain is much larger in proportion to the body than in any reptile, and the size of the cerebral hemispheres rivals that of mammals. The hind part of the brain, the cerebellum, is also large. The eyes and ears are very well developed, but few birds have any appreciable sense of smell.

The behavior of birds, especially in connection with reproduction, nesting, and migration, shows an elaboration far beyond anything found in reptiles, and it is presumably largely through the selective advantage of this that the brain has been developed. Much of this behavior is instinctive, that is, it is acquired by the individual without learning or practice, and many authors say that birds are, by comparison with mammals, instinctive rather than intelligent. This is not true in the sense in which it is meant, for while the instincts of birds are more complicated than those of mammals, most birds are probably as intelligent as any mammals except the primates. The acquisition and spread of new habits shows this. It became customary in England in the 1930's for milk to be delivered and left on doorsteps in bottles with a cardboard stopper. Before long, blue and great tits learned to open the bottles to drink the cream; and when the type of bottle was changed to one with an aluminum cap they learned to deal with this too. There is some evidence that this habit first arose accidentally and then spread by imitation.

There are relatively few fossil birds, and little is known of their immediate ancestry, but three specimens of a single species of one Jurassic bird have been found in two neighboring quarries in Germany. This is *Archaeopteryx lithographica* (Figs. 6.9, 6.10). It was a creature about the size of a crow, with an opposable first finger and so presumably arboreal, but in almost every other feature quite reptilian. There are teeth, the vertebrae are not heterocelous, there are no uncinate processes, and there is a long tail. The condition of the wrist and ankle is not certain, but it is probable that there was only a third carpometacarpus but four separate tarsometatarsals. If this was so the hind-limb was in advance of the fore-limb in this respect, and the suggestion made above that the single fused carpometacarpus of modern birds is not a direct adaptation to flight, but follows on the condition of the tarsometatarsus, is made more probable. The animal would be a reptile but for one thing: it had feathers of exactly the same type as those of modern birds. Some covered the body, and long ones, the bird's primaries and secondaries, were arranged to form a wing. The

FIG. 6.9 *Archaeopteryz lithographica*, x 1/3. (Based on a restoration by M. Wilson in *Fossil Birds*, British Museum (Natural History), 1962.)

sternum probably had no keel, so that *Archaeopteryx* is unlikely to have been able to fly very actively, but it presumably used its wings in gliding downward from one tree to another, in the manner of the so-called flying squirrels and flying lizards. This confirms the suggestion made above, that feathers were concerned with temperature regulation before they were used for flight.

There are many pseudosuchian reptiles in the Triassic which are near enough in structure to *Archaeopteryx* to have been close relatives of its ancestors, but none is known which could itself be an ancestor. The general view is that some of these small, active, and at least incipiently warm-blooded animals took to climbing trees and then to gliding. The alternative view that a bipedal reptile ran and flapped its fore-limbs until it became air-borne is not now held. Any direct derivation of the ostrich-like birds from bipedal reptiles is ruled out, in spite of their superficial similarity, by the many points in which their skeleton appears to be a reduc-

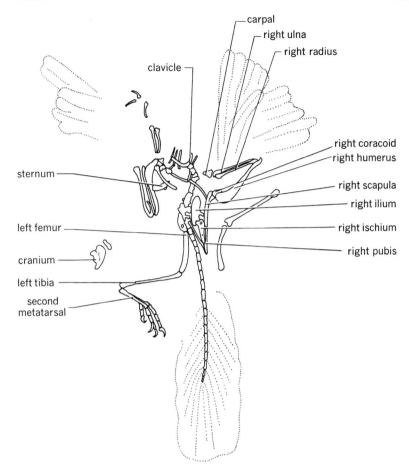

FIG. 6.10   *Archaeopteryx lithographica*, (British Museum specimen), x 1/3.

tion from that of the flying birds. Some of these are paralleled in other
flightless birds.

Aerodynamics is a difficult science, and the theory of a moving airfoil is
not completely worked out. Because of this, and because relatively little
experimental investigation has been done, our knowledge of bird flight is
incomplete. The bird's wing (Figs. 6.11, 6.12) is mainly supported by the
metacarpus and the second digit, and there is a small tuft of feathers, the
bastard wing, or alula, supported by the thumb. The wing can be bent at
elbow and wrist, and also rotated on the shoulder girdle. These movements enable it to go through a complicated figure-of-eight path in each
stroke. In the pigeon in slow flight, as at take off, the amplitude is only
about 90°, from vertically upward to a little below the horizontal, and ob-

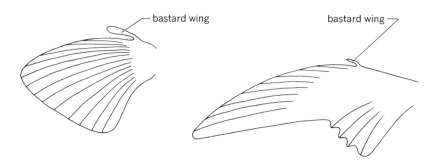

FIG. 6.11   A wing of low aspect ratio (length over breadth), the wren, *Troglodytes troglodytes*, x 2/3.

FIG. 6.12   A wing of high aspect ratio, a young swift, *Apus apus*, x 1/2. In an adult bird the ratio is even higher.

servation of the bending of the feathers shows that during the stroke forces are exerted both backward and downward (Fig. 6.13). This tells us no more than we could have forecast from physical principles, but the photographs do suggest that the bird does something to even out the forces during the cycle, driving itself forward, as does the good breast-swimmer, even during the recovery stroke. This may become more important in steady flight, when propulsion is more important than lift. Different shapes of wing, which are roughly expressed by the ratio of length to breadth, or aspect ratio, are undoubtedly important in different types of flight, but the relationships are obscure. In general, strong fliers and birds of open spaces have a higher aspect ratio than weak fliers and woodland birds (Figs. 6.11, 6.12).

The alula is undoubtedly important, probably in preventing stalling, since it is opened especially in slow flight and in hovering. It then produces the device known as a slotted wing, which may be seen in action when an aircraft comes in to land. The separated primary feathers of soaring birds have a similar function. These birds make use of large wings and rising air currents. Gliding is lateral movement on extended wings without vertical currents. Lateral velocity produced by previous flapping of the wings may, by alteration of the angle of the wings, be changed into vertical motion, so that the bird rises.

The classification of birds is difficult, not, as is that of reptiles, because there are many diverse forms which cannot confidently be associated in a phylogenetic tree, but because most birds are so very much like each other; taxonomic groups that are for convenience called orders are the equivalent of families in other vertebrate classes. There are nearly nine

FIG. 6.13   A pigeon (*Columba livia*) in slow flight. (A) The wings have just begun the down beat; the curve of the primary feathers shows that they are pressing backward against the air. At this stage the bastard wing (not shown) is slightly open. (B) The wings are near the bottom of the down stroke; the primaries are still pressing down, but the humerus has begun to rise. (C) The humerus is still rising, but the wrist has begun a sharp downward flick. (D) The wing is fully extended near the top of the up-stroke; there is little pressure on the primaries in either direction. (Redrawn from Brown, *J. Exp. Biol.* 25, 1948)

thousand living species of birds, and although the division of these into about thirty orders is for the most part fairly clear, no very satisfactory grouping of these orders is agreed. The penguins are usually separated as a superorder, Impennes, leaving the rest as the superorder Neognathae. It is still convenient to refer to the flightless birds—ostriches, kiwis, etc.—by the old name of Ratites, even though they are now placed in half a dozen orders which are probably not closely related (the capacity for flight having been lost several times) and similarly all the other orders of the Neognathae, the typical birds, may be called Carinates. The Impennes and the Neognathae, together with some rather problematical fossil birds which probably had teeth and are put into another superorder, the Odontognathae, constitute the subclass Neornithes. This leaves *Archaeopteryx* in a subclass by itself, the Archaeornithes.

7

Mammals

JUST AS the birds may be recognized by the possession of feathers, so all mammals, and no other animals, have hair. It is, however, sometimes very much reduced—to a few whiskers, for example, in whales. Hair, like feathers, is primarily an insulating layer.

Although the skeleton of a mammal is usually easily recognizable as such, there are few characters in it that are diagnostic. The best is in the lower jaw, which consists of one bone only, the dentary, on each side; in reptiles and birds there are always several. The dentary articulates with the squamosal, whereas in all other tetrapods the articulation of the jaw is between articular and quadrate, two bones that are absent from the jaws of mammals. Less obvious, but equally diagnostic, is the mechanism that conveys sound across the middle ear. In mammals there is a chain of three little bones or ear ossicles in place of the single bone possessed by all other tetrapods. As we shall see in Chapter 16, the changes in the ear and lower jaw are connected.

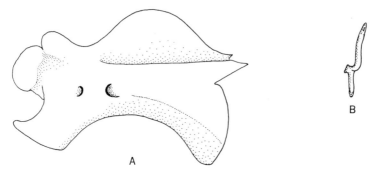

FIG. 7.1   Cervical vertebrae (A) Giraffe (*Giraffa camelopardalis*) x 1/4. (B) Porpoise, *Phocaena phocaena*, x 1/4.

The neck of mammals is peculiar in that, however short or however long it may be, the number of vertebrae is almost always seven (Fig. 7.1). The only exceptions are two genera of sloths (*Bradypus* and *Choloepus*) which have nine and six respectively, the ant-bear (*Tamandua*) with eight, and the aquatic manatee (*Manatus*) with six. There is a general tendency to reduction of the shoulder girdle, sometimes to scapula only,

sometimes to scapula and clavicle, and only rarely is there a separate coracoid element.

The skull is basically synapsid, but with a greatly expanded brain-case,
paralleling in this respect the diapsid skull of birds. The teeth are nearly
always of several different types, having different functions in eating.

The characteristic features of the internal organs also parallel those of
birds, although the same or similar functional effects have been achieved
by different morphological means. The lungs have many small chambers,
so that the internal surface is greatly increased, but there is nothing like
the air sacs of birds. Instead, the partition between the thorax and the abdomen is developed into a muscular diaphragm, so that breathing is vigor-
ous. The blood is peculiar in that the red cells of the adult lose their nuclei
before they become functional.

The heart has two completely separate ventricles, and there is only one
systemic arch, but this time it is the left, which comes from the left ventricle. There is therefore exactly the same separation of oxygenated and
deoxygenated blood as has been achieved by birds, but the relationship of
the arches to the heart shows that it must have been brought about in
quite a different way.

The brain has even larger cerebral hemispheres in proportion to its size
than in birds, but the cerebellum is not so well developed. Eyes and ears
are usually important sense organs, and so is the nose. Many mammals in
fact live by smell as much as or more than by vision, and in comparison
with birds their eyes are relatively poor in discrimination and in color
sense.

The vast majority of living mammals have the characteristic that gives
the class its name: the female feeds the young on milk which is ejected
from the glands that produce it, called mammae, through openings on various parts of the ventral surface. This habit is connected with the fact that
the typical mammal is viviparous. In most, the unborn young, known as
a fetus, is firmly attached to the mother by a structure called a placenta
(Fig. 7.2), formed partly from the allantois and partly from the uterine
wall. Through the placenta food and oxygen are taken to the embryo, and
its waste products are led away through the blood of the mother. Such
mammals are placed in the subclass Placentalia or Eutheria (Fig. 7.3).

Mammals of another type, the subclass Marsupialia or Metatheria (Fig.
7.4), have mammae but no placenta, or only a very temporary one. The
young is born precociously (that of a six-foot kangaroo is about half an inch
long at birth) and is capable only of crawling up the mother's belly, along a
track that she licks with her tongue, to a nipple, to which it becomes firmly
attached and from which milk is pumped into it. The nipples of a marsupial
are enclosed in a fold of the body wall, or pouch, from which the group gets
its name. Many features of the skeleton and other parts of the body show
that the marsupials diverge rather widely from the placentals. They ap-

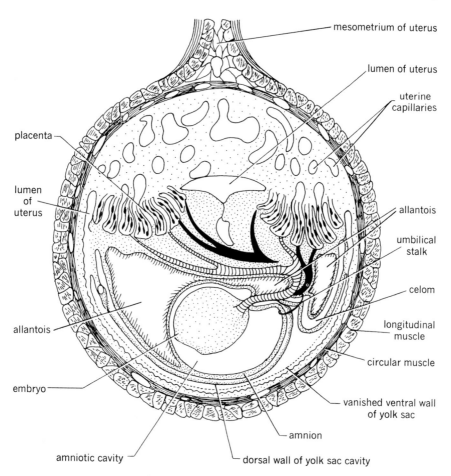

mesometrium of uterus

lumen of uterus

uterine
capillaries

placenta

lumen
of
uterus

allantois

umbilical
stalk

celom

longitudinal
muscle

allantois

circular muscle

embryo

vanished ventral wall
of yolk sac

amnion

amniotic cavity

dorsal wall of yolk sac cavity

FIG. 7.2 A section of a mammalian uterus and fetus, to show the placenta.

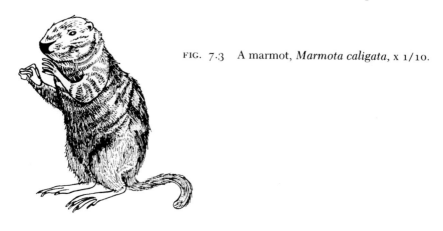

FIG. 7.3 A marmot, *Marmota caligata*, x 1/10.

FIG. 7.4   The great gray kangaroo, *Macropus major*, x 1/16.

proach most closely to the order known as Insectivora, as is shown, for example, by a ventral view of the skull (Figs. 7.6, 7.7, 7.8).

There are two or three mammals, the duck-billed platypus (*Ornithorhynchus*) of Australia and Tasmania (Fig. 7.5) and one or two species of
spiny anteater (*Echidna*) of Australia and New Guinea, which fit neither
into the Placentalia nor the Metatheria. They lay eggs like those of reptiles, and are placed in the subclass Monotremata or Prototheria. Their
mammae are glands of a different type from those of other mammals; they

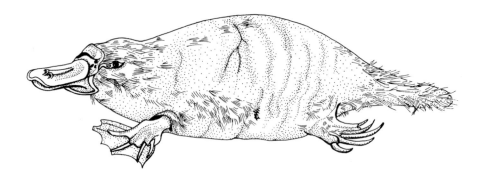

FIG. 7.5   The duck-billed platypus, *Ornithorhynchus paradoxus*, x 1/3.

are enclosed, like those of the marsupials, in a pouch, into which the female anteater transfers her eggs. There are many reptilian features both in the skeleton and in the soft parts. For example, the ventral part of the pectoral girdle has both a coracoid and a procoracoid, and there is a cloaca. The characteristic mammalian features of the lower jaw and ear, the seven cervical vertebrae, the diaphragm, and the single left systemic arch, as well as hair, leave no doubt that they are mammals, however early they may have diverged from the main line. Many of their features are obvious specializations, for *Echidna*, is, as its English name tells us, one of those peculiar animals that subsist almost entirely on ants, and has many similarities, in feet and skull, to other mammals that do the same thing, while the platypus is largely aquatic, with webbed feet and thick epidermal snail-crushing plates in the mouth instead of teeth. We need not suppose that the first mammals were either ant-eating or aquatic.

It is obvious that we cannot hope to trace in fossils the change of the soft parts from the reptilian to the mammalian condition, and since the limbs of many mammals are relatively unspecialized—or, rather, since they have no common pattern of mammalian specialization—the things that we must look out for in the fossils are the changes in the skull and shoulder girdle. The later therapsids had several mammalian features: the brain case was enlarged; the postorbital was reduced, as in *Cynognathus*, or missing, as in *Bauria*, so that the temporal vacuity had broken into the orbit; the bones in the lower jaw, other than the dentary, were reduced in size and lay almost free at the back of the jaw, and there were different sorts of teeth, including large canines which give the skull the dog-like appearance from which *Cynognathus* gets its name. Between the last of these animals, which were certainly reptiles—they disappear in the early Jurassic—and the first of the modern mammals in the Cretaceous, there is a long gap, which is only partly filled by a mixed collection of fossils known generally as Mesozoic mammals. All had the jaw articulation between dentary and squamosal, and it is this feature which leads to their being grouped as mammals, but we do not know whether or not they had hair and a single aortic arch. Many are imperfectly known, usually by parts of the skull only, and some have been classified alternatively as reptiles. With only one feature to go by, and that not a very important one, the decision must be to some extent arbitrary. In *Diarthrognathus* (Subclass Ictidosauria) the dentary articulates with the squamosal, a good mammalian feature, but the old reptilian articular-quadrate joint persists alongside it. Clearly, by our criterion this animal was both mammal and reptile, or neither.

There are five other groups. The Docodonta, from the Jurassic and Triassic, have a reptilian shoulder girdle rather like that of the monotremes. Their teeth have three cusps in a row, a condition known as triconodont. Similar teeth were present in another group of Jurassic mammals, which have the group name Triconodonta. They are less well known, and had a rather different type of jaw.

The Allotheria or Multituberculata are found from the Jurassic to the lower Eocene, and had a skull superficially similar to that of a rabbit, with broad attachments for muscles, long, chisel-like incisors, a diastema, and cheek teeth with several cusps. One can little doubt that they chewed vegetable food.

The Symmetrodonta and the Pantotheria (= Trituberculata), both from the Jurassic, resemble each other fairly closely. Both have cheek teeth with a triangular surface, but while the symmetrodonts have three cusps on this regularly arranged at the corners of an equilateral triangle (hence their name), the pantotheres have extra cusps on the inner border. The cheek teeth of most modern mammals have several cusps, and much ingenuity has been devoted to deriving them from the tritubercular pattern. This is all very theoretical, but it does seem possible that the marsupials and monotremes were descended from one or other of the last two groups, perhaps from the symmetrodonts through the pantotheres. Some modern classifications include all four of these types of mammal in one subclass, the Theria, but this seems premature in the present stage of our knowledge, and is certainly awkward for students. The monotremes are generally left as a separate line, perhaps connected with the docodonts. The multituberculates have been claimed in the past as ancestors to the monotremes, to the marsupials, to the placentals, and to both the monotremes and the marsupials. If we now, as most paleontologists do, think these supposed connections to be quite impossible, we should also remember that our successors may think the same of some of our popular lines of descent. Looking at things from the outside, all one can believe with confidence is that between the Jurassic, when the therapsids became extinct, and the Eocene, when the placental mammals were present in abundance, there were several groups which, in their skeleton, were more or less mammalian. They may have had hair and mammae, and a single left systemic arch, or they may not. Some may have led on to the surviving mammals, or some of them; others certainly did not, and may indeed, have been merely reptiles with a larger brain and better teeth than most.

The important feature of the eutherian mammals is the great development of the allantoic placenta, so that the young are relatively large at birth, and in some species, such as the deer, able to run nearly as fast as their parents almost at once. The skeletons can be recognized by a number of features, chiefly in the skull. The middle ear is surrounded by the tympanic bone, which may be ring-like but is more often swollen up so that it resembles a flask without a base, making what is called a bulla. This never happens in marsupials, which may have instead a bulla formed from the alisphenoid bone. The optic foramen, through which the optic

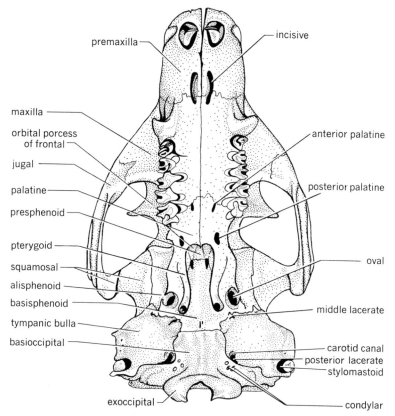

FIG. 7.6 The skull of a marmot, *Arctomys marmota*, ventral, x 1. Bones are
labeled on the left, foramina on the right.

nerve runs from eye to brain, usually pierces the orbitosphenoid bone,
whereas in marsupials it has moved back to join another foramen, the
anterior lacerate, as a space between orbitosphenoid and alisphenoid. The
palate is complete (Fig. 7.6), whereas in marsupials it is incomplete or
fenestrated and the posterior border tends to be thickened. The lacrimal
foramen, through which the tear duct runs to the nose, is within the orbit,
not, as in marsupials, over its edge, on the face. The jugal does not take
part in the articulation of the lower jaw, as it does in marsupials. The
dentary is a vertical plate of bone, without the horizontal shelf at the
lower posterior corner, known as the inflected angle, which marsupials
have. There are never more than three teeth, the incisors, in each quarter
of the mouth in front of the canines. Since there is no pouch for the
young, there are no bones to support it. The marsupial or monotreme has
these, called epipubic bones, attached to the pelvic girdle.

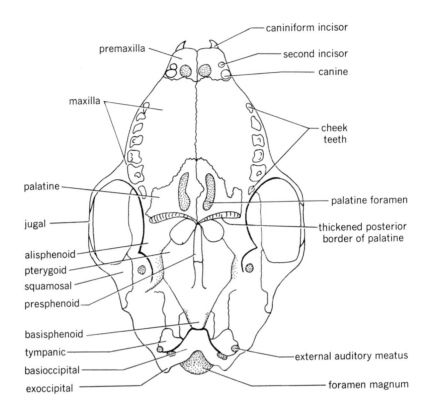

FIG. 7.7 The skull of an insectivore, the hedgehog, *Erinaceus europaeus*, ventral, x 3/2. Bones are labeled on the left, foramina on the right.

Many of the marsupial features of the skull are present in some placentals, especially in the order Insectivora (Fig. 7.7). Skulls ascribed to this order, which on other grounds also is regarded as the most primitive and nearest to the reptiles, are found in the Cretaceous, and there is no doubt that the placentals had evolved by this time. By the Eocene all the existing orders of mammal, as well as some that have since become extinct, were established.

One interest of the mammals lies in what is called their adaptive radiation, that is, the way in which, while retaining the general plan of structure, they have made use of different types of food and different ways of living, and have altered some parts of the body accordingly. This radiation is best seen in the feet and the skull, and it is possible, with very little practice, to assign any mammalian limb or skull to its order with complete confidence. Study of mammalian skulls is of great interest to the ecologist as well as the comparative anatomist.

Attempts have been made to group the orders of mammals into cohorts and superorders indicating common ancestry, but these are not very convincing and we shall not use them here. Everyone agrees that, both on ecological and paleontological grounds, the order Insectivora is the most primitive. Its members are all small, they feed chiefly on invertebrates ('insects,' as that word was used in the eighteenth century) and for the most part have unspecialized feet with five digits. They possess clavicles. The skull has many features characteristic of marsupials (but not the inflected angle), and there is often a full set of teeth, that is, three incisors, a canine, four premolars, and three molars in each quarter jaw—a dentition which is represented by the formula $\frac{3143}{3143}$. Within this general pattern they show considerable specialization, so that they have an adaptive

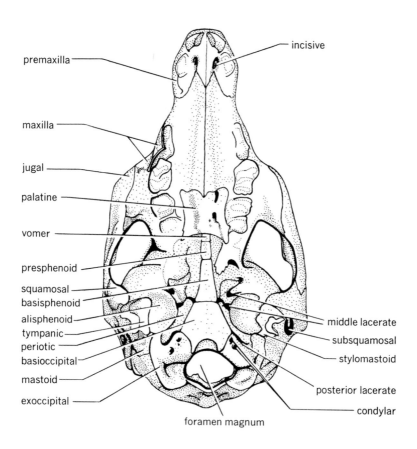

FIG. 7.8 The skull of a marsupial, the bandicoot, *Hypsiprimnus* sp., ventral, x 3/2.

radiation of their own. Even the central types, the shrews (*Sorex*) and hedgehogs (*Erinaceus*), have much specialization, for example, in the flexible snout of the former and in the spines and teeth of the latter. The shrews have, too, reversed the usual trend of evolution by becoming smaller and smaller, so that some of them are the smallest mammals and, except for the hummingbirds, the smallest homeotherms known. They lose so much heat from their relatively large surface that in temperate climates they must feed at least every four hours, and have given up the usual daily rhythm. Many insectivores, such as the water shrews (*Neomys* of Europe and Asia, *Sorex palustris* of America) and the two-foot-long *Potomogale* of Africa, are aquatic. The desman (*Myogale*), which is related to the moles and lives in Europe and Asia, has webbed feet. Others, such as the moles (Talpidae), burrow in the earth and are called fossorial. They are blind and have greatly strengthened fore-limbs which are turned backward to shovel the earth behind them as they dig. The golden moles (*Chrysochloris*) of South Africa have many similar features. Others, such as the tree shrews (Tupaiidae) of the East Indies, are arboreal, and are diurnal, with large somewhat forward-looking eyes which are bounded behind by a complete bony arch where the jugal and frontal bones have met. In this and other features they resemble the more primitive monkeys, or lemurs, with which they are sometimes grouped. The elephant shrews (*Macroscelidae*) of Africa resemble them in some ways, but are jumping or saltatorial, with long hind-legs. The semi-volant *Cynocephalus* (= *Galeopithecus*), the flying lemur of Malaya and the Philippines, is now usually placed in a separate order, the Dermoptera, but is not greatly different from the insectivores. It jumps and glides from tree to tree, helped by a broad fold of skin and muscle stretching between its limbs.

It is obvious that although the insectivores have remained primitive, with a small brain, they have been able to spread into and hold their own in a wide variety of environments. Aquatic and fossorial forms, for instance, have each developed at least four times, and probably more often.

Some early arboreal insectivores probably developed into bats (Cheiroptera, or Chiroptera). They were distinct in the Eocene, but how they arose is unknown. They are the only truly flying mammals, with large wings supported by both fore- and hind-limbs, but chiefly by the elongated second, third, fourth, and fifth fingers. There is a strong pectoral muscle attached to a small keel on the sternum. Instead of becoming bipedal, like the birds, the bats have lost the power of walking, as the pterodactyls also had presumably done. When at rest they hang upside down by the claws of the hind-limbs. Some of the larger fruit bats are, however, surprisingly active in climbing, using the claws of the feet and of the thumb.

Bats are nocturnal and their eyes are poor, but they have developed a very efficient system of sonar. As they fly they give out very high-pitched notes, which are reflected from solid surfaces and picked up by the ears. By this means bats can detect the whereabouts not only of obstacles like walls and trees, but of the large insects, such as moths, on which they feed.

Two aberrant orders of mammal which are usually placed close to the insectivores are the Edentata, or armadillos, sloths, and anteaters, and the Pholidota, containing only the genus *Manis*, the pangolin. The armadillos are omnivorous animals, mostly fossorial, with protective bony plates in the skin overlaid by horny scales, so that there is superficial resemblance to a tortoise. One species can roll itself up like a hedgehog. They range from the southern United States to Paraguay. The sloths live upside down in American tropical forests, hanging from branches by hooked claws, eating leaves, and moving very slowly. The anteaters, also from tropical America, have a long snout with jaws which hardly open and a long tongue with which they collect the ants and termites on which they feed. Several fossils show intermediate stages between these apparently diverse forms.

The pangolins live in Asia and Africa, and their resemblances to the anteaters come from the fact that they eat similar food. The body, which can be rolled up, is covered with rows of large scales, which may be formed of fused hairs.

A third type of anteater, the aardvark (*Orycteropus*) of South Africa, is placed in a separate order, the Tubulidentata. It used to be put near the edentates, but the resemblances do not seem to be fundamental and it is now usually associated rather with the hoofed animals than with the insectivores.

The last order to be associated with the insectivores is the Primates. (If this word is read, as it should be, as Latin, it has three syllables; the same spelling, without an initial capital letter, is English and pronounced as two syllables.) As we have seen, the tree shrews connect the two orders, but most primates differ from insectivores in having the orbit surrounded with bone and in being able to oppose the thumb and big toe to the other digits, so that objects can be grasped both with hands and with feet. In other respects the primates are primitive. There is a large and unspecialized clavicle, and the radius and ulna remain separate.

The most striking feature of the primates is the great enlargement of the brain, and the changes which that imposes on the skull. There can be no doubt that the primates are the animals best able to learn from experience, and that it is the great size of their cerebral hemispheres that enables them to do this. If one can transfer a word from human psychology, many of them are able to think. Various people have suggested that before thinking could be developed there had to be something to think about. This was provided, they say, when the early primates developed the opposable thumb and moved their eyes from the side to the front of the head. Things could then be picked up and held in front of the face to be seen and to become objects of contemplation. It is certainly remarkable that the most intelligent of birds, the parrots, also have some degree of binocular vision and are able to hold food to the mouth in one foot while they stand on the other. Primates are the only mammals with fully developed color vision, although this sense is, so far as is known, universal in birds and is present also in some reptiles and in urodeles and some fish.

The primates are divided into the suborders Prosimii (Lemuroidea), or lemurs and lorises, and Anthropoidea, or monkeys, apes, and man. The former are more primitive, with no tendency to walking on their hind-legs, and long dog-like faces. The lemurs live in Madagascar, the lorises in Africa and Asia. *Tarsius*, the spectral tarsier, a small East Indian animal with forwardly directed eyes, is sometimes associated with them, sometimes placed in a group on its own. All these creatures are arboreal and nocturnal, and probably resemble in habits, as they do in skeleton, the earliest primates from the Paleocene.

The Anthropoidea take further the characters foreshadowed in the Prosimii, and especially in the tarsier. They come to depend more and more on their eyes, and the sense of smell is reduced, until in man it is vestigial. Although monkeys use all four limbs in running as well as climbing, there is a general tendency to sit on the haunches so that the fore-limbs are freed for handling things, and this presumably led on to the bipedal progression of apes and men. The gibbons move rapidly through the trees by swinging from the arms alone. The American monkeys, placed in a separate superfamily, the Platyrrhini or Ceboidea, include some that can swing from branches by their prehensile tails, a facility their cousins in the old world, the Catarrhini or Cercopithecoidea, have never acquired; other American monkeys, the marmosets, have lost the opposability of the thumb.

The chief zoological characteristics of man are his upright stance, with flat feet, no opposable big toe, and huge buttock muscles to prevent himself from falling over; naked skin; and big brain behind a much flattened face. All these features are approached by the great apes.

Alongside the insectivores of the Paleocene there were other small mammals called creodonts, which showed by the big canine teeth and the crest on the top of the skull (which was presumably an attachment for a muscle so that they could carry things in their mouths), that they were probably carnivorous. They were at one time classed as Insectivora, then put in an order of their own, but are now usually grouped with modern flesh-eating forms as the Carnivora.

The typical modern carnivores, or suborder Fissipedia, are usually easily recognized. They walk on their toes (i.e. are digitigrade); they have big canine teeth; the skull has a big, Y-shaped sagittal crest on top; and the joint of the lower jaw is cylindrical, so that there is no sideways or to and fro movement. The cats (Fig. 16.17) show all these features very well, the dogs less so, and the bears least of all. Bears are in fact omnivorous rather than carnivorous, and, like man, who is also omnivorous, they are plantigrade and have flat cheek teeth.

The seals, sea lions, and walruses are marine carnivores, and are placed in the suborder Pinnipedia, which is not closely related to the others. They feed on fish or shellfish, and the teeth are sharp-pointed to hold the prey. They swim by their limbs, chiefly using the back-turned hind-legs as the equivalent of a tail, but can move quite fast on land, to which they come to breed.

Looking at the existing Carnivora, we can see little resemblance to any other group of mammals, but study of the Paleocene fossils suggests that the creodonts gave rise not only to the Carnivora but to several orders of hoofed mammals, all herbivorous and tending to be large. Some zoologists therefore associate all of these orders in one cohort, the Ferungulata.

Eight orders of ungulate or hoofed animals have no living members; we shall not consider them here, merely noting that there is a general tendency for the members of each order to increase in size until they become extinct, and that some of the large species parallel the features that we see today in the rhinoceros and elephant.

By far the most successful of the existing ungulate orders are the Artiodactyla, including the cattle, deer, antelope, camels, and llamas. The limbs are elongated on an axis that runs between digits three and four. The first digit is absent from all modern forms but it is present in many embryos; in the pigs and hippopotamus, though all four digits reach the ground, numbers two and five are smaller than three and four, while in the cattle, antelopes, and deer there is much reduction of numbers two and five; in the camels, these are missing, so that the animal walks on digits three and four only. There are associated changes in the bones of the legs; the joints are pulley-like, allowing movement in a fore-and-aft direction only, and the clavicle, which would have no function in this type of movement, is absent. The third and fourth metacarpals tend to be fused, so that in the cattle and camels there is a single cannon bone. Most artiodactyls walk on the expanded nails, or hooves, and are called unguligrade, but the camels have instead a broad spreading pad of skin, more suited to use in yielding sand.

These features of the artiodactyls are associated with speed, presumably to escape from carnivorous pursuers. Their other main features are connected with their food. The teeth are flattened and the jaw has a very free articulation, so that the hard cellulose of which their food largely consists can be thoroughly chewed. Digestion is always assisted by bacteria, and in all there is some degree of complexity in the stomach, reaching its greatest development in the four-chambered stomach, associated with chewing the cud, in cattle and deer.

The horns and antlers of artiodactyls (Chapter 18) are mainly used in sexual combat.

The Perissodactyla have achieved a very similar mode of life to the artiodactyls by quite different means, and since there are not more than twenty existing species, against about three hundred artiodactyls, it seems that their methods are not so good. There are now only five species of tapir, four of them in tropical America, perhaps five of rhinoceros in Africa and Asia, mostly on the verge of extinction, and a doubtful number of species of horse in the genus *Equus,* of which only the zebras of Africa exist in the wild state in any numbers. The limbs are elongated through the third digit, which is always symmetrical and the largest. The first digit is absent from all existing species and most extinct ones, so that either four digits touch the ground, as in tapirs, or three as in the rhinoceros, or one, as in horses. The clavicle is absent and there are similar pulley-like joints to those of the artiodactyls, but there is no cannon bone, as the axis is through one digit, not between two, and the same effect is produced by enlargement of the third metapodial and reduction of the second and fourth.

The other ungulates have been even less successful than the perisso-dactyls. The Proboscidea, or elephants, have only two living species, in Africa and Asia. Noted for their great size, with many consequential changes in the skeleton, such as having the proximal elements of the limbs (humerus and femur) longer than the distal, they have also several other peculiar features, such as the trunk, the big external ears, and peculiar compound teeth. The Hyracoidea (the conies of the Bible), which are small rabbit-like animals living in Africa and western Asia, are generally placed near the elephants. They can always be recognized by their incisor teeth, which are triangular in cross section. They are vegetarian and plantigrade, but do not burrow.

Also placed in this cohort, but not very obviously hoofed mammals, are the Sirenia, or sea cows, of which there are only two genera, *Manatus,* the manatee, on both sides of the Atlantic, and *Dugong* (= *Halicore*), the dugong, in the Indian Ocean and Pacific Ocean. Both are completely aquatic, producing their young in the water, but, like all mammals, still breathing air. They swim by means of the tail, which has a horizontally flattened fin; the fore-limbs are large paddles but there is no hyperphal-angy or hyperdactyly; there are no hind-limbs. They approach the condition of whales in many ways, but are not so successful, being able to stay below the water for only about ten minutes, little longer than a well-trained man.

The Cetacea, or whales, which probably came off from some of the early creodonts but are not generally associated with the Ferungulata, are the other fully aquatic mammals. They also swim by a horizontal tail, with fore-limbs as paddles and no hind-limbs. The digits are four or five, but there is hyperphalangy, especially in the second finger—which may have ten or more joints—and in the third. In many there is an unpaired dorsal fin, presumably to prevent rolling, but unlike the unpaired fins of fish it has no skeletal elements. Whales can stay under water for as much as half an hour and can descend to depths of 1500 feet or more, but very little is known of the physiology which enables them to do this. The ear is large, though its external opening is small, and is probably the major sense organ.

The remaining mammals are the rabbits and their allies, or Lagomorpha, and the rats, mice, and others called Rodentia. They were formerly placed in one order but are probably not closely related. Both orders are herbivorous or omnivorous, with grinding cheek teeth and a long gap or diastema between these and the incisors. There are no canines. The jaw muscles are large, and there is a flat articulation for the jaw, associated particularly with the habit of gnawing wood. The Lagomorpha have two pairs of incisors in the upper jaw, one in the lower, the rodents only one pair in each. Both have developed the habit of re-ingestion (p. 169). Both are also remarkable for producing several litters of young in the year, so that their number can increase very rapidly. The rodents especially are a very successful group, probably outnumbering all other mammals put together, and are almost world-wide in distribution. They are the only placental mammals in Australia except for those introduced by man. They have undergone some adaptive radiation, with arboreal forms, such as squirrels (*Sciurus*), fossorial forms, such as the marmots (*Arctomys* and *Marmota*), and aquatic species, such as the beaver (*Castor*). The jerboas (*Dipus*) of Africa, and kangaroo rats (*Dipodomys*) of America, are saltatorial desert forms.

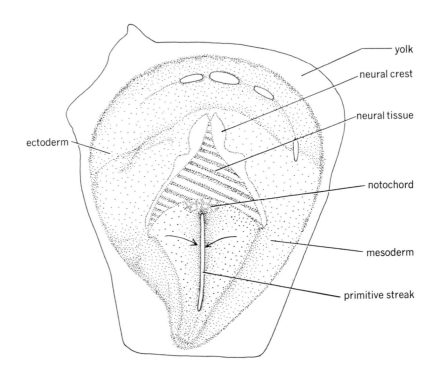

FIG. 8.1   The embryo of a chick, at about 18 hours' incubation, to show the presumptive areas, x 12.

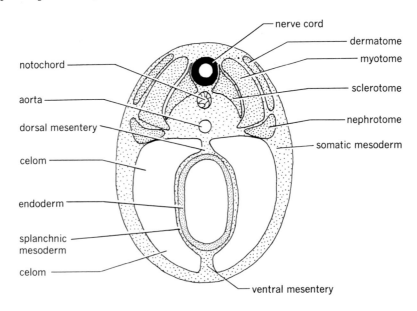

FIG. 8.2   Diagrammatic transverse section of a late vertebrate embryo.

8

Mesoblast and Celom

IN VERTEBRATES the middle layer of the embryo, or mesoblast, arises
in two different ways. At gastrulation a large sheet of cells moves inward at the blastopore so that they come to lie between the wall of the
gut or hypoblast and the external surface or epiblast. In those vertebrates
such as Amphibia where there is a spherical blastula the sheet of cells,
which may be called presumptive mesoderm from its usual fate, is originally a broad crescent (Fig. 1.1A), while in the birds and mammals it is a
flat plate on each side of the main axis (Fig. 8.1). Wherever it starts, it
comes to lie as two sheets, roughly quarter-cylindrical in shape, one on
each side of the notochord, which has been formed at the same time by
cells moving in the same way. These sheets do not at first meet ventrally,
and the mesoderm here may have quite a different origin, being formed
by a condensation of loose cells, called collectively mesenchyme. Some
of these have rolled in with the dorsal mesoblast, but others come from
hypoblast and especially from the neural crest. This origin of mesoderm
from mesenchyme is most notable in the Amphibia, and the tissue is so
liquid in the head of frogs as to have been called mesodermal porridge.

The dorsal part of the mesoblast early becomes divided into a series of
large individual blocks, the somites, which determine the primary segmentation of the animal. Some of the cells of these migrate upward, coming to lie on each side of the notochord as the sclerotomes and forming
also some mesenchyme. The remainder becomes divided into three; there
is a main block, or myotome, and outside this a dermatome and below a
nephrotome (Fig. 8.2). These will give rise in the adult to the structures
suggested by their names; myotome to muscle, sclerotome to skeleton,
dermatome to the dermis, and nephrotome to the kidney. In many vertebrates this fourfold division of the somite is not clearly present, the dermatome especially being often missing. In this case the dermis is formed
from mesenchyme budded off from the myotome; the developing chick
shows the full arrangement, and according to some embryologists a fifth
block of segmental mesoblast, the gonotome, which will give rise to the
gonads, can be distinguished. There is, however, enough similarity in all
vertebrates for us to be confident that we are dealing with segmentation
that is homologous throughout the phylum. We cannot be so certain when
we come to the protochordates. In *Branchiostoma* the mesoblast arises

in a different way, as pouches growing out from the wall of the primitive gut, and is segmented from the beginning. The mesoblast of tunicates and *Balanoglossus* also is formed from the gut wall, but in different ways. Although attempts have been made to reconcile these divergent modes of development, so that homology of the mesoblast in all chordates, if not in all Metazoa, is usually assumed, they are not entirely convincing.

Between the successive somites a few cells are left. These will become the fibrous myocommata which separate the segmental muscles and to which they are attached. In the head the segmentation is incomplete and difficult to make out. We shall deal with it in Chapter 19.

The ventral portion of the mesoblast remains unsegmented, and is known as lateral plate. The plates of the two sides grow downward until they meet ventrally.

Cavities which appear in the mesoblast are known collectively as celom. In *Branchiostoma* there are several pouches, and in *Balanoglossus* five, whose hollows are there from the beginning as cut-off portions of the gut cavity. In vertebrates the celom always arises by the moving apart of cells of mesoblast to leave a space filled with fluid. The main part of it begins through a split in each lateral plate, so that this has an outer or somatic sheet, and an inner or splanchnic one. These sheets are sometimes called somatopleure and splanchnopleure, but these terms are also used for the sheet of mesoblast plus the other material, epiblast or hypoblast, with which it is in contact. We shall therefore as far as possible avoid the words.

The origin of the celom in this way means that there are originally two spaces, one on each side of the gut. As the celom enlarges, the gut is left hanging from the dorsal part of the body by a double fold of splanchnic mesoblast, and it is anchored ventrally, where the two lateral plates have met, by another double sheet. These are called the dorsal mesentery and the ventral mesentery.

Meanwhile other spaces have appeared in the mesoblast elsewhere. In each myotome there may be a myocele, in the nephrotome a nephrocele, and in the gonotome a gonocele. Only the nephrocele, which may open into the general celom, is of any great importance, and we shall deal with it in Chapter 11.

The myotomes form the muscles of the dorsal region of the body—which in fishes remain segmental throughout life—and they grow out also into the limbs, where segmentation is lost. The sclerotomes will form, in a somewhat complicated way, the vertebrae (Chapter 15), but much of these is formed of mesenchyme.

The splanchnic wall of the lateral plate forms the whole of the gut except its secretory and absorptive lining, which is of hypoblast; most of the splanchnic mesoblast therefore becomes smooth muscle, but this is covered by a layer of flattened cells, the peritoneum or serous membrane. This layer continues over the inner surface of the somatopleure, the outer part of which forms the muscles and other structures of the dermis. The somatic mesoblast forms also the buds from which the limbs grow, and takes some part in the formation of the kidney and gonad.

Mesoblast everywhere also forms the walls of the blood vessels, which become laid down as walls surrounding lines of liquid which has been produced from mesenchyme. Some of the cells of this remain as the white cells of the blood. There does not seem to be much formal distinction between the mode of origin of the blood vascular system and the celom, the difference lying rather in the circulation of fluid in the former. It is not surprising that in molluscs and arthropods the organs have come to be suspended in the vascular system (now called a hemocele) just as they are in the celom of annelids and vertebrates.

The main part of the celom is the peritoneal cavity, extending originally from the posterior limit of the head to the far end of the body. The ventral mesentery breaks down either entirely or for most of its length, so that there is one continuous space. The volume bounded by its walls is large, as is obvious when the gut, kidneys, and others organs of an animal are removed in dissection, but there is little free space. The contained organs or viscera nearly fill it, leaving only a small part which is occupied by celomic fluid with a few amoeboid cells.

The celom has two types of opening to the exterior, the celomoducts, which we have already mentioned as characteristic of vertebrates and which will be dealt with in Chapters 11 and 12, and abdominal pores. These are openings, usually paired but occasionally, as in the Dipnoi, single, which open on either side of the anus, sometimes into the cloaca, sometimes directly to the exterior. They are present in many elasmobranchs, in Dipnoi, in sturgeons and other primitive bony fishes, and in a few teleosts. No Amphibia have them, but they occur in crocodiles and turtles. They are probably always secondary, and in the dogfish, where they are easily seen in dissection, they are formed only when the fish is approaching maturity. In some teleosts they serve for the escape of sperm, but their function is otherwise unknown. They must allow celomic fluid to escape when the body is compressed, and possibly water may enter through them, but it is difficult to see how either of these happenings can benefit the animal.

The simple condition of the celom is lost in all adult vertebrates, partly by the growth of the gut and its offshoots, which leads to a complicated twisting of the dorsal mesentery, and partly by the formation of more or less vertical transverse partitions that divide the celom into two or more cavities. *Branchiostoma* is of no help in understanding how the division comes about, since instead of a simple division there is in that animal a complicated splitting up of the celom in the metapleural folds and primary gill bars.

There are three main types of subdivision. In the simplest, a transverse partition separates a smaller anterior pericardium containing the heart, from the larger main peritoneal cavity containing the rest of the viscera. This partition is present in all vertebrates and is always formed in the same way, by the splanchnic mesoderm swelling out just behind the heart, largely because of the veins that form in it, so that it meets the somatopleure and forms a bridge across the celom, in which the Cuvierian ducts (p. 172) develop. This leaves the pericardial and peritoneal portions of the celom connected by a dorsal and a ventral passage. The latter soon closes by the growth of the bridge and of mesoderm from the region of the ventral mesentery, in which the liver is forming, until they meet. There is thus formed a transverse septum with a connection between the pericardium and the peritoneal cavity. This is the condition that persists in some cyclostomes and in elasmobranchs throughout life, although there is always some constriction of the pericardio-peritoneal passage. In *Myxine* it is confined to a wide opening on the right side, in dogfishes to a narrow Y-shaped canal with a single opening immediately behind the heart and one into the peritoneal cavity on each side of the liver (Fig. 8.3A). This odd arrangement is formed by the anterior fusion of two lateral passages which are themselves what is left of the original wide opening. The sturgeons also possess a pericardio-peritoneal canal, but its development seems to be unknown.

In all other vertebrates the transverse septum becomes complete. In lampreys the ammocoete has a pericardio-peritoneal canal, which is obliterated at metamorphosis. The relationship of the cavities in bony fishes is very similar to what would be produced in the dogfish if the canal were closed. In amphibians there is a slight complication because the lungs, enclosed in their mesoblastic coverings or pleura, grow back into the peritoneal cavity on each side of the heart. In frogs the heart also projects into the peritoneal cavity, and the wall of the pericardium is reduced to a thin membranous covering for the heart (Fig. 8.3B).

Most reptiles (Fig. 8.4) are not greatly different from the amphibians, but the lungs tend to be larger, so that the recesses of celom between them and the gut are bigger too. Moreover, the transverse septum is carried back ventrally so that it lies obliquely across the body. In some lizards a new incomplete septum partially separates the portion of the peritoneal cavity in which the lungs lie from the rest. In crocodiles an oblique septum completely isolates the lungs, leaving the liver in a space below. A septum in the same position, which is probably homologous, is present also in birds, and in these it is invaded by muscle fibers that grow in from its circumference. Readers will remember that the crocodiles are in their heart and circulatory system the nearest of all living reptiles to birds. Birds are, however, complicated by the presence of the air sacs. These originate as paired outgrowths from the bronchi, grow into the

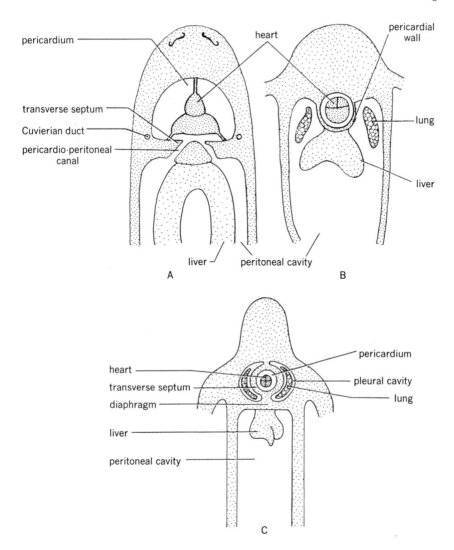

pericardium

heart

pericardial wall

transverse septum

Cuvierian duct

pericardio-peritoneal canal

lung

liver

liver   peritoneal cavity

A   B

heart

transverse septum

diaphragm

liver

peritoneal cavity

pericardium

pleural cavity

lung

C

FIG. 8.3   (A) Diagrammatic frontal section of an elasmobranch. (B) Diagrammatic frontal section of an amphibian. (C) Diagrammatic frontal section of a mammal.

mesoderm which is forming the oblique septum, and communicate with the lungs by secondary recurrent bronchi as well. In a transverse section (Fig. 8.4D) they must not be mistaken for part of the celom.

The mammals also have pleural cavities completely separated from the peritoneal, but the lungs lie on each side of the heart without projecting backward into the abdomen (Fig. 8.3C). The pleuro-pericardial membrane

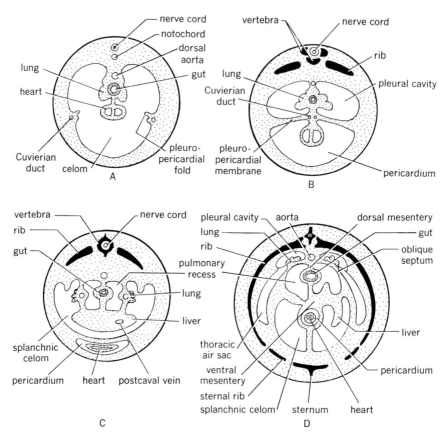

FIG. 8.4   (A) Diagrammatic transverse section of a reptilian embryo, to show the formation of the pleural cavities. (B) The same, later. (C) Diagrammatic transverse section of an adult reptile, to show the celomic cavities. (D) Diagrammatic section of a bird, to show the divisions of the celom.

is formed between lung and heart as the former expands (Fig. 8.5A). The final result, as seen in section, is shown in Fig. 8.5B. The pleural and pericardial cavities come to be separated from the peritoneal celom by a thick muscular sheet, the diaphragm, which in this form is diagnostic of mammals. It is formed in part from the original transverse septum, in part from the pleuro-peritoneal membrane, and in part from various other folds. The muscles begin to grow into it at a very early stage, when the heart is still in the part of the body that will become the neck. Their exact origin is unknown, but they come from some of the anterior cervical segments, so that they are not homologous with those in the transverse septum of birds. As the heart moves backward in development to come to lie in the chest, they carry their nerve fibers with them, and these can be seen in dissection as the conspicuous phrenic nerve running back from the neck, past the heart, to the diaphragm.

The formation of the diaphragm leads to the very conspicuous division of the trunk of mammals into the chest or thorax, and the belly or abdomen. This division is marked in several ways, but especially by the presence in the thorax of long ribs articulating ventrally with the sternum. Both ribs and diaphragm are used in breathing, and the diaphragm presumably evolved because it gave its possessors more efficient respiration. The origin of the muscles from those of the neck is difficult to explain, since that part of the body does not otherwise take any part in breathing.

The method of origin of the celom from two splits in the lateral plate mesoblast shows that there must be, in the middle, a double sheet of mesoblast surrounding the gut and enclosing above this the dorsal aorta and below it the ventral aorta. The gut drops down from the roof of the celom, so that it comes to be slung by the double sheet, which becomes thin and fibrous, and is the dorsal mesentery. The portion of the double sheet below the gut, in which lies the ventral aorta, is the ventral mesentery. Except in the Dipnoi and a few other fish it disappears almost completely, leaving the gut free to coil as it elongates.

The parts of the dorsal mesentery are given names corresponding in general to the parts of the gut that they support, but that supporting the stomach is usually called the great omentum. Diverticula of the gut, such as the lungs and glands, must be covered with mesoderm as they form, and must begin by growing into the mesentery unless this breaks down.

The liver is ventral to the gut, and where it begins, a little way behind the transverse septum, the ventral mesentery persists, so that the liver is

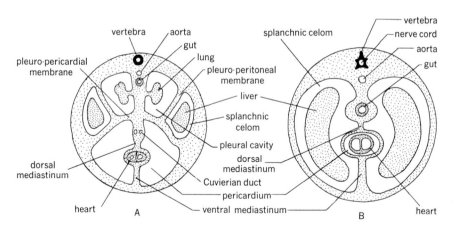

FIG. 8.5 (A) Diagrammatic transverse section of a mammalian embryo, to show the formation of the pericardium and pleural cavities. (B) The same, later.

attached to the duodenum by the hepato-enteric ligament, or lesser omentum, while it is anchored below to the body wall by the hepatic or falciform ligament, both of these being derived from the ventral mesentery. In cyclostomes and elasmobranchs the pancreas grows into the dorsal mesentery just behind the liver. In other vertebrates there are also two ventral pancreatic outgrowths which grow up to fuse with the dorsal one.

The fact that the anterior end of the duodenum is anchored by the remains of the ventral mesentery (hepato-enteric and hepatic ligaments) means that as the stomach elongates it must bend; as it does so, it bulges out to the left. This inevitably pulls the dorsal mesentery out of position, so that there is a pocket opening out of the celom dorsal to the stomach. This becomes large in the tetrapods.

The lengthening and coiling of the intestine also cause twisting of the dorsal mesentery, which in the adult mammal, where the gut is many times the length of the abdomen, is so complicated as to be almost impossible to follow. In most animals the mesentery breaks down in places, so that there is not a continuous sheet of tissue and parts of the gut are unattached.

In the anterior part of the body the heart is formed in the ventral mesentery. Its swelling below the esophogus leads to the division of the mesentery into two parts, the dorsal and ventral mediastina, between which the heart is slung. Later both break down, so that the heart is attached to the pericardium only at its anterior and posterior ends, where, initially, blood vessels enter and leave it. In the dogfish the pericardium is a conspicuous chamber in which the heart can be pushed about in dissection, its posterior wall supported by the cartilage of the pectoral girdle; in tetrapods it is reduced to a thin membrane closely investing the heart, from which it can be peeled off only with care.

The mesoblast which is going to form the kidney and that which is going to form the gonad may also grow so that the organ projects down into the celom or hangs from the roof by a double fold of peritoneum. Such a fold enclosing the kidney is called the nephric fold, and is seldom conspicuous. That which slings the ovary is called the mesovarium and that which slings the testis, the mesorchium. (It is to be noted that the mesonephros is not a membrane slinging the kidney, but a particular type of kidney, see p. 204 ff.) These gonadial folds are very conspicuous in the dogfish, less so in amphibians, and hardly visible in mammals, where the ovaries are very small and the testes have usually moved back out of the abdominal cavity.

9

The Gut and Its Derivatives

WE HAVE already seen that at an early stage in its development the vertebrate embryo becomes a gastrula, in which is a hollow longitudinal space called the archenteron, with walls of hypoblast. In animals with yolky eggs, such as reptiles and birds, the gastrula is not easily recognizable as such, and the floor of the archenteron is made, not by a discrete wall of hypoblast, but by a large mass of yolk. The embryo feeds on this yolk, so that it is gradually reduced, and as it goes the hypoblast closes in to complete the floor. Eventually, therefore, every vertebrate embryo may be said to have a tubular archenteron, from which a large part of the gut is derived (Fig. 9.1A). The only parts that do not come from this structure arise from dimples of epiblast that grow in and meet the archenteron; one, the stomodeum, is anterior, and the other, the proctodeum, is posterior, but both are on the ventral surface of the animal.

There is an unfortunate confusion in the nomenclature of the parts to which these three structures give rise. The simplest terminology, which will be followed in this book, is to say that the anterior part of the gut, formed from stomodeum and so lined with ectoderm, is the fore-gut; that formed from the archenteron and lined with endoderm is mesenteron or mid-gut; and that formed from the proctodeum and ectoderm-lined is hind-gut. This usage has the advantage that it is in line with the way in which the words are used in other Metazoa in which the gut arises in the same triple way.

In the embryos of birds and mammals the archenteron, soon after its formation, bulges forward into the head, and a little later backward toward the tail. Since the floor of the archenteron is incomplete in these animals, these bulges have distinct ventral edges, and these are known as the anterior and posterior intestinal portals (Fig. 9.1B). Embryologists tend to use the name 'fore-gut' for every part of the gut that develops in front of the anterior intestinal portal, 'hind-gut' for the part of it behind the posterior intestinal portal, leaving 'mid-gut' for the part between them.

Whichever system one uses, most of the gut is lined with endoderm, and from this are derived also all the more important branches from the gut, whether they become liver, digestive glands, gill slits, or lungs. This endodermal layer is known as the mucosa or mucous membrane, and its

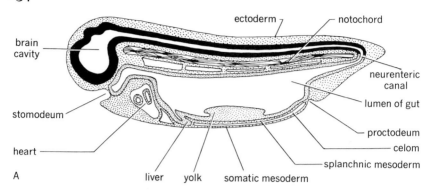

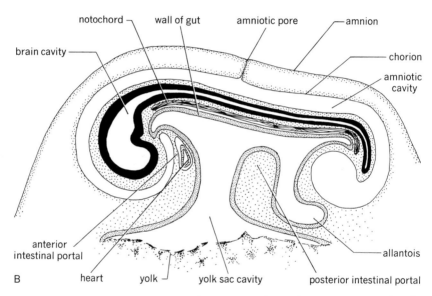

FIG. 9.1   (A) Diagrammatic sagittal section of the embryo of a frog at hatching. (B) Diagrammatic sagittal section of a chick, at about seven days' incubation.

cells often become glandular in various ways. Outside it there is a much thicker wall which is made of splanchnic mesoblast. It has several layers (Fig. 9.2), all in contact. The innermost is the submucosa, which is usually richly supplied with blood vessels and has also a nerve supply in the form of Meissner's plexus. It is almost one with the mucosa, for all the material brought to the glands of the gut and all the food materials absorbed from its lumen must use its blood vessels. Outside it there is a layer of circular muscles, and outside them is a layer of longitudinal ones, which together move the contents of the gut. The nerve fibers that supply these muscle layers ramify between them as Auerbach's plexus. Outside

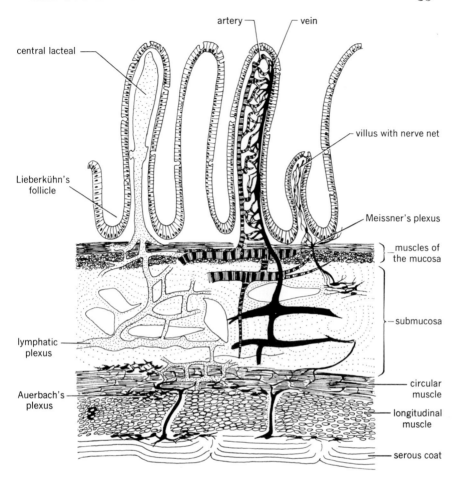

FIG. 9.2 Diagrammatic section through the wall of a mammalian small intestine.

the muscles is the serosa, or serous coat, which consists of connective tissue which is condensed on the surface to make a wall of flattened cells. This, since it is made of mesoderm, is called mesothelium.

The function of the mesoblastic wall of the gut is to contain and support the relatively weak endodermal part, to supply it with blood vessels, and to move the contents. It is obvious that circular and longitudinal muscles are antagonistic; contraction of the former will reduce the diameter of the space or lumen in the middle, while contraction of the latter will reduce its length. Since the liquid it contains is relatively incompressible and the volume of a cylinder is proportional both to its length and to the square of its diameter, the two types of contraction could not occur at once without bursting the tube. In fact they generally alternate in such a way that the contents are continually driven from head to tail. Waves of contraction of circular muscle are continually passing down the gut, followed by contractions of the longitudinal muscles, a mechanism known as peristalsis. Since stimulation of the gut, as by the presence of anything in it, causes contraction of the circular muscle on the oral side of the point of stimulation, food to some extent initiates its own movement. There cannot, however, be continuous movement of the food in one direction, since the anus is normally closed, and there must be axial reflow. There are also other types of muscular contraction, leading to complete mixing of the gut contents.

There are variations in the form and thickness of the muscle, and in some parts the longitudinal muscles run spirally, so that the gut is twisted when they contract. At intervals down the length of the gut the circular muscle is greatly thickened, so that when it contracts the lumen is almost or entirely closed off. These regions, called sphincters, occur between parts of the gut which have different functions and so different shapes. One of the most powerful sphincters is at the anus, where it stops the escape of feces except when it is relaxed.

In all vertebrates three broad functional parts of the gut may be recognized, but they do not correspond to fore-, mid-, and hind-gut as defined above. Anteriorly there is a part into which food is taken and in which it is held in preparation for digestion. There may be mechanical churning or grinding in this region, but there is seldom much chemical attack on the food. Then comes a length where there are many enzymes and where there is intense chemical attack on the substances of which food is composed. Absorption begins here, but may continue lower down after digestion has ceased. As there is so much overlap the regions of digestion and absorption are usually considered together. Lastly, there is a stretch of the gut where the remnants of the food await expulsion from the anus as feces, and where nothing important happens except the absorption of water.

As one goes through the series from fish to mammal the gut tends to become more complicated and to have more recognizable parts and more specialization in these parts. This evolution is especially noticeable at the anterior end, where the development of special structures for feeding is part of the cephalization which we have seen on p. 47 to be characteristic of vertebrates.

Mouth and Buccal Cavity

The stomodeum is always formed on the ventral surface, and the mouth to which it gives rise may remain there, as it does in the dogfish and man. More often the ventral surface of the body grows in such a way as to bring the mouth to the extreme anterior end of the body, the position it has in most bony fish and most mammals.

The word 'mouth' has some ambiguity in ordinary English, and according to the dictionaries this goes back to the very early use of the word. It may mean simply the opening at the front end of the gut (which is bounded in man by the lips), or it may mean the space into which this leads (containing, in man, tongue and teeth), or it may mean both of these together. In this book we shall use it in the first sense only, and for the space, the first part of the alimentary canal formed from the stomodeum and lined with ectoderm, we shall use the term buccal cavity.

The mouth of cyclostomes is, as their name implies, circular. It is surrounded in lampreys by a muscular structure which makes a single circular lip, while in hagfishes, where it is further on the ventral surface, there are six or eight fleshy barbels (or barbules) standing at a little distance from it. There are small teeth inside the lips, and inside the ventral (or posterior) rim is a short tongue, on which the teeth are larger. These teeth are quite different from those of any other vertebrates. Their main part is a hardened thickening of the epidermis, but this is supported by a pad of cartilage, with many cells, formed in the dermis. They are used to make a wound through which the animal sucks the blood or other tissues of its prey.

There is a strong muscle that can pull the tongue inward, and it appears that this is the chief source of the suction by which the animal holds onto its victim. The cutting of the skin is achieved by an up and down movement of the tongue. At the center of the sucker is a small gap leading to the buccal cavity.

In gnathostomes the mouth has distinct upper and lower edges which can be brought together or moved apart by muscles running either from the cranium or from the upper jaw to the lower jaw. In a few animals, notably snakes and parrots, there is also a joint between the upper jaw and the cranium and between the facial portion of the skull and the rest, so that the upper jaw can be lifted. This is dealt with more fully in Chapter 16.

In elasmobranchs the edges of the jaw are covered with teeth, which make a continuous series with those of the buccal cavity and the placoid scales of the skin.

In most bony fish the mouth is terminal and large, and it is sometimes continued backward along the sides of the head, the margins being supported either by the maxillary and premaxillary bones or by the latter alone. Its edges often have barbels, which are sensitive to touch. Teeth are nearly always present and numerous, and may be large and varied in shape to make complicated patterns. They are generally fastened to the underlying skeleton by the growing together of the bones from the two structures, but are only rarely embedded in sockets. Where they are attached to the sides of the jaw they are called pleurodont, or if to the edges acrodont. They may be attached not only to the bones of the jaw (pre-maxilla, maxilla, and dentary) but to those of the palate (palatine and vomer) and branchial skeleton, and rarely to the pterygoid and parasphe-noid. They are continually worn down and cast off, and are replaced by new ones which begin just behind the old. In a few, such as the wolf fish (*Anarrhichas lupus*), there are teeth of several different shapes. They are of the standard vertebrate construction which is described in Chapter 18.

In some fish the mouth is short and wide, so that it appears round and sucker-like. In the sturgeons it is ventral and is small and without teeth, though there are four anterior barbels. The animals feed by sucking mud into the buccal cavity.

Fish never have a well-developed tongue with its own muscles, but the center of the floor of the buccal cavity is usually raised as a ridge and supported by the hyoid bone or cartilage.

The mouth and buccal cavity of tetrapods show on the whole a progres-sive evolution, which in some ways reaches its highest peak in man. In Amphibia the lips are not conspicuous, but in reptiles and mammals they are often thick and massive. In tortoises and birds they are covered with a thick shell of keratin, so that the term 'lip' becomes inappropriate, and we speak of a beak, or bill, instead. Similar structures are found in the platypus among mammals and in some extinct reptiles, such as some Ornithischia and therapsids. Although the beak is often hard and insensi-tive, as anyone who has been bitten by a parrot knows, this is not always so. In many ducks and wading birds it is soft and well-provided with nerve endings. The way in which birds probe the mud when feeding sug-gests that they can in some way recognize the presence of the burrowing worms and molluscs on which they feed, but the sense that is employed is unknown. In some the bill can be bent slightly upward. Birds presum-ably lost their teeth because they fed in a manner that made them unnec-essary; some, which feed on fish, for holding which teeth would be useful, have developed serrations along the edges of the beak which take their place. Bills of this sort are best developed in the ducks called mergansers.

In many mammals the lips are muscular and help in feeding; this is very noticeable in the horse, camel, and giraffe. Presumably such use led to the development of the upper lip into a prehensile trunk, which is incipient in tapirs and fully developed in elephants. The lips are important in hu-man speech.

The teeth of amphibians are simple and fused to the jaw like those of bony fish. Frogs are remarkable for having none in the lower jaw, so that the bone called the dentary (because in reptiles it is the only one that bears teeth) has an inappropriate name. The Stegocephalia had larger teeth which had vertical ridges on their surface, and sections of these fossil teeth show that the furrows between the ridges are deep and complex. From this pattern some of these early amphibians were given the name of Labyrinthodonta. The early crossopterygians had teeth of the same pattern, which is one piece of evidence for the descent of the tetrapods from these fish.

Most reptiles also have simple teeth, stuck to the side of the jawbone and so called pleurodont. The Squamata and *Sphenodon* still have palatal teeth, but these have been lost by crocodiles; in the chelonians there are no teeth.

Snakes show some specialization in the teeth, with the development in many genera of the poison fangs as enlarged teeth on the maxilla. In the Viperidae, such as the rattlesnake, *Crotalus horridus,* of North America and the adder, *Vipera berus,* of Europe, these have a canal, open at both ends, running their length. Poison from a gland inside the lip passes into the base of the canal, and is injected into the wound from the tip of the tooth when the snake strikes.

The greatest development of teeth is found in mammals, though complication of form has been accompanied by reduction in numbers. All the teeth become surrounded by the bone of the jaw as they grow, so that they come to have their bases in sockets, a condition known as thecodont. At each point where a tooth develops there may be only one throughout life, a condition known as monophyodonty, or the tooth may be shed and replaced by one other, but no more; this is diphyodonty. Since most of the teeth are replaced once, the mammals are generally, but not entirely accurately, said to be diphyodont, with two sets of teeth, called milk and permanent. The condition of many embryos suggests that this state is derived from the polyphyodonty, or continuous replacement, of reptiles and earlier vertebrates, for it is often possible to find tooth germs, before or after the functional teeth, which never cut the gum. The toothed whales have achieved complete monophyodonty, while the elephants have acquired what can be called either monophyodonty or polyphyodonty, according to which way it is looked at. Teeth are formed in a crescent at the back of the jaw, and gradually move forward, so that about one and a half cheek teeth are in use in each quarter jaw at any one time, while another is always forming behind the half that is still within the gum. After the old tooth wears down in front it is shed, and the next takes its place.

The teeth of mammals are named not according to their pattern or shape but according to their position in the jaw. Those in the upper jaw which are borne on the premaxilla are incisors; that borne either in the suture between premaxilla and maxilla or immediately behind it is the canine; and all the rest, which are borne on the maxilla, are cheek teeth. The teeth of the lower jaw are given the names of those against which they strike, but the lower canine usually comes just in front of the upper when the mouth is closed. Each of these groups has a characteristic form to which there are many exceptions. The incisors are usually small and flattened along the curve of the premaxilla, the canines are long and pointed, while the cheek teeth are flattened on their biting surface or elongated along the line of the jaw, in either case having knobs, points, or ridges, called cusps. There are many exceptions to these general patterns. The European hedgehog (*Erinaceus*) is a well-known catch for students because its third upper incisor is long and the shape of a typical canine, while the canine itself is quite small. The tusks of elephants also are incisors, not canines, which these animals do not possess.

The cheek teeth may be all alike, perhaps differing slightly in size, or there may be two distinct sorts, the anterior few being different from and usually simpler than the remainder. There is another and more constant difference in that the anterior cheek teeth usually appear in two sets, like the incisors and canines, while the posterior teeth appear as a single set, which is not replaced. Those with two sets are called premolars, those with only one are molars. Since the molars usually arrive at the same time as or after the second set of premolars they are usually called permanent, but study of the development suggests that they correspond more strictly to the milk set.

We thus have four types of teeth, and since the jaw is nearly always symmetrical we can express the dentition of a mammal by a formula in which the teeth of one side of the upper jaw are written as the upper line of a fraction, those of one side of the lower jaw by the lower line. The full dentition of a placental, that is to say, the maximum to be expected, or that present in the most primitive forms, is $\dfrac{\text{i3. c1. pm4. m3.}}{\text{i3. c1. pm4. m3.}}$, where the letters are the initials of the types of teeth. Since there is no ambiguity (provided that a zero is inserted when any type of tooth is missing) the letters may be omitted and the formula written as $\dfrac{3143}{3143}$. The variations on this formula are many, and orders and families sometimes have values that are quite typical for themselves. The only mammals with more than three incisors are the polyprotodont marsupials, whose four or five teeth in the prexamilla make them instantly recognizable. Some of the toothed whales, such as the dolphins (*Delphinus*), have returned to an almost reptilian condition, with as many as sixty uniform peg-like cheek teeth in each quarter jaw, but with no incisors or canines. The canines are usually longer than the others and in the extinct saber-toothed tigers were as much as eight inches long; but occasionally some of the other teeth are extreme in size, often in the male only. We have referred to the tusks of the elephants, which are upper incisors; the male nahrwal (*Monodon monoceros*), a peculiar toothed whale of the Arctic, has a single, twisted tusk, which may be six feet long; it is usually described as a canine, but as its base is surrounded by the maxilla it appears to be more strictly a cheek tooth. The tusks of pigs, usually best developed in the males, are curled canines.

Herbivorous mammals tend to have premolars and molars alike, with ridges, a shape called lophodont if the ridges are straight—as in rabbits—selenodont if they are curved—as in cattle. Their incisors and canines are generally small (unless developed into tusks) and may be absent. There is often a space or diastema between incisors and cheek teeth. Carnivorous mammals have large canines, and cheek teeth elongated as cutting edges, and the degree of development in these directions is usually a fair indication of the degree of dependence of the animal on living prey. Thus cats, which in nature kill their food, have sharper teeth than dogs, which tend to be scavengers and feeders on carrion; while the bears, which, though Carnivora, are largely vegetarian, have relatively blunt teeth. In modern Carnivora two cheek teeth in each jaw, the fourth upper premolar and the first lower molar, are larger than the others and are known as carnassial teeth. Omnivores, such as man, tend to have a fairly full and unspecialized set of teeth, with the canines little developed. Man's dental formula is $\frac{2123}{2123}$. Insectivorous animals are rather similar, but with sharper cusps on the cheek teeth. More unusual types are the frugivorous, with flat-topped cheek teeth without cusps, as in the kinkajou (*Potos*), an arboreal member of the Carnivora living chiefly in South America; piscivorous, where the teeth are all alike and usually simple, as in whales and to a lesser extent seals; and those peculiar types of feeding such as ant-eating and the plankton-feeding of whalebone whales, in which teeth are not used and are nearly or quite absent.

We have seen that many of the therapsid reptiles had a varied dentition very similar to that of the mammals, so that it is reasonable to suppose that mammalian teeth are simply a development from the reptilian state. This would imply too that the complicated cusp patterns of mammaliam molars are derived from the relatively simple pattern in the reptiles. The three cusps of the teeth of symmetrodonts (p. 114) have been given names, and from this or a similar condition all the later types of teeth are supposed to have arisen by addition, fusion, or suppression of cusps. There seems no reason to doubt that in a general way this is true, but the details are obscure.

Most mammalian cheek teeth have long roots in the jaw and a relatively short exposed part or crown, a condition called brachydont, and, once formed, they cease to grow. Those of herbivores are usually high crowned, or hypsodont, and grow throughout life; most of the crown consists of tall ridges of enamel-covered dentine with deep valleys filled with cement between them. The wear on enamel, dentine, and cement is unequal because of their different degrees of hardness, and so an irregular grinding surface is produced, which is continually renewed as it is worn away.

Some other teeth, such as the incisors of rodents and lagomorphs and the tusks of pigs, also grow throughout life.

Near the mouth there are always external nostrils, and in many embryos these arise as little sacs on the dorsal wall of the stomodeum, so that they are part of the gut and are not really external at all (Fig. 9.3). This is such a common situation that it was probably their original condition. Presumably they arose in connection with the chemical appreciation of food-in-the-mouth, or taste, and only later became distance receptors (Chapter 14). Between and behind them in the stomodeum is another in-pushing, the hypophysial sac. This loses its connection with the mouth and becomes part of the pituitary body (Chapter 20).

The condition of the external nostril of Agnatha is peculiar in that there is only one, which is generally situated on the mid-line on top of the head. In lampreys this starts in the usual way as a pocket on the roof of the stomodeum and then moves forward, but as it goes it remains connected to the hypophysial sac by a line of cells which later becomes hollowed out to form a tube. The hypophysis thus remains open to the exterior, but the value and function of this arrangement are unknown. In the hagfishes the nasal tube opens secondarily into the pharynx, so that there is an internal nostril. This appears to have nothing to do with the internal nostrils of the tetrapods, which are described below, and to be an adaptation to the fish's semi-parasitic mode of feeding. The external nostril is on the tip of the snout, just above the mouth, so that when the animal buries the front end of its body in the fish on which it is feeding, no water can enter the nostril. The gill slits, however, are far back, and some of the water which enters them as the respiratory current is taken forward through the internal nostril to the olfactory sac, which lies about halfway between the two nostrils.

Some degree of connection between mouth and external nostrils remains in the adults of many forms, and is well seen in the dogfish (Fig. 4.11) and in the harelip of many mammals, notably cats, rodents, and lagomorphs (Fig. 9.4). A similar stage is passed through by the human embryo, and occasionally persists as an abnormality after birth. In other animals, including the teleosts, amphibians, reptiles, birds, and most mammals, nostrils and mouth are separate. The original position of the nares ensures that some of the water taken in as the respiratory current passes to the sensitive cells in the olfactory sac, but in the bony fishes, where the nostrils are usually widely separated from the mouth and situated just in front of the eyes, this is not so. Each nostril is double here, the two halves being separated by a band of skin, an arrangement which enables a current of water, which has no other function than to carry any chemicals in it to the sense cells, to enter the anterior opening and leave the posterior. This current is produced in some species by muscular action, in others by cilia.

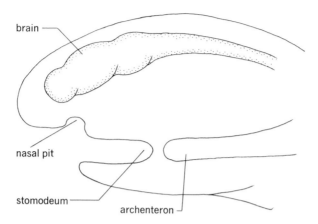

FIG. 9.3 Diagram of a vertebrate embryo, to show the primitive position of the external nostrils.

In the Crossopterygii and tetrapods each nasal passage opens posteriorly into the buccal cavity or pharynx, so that there are internal as well as external nostrils. These are associated with the development of lungs as respiratory organs, and they enable air to be taken to the lungs when the mouth is full of food or even when it is under water, though the last is only possible if the external nostrils are on the top of the head; this is well seen in secondarily aquatic animals such as crocodiles and whales. There seems no reason to think that, apart from the hagfishes, which, as we have seen, have a different arrangement for a different purpose, internal nostrils have arisen more than once, so that they are all homologous.

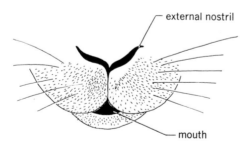

FIG. 9.4 The hare lip of a rabbit (*Oryctolagus cuniculus*) showing the connection between the mouth and the external nostril.

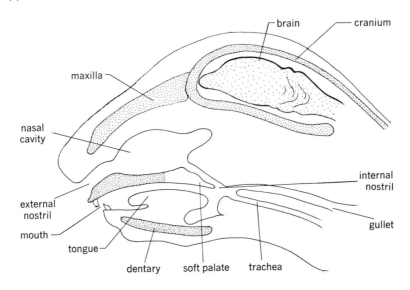

FIG. 9.5   A longitudinal vertical section through the head of a mammal, to show the nostrils. Bone is in fine stipple.

It is impossible to be certain whether the extinct crossopterygians had internal nostrils, but as there is a pair of gaps in the bones of the palate in an appropriate position it is probable that they did. There are none in the living *Latimeria,* but as this fish lives in the sea at considerable depths and has hardly any gas in its air bladder this is not surprising. They are present in Dipnoi. In these and in urodeles the nasal passage is simple, but in anurans it is divided into an anterior respiratory part and a posterolateral pair of pouches which are olfactory in function. This development is elaborated in the reptiles and mammals, where there are special bones, called turbinals, which support the nasal epithelium. The olfactory chamber is small in birds, in accordance with their poor sense of smell.

In the mammals (Fig. 9.5) the maxillary and palatine bones (Chapter 16) grow downward and inward at their outer edges, so that they come to meet again in the mid-line, and shut off the upper part of the stomodeum from the region below, which is the functional buccal cavity, by what is called the hard palate. The practical effect of this is to extend the nasal passage posteriorly, so that the functional internal nostrils are now much further back; a further growth of the epithelium and connective tissue, the soft palate, carries the nasal passage, which at this level is often single, right back to the pharynx. The hard and soft palates can, with care, be felt in one's own buccal cavity by the finger. All this helps in the separation of the respiratory and feeding passages, so that a mammal can breathe continuously while eating, except just at the moment of swallowing. A similar hard palate occurs in crocodiles, which can as a result breathe while eating under water.

The olfactory epithelium would not function unless it was damp, and in terrestrial vertebrates a secretion to ensure this is produced by a number of nasal glands. These are present in Dipnoi, adult amphibians (except perennibranchiates), reptiles, birds, and mammals. They may be small and scattered, or concentrated as the glands of Steno. The excess secretion of the lacrimal glands is also carried into the nasal passages through the lacrimal duct. Many sea birds, such as penguins and cormorants, have put their nasal glands to the special use of secreting the excessive sodium chloride which they have taken in with their food.

On the floor of the buccal cavity of lampreys is a pair of glands that produce an anticoagulant which prevents the clotting of the blood which is their chief food. Fishes have cells in the mouth that produce mucus, but have no specialized glands within the mouth. All terrestrial vertebrates have at least one gland that produces enough secretion to moisten the food and so take the place of the water that in aquatic forms is inevitably mixed with it. In the frogs there is an intermaxillary gland in the fore part of the palate, and the structure of the skull suggests that a similar gland was present in labyrinthodonts. Reptiles have glands in various positions in the buccal cavity—on the palate, on or under the tongue, and inside both upper and lower lips—and in the poisonous snakes the upper labial glands are specialized to produce the venom.

Most birds have a number of mucous glands collected into groups, but they are reduced in aquatic species, and even absent from the pelican and related forms. Woodpeckers have a very large pair—up to seven centimeters long in the green woodpecker (*Picus viridis*) of Europe—which produce not only mucus but a sticky secretion by which the birds can pick up with their long tongue the insects on which they feed. Many martins and swallows also have large glands which increase in size in the breeding season and produces a secretion which is used to bind together the mud of which their nests are built. In the swiftlets (*Collocalia*) of Asia the mud is dispensed with, and the secretion of the glands sets by itself to make the nests of which bird's nest soup is made.

In mammals there are usually four relatively large pairs of salivary glands—submaxillary, between the angles of the jaws; sublingual, inside the dentaries; parotid, behind the angles; and infra-orbital, below the eyes —but the last are absent from man.

The secretion of the salivary glands seldom has anything to do with chemical digestion, but in a few animals it contains a starch-splitting enzyme or amylase, usually called ptyalin, which helps a little in softening food. Salivary amylase is chiefly found in animals that eat much hard carbohydrate food: among mammals, in primates, pigs, elephants, and some rodents; among birds in the graminivorous game birds and finches.

There is also a little amylase, as well as a weak protein-splitting enzyme, in the saliva of frogs and toads. Here its function may be to bring into solution just enough of the food to be tasted.

The chief voice-producing region is behind the buccal cavity, but this and its associated structures are important in modifying the primary sounds, as is clear from the use of the tongue, lips, and teeth in the speech of man. Above all it is a resonator, the quality of the sound produced being determined by its shape and size. Many anurans have vocal pouches at the sides of the mouth which are blown up for this purpose.

Most tetrapods have on the floor of the buccal cavity a muscular and more or less protrusible tongue. Its development shows that it really belongs to the next section of the alimentary canal, the pharynx, but as it is functionally associated with feeding we will consider it here. The branchial skeleton of fishes (p. 388) has muscles attached to it whose contraction assists in maintaining a flow of water over the gills for respiration. With the transference of oxygen-uptake to the lungs some of these muscles became freed for other uses, and they developed into the tongue. The skeleton of the tongue is derived from the hyoid arch (p. 388) with some contribution from the branchial arches.

The tongue is used in feeding in two principal ways, to manipulate food already in the mouth, and to pick up or help in picking up food from the outside world. In the first case it tends to be relatively short, a condition well seen in parrots and in man. Protrusible tongues vary in form from the squat type of most frogs (Fig. 9.6A), which is anchored in front and is flipped out by a forward bend, to the very long and thin type found in woodpeckers and flickers (Fig. 9.6C), or the somewhat similar tongue of the chameleon, which is expanded at the end. All these are used for picking up insects, and have sticky tips. The tongue of a cat (Fig. 9.6D), with rough file-like surface with which flesh is scraped from bones, and the very flexible tongue of cattle, with which grass is drawn into the mouth, are intermediate in relative length.

While most tongues are entirely muscular in action, that of chameleons is stiffened by blood sinuses, the expansion of which under pressure derived from the heart causes its sudden elongation. The tongues of amniotes are free in front, attached posteriorly, but those of amphibians may be attached anteriorly, or posteriorly, or along their whole length. Frogs of the family Pipidae have no tongue, and it is very small in some toads. This loss seems to be an adaptation to a secondarily aquatic life.

The long tongue of the Squamata is forked (Fig. 9.6B), and in snakes it has acquired the new function of sampling the air for its chemical composition. Odorous particles are picked up as it flicks in and out, and the forked tip fits into two pockets on the roof of the mouth which are lined with a sensory epithelium.

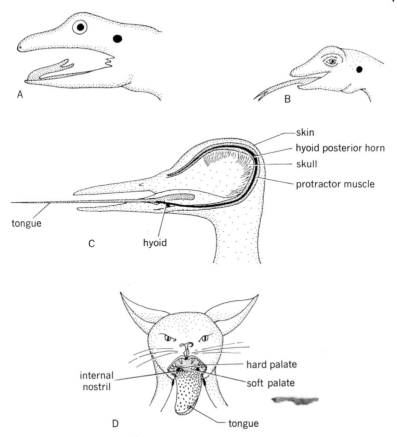

FIG. 9.6 (A) Tongue of a frog, *Rana temporaria*, x 2. (B) Tongue of a green lizard, *Lacerta viridis*, x 1. (C) Dissection of the head of a green woodpecker, *Picus viridis*, to show the tongue and the posterior horn of the hyoid, x 2/3. (D) Tongue of a cat, x 1/4.

Pharynx

At a fairly early stage in the development of the embryo the stomodeum breaks through into the archenteron, so that the buccal cavity, and the anterior part of the endodermal region of the gut, or pharynx, are continuous with one another. In the adult there is in fact hardly any distinction between these two sections, but the pharynx is functionally important because of its connection with respiration or breathing.

In the cyclostomes and fishes a series of paired pouches grow out from the sides of the pharynx to meet corresponding inpushings from the external surface. When these meet there are formed the gill slits, gill clefts, or branchial clefts which are diagnostic of chordates. When, as often happens, the middle portion of these is expanded so as to become wider than the internal and external openings, they are known as gill pouches. On the walls of the gill slits, or pouches if present, are developed the gills, structures richly supplied with blood vessels and with thin walls through which oxygen can be absorbed. Although called internal gills, they are formed from the ectodermal portion of the slits. The portions of body wall between the slits, known as gill bars, branchial bars, or gill arches or branchial arches, obviously have endoderm on their inner surface, ectoderm on their outer surface, while most of their bulk consists of lateral plate mesoderm. In this there is originally a part of the celom, which is soon obliterated, and from it there develop skeletal elements of bone or cartilage (p. 51) with muscles attached to them, and in the arches also run nerves and blood vessels. The lateral plate mesoderm is unsegmented, but the gill slits form in an intersegmental position so that the gill arches correspond to the somites above them.

If, as is generally assumed, the gill slits of vertebrates are homologous with those of the protochordates, they were not originally respiratory in function but were formed in connection with the method of continuous feeding on small particles in a current maintained by cilia. It is possible that this method was still used by the ostracoderms, although in view of their size some of the current must have been produced by muscles, since cilia can only work efficiently in a tube of diameter a little more than twice their length. In the ammocoete larva of lampreys, which also retain this type of feeding, most of the current is produced by muscles, though cilia are still present. In adult vertebrates the feeding function is lost, and the gill slits are solely respiratory. The view that the mouth of vertebrates represents a pair of gill slits that have fused, for which there is some evidence from comparative anatomy, is in keeping with this primary function.

Cyclostomes have more gill slits than most vertebrates, for there are six or seven in *Myxine*, six to fourteen in *Bdellostoma*, seven in lampreys. In all of them the first gill slit has been lost. The branchial pouches containing the gills are almost spherical, and open to pharynx and exterior by narrow ducts with small circular pores. In *Myxine* the ducts of one side join and have a common opening just behind and below the last gill pouch; on the left side the common duct receives, or opens near, a short duct without gills which is presumably a functionless gill slit. A current of water—in at the external nostril, through the pouches, and out at the gill pores—is maintained by muscular action, largely of the walls of the sacs. Some authors say that when the hagfish's head is buried in its prey, similar contractions pump water in and out of the external openings of the gill slits, but others deny this, and say that under these conditions the animal respires through its skin. This tidal method of breathing is, however, normal in lampreys, though water can also enter by the mouth. Their gill slits open internally into a single median tube below the esophagus, blind posteriorly but opening into the pharynx in front. The gill lamellae of cyclostomes make an almost complete ring around each pouch, interrupted only dorsally and ventrally.

The usual number of gill slits in elasmobranchs is five, as in the common *Squalus* and *Scyliorhinus,* but in other sharks there are six or seven, this being the highest number found in any living gnathostome; some extinct forms had more. In most elasmobranchs there is also an anterior pair without functional gills, called spiracles. These are usually small, though they are large in the rays. The functional gill slits are elongated in a dorsoventral direction, and there is little in the way of a gill pouch. There is a gill—called rather stupidly a hemibranch because there are two inside most gill slits—on the anterior and posterior walls of each pouch except the last, where only the anterior wall has one. A fish with five slits therefore has nine hemibranchs. There is also a small and probably functionless gill on the anterior wall of the spiracle. The term holobranch, sometimes used for the two hemibranchs of a slit taken collectively, is best avoided, since it implies a single structure when in fact two separate ones are present.

The gills of elasmobranchs are described as lamellar, that is, they are developed as plates of vascular tissue, though with a deeply corrugated surface, on the gill arches. They do not project out of the slits, though the connective tissue and epithelium between each back-to-back pair of hemibranchs extends a little way out to act as a valve to cover the gill slit behind it. (Fig. 9.7A).

The two hemibranchs of a slit meet across the gill pouch, and it is by forcing a current through the gaps left where the corrugations meet that the dogfish breathes. There are two mechanisms. In the first, the contraction of the hypobranchial muscles lowers the floor of the pharynx, so increasing its volume and drawing water in through the mouth and spiracles; the flaps of skin close over the external openings of the gill slits and prevent water from entering. The mouth and spiracles then close and muscles draw the epibranchial and ceratobranchial cartilages (p. 51) closer together, so reducing the volume of the pharynx and forcing water out between the hemibranchs. In the second mechanism, contraction of various muscles in the gill arch alternately enlarges and contracts the outer part of the gill pouch. Since the skin valves close as before when the internal pressure is reduced, water is drawn across the gills into the outer part of the pouch; then, when the outer chamber contracts, the small spaces between the hemibranchs have a higher resistance to flow than have the external gill slits, and so water is expelled to the exterior. This second method is used chiefly when the animal is feeding, since it can go on when the mouth is open.

The Holocephali have an arrangement in general similar to that of other

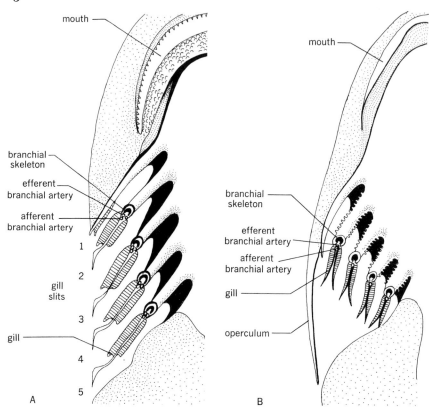

FIG. 9.7   (A) Thick frontal section of one side of a dogfish, to show the lamellar gills. (B) Similar section of a teleost, to show the filamentar gills.

elasmobranchs, except that a flap of skin extends back as an operculum to cover all the gill slits of each side.

There is a general tendency to reduction of gill slits and gills in the Dipnoi. *Epiceratodus* has five slits, but the first has only a vestigial gill on its anterior wall; in *Lepidosiren* the first gill slit is closed, and, though there is individual variation in the number of gills present, there are generally only a posterior hemibranch in the third slit, two in the fourth, and one on the anterior wall of the fifth. *Protopterus*, though it has five gill slits, has the same number of gills as *Lepidosiren*, except that there is one on the posterior wall of the fifth slit and one on the anterior wall of the first. This reduction is presumably connected with the muddy water in which the fish live, and is associated with lung-breathing; in *Protopterus* there are also usually three filamentar external gills, which are extensions of the body wall projecting just above the pectoral fin. The gill slits of Dipnoi are covered by an operculum, but the gills are lamellar like those of dogfish, except that they project a little way beyond the gill bar.

The Actinopterygii have a large operculum strengthened by several opercular bones, and the gills are filamentar, stretching out under the operculum as vascular tufts, which project into a chamber which is really part of the external world (Fig. 9.7B). In association with this the gill bars are thin and feebly supported, and there are no gill pouches. There are usually five gill slits, but in teleosts the hemibranch of the anterior wall of the first has been lost. Otherwise the arrangement is similar to that in sharks. There is no spiracle, and breathing depends on the presence of two folds of tissue in the mouth, one, the maxillary, hanging down, and another, the mandibular, rising up to meet it and so forming a valve. In inspiration the folds open and the opercula are brought close to the sides of the body, in expiration the folds meet and the opercula are lifted up. The fish can thus breathe with its mouth continuously open. Similar valves are present in the lungfishes *Polypterus, Amia,* and *Lepidosiren.*

Although the chief function of gills is to take up oxygen, those of teleosts have acquired also the power to excrete chlorides, and probably ions of sodium and potassium, so that when the fish is in sea water and these solutes are taken up by the blood (which has a lower concentration of them), they can be got rid of so that the composition of the blood does not change.

Gill slits very similar to those of fish are present in the embryos of amphibians, but they are only four in number; at metamorphosis they usually close, but some of them remain open throughout life in the perennibranchiate urodeles. In *Necturus* there are two, the second and third. The slit that corresponds to the spiracle of fishes seldom if ever opens, and its fate is discussed below. The larvae are active before the gill slits become perforate, and perhaps because of this they develop external gills, three pairs of muscular tufts which grow out from the skin of the gill arches between the four slits. They last only for a short time in the anurans, and are replaced by internal gills, which, like those of fish, are ectodermal but within the gill slits. Urodeles have no internal gills, and, in the perennibranchiates such as *Necturus* the external gills are present throughout life.

Amniotes never breathe by gills, and, except as an abnormality, the adults never have open gill slits, but traces of them can usually be found in development. In the chick, for example, five begin to push out from the pharynx, but only the first three perforate the gut wall, and then only for a few hours. In most mammals no slit breaks through.

The slit corresponding to the spiracle is of special interest in tetrapods, because, although it has been diverted to other uses, it is the only one that persists throughout life. It becomes the Eustachian tube, a narrow membranous passage that leads from the pharynx (the throat of man) to the cavity of the middle ear. In reptiles and birds it is open to the outside

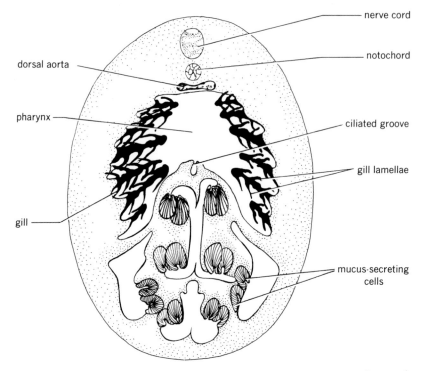

nerve cord

notochord

dorsal aorta

ciliated groove

pharynx

gill lamellae

gill

mucus-secreting
cells

FIG. 9.8   Semi-diagrammatic transverse section of an ammocoete larva of a lamprey, x 40. The complicated structure on the floor of the pharynx, including the pockets of mucus-secreting cells and the ciliated groove, is the endostyle.

for a short time, but not in mammals, although the endoderm grows out far enough to come in contact with the ectoderm. The details of the formation of the middle ear are different in the different classes, but the important point is that its cavity is essentially a gill pouch. The function of the Eustachian tubes is to maintain atmospheric pressure on both sides of the ear-drums. We are not in general conscious of their existence, but, since they are normally closed and are opened only in the act of swallowing, or, in some individuals, voluntarily, we experience an unpleasant sensation in the ears when ascending rapidly in a non-pressurized aircraft; this sensation can be relieved by opening the tubes, which act can be heard as a faint click. If, as sometimes happens, they have become blocked, the unpleasant sensation continues. As will be discussed more fully in Chapter 19, some zoologists think that the mouth represents two anterior gill slits that have fused. The formation of the stomodeum is certainly similar in principle to the formation of a gill slit.

Although the gill slits of tetrapods close, so that they lose their connection with the endoderm of the gut and the ectoderm of the skin, their middle endodermal portion may swell up and, as described in Chapter 20, give rise to the thymus gland and the parathyroids.

On the ventral surface of the pharynx of the lancelet there is, as we have seen on page 18, a ciliated grooved structure called the endostyle, and a similar but more complicated organ occurs in the ammocoete larva of the lamprey (p. 42) (Fig. 9.8). These endostyles are used in feeding, but at metamorphosis that of the lamprey becomes closed up into a row of sacs lying below the pharyngeal floor. The substance contained in these sacs is rich in iodine and acts like thyroxin in accelerating the metamorphosis of amphibian tadpoles (p. 79). Although it is not known to have any effect on the metamorphosis of the lamprey itself, there can be little doubt that we have here the beginning of the thyroid gland, which in all other vertebrates begins as a groove in the floor of the pharynx.

Apart from a few aberrant species, all gnathostomes except the elasmobranchs have a diverticulum from the pharynx that contains gas. Since the question of its homology in all the classes is a difficult one, and can only be considered in the light of the facts, we will first describe it in the teleosts, where it is known as the swim bladder, then in the tetrapods, where it is a pair of lungs, and finally in the Choanichthyes, after which we can discuss the homology.

In nearly all teleosts there grows out from the roof of the pharynx an endodermal pouch. It is almost surrounded by mesoderm of the splanchnopleure, and this is invaded by a branch of the celiac artery and sometimes by smaller vessels direct from the dorsal aorta. The blood is collected into veins which run into the hepatic portal system or into the posterior cardinal veins. Later, mesoderm from the somatopleure grows round the pouch and makes a tough external coat. The resulting bladder is of considerable size, and lies in the dorsal part of the celom, usually running its whole length. The connection with the gut becomes narrowed to a short pneumatic duct, and this may shift backward, even so far that it opens not from the pharynx but from the next part of the gut, the esophagus. The bladder then extends in front of as well as behind its point of connection with the duct. When the duct remains open throughout life the fish is said to be physostomatous, but in the more advanced fishes, such as cod and perch, it closes, and the fish is called physoclistous. In all the physostomatous species and most of the physoclistous species that have been studied, the larva gulps air at the surface, and so fills the bladder with gas. In all, gas can be obtained from the blood and also given up to it, secretion taking place chiefly in the anterior part, absorption posteriorly. It is in this way that the bladder of some physoclistous forms is filled. In general, fresh-water fish are physostomatous, marine ones, physoclistous; but there are many exceptions, and no physostomatous forms are known from below 600 feet. The air bladder is not present in many bottom-living species, both fresh water and marine, including the common flatfish, nor in a few species living in fast-flowing mountain streams. In a few fish, such as the herring (*Clupea harengus*), the bladder acquires a secondary opening direct to the exterior near the anus.

There is now little doubt that the chief, and in most teleosts the only, function of the swim bladder is to adjust the density of the fish so that it is the same as that of the water at whatever depth it may be. This has been shown by observations on secretion and absorption and by calculations of density. The gas secreted is partly oxygen and partly carbon dioxide, and nitrogen follows these by a purely physical effect. Absorption takes place over a special area, the oval, which is cut off from the rest of the bladder by a sphincter when secretion is taking place. When the sphincter relaxes absorption continues slowly by physical processes. The mechanism of secretion is not clear, but it is under nervous control, since it can be stopped by cutting the vagus nerve and started by cutting the sympathetic nerve supply (Chapter 13). There is no evidence that muscles in the bladder itself take any part in altering its volume, but physostomatous species may swallow or release gas from the mouth, and as the duct is muscular it probably pumps air in.

There is no evidence that the swim bladder is ever itself a sense organ, but in some fishes it becomes connected with the inner ear, and then helps in the perception of pressure and sound. These functions are best developed in the Ostariophysi, including the roach (*Rutilus rutilus*), in which a chain of three small bones, called Weberian ossicles, runs from the anterior end of the bladder to a median extension from the sacculus of the ear (Fig. 9.9). These ossicles are derived from the first three vertebrae, and are not homologous with the ear ossicles of mammals. Fish that possess them respond to sounds of higher pitch and lower intensity than do other fish.

In some fish the swim bladder is concerned with sound production, either directly through the vibration of its walls or by expelling bubbles, or indirectly by acting as a resonator for sounds produced in other ways.

A few teleosts, all living in swamps, use their swim bladder as a lung, taking in air at the surface. *Erythrinus unitaeniatus* of South America, for example, habitually comes to the surface to breathe, and if prevented from doing so in poorly aerated water it dies, though it can survive indefinitely below the surface if the water is well oxygenated.

In one swamp teleost, *Gymnarchus*, that breathes in this way, the swim bladder is supplied with blood by an artery formed from the fifth and sixth aortic arches of the left side; meanwhile the right fifth and sixth arches have formed the celiac artery, so that the blood supply can hardly be considered to be different in principle from the normal arrangement.

Tetrapods have nothing that corresponds functionally to the swim bladder, for, even when they are aquatic, they are always dependent on coming to the surface to breathe, and their diving is an active process. But in much the same position they have a pair of gas-filled bags, the lungs, which open into and are filled from the pharynx. Though there is a pair of lungs (except where, as in some snakes, one has clearly been suppressed as a specialization), the tube or bronchus from each unites with its fellow to form a single tube, the trachea, which connects them to the ventral surface of the pharynx. In some mammals they apparently arise in development as a single ventral outgrowth which soon divides into two, but in many amphibians, reptiles, birds, and mammals the first trace of them is a pair of pouches, slightly lateral, which join with a median depression between them, which will form the trachea. In the amphibians these pouches occupy a position in series with the gill slits; first come the vestigial spiracles, then four pairs of bulges that become perforated as gill slits, then a pair that never develop beyond shallow pockets, then the ones under discussion. This has led to the not improbable suggestion that the lungs are in fact modified gill pouches. This interpretation is supported, as we shall see, by their blood supply.

The general form of the lungs, endoderm covered by mesoderm, is similar to that of the swim bladder, but there is little muscle, and the detailed structure differs considerably in the different classes. In all, the inner surface is highly vascular, the blood supply coming from a new vessel, the pulmonary artery, which can be traced in development as derived from

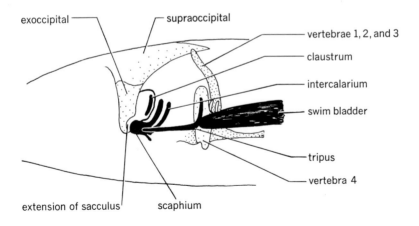

exoccipital — supraoccipital — vertebrae 1, 2, and 3

claustrum

intercalarium

swim bladder

tripus

vertebra 4

extension of sacculus — scaphium

FIG. 9.9 Diagram of the Weberian ossicles of the Ostariophysi. The scaphium, intercalarium, and tripus are connected by ligament; the claustrum is detached and lies in the wall of the extension of the saccule.

the sixth aortic arch (Chapter 10). Drainage is direct to the heart by the pulmonary vein. The inner surface of the bronchi and trachea is ciliated. In amphibians the lungs are simple membranous bags, with at most only a few folds stretching inward to increase the surface. When a frog or a mud puppy is dissected under water and the lung is cut open, all the air contained in it can be squeezed out in a single bubble. The lungs of reptiles have a somewhat greater subdivision, but it is still possible to squeeze all the air out of them.

Mammals and birds have highly developed and specialized lungs which,

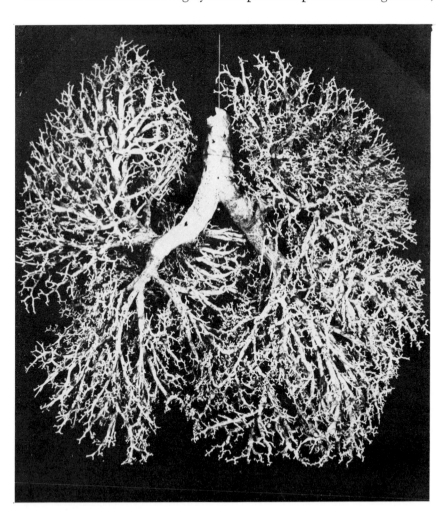

FIG. 9.10   The human lungs, injected with latex, x 2/3. (From a photograph by Mr. W. J. Pardoe)

like so many other features of their bodies, have achieved similar results by different means. The chief function of lungs is to take up oxygen, and anything that increases their surface, or the flow of air over it, will assist in this. Since the lungs of mammals are simpler, and presumably less efficient, than those of birds, we will take them first. The bronchi branch

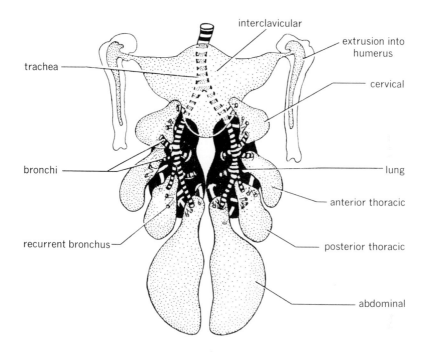

trachea

interclavicular

extrusion into humerus

cervical

bronchi

lung

anterior thoracic

recurrent bronchus

posterior thoracic

abdominal

FIG. 9.11 Diagram of the air sacs of a bird.

and branch again and again until there is a complicated respiratory tree. All this is lined with cilia and is not vascular, but at the tips of the five branches (or bronchioles) are alveolar ducts which expand into air sacs, the walls of which are scooped out into alveoli or air cells. The epithelium of the ducts, air sacs, and alveoli is very thin, with a network of capillaries on the outer surface, and it is here that gas exchange takes place (Fig. 9.10).

The arrangement in birds is quite different. The primary bronchi give off several branches or secondary bronchi, some dorsal and some ventral. Each main ventral branch leads to a membranous air sac which is not vascular (Fig. 9.11). The cervical sacs extend into the neck; the interclavicular sacs are beneath the shoulders and are sometimes fused; anterior and posterior thoracic sacs lie above the sternum; and the abdominal pair extend back into the abdomen. They can be inflated with a blow-pipe when the pigeon is dissected. Some of them send extensions into the hollows of the long bones, so that marrow is replaced by air. The dorsal and ventral secondary bronchi are connected by tertiary or parabronchi, which pass through the lungs and give off minor branches which lead to the alveoli. In active birds these may join with each other, so that there is a continuous network of fine respiratory passages. Recurrent bronchi connect the air sacs to the secondary bronchi, especially the dorsal ones.

The effect of this structure is that although the lung has a very large internal surface there is very little dead space. The air passed over the respiratory surface is almost the same as that in the atmosphere, whereas in mammals the oxygen tension in the lung is never more than two-thirds of that of the atmosphere, because of the quantity of air that can never be expelled from the lung, however deeply the animal breathes out.

Although all tetrapods use their lungs for breathing, the mechanism by which they produce the flow of air is not always the same. Frogs use a force-pump system, pushing air into their lungs by raising the floor of the mouth while the mouth and nostrils are shut—but the details are not clear. Most of the frog's oxygen is taken in through the general surface of the body and through the epithelium lining the mouth, and a resting frog uses its lungs only about once a minute. In any case the system must be very inefficient, since the volume of air pumped in from the buccal cavity is less than that already present in the lungs. Urodeles breathe in a similar way, but the perennibranchiates probably use their lungs little if at all. Some urodeles have even lost their lungs and trachea completely and respire through the skin, or through that and the mouth and pharynx. Most reptiles also fill their lungs by a force pump, but the turtles expand the lungs by movements of the limb girdles.

Mammals have two methods of breathing. Contraction of intercostal muscles swings the ribs forward (upward in man) on the vertebral column, and contraction of the muscular diaphragm, which is convex forward in rest (above in man), flattens the division between the two parts of the celom. The result of both of these actions is to increase the volume of the pleural cavities. Increase in volume means, according to Boyle's law, a reduction in pressure. The lungs, containing air at atmospheric pressure, must swell out to maintain equilibrium, and in so doing they reduce the pressure inside them so that air moves in from outside. Inspiration is thus the active process, and when the muscles relax, passive expiration follows by the contraction of the elastic walls of the lungs. Breathing is normally controlled automatically, partly by proprioceptors in the lungs themselves which maintain an alternation of contraction and relaxation, and partly by chemical stimulation. Carbon dioxide (or acid) reaching the medulla of the brain causes deeper and more rapid breathing, and so does a lowered oxygen concentration in the blood flowing through the aorta and especially through the carotid body, a small structure derived from the first gill. As a result of these responses breathing is strongest when it is most needed.

In birds, expiration is the more active process, but both inspiration and expiration are produced by muscular contraction, which is controlled in a similar way to that of mammals. In both movements some of the air passes through the lung, so that the efficiency of the system lies not, as is commonly said, in a circulation of air through sacs and lungs (there are no valves to make this possible), but in the fact that there is almost continuous exchange of gases across the respiratory surface.

The bronchi and the trachea are supported by rings or incomplete hoops, usually of cartilage but occasionally, as in some birds, containing a little bone. The anterior ones are usually the largest and can be traced as coming from the segmental cartilages which form in fishes the branchial skeleton (Chapter 16.).

The opening of the trachea from the pharynx, the glottis, often has specializations in or associated with it, which may be divided into two groups. First are those which make breathing easier or allow it to be carried on under special conditions. In many species it can be closed, or partially closed, during swallowing, by a flap, the epiglottis, which grows out from its ventral rim. In many aquatic forms, such as whales, the epiglottis grows out as a tube which extends into the narial passage, so that there is a continuous channel for air from nostril to lung, unaffected by the fact that the mouth may still be under water. An intranarial epiglottis is present also in the pouch young of marsupials, so that the milk can be pumped into them by the mother without risk of their choking. It is later lost, so that it is a true larval character, the only one known in mammals. Surprisingly, crocodiles have no epiglottis. That of man is small, and although it helps in closing the larynx, the chief way in which this is done is by a sphincter.

Secondly, the fact that air flowing through a tube easily produces sounds, has been used by a number of tetrapods, which have developed a voice-producing organ, the larynx. In frogs the wall of the trachea is raised into two ridges, and the vibration of these produces a sound which, magnified by the resonance of chambers bulging out of the mouth, can in some species be heard nearly half a mile away.

No reptile has a highly developed larynx, but mammals have vocal cords, which are two bands of muscle attached to the arytenoid cartilages. In most, the sound produced by the vibration of these varies little in pitch, but in others, and most notably in man, variation in the tension, aided by alterations in the shape and size of the resonating chambers of buccal cavity and nose, enables the animal to produce a range of sounds varying widely in both pitch and quality.

The best organ of voice is found in the birds, where it is situated at the fork of the trachea into the two bronchi and is known as the syrinx. It has different forms in different groups, but always involves modifications of the cartilaginous rings and of the muscles, and the development of vibratory vocal cords. It is not possible always to associate the degree of complexity of the syrinx with the quality of the voice, but the most complicated organs are found in the songbirds (Passeriformes, suborder Oscines), which mostly have a highly developed and musical voice, and in the parrots, which, whatever sounds they make in a state of nature, are excellent mimics.

The chief use of the voice, in amphibians, birds, and mammals, is for sexual communication, and often, as in bull frogs and most songbirds, the full elaboration occurs in the male only.

The Dipnoi get their name from their two methods of breathing, and their lungs are very similar to those of amphibians, though rather more elaborate. *Epiceratodus* has only one (on the right side), with a small vestige of the left in the embryo, the others have two; but in all the trachea opens ventrally from the pharynx and the lung or lungs lie dorsally above the gut. *Epiceratodus* breathes air, and the others get 98 per cent of their oxygen in this way. The walls of the lungs have many pouches or alveoli. The blood supply comes through a pulmonary artery which is a branch of the last branchial arch (Chapter 10), but in *Protopterus* and *Lepidosiren,* owing to the absence of gills from the second gill slit and the shortening of the lateral dorsal aorta, much of the blood that reaches the lungs has probably passed through the anterior arches. Blood drains by pulmonary veins direct to the sinus venosus.

We do not know the condition of the lungs in the extinct crossopterygians, but they were presumably present. The air bladder of *Latimeria* has a ventral connection to the pharynx, but contains little gas and is clearly degenerate, as would be expected from the habitat of the animal in the deep sea.

Certain fish that are now usually grouped with the teleosts in the Actinopterygii, but which were formerly associated with the Crossopterygii, need special mention since their air bladders are in some respects intermediate between the lung and swim bladder. In *Amia* (the bow fin) and *Lepidosteus* (= *Lepisosteus*) (the gar pike) of the order Holostei the bladder is single but bilobed and arises laterally from the pharynx, the connection later shifting to become dorsal. In *Polypterus* (of the Chondrostei) there are two bladders with a ventral origin, but the left is reduced in size. The bladders of *Amia* and *Polypterus* are supplied with blood from the last branchial arch, but that of *Lepidosteus* comes from the celiac artery.

We can now summarize the similarities and differences of swim bladder and lung (Plate II).

SWIM BLADDER	LUNG
Present in most Actinopterygii	Present in *Polypterus* (? Actinopterygii); Dipnoi; presumably Crossopterygii; tetrapods
Dorsal outgrowth from pharynx; may be closed	Ventral outgrowth from pharynx
Single	Double
Usually vascular only in patches; gas-secreting	Highly vascular; not gas-secreting
Blood supply from celiac artery or dorsal aorta	Blood supply from last branchial arch
Veins drain to portal system or cardinals	Veins return blood direct to heart

Amia

Dorsal	Bilobed
	Blood supply from last branchial arch

Lepidosteus

Dorsal	Bilobed
Blood supply from celiac artery	

These facts can be explained broadly in four possible ways. (1) Lungs arose first, probably as an adaptation to life in poorly aerated fresh waters, and gave rise to swim bladders when the teleosts returned to the sea. (2) Swim bladders arose first, and later became lungs when some fish began to breathe air. (3) An air bladder was formed as a relatively unspecialized structure of unknown function, and the descendants of its possessors bifurcated into two lines, in one of which it developed into a swim bladder and in the other into lungs. (4) Swim bladders and lungs are independent evolutions.

The first is the view that has been commonly expounded in textbooks for the past half-century. It fits in with the fact that the Choanichthyes are the most primitive of bony fish, and that the teleosts seem to have originated from them, but it raises many detailed difficulties of morphology. That a double structure might become single and that the opening to the pharynx might shift from a ventral to a dorsal position are easy to imagine,

and states that are morphologically (though not phylogenetically) intermediate exist; *Epiceratodus* and many snakes have lost one lung and some
teleosts have a somewhat laterally placed pneumatic duct. The alterations
in the blood supply are more difficult to explain, and no one has ever satisfactorily accounted for them. Whatever purpose the bladder serves, supply
from the branchial arch should be adequate; yet in the teleosts, if the
theory be true, it has been entirely abandoned, without, apparently, leaving any trace either in adults (unless *Amia* is the one actinopterygian that
retains the original system) or in embryos. *Gymnarchus,* as explained
above, is not the exception that it appears to be. Blood vessels are, it is
true, things that are easily replaced, lost, or expanded, but where changes
of this sort occur, as in the neck of birds, for example, there is usually
much variation. By contrast, the constancy of pattern in lungs on the one
hand and swim bladder on the other is remarkable.

The derivation of lungs from swim bladder would be more plausible in
that the change in the blood supply could be explained as due to the functional necessity of supplying the lungs with deoxygenated blood, but it
would necessitate the existence of swim bladders in the ancestors of the
presumably lung-breathing crossopterygians; no such ancestors are known,
unless the early cartilaginous fishes and ostracoderms are assumed to have
had swim bladders. General consideration of their form is against this, and
in any case speculation with no facts to guide one is unprofitable.

The same objection applies to any hypothetical air bladder that was
neither a swim bladder nor a lung.

If one considers the animal knigdom as a whole it is obvious that evolution has been opportunist. The body wall can grow out into external gills
(annelids, crustaceans, echinoderms, fish, amphibians), and the gut can
develop various forms of respiratory organs (insects, echinoderms, chordates). As we shall see in Chapter 20, the wall of the pharynx has been
versatile enough to evolve into several endocrine glands. There is therefore no general reason for assuming that swim bladder and lungs are
homologous. The latter may well have arisen as accessory respiratory organs derived from the posterior gill pouches, and their origin in this way
accounts for their blood supply. The probable habitat of the early Choanichthyes, in shallow waters poor in oxygen, gives the conditions in
which such organs would be favored by natural selection. The swim bladder may have arisen independently as a help to an active fish in maintaining its position in the water. Or indeed, since the early teleosts lived in
water that was probably poorly aerated, it may have arisen as an accessory
respiratory organ from the roof of the pharynx, in which case it must have
lost that function when it was no longer needed and was changed to other
uses. If this were so, lungs and swim bladder would be parallel evolutions
for the same purpose, resembling in this the wings of birds and bats, or,
even more closely, the tracheae of insects and arachnids.

It is not, in the present state of our knowledge, possible to be certain of the relationship of lungs and swim bladder. That they are independent is the most economical hypothesis; but if one must regard them as homologous structures it is probable that lungs came first. On any view, *Amia* is a difficulty, and so, if it is correctly placed in the Actinopterygii, is *Polypterus*.

Gullet

Beyond the pharynx the gut is concerned almost solely with the passage and treatment of food, and its evolution can be seen as a gradual increase in the complexity with which digestion is carried out. Its morphological development is to a great extent accompanied by increase in the number and types of enzyme present. In certain circumstances there have to be places where food is stored while awaiting digestion, and in land animals water, as well as food materials, has to be absorbed. The fullest development of the parts of the gut, as well as of the glands that grow out of its walls, occurs only in mammals, and it is from these that the names of the parts are taken. Subsidiary functions of the gut, of which the chief is excretion, have little effect on its form.

We may imagine that the gut of the original ciliary-feeding vertebrate was straight and simple, with emphasis on secretion in the cells of the anterior part, and on absorption posteriorly, with few or no diversions or specialized glands. Something similar to this is found in the lampreys, but here there is a diverticulum corresponding to the liver (p. 166), and the internal surface is increased by a fold or typhlosole.

With the abandonment of microphagy complications arose, and in all the gnathostomes separate parts of the gut can be recognized.

The pharynx leads into a narrow esophagus or gullet. This is in origin a mere passage through which the food passes as quickly as it can and in which no digestion takes place. It retains this absence of function in most groups, but in long-necked animals, especially, at the present day, in mammals, it is necessarily of considerable length, and this was presumably also the case in the dinosaurs. A little proteolytic enzyme is apparently produced by the gullet in amphibians, but only in birds does this part of the gut have any important function; in some of these its lower portion is expanded into a thin-walled crop. In seed-eating birds, notably the gamebirds (Galliformes), pigeons (Columbiformes), parrots (Psittaciformes), and some finches (Fringillidae) and buntings (*Emberiza*), it is large and enables the birds to swallow a great quantity of food very rapidly. A pigeon, for example, can stuff its crop with some dozens of acorns, and then go away to rest and digest them. While the seeds are in the crop they become slightly softened by the action of the enzymes present in the food itself or produced by bacteria. In several flesh- and fish-eating birds there

is a less well-developed crop, and in some of these there is enough digestion of the prey by enzymes sent forward from the next division of the gut
for the skin to be stripped off so that it can be ejected as a pellet. In birds
which feed their young by regurgitation, the food is returned in a slightly
softened form from the crop. The pigeons have gone further. Some of the
cells of the wall of the crop have become glandular; they break down and
liberate their substance as a material the consistency of soft cheese, known
as pigeon's milk, which is fed to the nestlings. It is rich in casein, the same
protein as is present in the milk of mammals. This glandular development
occurs in both sexes, but only during the breeding season.

Stomach

The gullet leads into the stomach, a part of the gut which is usually the
widest in diameter of any and is often more or less bent into the shape of
a U, so that its exit, as well as its entrance, faces toward the head. This
bending comes about because the anterior end of the stomach is anchored
by the transverse septum (p. 128), and its posterior end by the hepato-
enteric and falciform ligaments, which are permanent parts of the ventral
mesentery (p. 132). Hence when the stomach increases in length it can
do so only by bending. It is large in sharks, but its function in them seems
to be little more than storage. Dipnoans have none, so that either they
have lost it or their ancestors must have been fish which, like the cyclostomes, never had one; many teleosts are also without a stomach. This
suggests that the stomach was originally simply a storage place for food,
and only important in those animals which, like the dogfish, were preda-
tory, taking their food in large mouthfuls. If this is so, the crop which has
developed in birds, which already had a stomach, is of a similar nature.

All tetrapods have a stomach, and in them it is in general a place where
digestion of protein goes on in an acid medium. The enzymes used are
called collectively pepsins, and there is nothing corresponding to them in
invertebrates, where digestion of protein is always in an alkaline or neutral medium. The acidity of the stomach varies, but it is seldom so extreme
as in man and the dog. The gland cells are concentrated in the middle
portion, known as the fundus, near the bend of the U. Acid and enzymes
are produced by different cells in mammals, but by the same ones in amphibians and elasmobranchs. The acid is perhaps the primary product,
serving to prevent too rapid bacterial attack on the flesh in the stomach.

In teleosts, amphibians, and reptiles the stomach is on the whole small,
unspecialized, and in some species even straight. In birds there is nearly
always some degree of division of the stomach into two parts, an anterior
proventriculus and a posterior gizzard. Gland cells are present only in the
former. The gizzard is fully developed only in grain-eating birds—largely
the same as those that have a crop—and then consists of two large masses

of muscle enclosing between them a narrow flat space lined with a tough membrane. In this space small stones taken in with the food accumulate. Birds that have had the gizzards removed can digest only part of the corn fed to them, whereas if it is first crushed they can use it all.

The stomach of mammals is large, and may be very large indeed. The cephalad end leads slightly to the left, and is known, from its relation to the heart, as the cardiac limb. The caudad end, which is on the right side, is known as the pyloric limb, because it ends in a sphincter called the pylorus. These names are used, so far as they are applicable, for the corresponding parts of the stomach in other groups. The artiodactyls have a complex stomach, and in cattle and deer there are four distinct chambers. First comes a larger rumen, and then a smaller reticulum, so called from the network of ridges on its inner surface. When the food is passed into these it undergoes considerable churning, during which it is largely split up by bacteria and much fatty acid is formed. This is absorbed directly from the walls of the rumen and may account for one-sixth of the total energy supply. The contents of the rumen are only slightly acid. After some time—four days in cattle—the food is returned to the mouth and chewed, the process being called 'chewing the cud.' Much saliva is produced at this time. The food is then swallowed again, but this time it bypasses the first two chambers of the stomach and goes to the third chamber or psalterium, which has longitudinal ridges on the inner surface to help in mechanical digestion. The food then goes to the fourth stomach, the abomasum, which produces pepsin and carries out chemical digestion in the usual way. In most mammals the stomach absorbs only a little water.

Intestine

The exit from the stomach, the pylorus, is constricted by a strong sphincter muscle, which allows food to pass on only when it relaxes, and so underlines the storing function of the stomach. It leads into the intestine, or rather into the anterior part of this called the small intestine; 'small' here is slightly misleading, since it refers to the diameter, not the volume, of this part of the gut, which may, in some animals, be the biggest section. Moreover, the description is taken from mammals, and in some animals the small intestine is wider, as well as bigger, than the large intestine that follows it.

The small intestine has the twin functions of breaking the food down chemically into small molecules of hexose, aminoacid, fatty acid, and glycerol, and of absorbing these into the blood stream or lymph; probably in the early vertebrates there was no differentiation of parts, secreting cells and absorbing cells being scattered over the walls in mixture. This is approximately true of lampreys, and also, perhaps secondarily, of teleosts, and certainly secondarily of some mammals. In other vertebrates the glandular part is concentrated in the first portion of the small intestine, which is differentiated as the duodenum, while absorption is the function of the longer remainder, the ileum.

In all gnathostomes there are not only glandular cells in the walls of the duodenum, but one or more branched tubular extensions of it which constitute the pancreas. This gland produces powerful digestive enzymes of the three main classes. It has associated with it cells of a different nature and origin, the islet tissue, which make an endocrine gland (Chapter 20). Cells with the same proteolytic function as the pancreas occur in the walls of the anterior part of the intestine of lampreys, and outside it are cells with the same function as the islets, but neither of these groups constitutes a definite gland.

The inner surface of both duodenum and ileum is increased by the presence of short finger-like processes, or villi, which are best developed in mammals, and also by coiling. The ileum may be many times the length of the animal and in general it is much longer in herbivorous animals than in carnivores of the same class and size.

In the dogfish the duodenum is short and undifferentiated. The ileum is relatively short, wide, and straight, but has its internal surface increased by a spiral valve. A similar valve is present also in the intestine of Dipnoi, sturgeons, *Amia, Lepidosteus,* and *Polypterus.* There is little differentiation of duodenum and ileum in the Amphibia, but the ileum has its surface increased by longitudinal ridges. The small intestine of frogs undergoes a remarkable shortening at metamorphosis, reflecting the change from a chiefly herbivorous to a carnivorous diet. Reptiles, because they too are carnivorous, also have a short and undifferentiated small intestine.

In all birds the duodenum is clearly marked off from the rest of the intestine as a single independent loop, while the ileum is thrown into many loops and disposed in the body cavity in various patterns. The pancreas is held in the mesentery in the loop of the duodenum, and usually has two ducts. There may, however, be more than two, or only one, and the number sometimes varies within a species.

The mammals show in the intestine another of their remarkable parallels to the birds. The duodenum is a single deep loop, containing the pancreas, and the ileum consists of many loops, and is longer and more convoluted in herbivores than in carnivores.

Opening into the duodenum or the anterior part of the small intestine by the bile duct, there is, in all vertebrates including cyclostomes, a structure known as the liver. The real origin of this is obscure. In the chick the bile duct begins, like the pancreatic duct, as an outgrowth from the gut, and then branches and expands, its walls forming secreting tissue, so that the liver has been usually interpreted as a glandular development from the walls of the gut. It seems, however, that the mass of the liver is formed directly, mostly from endodermal cells and in most species partly from mesoderm as well, so that except in the sense that all hypoblast is by definition at one time part of the wall of the gut, the liver has no primary connection with the intestine. In Amphibia it is formed from some of the undifferentiated cells on the floor of the archenteron which contains much yolk. In most embryos that have been examined the bile duct develops from the liver and grows into the duodenum. Whatever its origin, the liver is situated in the ventral mesentery below the duodenum, but it usually grows backward to project into the abdominal cavity, and may be large, with several lobes. It consists of masses of more or less cubical cells, with very fine channels between them. These join together and eventually form one or more bile ducts, through which bile is passed into the intestine, but the liver is not a digestive gland since it produces no enzymes for the purpose. At most, the bile assists in the digestion of fats by helping to bring them into solution without hydrolysis. In some animals the lower part of the bile duct is swollen up to form a gall bladder, in which bile is stored before being liberated; in others the gall bladder is formed independently, near the base of the bile duct, from the duodenal wall. In a few animals, such as man and anurans, the pancreatic and bile ducts join together to open in the duodenum by a single tube. The chief function of the liver is to carry out chemical processes, especially the deamination of proteins, the breakdown of fats, and the change of carbohydrates from a soluble to an insoluble form, and vice versa. It stores much glycogen.

The ileum leads into the large intestine, and this also has undergone a progressive differentiation into two or more parts. In lampreys there is really no large intestine at all, the undifferentiated gut leading straight to the anus. In dogfish, and in most other fish, there is a simple short tube usually called the rectum, though it has no great similarity of function to the structure of that name in mammals. After food has been digested in the duodenum and absorbed from the ileum there is nothing left but water, indigestible matter, bacteria, and mucus. The first is plentiful in fish, and the other three collectively make up the feces; under water there is no difficulty in their more or less continuous expulsion. The rectum in fish is then a mere passage to the exterior; in teleosts it opens directly by the anus, but in elasmobranchs and dipnoans it opens into a special structure, the cloaca, which receives also the openings of urinary and genital ducts; this will be considered more fully below.

The ileum of amphibians and reptiles leads into a short, wide, straight passage, usually called the rectum, which opens into a cloaca. The rectum of birds is similar, and often less well marked even than in the frog. There is a cloaca.

The large intestine of mammals is clearly divisible into two portions, an anterior colon and a posterior rectum, the former being the wider and often partially constricted by folds in the wall, so that it is said to be sacculated. The function of the colon is chiefly the absorption of water, and it has presumably become important because with warm blood and high activity the mammals take more food than reptiles of corresponding size, and at the same time have to conserve water as much as possible by re-absorbing it. High metabolism and conservation of water are features of the birds too, and to an even greater degree; little is known of how they achieve such a great degree of absorption, and one can only assume that the cells of the short rectum have a very high activity. The rectum of mammals is mainly a place where feces are stored so that they can be liberated only occasionally, when the anal sphincter relaxes.

It is characteristic of the pyloric region and of the large intestine that they often have one or more blind outgrowths, or ceca; in some animals those that occur below the ileum are taken to mark the limit between this organ and the colon or rectum.

In elasmobranchs there is a single short cecum opening dorsally from the rectum. Its function is unknown, but it has come to be called, misleadingly, the rectal gland. Most teleosts have pyloric ceca, in some as many as a thousand. Their function is uncertain, but the enzyme lactase has been found in them, and food may enter them. Dipnoi have no ceca, nor have amphibians. In some reptiles there is a short cecum on the large intestine, but crocodiles and turtles have none.

Most birds have two rectal ceca, which, especially in the more primitive orders, may be long and more or less lobulated. When they are large there is a well-marked sphincter at the base of the ileum, preventing matter going back into that part of the gut after it has been pushed into the ceca. In other birds they are reduced in size, or only one is present, or they are completely absent. It does not seem possible to associate their presence or absence with the food, since game birds have large ones but many pigeons have not, though both feed on seeds and shoots; nightjars have large ones, many swifts have none, though both feed on insects; owls have large ones, though in raptors they are much reduced.

Little is known of the function of the ceca, but in game birds they apparently absorb water and amino acids, and are also the seat of much bacterial digestion or carbohydrate. The ceca of the domestic fowl empty their contents only once for every seven to eleven defecations from the main part of the intestine.

In most mammals there is a single cecum at the beginning of the colon; it is long in kangaroos, rodents, lagomorphs, horses, and elephants; small in Carnivora and man; and absent from *Dasyurus* and bears. It is obvious that this distribution means that it is generally associated with a herbivorous diet. Wherever it has been properly investigated it has been shown to be very important in digestion, in that in it cellulose is split by bacteria so that the products can be utilized. No mammal, and indeed no vertebrate, can produce its own cellulase. In rabbits, for example, freshly eaten food by-passes the large cardiac part of the stomach and goes from the ileum to the cecum, where it remains for one or two days, after which it is voided as soft feces. These are eaten, a process called re-ingestion, and further digested in the cardiac portion of the stomach. On the second journey down the gut the material does not enter the cecum, but water is absorbed in the colon, and it is voided as hard feces. The artiodactyls, although herbivorous, have a short cecum, and are the exception that proves the rule, for they have achieved the same end, the digestion of cellulose, by other means.

The final portion of the gut is formed from the proctodeum, and is lined with ectoderm. In placental mammals it forms a small part of the rectum and nothing else, but in all other gnathostomes except the teleosts it contributes to a cloaca, which is the name given to a channel which conveys urinary and genital products as well as feces. The ducts that convey the former may be looked upon as originally opening on the surface and as having been carried in when the proctodeum was formed. The exact limits of the endoderm and ectoderm are not easy to determine and are probably unimportant, but the anterior part of the cloaca seems generally to be formed of endoderm, and in birds and mammals the ureters open into this part.

Opening from the ventral surface of the cloaca in Amphibia is a thin-walled bladder into which urine is passed and stored before being voided. A similar bladder is present in lizards and tortoises, and its development shows that it is a remnant of the allantois (Chapter 5). It seems therefore likely that this arose in the early land-living vertebrates as a storage place for urine when it became inconvenient to pass this out of the body continuously; later it was probably used for storage of excretory products in the embryo, as it still is in reptiles and birds; and finally became the important excretory, respiratory, and trophic organ that it is in mammals, where it makes up a large part of the placenta. Its original function has been retained in the lizards and tortoises, and in its stalk which forms the excretory bladder of mammals; its main part is shed at birth in mammals and it is completely lost in birds.

The cloaca of birds is partially divided by constrictions into three chambers, into the upper of which or coprodeum opens the intestine, into the second or urodeum the ureters and genital ducts, while the last or proctodeum, which alone is lined with ectoderm, bears the anus, and also a blind pouch called the bursa of Fabricius. This is of unknown function, but it contains much lymphoid tissue, which suggests that it manufactures white blood cells. In nearly all birds it closes and shrinks before adult life, so that it parallels the thymus of mammals (Chapter 20). The walls of the cloaca may absorb water, and so help to lead to the formation of the semi-solid urine mixed with feces so characteristic of birds, but there is no experimental evidence of this and some against it.

10

Circulatory System

SOME SORT of fluid that circulates, if only slowly and fitfully, within the body in order to carry food and other material seems to be a necessity for animals above a certain size; there is therefore no need to assume, as is sometimes done, that the circulatory or vascular systems of all Metazoa are homologous. That of the vertebrates, which are all, by invertebrate standards, large animals, has a characteristic and uniform plan which cannot easily be assimilated to that of any invertebrate (except amphioxus), and there is little use in trying to do so. Certainly it affords no evidence for any connection between the vertebrates and the echinoderms, which have neither blood nor blood system and have instead only a system of vessels open to the sea. The vertebrate vascular system has been described in outline in Chapters 1 and 2. It is derived from mesoderm and there is a very real sense in which the blood is its primary as well as its most important part. Along various lines much of the mesoderm becomes liquid; the cells that remain become blood cells, and around these, and the fluid in which they are suspended, walls of mesothelium one-cell thick form. Tough connective tissue, and in some cases muscles, are added on the outside of all but the smallest vessels. The result is a network of tubes, and out of this the final pattern of blood vessels is formed. Although the main lines are constant the minor ones are subject to much variation, and, since the network spreads throughout the mesoblast, major new vessels can be formed according to functional need almost anywhere, while old ones may be suppressed.

Two general features of the vascular system of Metazoa are that they often incorporate one or more specialized parts for pumping the blood, which may be called hearts, and that they have a special relationship to the organs which take up oxygen from the surroundings. The arteries, which are the vessels leading away from the heart, break up in the respiratory organs into capillaries, and these join up into arteries again which supply the body in general, where there are more capillaries. When these join together they form veins, which return the blood to the heart. Large and thin-walled veins are often called sinuses. In vertebrates, perhaps because of their greater activity or greater size, there is also a special relationship to the liver, and, in most groups, to the kidneys; in these organs there are intercalated sets of capillaries, the portal systems. Lung-breathing vertebrates have special pulmonary veins which return the oxygenated blood to the heart before it goes to the body. The method of formation of the vessels means that there is initially no difference between arteries, veins, and capillaries, for all begin by being capillaries. The major vessels that come from the heart develop muscular walls and become arteries, those that lead to the heart have less muscle, or none, and are veins, while the smaller arterioles and venules lead gradually into the capillaries, which retain their thin single-layered mesothelial walls. It is convenient, in the description that follows, to refer to vessels as growing in a particular direction, but this is misleading unless the reader remembers that a small vessel may be first formed simultaneously all along its length, and that the growth referred to is not the gradual progression of a new vessel, but the increase in size and importance of a pre-existing one in the direction shown.

Although there are many differences of detail, the early blood vessels of all vertebrate embryos follow the same plan, and this is very similar to that which is retained in adult fish (Plate III). The most interesting point is that both the main dorsal vessel and the main ventral vessel are primarily double. The first tubes to appear are usually a pair of ventral vitelline vessels, or vitelline veins, so called because they convey the food material derived from the yolk on which the embryo feeds. In the midpart of the body these meet and fuse to form a single subintestinal vessel, in which the heart will later form. The lengths behind the heart give rise to the hepatic portal and hepatic veins, their middle portions becoming the capillaries of the hepatic portal system. The anterior unfused parts develop directly into the lateral ventral aortae, although these are usually short and often unrecognizable in the adult.

A pair of lateral dorsal aortae also appear, and are joined to the ventral aortae in front of the heart by a series of branchial vessels, one running in each gill arch. Behind the heart a vessel, the vitelline artery, grows down from each lateral dorsal aorta into the yolk, where it breaks up into capillaries which are collected together into the vitelline vein. Behind the level of the heart or thereabouts the lateral dorsal aortae always fuse to form a single vessel, in which the blood runs posteriorly.

Meanwhile two more longitudinal vessels have formed. These are the cardinal veins, which run pretty well from end to end of the body at the top of the lateral plate mesoderm. A rather misleadingly named common cardinal drops down from each of these in the transverse septum, the two unite to form a transverse duct or sinus of Cuvier, and this joins with the anterior ends of the vitelline veins and opens into the heart. The portion of the cardinal vein in front of the common cardinal is called anterior, that behind it posterior. In the embryo blood leaks into the cardinal veins, and later they are connected to the dorsal aorta through the capillaries of the general body system.

From this simple plan there develop the different types of circulation found in the various classes of vertebrate, and we will now consider the fate of the chief parts. In general, those classes formerly included in one group as Pisces, or fish, deviate little from the basic plan, while the tetrapods diverge more and more widely from it.

Heart

The swelling of the ventral vessels to form the heart may begin, as in mammals, before the fusion. Histologically, the region is interesting for the development in the walls of the heart of a peculiar type of muscle, called cardiac (Fig. 21.4). It consists of fibers, cross-striped like those of skeletal muscle, but differing in that the fibers are branched and connected to one another, so that the heart is a single syncytium. The effective unit of contraction is not the single fiber but the whole heart; if any part begins contracting the rest must follow. It is a natural property of cardiac muscle to contract rhythmically, and this can be well seen in the two-day chick embryo, where the incipient heart can be watched beating long before any nervous tissue reaches it. The action of the nervous system even on the adult heart is only to alter its rate or amplitude of beat, usually to increase them. As the heart develops and becomes more complicated there is a loss of histological continuity between its various parts, but it is still obviously necessary for it to contract as a whole, though not all at the same time. There has developed therefore a mechanism called the pacemaker, whereby the rhythm is set by the morphologically posterior part of the heart, and is imposed on the rest through a special band of muscle fibers which runs to the other parts (Fig. 10.1).

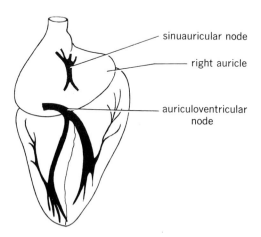

sinuauricular node

right auricle

auriculoventricular node

FIG. 10.1   Diagrammatic drawing of the pacemaker of the mammalian heart.

In all vertebrates the heart becomes divided into specialized parts, or chambers, which are primarily, from behind forward, the sinus venosus, the auricle (or atrium), the ventricle, and an anterior portion called variously conus or bulbus arteriosus, or bulbus cordis. The sinus venosus is thin walled and is chiefly a receptacle for venous blood; the auricle is also a receiving chamber, but is slightly muscular; while the ventricle is highly muscular and is the chief source of the beat that drives the blood forward. Valves, to prevent the blood flowing backward, are usually present between sinus and auricle, between auricle and ventricle, and in the conus. As the heart differentiates it elongates, and to fit itself into the space between gill slits and transverse septum it has to go into an S-bend, which brings the auricle to lie above and even slightly in front of the ventricle. A heart of this type is well seen in the dogfish (Figs. 4.11 and 4.13), which is almost diagrammatic. The anterior chamber of elasmobranchs is well developed and muscular, and it is solely for a chamber of this sort, according to some authors, that the name conus should be used. The conus of elasmobranchs has several rows of valves.

The heart of dipnoans will be considered later. That of the more primitive Actinopterygii—sturgeons, *Polypterus*, *Lepidosteus*, and *Amia*—is in general very similar to that of sharks, with a long conus with several valves. That of teleosts differs in a shortening of the anterior region and a loss of its valves. There is, however, a short muscular region in front of the ventricle, sometimes called the bulbus arteriosus to indicate the view that it is a new formation from the ventral aorta in front of the old heart. This may be so, but since the whole heart is a specialization of the ventral aorta to try to put limits to it in this way is not very wise. For the student it is simplest to call any chamber in front of the ventricle the bulbus, without adding any other Latin word, and to call it a conus if it has valves.

In the tetrapods and the dipnoans the heart is functionally complicated by the return of oxygenated blood from the lungs into the auricle, which means that oxygenated and deoxygenated blood would be, if the heart remained unaltered, present together in the same chamber. This would clearly be an inefficient arrangement, and in all the animals that possess lungs there is at least some secondary division of the heart into right and left sides, so that the two streams of blood are at least partially separated. Unfortunately, no simple account of the evolution of the tetrapod heart makes sense, and evidence is accumulating that the division has occurred more than once and in different ways. The hearts of the living amphibians, which are usually studied and taken as intermediate stages between the condition in most fish and the full division of the mammals and birds, appear to be degenerate and not very helpful. Of the hearts of the extinct crossopterygians and the stegocephalians, which might have been ancestral to living tetrapods, we know nothing and are never likely to know anything.

The dipnoan heart has an even more pronounced sigmoid bend than that of the dogfish, so that the auricle is almost entirely in front of the ventricle. The venous blood is returned as usual into the sinus venosus, but the pulmonary vein, bringing oxygenated blood from the lungs, opens directly into the left side of the auricle. The sinus venosus opens into its right side, and a vertical partition divides it almost completely into two unequal halves, of which the right is the larger. The ventricle also is incompletely divided by a septum, and so is the conus, but as the latter is spirally twisted the division comes to be horizontal, instead of vertical, in its anterior part. The effect of these partitions is that the blood which has been returned from the lungs to the left side of the heart goes into the ventral half of the conus and so to the carotid and systemic arteries (p. 187), while the deoxygenated blood from the sinus venosus goes through the right side of the heart to the dorsal channel of the conus and so to the pulmonary artery. The septa are more nearly complete in *Lepidosiren* than in the other two genera, and the histology of the gills in this fish suggests that they probably carry out no exchange of gases.

The heart of amphibians, though it resembles in general that of dipnoans, is much less suited to keep separate the two streams of oxygenated and deoxygenated blood. There is the same exaggerated sigmoid curve, with the auricle in front of the ventricle, and now the sinus venosus is above the auricle. In the anurans the auricle is completely divided into two, and it is usual to speak as if there were two, the right receiving blood from the sinus, the left from the lungs. This arrangement persists, as we shall see, in the amniotes. In the urodeles the auricular septum is always thin, may be perforated, as in *Salamandra*, and in some perennibranchiates is lost altogether in the adults, though present in the embryo. Perforations occur also in the auricular septum of cecilians. Whatever the condition of the auricles, no amphibian has any trace of a ventricular septum, so that in the ventricles the two streams of blood must at least come into contact, even if they do not mix. The anurans and terrestrial urodeles have a division, the spiral valve, in the conus, which, like its fellow (but not necessarily homologue) in the Dipnoi separates a ventral passage, leading to the carotid and systemic arteries, from a dorsal passage going to the pulmonary artery. The cecilians, and the aquatic urodeles with a much-perforated auricular septum, have no spiral valve.

Much speculation and imagination have been devoted to the problem of how far the two streams of blood that enter the amphibian ventricle remain separate from each other. For long the story expounded in the books was that, in the frogs at least, the slightly asymmetrical contraction of the heart, combined with the spiral valve, served to keep them almost entirely apart, so that deoxygenated blood went to the lungs, oxygenated blood to the carotids, and oxygenated blood, with some mixture from the right side of the heart, to the systemic. Experimental investigation has now shown that this is not so. In the European *Rana temporaria* there is almost complete mixing in the ventricle, and no difference between the types of blood in the three arches can be detected. Other, and on the whole less critical, work on other species of frog has not shown such complete mixing, or has shown it only in some experiments, but at least it seems clear that there is never complete separation. It seems unlikely that there is a greater degree of separation in urodeles, and in those with a very incomplete auricular septum there is likely to be less.

The persistence of the old story for so long—it was first put forward in 1852 and is hardly dead yet—is an example of the small attention paid by many zoologists to the living animal. It is obvious to anyone who dissects a frog that at least half the blood that leaves the heart by the pulmonary arch goes not to the lungs but to the skin, and it has been known for a long time that much, and under certain circumstances most, of the oxygen uptake of a frog is through the skin, not the lungs. Blood returning from the skin will therefore be as highly oxygenated as that from the lungs, and it travels by the cutaneous vein to the sinus venosus and the right auricle, not by the pulmonary vein to the left auricle. The blood coming into the right side of the ventricle is thus by no means deoxygenated, and there would be no advantage in channeling it all to the lungs. It is possible, but not proved, that the degree of mixing of the blood in the heart is under physiological control according to whether the animal is breathing chiefly by its lungs or by its skin.

Another reason for the persistence of the old story was the view that the Amphibia are ancestral to the amniotes, so that it was necessary to explain the heart of the frog as an intermediate stage between that of the fish and that of the reptiles. It is now clear, as many chapters of this book will show, that all the existing amphibians have lost many structures that their ancestors possessed, and can be used as links between fish and reptiles only with great circumspection. The probability is that all the modern amphibians except the Apoda, which are peculiar in other ways, are more aquatic than their ancestors, and their breathing and circulation have been modified accordingly. All, including the Apoda, have at least some degree of cutaneous respiration, and many of the urodeles have external gills. The presence of an auricular septum in the embryos of newts, and the association between its perforation in adult life and the aquatic habitat, suggest that it is in process of being lost. It is at least possible that the interventricular septum has been lost too. The Dipnoi are not ancestral to the tetrapods, but as they have a ventricular septum there is a likelihood that the crossopterygians had one also. That the heart of *Latimeria* is like that of most fishes, with single auricle and ventricle (though it is even more primitive than that of the dogfish, in that there is no sigmoid bend), does not argue against this view since the creature has given up using its lungs. There are, however, on any view difficulties

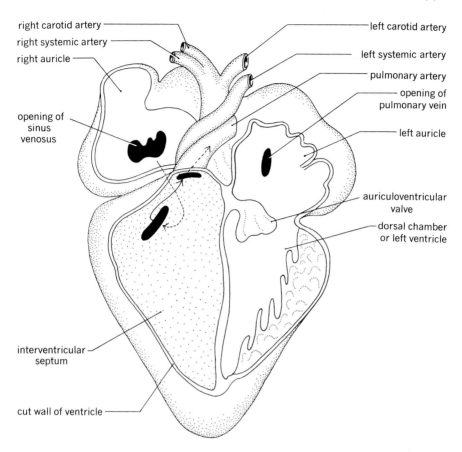

right carotid artery
right systemic artery
right auricle

left carotid artery
left systemic artery
pulmonary artery
opening of pulmonary vein

opening of sinus venosus

left auricle

auriculoventricular valve

dorsal chamber or left ventricle

interventricular septum

cut wall of ventricle

FIG. 10.2 Dissection of the heart of the green lizard (*Lacerta viridis*), ventral, x 10. The ventral wall has been removed. The arrows show the course of venous blood from the right auricle through the dorsal chamber of the ventricle to the ventral chamber (which lies between the interventricular septum and the reader) to the pulmonary artery.

in explaining the hearts of reptiles, with which we must now deal.

The heart of amniotes is, as it were, abbreviated at both ends. The conus is never present and in reptiles the sinus, though of the same general form as in amphibians, is smaller. In all reptiles (Fig. 10.2) there are completely separate right and left auricles, the pulmonary veins opening into the left. The ventricle shows an almost complete range of subdivision from the state of some lizards which have practically none, to the crocodiles which have a septum complete except for a small hole, the foramen of Panizza. This is not, however, the whole story, for the septum forms in different ways and in different positions in the various orders. In Squamata and Chelonia the ventricular septum is horizontal, dividing the ventricle into dorsal and ventral chambers; this arrangement probably arises because of a twisting of the heart, so that the dorsal chamber is probably morphologically left, and the ventral one, right. The septum stretches forward from the posterior wall of the ventricle, and is incomplete in front; its position is such that both auricles open on its dorsal side, and any blood from them that is going to pass into the ventral (or right) chamber must pass across its free lip. The blood most likely to do this is that from the right auricle, which is deoxygenated. Since the pulmonary artery arises from the ventral side of the ventricle, it looks as if this is a functional arrangement to separate oxygenated and deoxygenated blood; but it is quite different from the arrangement in the frog.

As will be shown below, the right and left systemic arches of the reptiles arise separately from the ventricle (in other words, there is no ventral aorta). In the Lepidosauria they are both in such a position that a completion of the ventricular septum would leave them beginning from the dorsal chamber, or left ventricle; in Chelonia, such an extension would separate them, so that the left arch would come from the ventral chamber (right ventricle), and the right from the dorsal chamber (left ventricle). This reversal of what might be expected arises because the systemic arches are twisted round each other.

Experimental observation of the heart of the European lizard *Lacerta viridis* has shown that there is a considerable separation of the oxygenated and deoxygenated blood in the ventricle, so that the latter goes chiefly to the lungs, while the right systemic artery (which is further from the pulmonary artery in its point of origin) conveys more highly oxygenated blood than does the left. There is thus considerable functional efficiency in the arrangement of the vessels and their relationship to the septa. This subject is returned to below when we discuss the comparative anatomy of the arches.

The ventricle of many reptiles has in addition a secondary incomplete septum which divides the dorsal (left) chamber vertically into right and left halves. Unlike the primary septum, it is not formed by an ingrowth of a ridge from the walls, but by the coalescence of the trabeculae, which are bars of muscle which in most reptilian and amphibian hearts run across the ventricle from one wall to another and give it something of a spongy character. In crocodiles this septum is practically complete, while the primary one disappears. The junction with the auricle is made in such a way that the right auricle opens into a right ventricle, from which spring the pulmonary artery and the left systemic, while the left auricle opens into a left ventricle from which springs only the right systemic. There is therefore complete separation of oxygenated and deoxygenated blood in the heart, the effect of which is somewhat vitiated by the fact that the left systemic, containing only deoxygenated blood, later joins the right. It is, however, much the smaller of the two. The foramen of Panizza is too small to allow much mixing of the blood. According to some authors it is a secondary perforation. An alternative explanation of the heart of reptiles, according to which most of the interventricular septum is the same in all groups, is much less well supported.

The heart of birds (Fig. 10.3) is essentially similar to that of crocodiles, with an interventricular septum formed from trabeculae and a right systemic coming from the left ventricle. There is no foramen of Panizza, and the sinus venosus is absorbed almost completely into the right auricle; in some birds, such as the ostrich, it is still recognizable, and sinu-auricular valves are present.

The mammalian heart (Fig. 10.4) is simpler than that of any other tetrapod, and appears to be completely efficient. The sinus is absorbed into the auricle, its tissue remaining only as the pacemaker, called the sinu-auricular node. Its valves remain in monotremes. Both auricle and ventricle are completely divided into right and left chambers, and as the ventricular septum is formed by a forward-growing ridge, it is presumably homologous with that of lizards and tortoises, but not with that of crocodiles and birds. It divides the auriculo-ventricular opening and the base of the arterial arches in such a way that deoxygenated blood flows through

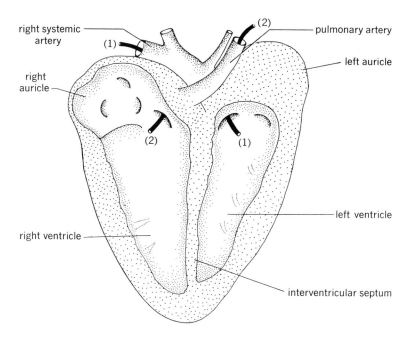

FIG. 10.3 Dissection of the heart of the pigeon (*Columba livia*), ventral, semi-diagrammatic, x 3. The left auricle has been cut open, and bristles have been placed in the right systemic artery (1) and the pulmonary artery (2).

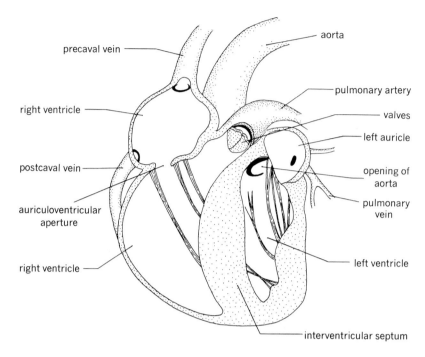

FIG. 10.4 Dissection of the heart of a kitten (*Felis catus*), ventral, slightly diagrammatic, x 4.

the right auricle and ventricle to the pulmonary artery, oxygenated blood through the left-hand chambers to the systemic and carotid arteries.

In all the amniotes the auricular septum, which is the first step toward a partial or complete double circulation, is established in the embryo before the lungs can be used for respiration. The embryo of a reptile or bird gets its oxygen through the allantois, which comes up against the inside of the egg-shell, while the mammalian fetus gets its oxygen from the mother's blood through the placenta. The blood from both allantois and placenta drains into the cardinal veins, so that it is mixed with deoxygenated blood and goes to the right auricle. It would be a waste of effort to send it to the lungs, and presumably for this reason the auricular septum becomes pierced by one or more foramina, that in mammals being called the oval foramen. In a number of mammalian fetuses (for example, sheep, cat, and guinea pig) an almost complete double circulation has been demonstrated. Blood from the placenta and the posterior part of the body goes into the right auricle and then almost entirely through the foramen to the left auricle, left ventricle, and by the carotid arteries to the head, while blood returned from the head goes from the right auricle into the right ventricle and into the pulmonary artery; this is still connected by the ductus arteriosus to the dorsal aorta (see below, p. 187), so that most of the blood goes this way and is taken by the aorta to the placenta and the posterior part of the body. This is an interesting example of a special embryonic adaptation, which must have been evolved independently of the life of the adult mammal.

Diagrams of the different types of circulation are shown in Fig. 10.5.

While the holes in the auricular septum of birds close at hatching by growth from their edges, the oval foramen of mammals is filled by a secondary septum; at birth, when the animal begins to breathe, the resulting changes in pressure in the heart and blood vessels cause it to act as a valve to prevent blood flowing through from one auricle to the other, and

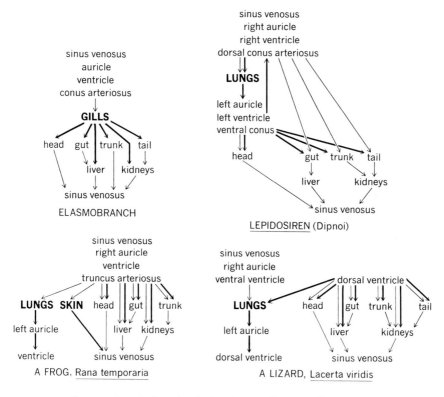

FIG. 10.5 Summaries of the circulation in vertebrates. The respiratory organ is shown in boldface caps; lightface arrows indicate deoxygenated blood; boldface arrows indicate oxygenated blood.

The pattern of circulation in the teleosts is generally similar to that in the elasmobranchs, but the conus arteriosus is replaced by a bulbus and there is some variation in the formation of the renal portal system. The degree of separation of the two streams of blood in the heart of the Dipnoi has not been experimentally analyzed, so that the scheme shown is tentative and shows only the probable main lines of flow.

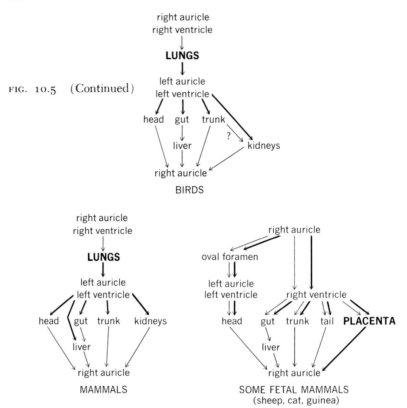

FIG. 10.5   (Continued)

eventually it becomes joined to the primary septum and the hole is obliterated. Its occasional failure to do so, leading to hole-in-the-heart babies, can now be dealt with by surgery.

Arteries

We must now return to the ventral aorta, in front of the heart, and its connection, through the gill arches, with the anterior part of the dorsal aorta.

In the simplest case, which is realized more or less in many embryos, including the dogfish, chick, and mammals, the anterior parts of the vitelline veins become transformed into paired ventral aortae running forward to the head, and from these branch a symmetrical series of branchial arteries which lead to the lateral dorsal aortae. In the anterior prolongations of these the blood runs forward to the head, but for most of their length the blood runs backward in them (Fig. 10.6). The number of pairs of branchial arteries varies, but corresponds in general to the number of gill slits. In accordance with the view that the mouth represents a pair of fused gill slits, the first branchial vessel runs in what would be the first branchial arch, that is, between mouth and spiracle. The series is then

mouth

mandibular artery

spiracle

hyoid artery

1st gill slit

3rd branchial artery

2nd gill slit

4th branchial artery

3rd gill slit

5th branchial artery

4th gill slit

6th branchial artery

5th gill slit

There is no artery behind the last gill slit, but where there are more than five gill slits extra arteries are present in the arches.

Complications are of three sorts. The ventral aortae tend to fuse to form a single median vessel, and in the tetrapods to shorten and disappear altogether, so that the arches come directly from the heart; the dorsal aortae tend to fuse and later largely disappear between the third and sixth branchial arteries; and the branchial arteries are complicated by the presence of gills and later of lungs.

The dogfish (Figs. 4.11, 4.12) shows a relatively simple modification. There is a single ventral aorta, and only a short part of the dorsal aorta is double, making what is called the cephalic circle below the skull. The dorsal or efferent part of each branchial arch is lost and is replaced by a new vessel, the epibranchial artery, which shifts so as to lie opposite the slit, not the arch. It becomes connected to the ventral portion of the branchial artery, now called the afferent branchial artery, by the capillaries in the gills. There are also simplifications and losses in the region in front of the functional gill slits. These changes are shown, in simplified form, in Fig. 10.6. The head is supplied only by the dorsal aortae, through a pair of vessels called internal carotids.

A rather similar state is found in the teleosts. The dorsal aortae remain separate rather further back, so that some or all of the efferent branchial arteries join the cephalic circle. The junction through the gills is made by the loss of the ventral or afferent portions of the branchial vessels and their replacement by new ones. The condition in sturgeons, *Lepidosteus*, *Amia*, and Dipnoi is intermediate, part of each vessel being lost.

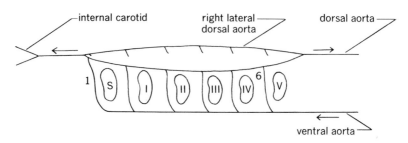

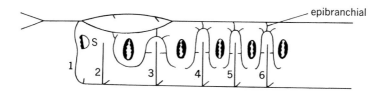

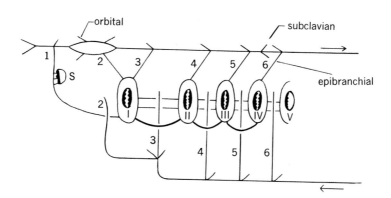

FIG. 10.6   Three diagrams to show the development of the epibranchial arteries in an elasmobranch, to be read from above downward. (Simplified from Goodrich) I to V, the gill slits; 1 to 6, the branchial arteries.

Those gill bars of dipnoans which bear no gills have, as would be expected, simple branchial vessels. These efferent branchial arteries (or epibranchials, as the case may be) of one side join together before they unite with those of the other side to form the dorsal aorta, but they are more or less widely separate from each other ventrally, so that the ventral aorta is short. A branch from the sixth branchial—or in *Protopterus* from the region where all the epibranchials join together—runs to the lung as a pulmonary

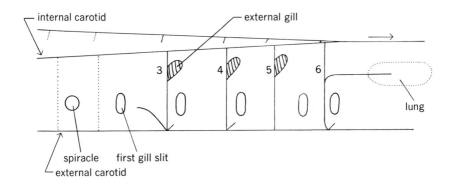

internal carotid

external gill

3   4   5   6

lung

spiracle   first gill slit

external carotid

FIG. 10.7   Diagram of the anterior arteries of a larval amphibian.

artery. The external gills of *Protopterus* are supplied from the fourth, fifth, and sixth branchial vessels.

At first sight the anterior arterial system of tetrapods seems to have little resemblance to that of fishes, but a study of the development shows that this is not so. The system in an amphibian larva is essentially fish-like (Fig. 10.7), with a single, though short, ventral aorta, arteries through the gill arches, and lateral dorsal aorta joining posteriorly. The chief differences are the prolongation of the ventral aortae into the head as the external carotid arteries; the absence of a cephalic circle; and the absence of first and second branchial arteries. There is, as development goes on, the same tendency to elimination of the ventral aorta by carrying the afferent vessels separately back to the heart as is seen in the dipnoans. The external gills are supplied by loops and capillaries from the third, fourth, and fifth branchial arteries. When the lungs are formed they are supplied from the sixth.

In the neotenous urodeles, the larval arrangement essentially persists. The only important changes are that the fifth arch may be absent and the dorsal aorta may disappear between the third and fourth and between the fourth and fifth branchials. The effect of these breaks is that the head is supplied only through the external carotid and the third branchial, the body only through the fourth branchial. *Necturus* is exceptional in that the lung is apparently supplied from the fifth branchial artery (Fig. 10.8).

In other amphibians there is greater reduction, seen at its maximum in a frog such as *Rana* (Fig. 10.9). All the blood supply to the gills is lost, though the knot of capillaries from the first internal gill remains as the carotid body; the fifth vessel disappears entirely, and the sixth no longer meets the dorsal aorta, so that it appears as an independent pulmonary artery; the dorsal aorta disappears between the third and fourth branchial vessels, leaving the former as the carotid arch and the latter as the sys-

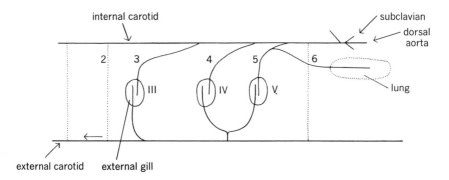

FIG. 10.8 Diagram of the anterior arteries of the mud puppy, *Necturus maculosus*. III to V, the external gills; 1 to 6, the branchial arteries; dotted lines show vessels that are not present.

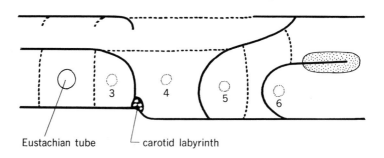

FIG. 10.9 Diagram of the anterior arteries of a frog, *Rana temporaria*. 1 to 6, branchial arches; dotted lines show vessels not present.

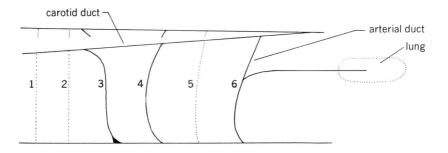

FIG. 10.10 Diagram of the anterior arteries of *Sphenodon punctatus*. 1 to 6, branchial arches; dotted lines show vessels not present.

temic. The carotid, systemic, and pulmonary arches are continued back almost to the conus, so that there is hardly any ventral aorta.

The same sort of reductions occur in most reptiles, but in some of them, as well as in some amphibians, pieces of the system that are lost in the frog persist (Fig. 10.10). There has been much confusion in the past in the naming of some of these relics, but there is now fairly general agreement. The two following lists show the names of the vessels that are present in tetrapods, with the part of the symmetrical system of fish embryos from which they are derived. Names that are not recommended are placed in square brackets.

First, the vessels that are always present in reptiles and amphibians are these:

External carotid artery [= lingual artery]	Anterior prolongation of ventral aorta
Internal carotid artery	Third branchial artery plus anterior prolongation of lateral dorsal aorta
Carotid body [= carotid gland = carotid labyrinth]	Remains of capillaries of gill between first and second gill slits
Systemic artery or arch	Basal portion of ventral aorta plus fourth branchial artery plus posterior part of lateral dorsal aorta
Pulmonary artery or arch	Split-off part of basal portion of ventral aorta plus ventral portion of sixth branchial artery

The first and second branchial arteries are always lost, but some of the other pieces of the system are retained here and there. They are, with their names when present, and examples of their occurrence:

Carotid duct or ductus caroticus [= duct of Botallus]	Dorsal aorta between third and fourth branchial arteries	Some urodeles, e.g. *Triton;* Apoda; Some reptiles, e.g. *Lacerta, Sphenodon;* Occasionally present in birds on the right side
Fifth artery or arch	Fifth branchial artery	Urodela (Fig. 10.11).
Arterial duct or ductus arteriosus [= duct of Botallus]	Dorsal portion of sixth branchial artery, or sixth epibranchial	Urodela; Apoda; Many reptiles, e.g. *Sphenodon, Alligator,* some Chelonia; it closes late, and can often be seen as a fibrous strand in dissection, e.g. in the frog and mammals

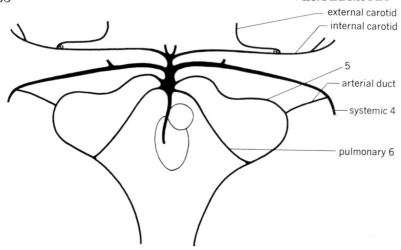

external carotid
internal carotid
5
arterial duct
systemic 4
pulmonary 6

FIG. 10.11 Dissection of the arterial arches of a salamander (*Salamandra maculosa*), slightly diagrammatic, x 1/5. The fifth arch (5) persists.

In addition to the modifications and reductions that they share with amphibians, the reptiles have a further asymmetrical development which is connected with the partial division of the ventricle that we have already described. The left systemic arch is always smaller than the right, and the common carotid artery, as well as both subclavians, comes off from the right systemic arch, the basal portion of which is strictly, as shown above, part of the ventral aorta. The spiral twist that separates left and right systemics also causes the left systemic to come from the right ventricle and the right systemic from the left ventricle. The effect of all this is, as we have seen, to cause a partial separation of oxygenated and deoxygenated blood, so that there is a higher oxygen concentration in the right arch, which alone supplies the fore-limbs and the head. The extreme of this development is found in the crocodiles, where the ventricular septum is nearly complete and the left systemic arch is very small.

The arrangement in birds is easily derived from that of the crocodile. There are two separate ventricles, and the left systemic is lost. The right systemic comes from the left ventricle, and there is a perfect double circulation. There are other peculiarities in the arteries of birds, especially in the carotids, which will be referred to below. A persistent left systemic has been seen in a number of species, and the right carotid duct occurs often enough for it to be ranked as a common abnormality.

The system in mammals (Fig. 10.12) cannot be derived from that of any living reptile and must be referred back to the more symmetrical arrangement of the amphibians. The right systemic is lost, but as there is no spiral twisting of the vessels, and the left systemic comes from the left ventricle, the same separation of the two circuits of blood is achieved as in the birds. Both carotids and both subclavians come off, in various patterns, from the left systemic.

The disposition of the anterior arteries and the division of the heart can be summarized in a series of diagrams (Fig. 10.13). In these the heart is shown diagrammatically with the sigmoid bend taken out so that the auricles are posterior, and from the ventral surface to correspond to an animal as usually seen in dissection. Owing to the twisting of the heart and to the sigmoid bend it is impossible to show the ventricular septum in a diagrammatic way which is strictly accurate, but an attempt has been made to place it in the drawings in such a way as to show its effect.

Goodrich, who first stressed the differences between the mammalian and avian arrangements, rightly pointed out that it meant that the mammals could not have evolved from any existing reptiles, or anything like them, and that their ancestors must be presumed to have diverged very early from the first reptiles, the cotylosaurs, which may be presumed to have had a more symmetrical arterial system, resembling that of the Amphibia. This view is confirmed, as will be shown in Chapter 16, by the skull. There are, however, difficulties in accepting the idea of a simple bifurcation of the reptiles into sauropsidan and theropsidan lines. In the first place, the

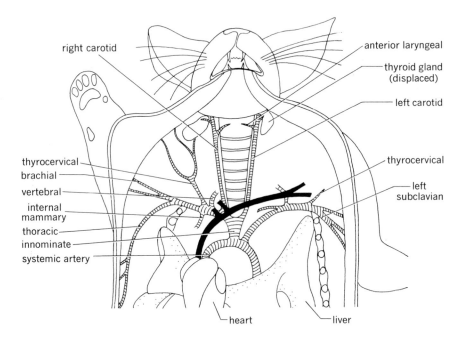

FIG. 10.12 Dissection of the anterior arterial system of a kitten (*Felis catus*), x 3/4.

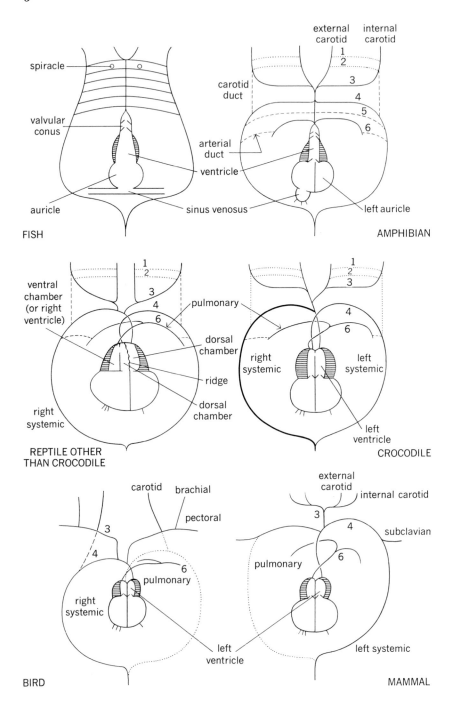

FISH

spiracle

valvular conus

auricle

sinus venosus

ventricle

arterial duct

AMPHIBIAN

external carotid

internal carotid

carotid duct

1
2
3
4
5
6

left auricle

REPTILE OTHER THAN CROCODILE

ventral chamber (or right ventricle)

1
2
3
4
6

pulmonary

dorsal chamber

ridge

dorsal chamber

right systemic

CROCODILE

1
2
3
4
6

pulmonary

right systemic

left systemic

left ventricle

BIRD

3
4
6
pulmonary

carotid

brachial

pectoral

right systemic

left ventricle

MAMMAL

external carotid

internal carotid

3
4
6
pulmonary

subclavian

left systemic

hearts of existing amphibians show every sign of being degenerate, so that it is possible that their symmetrical arterial arches may be a larval character that has been retained in the adult. This is in line with other features of their bodies, such as the retention of much cartilage in the skeleton. We certainly cannot have any confidence that the heart and arterial arches of cotylosaurs were like those of frogs. Since the dipnoans have a partly divided ventricle it is possible that the crossopterygians did also, and then so probably did the stegocephalians and cotylosaurs. Another difficulty comes from the nature of the ventricular septum, which is the same in mammals as in Dipnoi, Lepidosauria, and Chelonia, but which is of a different type in crocodiles and birds. This suggests that the latter have acquired a new type of septum, and that they are on a different line of evolution from the other reptiles. This would agree with the view that the Chelonia are persistent anapsids (Chapter 5) but would necessitate removing the Rhynchocephalia, as well as the Squamata, from the diapsid line. All we can say is that the problem of the double circulation needed by lung-breathers has been solved, or partially solved, in four different ways, by Dipnoi, by Chelonia and Lepidosauria, by crocodiles and birds, and by mammals, while the modern amphibia have hardly solved it at all.

Several small arteries branch off from the carotids to supply the various parts of the head in fish (Fig. 10.6), and attempts have been made to homologize these with the arteries in similar positions in amniotes. In view of the very great changes that have taken place in the form and segmentation of the head (Chapter 19), success in these seems unlikely. It is possible that some parts of these anterior arteries represent pieces of the first and second branchial vessels. The elongation of the neck in tetrapods produces complications, and there is much variation in the arrangement of the carotids. The external carotids of reptiles are small, and in crocodiles the internal carotids join, that of the left side then disappearing. Birds have a bewildering array of types of carotid circulation. The two internal carotids may be normal; they may meet and fuse, and one may be much smaller than the other or disappear as in crocodiles; either or both may disappear and be functionally replaced by a superficial vessel; and one of these may in its turn disappear.

FIG. 10.13   Diagrams of the arterial arches of vertebrates, ventral. The heart is shown flattened and pulled out, so that the auricles appear in their embryonic posterior position. Continuous lines show vessels that are always present in the group, broken lines those sometimes present, and dotted lines those never present. The position of the fifth arch is not shown in the diagrams of reptiles, birds, and mammals, in which it is never present, and some other absent vessels are not shown for birds and mammals.

After the anterior system the rest is relatively simple. The dorsal aorta has basically two types of branches; paired ones which are primarily segmental and run in the body wall, and unpaired ones which run in the mesentery. The former supply the muscles, limbs, and mesodermal structures such as kidneys and gonads, while the latter go to the alimentary canal and its offshoots.

In view of the ease with which, as explained above, any small blood vessel may be expanded and become important with use, it is pointless to try to make homologies except in the most general way between corresponding vessels in different groups of animals. The subclavian arteries, for example, which go to the fore-limbs, arise at various points. In elasmobranchs they are far forward, in front of the last epibranchials (Fig. 4.12), in frogs they are about halfway round the loop of the systemics, in *Necturus* they arise from the dorsal aorta just after the junction, while in reptiles, those of both sides come off from the right systemic just in front of the point where it joins its fellow. In birds a new subclavian grows out from the common carotid and joins the primary subclavian, the base of which then disappears, so that the fore-limb is supplied entirely from the secondary vessel. In mammals the original subclavians persist, but, as the heart moves backward during development until it is slightly posterior to the fore-limb, they come to lead off the systemic arch relatively far forward.

The renal arteries to the kidneys, and testicular or ovarian arteries to the gonads, vary in number and position according to the size and position of the organs that they supply. In the dogfish there are several renals, and the gonads are supplied, exceptionally, by a branch from the anterior mesenteric. The frog has four pairs of renals and one of gonadials, while in *Necturus* there are several of each. The lizard has one pair of renals, from which the gonadials branch off, but the grass snake *Tropidonotus* has three pairs of renals, and a separate pair of gonadials, with each pair staggered so that the vessel on the right side is in each case an inch in front of that on the left; this fits with the end-on instead of side-by-side arrangement of the gonads and kidneys of the right and left sides, which is presumably brought about by the elongated shape of the body. Birds have a pair of renal and a pair of gonadial arteries, but in addition the arteries to the legs run through the kidneys and give branches to them. In mammals also there is a pair of each, the left sometimes being a little way behind the right.

The arteries to the hind-limbs are a single pair, called iliac, but each divides in mammals into two main branches, the external and internal iliacs. The continuation of the dorsal aorta into the tail is called the caudal artery, which communicates only by capillaries with the caudal vein. It is short or absent in animals in which the tail is reduced.

All the unpaired arteries may be strictly called mesenteric since they run in the mesenteries, but this name is usually confined to the two that supply the small and large intestine. Other vessels are given names such as gastric or hepatic, according to the organ that they supply. There is a general tendency toward concentration of the arteries into a few main trunks each with many branches. Thus the dogfish has a celiac, with gastric and hepatic branches, an anterior mesenteric with several branches to the intestine as well as one to the gonads, a lienogastric with branches to the spleen and stomach, and a posterior mesenteric to the rectal cecum. In frogs the corresponding branches all spring from a single root, called the celiacomesenteric, which starts from the left systemic just at the point where it joins its fellow. *Necturus* has most of these vessels joined in a much more posterior celiaco-mesenteric, but has a separate anterior gastric. Lizards have a celiacomesenteric, but birds and mammals have separate celiac, anterior mesenteric and posterior mesenteric, while the grass snake has six main vessels.

The arteries called coronaries, by which the muscles of the heart are supplied with oxygenated blood, are of some interest. In *Squalus* they are relatively large, and run from the base of the efferent branchials of the second gill slit; branches from them supply the hypobranchial musculature (Fig. 4.11). In rays they come from subclavians. The heart is therefore well supplied with highly oxgenated blood. Those bony fish that have been examined have a similar supply, from the hypobranchial arteries, or the subclavian vessels, or both. In the dipnoans the coronary arteries come directly from the morphologically fourth branchial artery, which, it will be remembered, is the one that will become the systemic arch of tetrapods. The importance of this restriction is that if the coronary arteries came from the more posterior arteries, which will run to the lungs, the blood would be deoxygenated.

In some reptiles the coronary arteries come off the systemic arch, but in various species steps in the movement of their origin back toward the heart can be traced, and in most they come off from the right arch, which is really all that is left of the ventral aorta, below the point where the carotid arteries leave it. This is also the point of origin of the coronary arteries of birds, and in mammals they arise at a similar point on the left arch.

The frog has only a single small coronary artery, arising from the carotid arch, usually of the right side, and even this does not reach all the muscle of the heart. The heart is apparently supplied with oxygen from the blood which passes through it in the ordinary course, for there are spaces between the fibers of the ventricle in which blood can be seen. This method of supply is only possible because of the frog's use of its skin for respiration, which means that much of the blood returning to the heart is highly oxygenated, and is one more proof that the heart of the frog cannot be taken as an intermediate stage between those of fish and reptiles. The other living amphibians are probably similar.

Veins

We have already seen that four main trunks of the venous system, two ventral vitelline veins and two dorsolateral cardinal veins, appear in the embryo at an early stage; two others, a pair of ventrolateral abdominal veins running in the somatic mesoderm of the lateral plate, soon follow them. From these six vessels most of the large veins or sinuses of the adult are derived.

The anterior cardinal veins (Fig. 10.14A) run back from the outside of the head, where the anterior ends may be called lateral head veins, and carry the blood to the common cardinal veins and so to the sinus venosus. This condition remains virtually unchanged in adult fish (except dipnoans), the only developments being expansions in various parts of the anterior portion of the body and the collection of blood from various branches (Fig. 4.10). Most of the vessels are large and thin-walled and are called sinuses. An exterior jugular sinus, which is probably not homologous with the vein of that name in tetrapods, develops median to the anterior cardinal sinus and parallel to it, and opens directly into the duct of Cuvier.

The posterior veins undergo rather more change. The vitelline veins are invaded by the liver as it grows in size, so that their anterior part, emptying into the sinus venosus, is separated from the posterior part by a set of capillaries. As the yolk dwindles and loses its importance their most important posterior branch is one that comes from the ventral wall of the intestine. This, the subintestinal, is at first double, but the two lines early fuse. We are thus left with a vein draining the gut and taking blood to the liver, which is called the hepatic portal, the portal capillaries in the liver, and two hepatic veins carrying blood from the liver to the sinus venosus.

Meanwhile the posterior cardinal veins have been invaded and interrupted by the kidneys in a similar way (Fig. 10.14A). In the tail they fuse to form a single caudal vein, and the point where this divides makes two renal portal veins. After blood has passed through portal capillaries in the kidneys it is collected by renal veins which expand into the large posterior cardinal sinuses, which join with the anterior cardinals to make a very short common cardinal. Near the anterior end of each posterior cardinal a superficial lateral or cutaneous vein comes in. The abdominal or deep lateral or epigastric vein receives an iliac vein from the pelvic fin and a subclavian from the pectoral fin and opens into the duct of Cuvier. The two deep lateral veins are joined posteriorly.

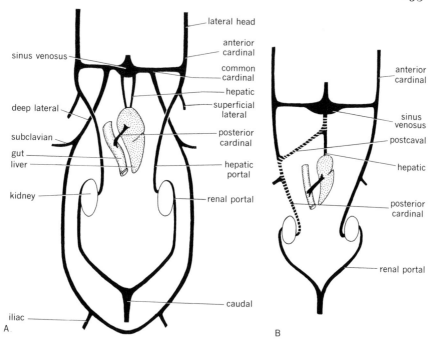

FIG. 10.14 (A) Diagram of the venous system of vertebrates. (B) Diagram of the origin of the postcaval vein.

The veins of teleosts are on the same general plan, but there is often reduction and asymmetry of the renal portal system, much of the blood for this coming from the iliac veins, while the caudal vein continues forward to become the posterior cardinal veins without supplying the kidneys. Abdominal veins are absent.

The venous system of dipnoans is modified by the presence of a pair of pulmonary veins returning blood from the lungs to the left side of the auricle, while the subclavian opens directly into the sinus venosus. There is a renal portal system which is asymmetrical in that the right posterior cardinal vein is much larger than the left. Moreover, it joins with the hepatic vein and opens directly into the sinus venosus, so that is foreshadows the condition in tetrapods and is sometimes called a postcaval vein.

In the tetrapods we find five main lines of development: the presence of pulmonary veins; the separation of the anterior and posterior cardinal veins so that each opens directly into the sinus venosus and the common cardinal and duct of Cuvier are lost; the loss of the left posterior cardinal; the gradual reduction of the renal portal system; and the fall in the importance of the abdominal veins. These changes have led to some change in the names of the vessels, which arose before the homologies were realized.

In all tetrapods a branch of the hepatic vein taps the right posterior cardinal vein and carries blood from it into the sinus venosus, or, in amniotes, into the right auricle. This leads to the formation of a large vessel, which is given the name of postcaval vein. It is made up of the posterior part of the postcardinal vein, of a branch of the hepatic vein, and then of the main right hepatic vein itself. With the loss of the left posterior cardinal it becomes median in position and symmetry is restored. The anterior bits of the posterior cardinal veins may remain as small rudiments (p. 197; Figs. 10.14B, 10.15A).

The formation of the postcaval vein leads to a break between the posterior and anterior cardinal veins. The latter now opens independently into the sinus venosus (the right auricle in amniotes), and the resulting compound vessel, consisting of the anterior cardinal, common cardinal, and duct of Cuvier on each side, is called the precaval vein. It does not differ essentially from the anterior cardinal vein of fish, but it does, however, now receive the subclavian from the fore-limb.

The urodeles, and especially the perennibranchiates like *Necturus*, are either descended from ancestors that never completely achieved these changes or else they retain a larval condition. In any case they are intermediate between the fish and the other tetrapods. There is a large median postcaval vein which takes most of the blood from the kidneys to the heart, but there is also a pair of small posterior cardinal veins which join the anterior cardinals and open into the sinus venosus through a duct of Cuvier as in fish. Anurans have a quite typical tetrapod arrangement.

There is considerable variation in the details of the anterior venous system in the different classes of tetrapods. The chief veins that join to make the precaval are usually an internal jugular that drains from the inside of the skull, an external jugular, from the rest of the head, and the subclavian. Of these the internal jugular, which runs back from the region of the eye outside or below the ear, represents the anterior part of the anterior cardinal vein. In frogs the subclavian receives a large musculo-cutaneous branch which brings oxygenated blood back from the skin. In mammals the primary internal jugular is replaced by a more dorsal vessel, running from the center of the brain above the ear, which also is called internal jugular. Another peculiarity of mammals is that the two precaval veins are joined in the neck by a cross vessel, the jugular anastomosis. In some, such as man, all the blood from the left side flows through this and only a single right precaval vein enters the heart. When this happens the name 'precaval' is usually restricted to the common path, and the short length bringing the blood from the internal and external jugular veins of one side is called the innominate vein. A similar jugular anastomosis occus in birds, and in some of these the left jugular vein may be lost.

Some relics of the piece of the posterior cardinal vein in front of the point where its main trunk joins with the hepatic vein to run direct to the heart can be seen in most tetrapods, where they appear as relatively small vessels carrying blood forward into the precaval veins. The most conspicuous in mammals is usually a vein on the right side only, called the azygos, which secondarily, by a cross connection, comes to drain the dorsal body wall of both sides.

The amphibians have a renal portal system on the same plan as that of fish, the cardinal vein dividing to take blood to the two kidneys. In addition the renal portal vein of each side receives a branch from the sciatic vein bringing blood in from the hind-limbs, and in the frogs, which have no tail, the renal portal vein is supplied solely from the legs, by the sciatic vein from the inside of the thigh and by the femoral vein from the outside. The two lateral abdominal veins of the embryo, also supplied partly and in frogs wholly from the hind-limbs, fuse to form a ventral abdominal vein which runs up the middle of the body wall, where it is a nuisance in dissection, and then plunges in to join the hepatic portal vein (Fig. 10.15B).

The posterior veins of reptiles are very similar to those of amphibians. In lizards the ventral abdominal vein drains the body wall only, and does not receive blood from the tail or hind-limbs. Lizards and *Sphenodon* have the posterior portion of the postcaval vein doubled, while the crocodiles have a single postcaval vein but paired abdominals. There is often a connection between the mesenteric vein and the renal portal.

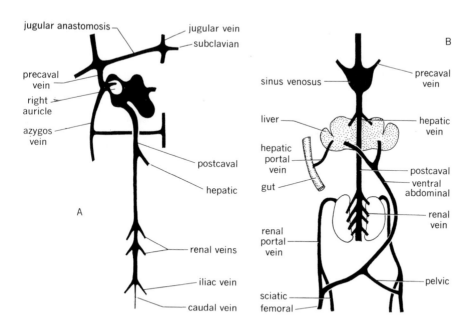

FIG. 10.15 (A) Diagram of the venous system of a mammal (B) Diagram of the venous system of a frog.

The posterior venous system of birds is peculiar and not fully understood. There appears to be a renal portal system, with two large renal portal veins formed from the hypogastric veins (which are the posterior parts of the posterior cardinals), small internal iliacs from the legs and the caudal. Each renal portal vein runs right through the kidney, and before it emerges picks up two more veins from the leg—the sciatic and the femoral or external iliac—and then joins with a renal vein to form a vein rather stupidly called 'iliac.' The two of these join to form the postcaval vein. At the point where iliac and renal veins join there is a valve, of different forms in different species of bird. There has been much controversy as to whether birds have a functioning renal portal system or not, which is well summed up in the most recent book on the physiology of birds, where the author of the chapter on excretion says they have capillaries to make this possible, while the author of the chapter on the blood system says they have not. The valve only makes sense if its function is to divert blood from the external iliac veins back into the renal portal vein, from which it could escape only if there were a capillary passage through the kidneys; a few experiments have been claimed to show that this is what happens. When the valve is open the relative sizes of the vessels must mean that little if any blood goes through the portal capillaries. No one knows under what conditions the valve is open or shut, nor what are the advantages in this step toward the loss of the renal portal system.

A further peculiarity is the great development, foreshadowed in reptiles, of a connection between the posterior part of the body and the hepatic portal system. From the base of the renal portal veins two short branches arise and join to form a large coccygeomesenteric vein which runs forward to join the hepatic portal system. Blood apparently flows in this from the legs to the liver. It may represent the ventral abdominal vein.

In mammals things are much simpler. The postcaval vein is a large median vessel (occasionally double posterior to the kidneys) made up of, or receiving, branches from tail, hind-limbs, body wall, gonads, kidneys, and liver, in due order from back to front. There is sometimes a degree of asymmetry, some of the veins on the left joining together before they enter the postcaval, and the right renal vein is usually in front of the left. There is no trace of a renal portal system, and the hepatic portal system is fed only from the veins that drain the alimentary canal. The abdominal veins are lost.

Lymph

Since the blood system of vertebrates is closed, the blood nowhere comes in contact with the cells of the body other than those that line the blood vessels. Food and oxygen are conveyed to the other cells through the medium of an intercellular fluid or lymph which is basically the plasma of the blood that has leaked out through the walls of the capillaries. The white blood cells can also force their way between the cells of the capillaries, a process called diapedesis, so that they too are present in the intercellular fluid. Obviously this fluid must somehow be returned to the blood, and it does so through a tree of thin-walled vessels that make up the lymphatic system. The lymph which this contains is reinforced by new blood cells that are made in lymphatic tissue, such as that of the spleen and bone marrow, and by this means the blood is renewed.

The origin of the lymphatic system in the embryo is similar to that of the blood system. Indeed, it is perhaps in origin only a branch of the venous system in which red cells do not form. It always opens into the venous system in the jugular region, and sometimes elsewhere. Its walls are even thinner than those of the capillaries, and are permeable to proteins, which can pass through the walls of the blood vessels only in small quantities. The outer ends of the lymphatic system end blindly.

No lymphatic system has been described in protochordates, and in cyclostomes and elasmobranchs it is incompletely separated from the venous system. That of teleosts is well developed and opens into the anterior cardinal veins or the duct of Cuvier. For the most part the movement of lymph is brought about simply by the massaging action produced by alternate contraction and relaxation of the muscles. The closed system, and valves in the larger channels, determine the direction of flow, but a few fish have a pulsating lymph heart at the base of the tail, which discharges direct into the caudal vein.

Amphibia have a well-developed lymphatic system, characterized by the presence of lymph hearts. In the cecilians there is one pair of these in each segment, opening into the segmental veins. There are also others in various parts of the body. Anura have two pairs, one opening by several pores into the subscapular veins (branches of the jugulars), the other similarly into the femoral veins. Much of the lymph of the frog is in a few large lymph sacs, subcutaneous and intramuscular, into which the fine vessels open and from which the hearts lead. The lymph sacs below the skin and those in which the kidneys lie are easily seen in dissection.

Reptiles have a system somewhat similar to that of urodeles, with two posterior lymph hearts opening into the renal portal system. The lymph vessels of birds open into the precaval veins and by smaller openings elsewhere. There is usually a pair of lymph hearts in the sacral region, but in some birds these disappear after hatching. There are on the course of lymph vessels some knots of lymphoid tissue, or lymph glands or lymph nodes, but these are not so well developed as in mammals.

The lymphatic system of mammals, on account of its medical importance, is much better known than that of other animals. The main vessels

11

Excretory System

THE EXCRETORY system of vertebrates is in principle simple, but it never retains a simple plan in the adult, and in the amniotes particularly there are complications which completely obliterate any relationship to the simple scheme. The student's confusion has been made worse by a careless use of nomenclature. Comparative anatomy and embryology both suggest that the system is based on the celomoduct (p. 34) and that this is a segmental organ. We shall begin by describing the celomoduct as it appears in those vertebrates that show it best, then consider the theoretical changes that it may be supposed to have undergone, and finally return to see how far existing vertebrates can be fitted into the scheme.

The celomoduct comes from a part of the mesoderm called the intermediate cell mass, which lies between the myotome and the lateral plate (p. 126). When typically developed it consists of a discrete mass of cells, the nephrotome, which soon becomes hollow to contain its own piece of the celom, the nephrocele. This may have a connection with the myocele, the part of the celom in the myotome, but any such connection is of no great importance since the myocele soon disappears. There is also a connection, the peritoneal funnel, with the general celom. There are now all the elements of a celomoduct except the opening to the exterior. We may suppose that in the original vertebrate, as in the annelids, the nephrotome grew until its canal opened to the outside, when there would have been a typical celomoduct, running from the peritoneal cavity, or general celom, to the exterior, but no vertebrate, embryo or adult, so far as is known, has a duct in this condition. Instead, the hollow of the nephrotome grows backward to form a longitudinal mesoblastic duct, and as it does so it joins with the ducts of other nephrotomes which are doing the same thing. We then have, instead of a segmental series of paired celomoducts each opening to the exterior, many segmentally arranged celomoducts opening into an unsegmented duct. This duct eventually opens either on the ventral surface of the body or into the posterior end of the alimentary canal. Celomoducts of this sort may be formed in segments running from the level of the heart back to the anus or even beyond.

We now have the stage shown diagrammatically in section in Plate IV.1. At this point we may consider what might have been the function of such a system if it went no further. In most invertebrates with a comparable structure (similar except that in them the duct is segmental not longitudinal) the celomoducts are the passage by which the eggs and sperms are sent to the outside, and this could have been the primitive function in vertebrates. As we shall see, eggs and sperms still go out through ducts derived in some way, usually complicated, from the celomoduct system. In many invertebrates the celomoducts are used also for the discharge of excess water, especially in animals that live in fresh water or estuaries where the osmotic pressure is less than that of the blood, so that water is continually being absorbed. This is so in many crustaceans and in annelids such as *Nereis diversicolor*, although in the latter the celomoduct is associated with a nephridium. Water regulation is probably still one of the functions of the celomoducts of fresh-water teleosts and of larval amphibians, and perhaps of adult amphibians.

Lastly the celomoducts of annelids (in association with nephridia) and of arthropods (by themselves) are organs for nitrogenous excretion. In these animals this does not seem likely to have been their primitive function, since it was presumably earlier carried out, as in the flatworms, by the nephridia alone. But in spite of their unexplained occurrence in amphioxus there is no evidence that the vertebrates and their ancestors ever possessed nephridia, and their celomoducts might well have been from the first excretory in function. This possibility is reinforced by their constant association with a special part of the blood system, to which we must now return.

The simple condition of Plate IV.1 does not last long, and so far as is known is quite useless by itself. Near the opening of each peritoneal funnel the renal artery forms a ball of capillaries, which projects into the celom to form the glomerulus, which, from its position away from the celomoduct, is said to be external (Plate IV.2). A later stage is for the glomerulus, now called internal, to be formed on a side-branch of the celomoduct, which becomes hollowed out to receive it (Plate IV.3). We now have the beginnings of the structure of the typical vertebrate kidney unit or nephron. The cup-shaped portion of the celomoduct surrounding the glomerulus is Bowman's capsule, and the opening of this to the main part of the celomoduct is the nephrocelostome (the word nephrostome, sometimes used for this, is best abandoned, as it is used also for the quite different opening, more properly called a nephridiostome, from the nephridium of annelids into the celom). Glomerulus and Bowman's capsule together constitute a Malpighian body, or renal corpuscle.

The next stage is that the peritoneal funnel, which no longer has any function, closes (Plate IV.4), and then the part of the celomoduct between Bowman's capsule and the longitudinal duct elongates and coils, forming what is now called the renal tubule. Generally the coils are in two parts, proximal against the capsule and distal against the duct, with a relatively uncoiled part between them (Plate IV.5). At this stage a second blood supply comes in, the renal portal, which supplies capillaries surrounding the tubule only, whereas the renal arteries supply blood to the whole structure as well as the glomerulus.

Further developments of the celomoduct are that the glomerulus may be lost, as in many marine teleosts, and that a long loop of Henle may be inserted between the proximal and convoluted tubules, as in birds and mammals (Plate IV.6).

Before we consider how these celomoducts are arranged in the different classes we must see how they function. Their physiology has been investigated chiefly in frogs, *Necturus*, reptiles, and mammals, but the results are so uniform that there can be little doubt that the kidney works in the same general way in all vertebrates. Fluid extracted from Bowman's capsule by means of a micropipette has been found to have the same composition as dialyzed blood, that is to say, of blood plasma without its colloids. More strictly, a little colloid may be present, but it has a molecular weight of less than 70,000. There can therefore be no doubt that the combined walls of the glomerular capillaries and Bowman's capsule are acting as a dialyzer, allowing water and crystalloids to pass through and holding back the colloids. For this to happen the pressure of the blood in the capillaries must be greater than the colloid osmotic pressure of the blood, and there is evidence that this is so, and that if the blood pressure falls too far filtration stops. Since the blood pressure is maintained by the heart, which is in a distant part of the body, no energy need be supplied by the Malpighan bodies themselves, and the rate of filtration should not affect the rate at which they use oxygen. This has been found to be so.

The urine has a very different composition from the glomerular filtrate; it is generally more concentrated, and in a healthy animal it contains no glucose, bicarbonate, or protein. It is poorer in amino acids, sodium, and chloride, but richer in potassium, phosphate, urea, and other compounds of nitrogen. Clearly therefore water and other things must have been absorbed and some things must have been added, presumably by the tubule. Extraction and analysis of fluids from various parts of this show that most of the absorption takes place in the proximal tubule, and, if it is present, in the loop of Henle. From 90 to 99 per cent of the water is absorbed, and many substances, especially the nitrogenous excretory products, such as urea and in birds and reptiles uric acid, are added. Obviously, in teleosts without glomeruli all the solids must come through the walls of the tubules.

Apart from the form of individual celomoducts, their arrangement differs much in different vertebrates. Since the end of last century there has grown up a somewhat confused and at times misleading nomenclature for kidneys of different types, in which any strict interpretation of homology has often been forgotten. Since the object of nomenclature is to make things easier to understand, or at least to describe and remember, and the kidney nomenclature does none of these things, it would be best if most of it were abandoned, but it is too firmly stuck in the books for the student to avoid it. In the account that follows therefore, emphasis is on what the kidney is like; what it is called is of minor importance.

Since there is no evidence that there ever was a vertebrate with a regular series of segmental celomoducts, each with its own opening to the exterior, we shall not name this type of kidney (Fig. 11.1A) and shall say no more about it. A regular series of celomoducts extending most of the length of the body and opening into a single duct on each side has been called a holonephros (Fig. 11.1B). It is found only in the embryos of hagfishes and cecilians. In *Bdellostoma*, for example, the celomoducts extend from segment 11 to segment 82, and although some at each end have only a short existence and then atrophy the rest are all very similar to one another. Glomeruli are present only from about segment 25 back, and some of these are external. The early kidney of *Hypogeophis*, a cecilian, is much the same, but all the glomeruli are internal. The duct of a holonephros is a holonephric duct. (Some authors call it an archinephric duct, but there is no need to double the load on the students' memory).

Some specializations take place as the kidney of cyclostomes and cecilians develops; especially in the former some of the anterior glomeruli fuse to form a single large external glomerulus, but there hardly seems enough to justify giving any special name to the adult organ.

In all other vertebrates the kidney is divisible into at least two, and sometimes three, portions, which develop at different times and come to have different functions (Fig. 11.1C). Development always takes place in a general head-to-tail direction, and as it goes back there is a general tendency for segmentation to be lost.

Those vertebrates which have a larval stage—the bony fish and the amphibians—early develop a few anterior celomoducts which are functional, form a common duct similar to the holonephric duct, and are usually clearly derived one from each nephrotome. Such a kidney is called a pronephros and its duct pronephric; it may be regarded as a precociously developed larval excretory organ. That of the tadpole of the European frog *Rana temporaria*, for example, consists of three tubules, which can be seen in a careful dissection in the anterior part of the body cavity. At or before the time when the larva metamorphoses, the pronephros usually degenerates, but it persists into adult life in a few teleosts, notably the little fish *Fierasfer*, which lives for most of its time in the rectum of holothurians.

Later, in preparation for adult life, more celomoducts develop in a position posterior to the pronephros. They have been given the general name of opisthonephros, but it is probably better to use the earlier nomenclature by which they are regarded as falling into two series: a posterior set, or metanephros, which is not always present, and a middle set, or mesonephros, which is always present (although, as will be seen shortly, often much modified) and may be all that is left after the pronephros has degenerated. The segmental arrangement of the mesonephros is often obscure, but it can generally be inferred to be present, while the metanephros never has any trace of segmentation. This is enough to distinguish them.

Where, as in elasmobranchs and amniotes, there is no larva, there may be a few vestigial celomoducts in front of those that form the mesonephros; such abortive structures may be regarded as a part of the mesonephros that fails to develop. They are sometimes called a pronephros, but it seems best not to use the word in this sense but to restrict it to the functional kidney of larvae.

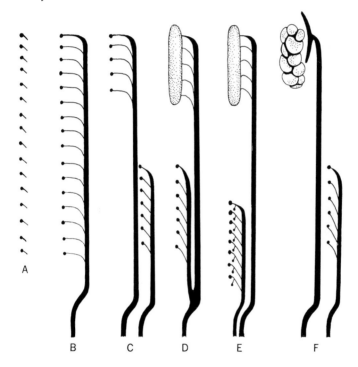

FIG. 11.1   Diagrams of kidney tubules. (A) Theoretical ancestral scheme, with separate segmental celomoducts. (B) Holonephros; embryos of hagfishes and cecilians. (C) Pronephros and mesonephros with separate ducts; larval teleosts and amphibians. (D) Mesonephros of a male, with anterior sexual portion; elasmobranchs and adult amphibians. (E) Metanephros, with the mesonephros having a sexual part only; male amniotes. (F) Mesonephros of a female elasmobranch or amphibian. The oviduct is perhaps derived from the pronephric duct.

The mesonephric celomoducts of teleosts and amphibians sometimes develop from definite nephrotomes, sometimes from an unsegmented intermediate cell mass which is in the same position. In any case regular segmentation is lost, because each tubule buds off two or three branches, so that there is more than one Malpighian body per segment. The ducts grow backward and fuse together to form, as before, a single duct on each side. Usually the duct formed from the first few segments has grown right back to the cloaca before the more posterior ones are formed. They then tap the pre-existing duct as they grow. In those animals in which a pronephric duct is already present this is usually joined by the mesonephric tubules, although complications come in here which we will consider later.

The mesonephros is the functional kidney of elasmobranchs—where it is all that there ever is—and of adult bony fish and amphibians. It forms also, in a very similar way, in the embryos of amniotes, but in these it either disappears or becomes much modified. It acts as the excretory organ of the embryo, and is active for a short time after birth in reptiles, monotremes, and marsupials.

There is a general tendency for the anterior tubules of the mesonephros to lose their excretory function and to become associated with the testis. When this happens they become simply channels by which the sperms travel to the exterior, so reverting, if reversion it is, to one of the possible original functions of the celomoduct (Fig. 11.1D). This is seen in elasmobranchs (Fig. 4.14A) and amphibians. The same thing happens in amniotes, but here nothing is left of the mesonephros except the part that becomes sexual in function. The mesonephros of mammals, for example, forms the epididymis and the efferent ducts of the testis (Fig. 11.1E). The result of this is that the sperms are carried into the mesonephric duct, but the form and fate of this duct are complicated and will be discussed below. The association of mesonephros with testis does not occur in teleosts. In the female vertebrate (Fig. 11.1F) the anterior part of the mesonephros, corresponding to that which in the male becomes sexual in function, is never well developed. Small tubules opening into the mesonephric duct persist in some elasmobranchs, but in others they disappear completely. They disappear also in amphibians, and in female amniotes the whole of the mesonephros is lost, except that in the larger mammals traces can still be found in the neighborhood of the ovary in the form of structures called paro-ophoron and epo-ophoron; so far as is known, these vestiges have no function (Plate V.3).

Before birth or hatching the amniotes develop a metanephros, which has a quite different origin from that of the pronephros and mesonephros, but comes to be made up of tubules of the same general form. From the distal end of the mesonephric duct, near where it opens into the cloaca, a new duct grows forward. This is the metanephric duct, and the mesoblast into which it grows becomes organized into Bowman's capsules and tubules, which join together and open into the duct. The result is a mass of compound tubules which never have any opening into the general celom and never have any trace of segmentation. They constitute the metanephros, and become the functional kidney that replaces the mesonephros of the embryo (Fig. 11.1E). The metanephros differs also from the other two in that its direction of development and growth is from tail to head.

We still have the fate of the ducts to consider, but before doing so we must deal with the reproductive organs, with which they are so closely connected.

The actual form of the kidney tends to show a gradual concentration of its mass as one ascends through the classes. In cyclostomes it originally occupies most of the segments of the body, but disappears both anteriorly and posteriorly so that it becomes more compact in the adult. In *Bdellostoma*, for example, of seventy-one original nephrotomes the first thirteen and the last twenty-seven do not give rise to functional tubules. The kidney of the adult *Petromyzon* is even more compact, and its segmentation is recognizable only in its arteries. It is unusual in having no renal portal system.

The remaining vertebrates show no trace of a segmental arrangement in the adult, largely because of the formation of secondary and tertiary nephrons as outgrowths from each segmental tubule. The organ occupies most of the length of the body cavity in elasmobranchs, but its anterior portion is narrowed and in the male is sexual in function, not excretory. The kidney of teleosts is very variable. In a few, such as *Cyclosthone*, there is only a single anterior nephron, which is the persistent pronephros, so that the animal may be considered to be neotenous. In the majority the mesonephros occupies a fair part of the body cavity; it may extend throughout its length, or be more or less concentrated toward either the anterior or the posterior end. The posterior part of the kidney sometimes possesses its own duct, probably split off from the original mesonephric duct, which has led to its being described by some authors as metanephric. Since it must, whatever its nature, be a different evolution from the metanephros of amniotes, this name is probably best not used for it. The kidneys of some teleosts are peculiar in possessing no arterial blood supply.

The kidneys of amphibians, all mesonephric in the adult, are more compact in the anurans than in the urodeles, and more compact in these than in the coecilians. The anterior portion, like that of the dogfish, is narrowed, and sexual in the male.

The kidneys of the amniotes, always metanephric, are generally more or less compact, with the ureter running from a notch or hilum on their medial surface. Only where the body is elongated, as in snakes, are they secondarily stretched out. There is a common tendency, well seen in snakes and mammals, for the right kidney to be in front of the left, with consequent asymmetry of the blood vessels and ureters. The method of formation of the metanephros leads to the expansion of the inner end of the ureter into a definite sinus, from which branches extend into the lobes of the kidney (where these are present), and into which the collecting ducts open. In some mammals, such as man, sheep, and rabbit, the kidney has the shape which is so well known as to have become a common term of reference for beans and dishes; in others, such as cattle, it is more elongated and lobulated. This is also its shape in birds. It does not seem possible to associate the shape with any particular habit of life.

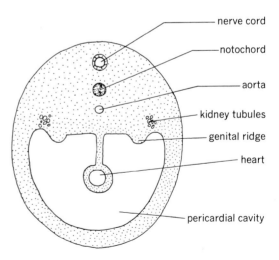

FIG. 12.1   Diagrammatic transverse section of
a vertebrate embryo to show the genital ridge.

12

Gonads

ACCORDING to a hypothesis that was popular at the beginning of this century, the germ plasm, the part of the body that was to give rise to future generations, was from the first set aside from the soma, or rest of the body, so that it alone was potentially immortal and was freed from outside influences. This is clearly not true, since many invertebrates can regenerate whole bodies from small bits of themselves, and even early vertebrate embryos can, under certain circumstances, be divided to give more than one adult animal. This can be done experimentally, for example, by separating the two or four cells of an early frog embryo without damaging them; each may develop into a tadpole. The same sort of thing appears to happen regularly and naturally in the nine-banded armadillo (*Dasypus novemcinctus*), which produces four young at a birth, all exactly like each other, and occasionally in man and other mammals to produce identical twins. The tissue from which the gonads will be formed, however, appears early in development, as a pair of genital ridges running along the roof of the peritoneal cavity on each side of the gut and medial to the nephrotome (Fig. 12.1). In this position it is mesodermal, but according to some authors the ancestors of the cells that are actually going to form gametes are first recognizable in the endoderm, and afterward migrate into the genital ridges. There is, however, some doubt about this, and critical experiments do not seem to have been done. Since the burden of proof rests with those who maintain that this migration happens, the student may well be permitted to start with the germ cells in their proper place. The ridges generally become concentrated in the anterior part of the body cavity, fairly close behind the transverse septum, but the left is often more posterior than the right. The wall of splanchnic mesoderm that covers the germinal cells constitutes, as they grow, a mesentery that slings the organ from the roof of the cavity, just as the median dorsal mesentery slings the gut; from the position of the genital ridges it is obvious that they have no ventral mesentery. The fold slinging the male organ, or testis, is called the mesorchium, that supporting the female organ, or ovary, is the mesovarium.

Once established, the genital ridges develop slowly, and the organs do not become functional until much later, although there is a period of rapid

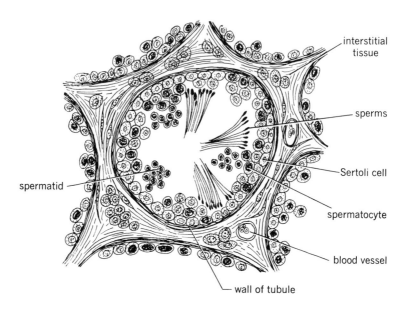

interstitial
tissue

sperms

Sertoli cell

spermatocyte

blood vessel

spermatid

wall of tubule

FIG. 12.2   Semi-diagrammatic transverse section of a seminiferous tubule of a mammalian testis, x 40.

development around the time of metamorphosis in Amphibia and of birth in mammals.

The important part is at first on the surface, but it becomes invaginated and differentiates according to sex and class. The general pattern is that in the male the invagination forms hollow sex cords, and the spermatozoa are formed from the walls of these, while in the female the organ forms a more definite cortex, into which individual cells fall and become ova. The structure is well shown in sections of the organs in a mammal. The testis (Fig. 12.2) shows a large number of hollow cylinders, the seminiferous tubules, which have been formed from the sex cords. They are long and much coiled, so that each is cut several times in one section. Their inner walls are formed of cells which are descended from those of the germinal epithelium; they undergo a rapid multiplication and eventually a meiosis so that the spermatozoa or sperms are produced, with their heads in the walls and their tails projecting into the lumen, giving a very characteristic appearance to the section. During the process of maturation the developing spermatozoa throw off a part of their cytoplasm, so that when fully formed they consist of little but nucleus and tail, the latter being in structure a flagellum. Some of the cells of the lining epithelium of the tubules develop not into spermatozoa but into cells of Sertoli, to which the spermatozoa for a time become attached. Except that the cells of Sertoli have large nucleoli, which suggests that they are active in the synthesis of protein, nothing is known of their function.

The tubules join together and pass into the efferent vessels of the testis; these all open into a single long coiled epididymis, which is divided into two regions, one above and one below the testis. As has been said above, efferent vessels and epididymis are derived from the tubules of the mesonephros. Originally a simple channel for the passage of sperm, the epididymis has become also secretory in function, and produces part of the liquid semen in which the spermatozoa are ejaculated. The semen is of great importance in land animals, since without a fluid in which to swim the sperms would be immobile. Most of it is made by the walls of the lower duct, the vas deferens. Sperms do not start swimming until after ejaculation, and though the value of this is obvious, for they have little reserve of food and swimming uses up energy, the mechanism by which it is brought about is not clear. In the salmon the semen contains a substance which inhibits their movement, but it loses its effect on dilution so that activity begins when the sperms reach the sea water. Most of the respiration of sperms depends on carbohydrates, especially fructose, which they absorb from the semen.

Between the seminiferous tubules is connective tissue, and in this are embedded the interstitial cells of the testis. These are derived from the mesoblast of the region of the intermediate cell-mass, or of the nephrotomes, and are active in secreting hormones that determine the secondary sexual characters (Chapter 20) and the pattern of development of the gonad itself.

Once begun, activity of the testis and production of sperms continue throughout life, or at least until senescence sets in.

The ovary (Fig. 12.3) retains most of its germinal epithelium on the surface, but pockets of this fall in and become pinched off to form hollow spheres, the Graafian follicles, from whose walls the ova are developed. It is unlikely that new follicles are formed after birth, and in nearly all the mammals that have been examined, including man, the ova are themselves well on the way to being produced before this occurs, only the later stages of maturation occurring in adult life.

A nearly ripe Graafian follicle has an outer wall or theca of connective and supporting tissue, surrounding the sphere of epithelium, or membrana granulosa. At one point the epithelium has proliferated to form a knot of cells, the discus proligerus, and one of the cells of this expands to become an ovum. With further growth it comes to project on the surface of the ovary, and is eventually discharged into the celom, a process called ovulation. The hollow of the follicle contains liquid.

The spaces between the follicles are filled by connective tissue which, as in the male, includes interstitial cells which produce hormones.

interstitial cells

tunica albuginea

small follicle

germinal
epithelium

Graafian
follicle

nucleus
of ovum

wall of
follicle

vein

artery

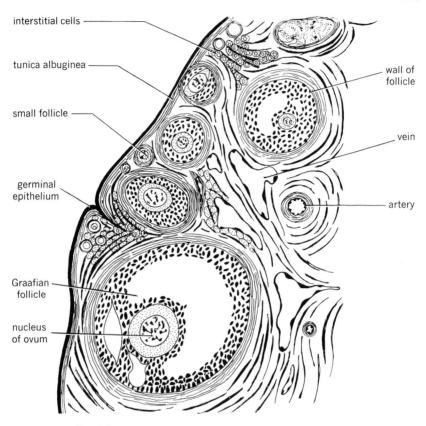

FIG. 12.3   Semi-diagrammatic transverse section of a mammalian ovary, x 40.

The gonads of other vertebrates, although having many differences of detail, do not differ in principle from those of mammals. The ovaries have usually much less connective tissue and the eggs themselves are larger, so that the ripe ovary of a frog or a bird consists, to the naked eye, of nothing but a mass of eggs. It is common for one ovary to fail to develop.

The fact that the testis and ovary arise in the same position and develop in comparable ways suggests that they are homologous organs, developed from an indeterminate ancestral form. The sex of vertebrates, like that of other animals, is mainly determined genetically, but the conditions of the environment may alter the direction of development so that intersexes are not unusual, and even occasional functional hermaphrodites have been described (see below, p. 233). In the cyclostomes some degree of hermaphroditism is normal. In the larva of lampreys both developing ova and developing sperms are present, but in the adult one sex or the other takes over, and either a testis or an ovary alone becomes mature. The gonads of the two sides fuse to form a single structure. In the hagfishes the double nature of the organ persists in the adult, the front part producing eggs and the posterior having seminiferous tubules. According to some authors *Myxine* is a protandrous hermaphrodite, producing sperms before eggs, but this has not been proved, and it may be that the indeterminate phase merely persists rather long and that either eggs or sperms, but not both, are eventually produced in one animal. In cyclostomes both eggs and sperms are shed into the celom and then go through temporary pores, which open only in the breeding season, into the lower ends of the kidney ducts and so to the cloaca and the outer world.

The gonads of the elasmobranchs are large, and hang from the body wall by conspicuous mesorchia or mesovaria (Fig. 4.14). There is a tendency for the two testes to fuse, and the left ovary disappears in many species. The oviducts are large and conspicuous and join to open into the cloaca by a single pore. The sperms as usual go through the anterior part of the mesonephros, and then, by a duct that is independent of that carrying urine, to the cloaca. On or near the lower end of this develop various swellings. The lower end of the duct itself is swollen to form a seminal vesicle, and branching off from the base of this is an expanded blind tube, the sperm sac. The two ducts join to form a slightly inflated urogenital sinus, which receives the openings of the kidney ducts, and opens into the cloaca by a single papilla on its dorsal surface.

Elasmobranchs are unusual among aquatic animals in having internal fertilization. The pelvic fins of the males are fused on the ventral surface, and near the junction there projects backward from each of them a rod called the clasper. It has a groove on its inner surface, and is in effect a rolled-up extension of the fin. It contains muscle and is supported by a cartilage attached to the pelvic girdle (Fig. 4.6), but there is in it also erectile tissue consisting of blood vessels which can be inflated under stimulation. This happens in sexual excitement, and the resulting erection of the organ can be produced experimentally by the injection of adrenaline (p. 463). In copulation the two partners lie twisted spirally round each other with the heads back-to-back and the claspers inserted into the cloaca of the female, where their dilation holds the two fishes together. The semen is probably injected by muscular action, accompanied by a certain amount of sea water which is washed through the grooves of the claspers. This mechanism is more complicated, and so one must presume more efficient, than anything of the sort in any other vertebrates except the mammals. It suggests that the elasmobranchs, though they are in many ways typical vertebrates and in others the most primitive living gnathostomes, may be too specialized to be ancestral to any of the other vertebrate classes. On the other hand, if, as some zoologists think, pelvic fins were developed not for swimming but as copulatory organs (p. 393), the elasmobranchs would be primitive in this as in other ways.

As is usual with animals in which there is internal fertilization, the eggs are large and the number produced in a season is relatively small. The upper part of the oviduct is glandular, and produces first albumen and then in some a horny egg shell, in which the egg develops at the expense of the yolk (Fig. 4.15).

In most elasmobranchs, including the common dogfish *Squalus acanthias*, the egg develops in the oviduct, there is no mermaid's purse, and the young are born alive, so that the species is said to be viviparous. The method by which the developing embryo is nourished is not always the same. In some, such as *Squalus*, material secreted by the walls of the oviduct is conveyed, by one route or another, into the intestine of the young, where it is absorbed. In a few, such as *Mustelus laevis*, the yolk sac of the embryo puts out villi which grow into depressions in the walls of the oviduct. There is therefore a structure which can only be considered as a placenta, and the oviduct has become a uterus. Here again we have a state of affairs that is close to the condition in the mammals, but produced quite independently. The various species can be put in a series of decreasing dependence on the external environment and increasing dependence on the mother. Eggs of the oviparous *Scyliorhinus caniculus* obtain 60 per cent of the salts that they need, and 70 per cent of their water, from the sea, and lose much organic material by respiration. *Squalus* has only a slight loss of organic matter, while in *Mustelus laevis* there is a gain.

The gonads of teleosts are somewhat different, and are simpler. There are usually two testes and two ovaries, and from each pair there usually leads backward a short median duct, which is continuous with the gonads from which it comes. It may open into the cloaca or into the lower end of the excretory duct. In a few fish, such as salmon, the eggs are shed loose into the body cavity, and then enter the oviducts by two funnels which soon join to form the usual median tube.

In nearly all teleosts the eggs are discharged into the river or sea, and sperms discharged near them at the same time take their chance of finding them for fertilization. In a number there is some degree of association of the sexes, so that the eggs and sperms are discharged simultaneously and close together, and in a few fertilization has become internal. There may be some sort of copulatory organ, or gonopodium, developed from the anal fin, or merely close apposition of male and female openings. A few have become viviparous. Fertilization in these species takes place within the wall of the ovarian follicle before the ova have been shed, and further development of the embryo takes place either here or outside the follicle but still within the ovary. There is never, so far as is known, any development of the oviduct into a uterus. Some species of the teleost families Sparidae and Serranidae are hermaphrodite and self-fertilizing, the testicular and ovarian tissue of the gonad sometimes being in separate zones, sometimes being intermingled.

PLATES

PLATE I

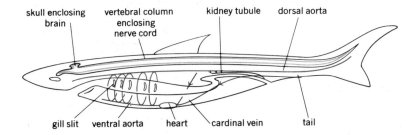

1 A simplified diagram of a vertebrate. Notochord, hollow dorsal nerve cord, gill slits, tail, main ventral blood vessel; skull and vertebral column, kidney tubules. Only three tubules are shown.

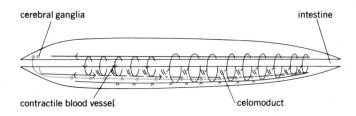

2 A simplified diagram of an annelid, as an example of the invertebrates.

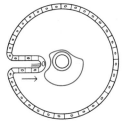

3 A diagram of a celomoduct. Meso-dermal, centripetal, intracellular lumen, extracellular cilia, open to celom.

4 A diagram of a nephridium. Ectodermal, centrifugal, intracellular lumen, intracellular cilia, primitively not open to celom.

PLATE II   LUNGS AND SWIM BLADDERS

All the diagrams are in transverse section, and seen from in front. See pp. 153-62.

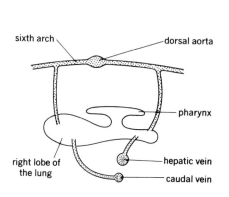

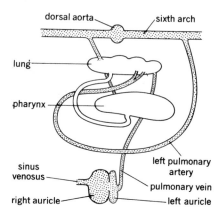

1   *Polypterus.*

2   *Epiceratodus.*

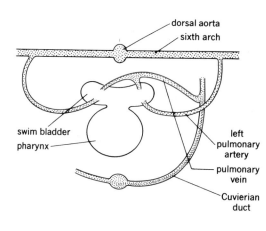

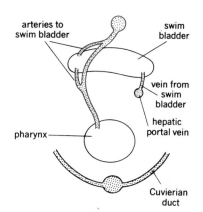

3   *Amia.*

4   A physoclistous teleost.

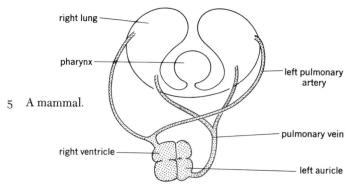

5   A mammal.

PLATE III

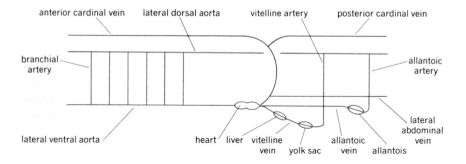

anterior cardinal vein   lateral dorsal aorta   vitelline artery   posterior cardinal vein

branchial artery

allantoic artery

lateral abdominal vein

lateral ventral aorta   heart liver vitelline vein   yolk sac   allantoic vein   allantois

1   A diagram of the blood system of the embryo of an amniote.

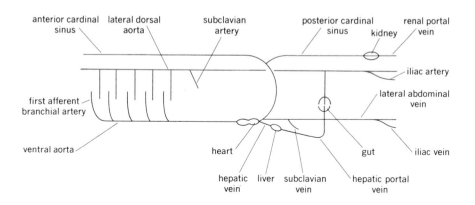

anterior cardinal sinus   lateral dorsal aorta   subclavian artery   posterior cardinal sinus   kidney   renal portal vein

iliac artery

first afferent branchial artery

lateral abdominal vein

ventral aorta   heart   gut   iliac vein

hepatic vein liver subclavian vein   hepatic portal vein

2   A diagram of the blood system of a fish.

PLATE IV   THE EVOLUTION OF THE KIDNEY TUBULE

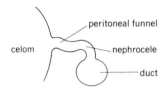

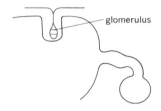

1   The first stage, a simple celomo-duct.

2   An external glomerulus has formed in the wall of the celom, a little distance from the peritoneal funnel. An example, the holonephros of the embryo of *Bdellostoma*, a hagfish.

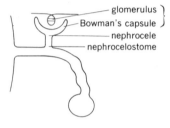

Malpighian body = renal corpuscle

3   More often, the glomerulus is internal, on the wall of the peritoneal funnel, which becomes specialized with the parts shown. For example, the holonephros of *Hypogeophis*, a cecilian. Most pronephric tubules are somewhat similar.

4   Usually the peritoneal funnel loses its opening to the celom.

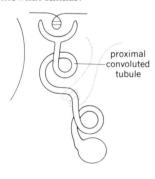

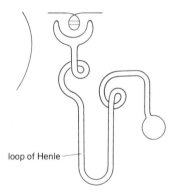

5   The tubule is coiled, and has acquired a new blood supply from the renal portal vein. This is the usual condition of the mesonephros, e.g. of amphibians, and of the metanephros of reptiles.

6   The two coiled parts of the tubule are separated by a straight-sided loop of Henle, and the renal portal supply has been lost. This is the condition in birds (probably) and mammals.

(Metanephric ducts are not shown).

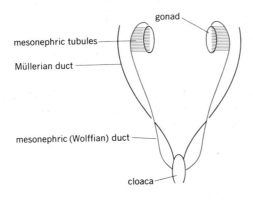

1 The undifferentiated embryonic stage.

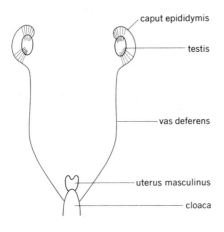

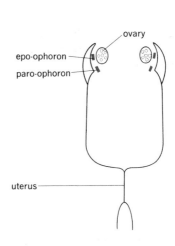

2 The male; mesonephric duct persists as the vas deferens, the Müllerian duct is lost or is represented by the uterus masculinus.

3 The female; the Müllerian duct persists as the oviduct and uterus, the mesonephric duct is reduced to remnants as the paro-ophoron and epo-ophoron.

PLATE VI

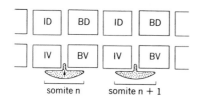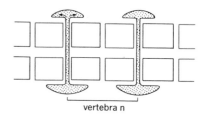

1 The development of a vertebra. The posterior parts (basidorsal and basiventral) of one scleromere join with the anterior parts (interdorsal and interventral) of the one behind to form a vertebra.

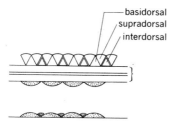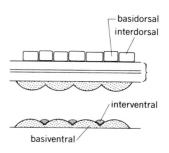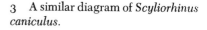

2 A portion of the vertebral column of *Squalus acanthias* in sagittal section, diagrammatic.

3 A similar diagram of *Scyliorhinus caniculus*.

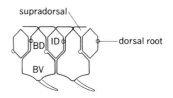

4 Two trunk vertebrae of *Squalus acanthias*, lateral.

5 Two trunk vertebrae of *Scyliorhinus caniculus*, lateral.

PLATE VII

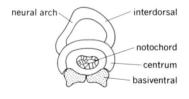

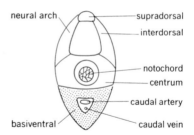

1   A diagrammatic transverse section of a trunk vertebra of *Squalus acanthias*.

2   A diagram of a transverse section of a tail vertebra of *Scyliorhinus caniculus*.

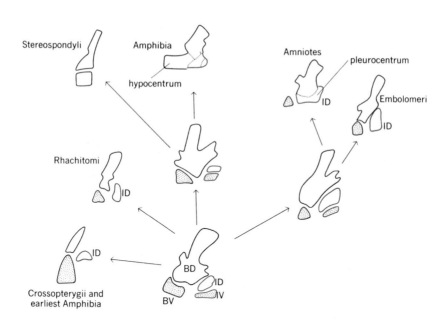

3   A diagram of the main lines of evolution of vertebrae.

PLATE VIII

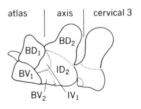

1   The origin of the atlas and axis in amniotes.

DIAGRAMS OF REPTILIAN SKULLS

The abbreviations for the bones of the skull are: PreMaXilla; MaXilla; NAsal; LACrimal; PReFrontal; FRontal; PARietal; POstFrontal; POstOrbital; Jugal; QuadratoJugal; Quadrate; SQuamosal.

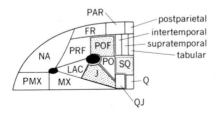

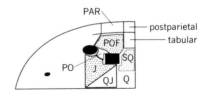

2   Anapsid, no temporal cacuity.

3   Synapsid, lower temporal vacuity, below the postfrontal and postorbital.

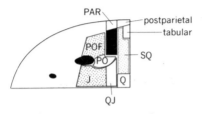

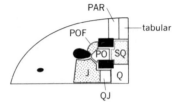

4   Parapsid, upper temporal vacuity, above the postfrontal and postorbital.

5   Diapsid, two temporal vacuities, in the positions of those parapsid and synapsid skulls.

The gonads of amphibians are large and paired, the ovaries of frogs especially swelling up in the breeding season and filling the abdominal cavity with a mass of darkly colored eggs. There is a general similarity to the system in elasmobranchs. The testis is connected with the anterior part of the mesonephros, and its duct is clearly derived from the duct of this. In anurans the kidney and testis are both more compact than in urodeles, and their connection is less obvious. The oviducts are large and glandular, usually opening separately into the cloaca. Fertilization is generally external, but there is a form of quasi-copulation called amplexus, in which the male embraces the female and sheds his sperms over the eggs as they are laid. In the salamanders and cecilians, fertilization is internal, and the sperms, made up into packets called spermatophores, are either inserted into the cloaca or passed out by the male and then picked up by the female with the lips of the cloaca. When this happens some degree of development may go on in the oviduct, and the young may be born able to swim, but there is no nourishment of the embryo by the mother. In a number of anurans, however, the eggs are carried about, sometimes by one sex and sometimes by the other, and undergo their development in such unlikely places as twined round the hind legs of the male (*Alytes*), on the back of the female (*Pipa*), or in the vocal sacs of the male (*Rhinoderma*).

The gonads of amphibians are at first sexually indifferent. If the cortex increases relatively to the medulla the germ cells remain in the former and become oocytes, but if the medulla increases they migrate into it and become spermatocytes. This development is dependent on hormones, but it can also be affected by changes in temperature. In several species of toad there is at the anterior end of the testis a small structure called Bidder's organ, which has the structure of a rudimentary ovary (Fig. 12.4). It has been known on occasion to become functional and produce eggs.

The reptiles also have gonads built on the same pattern, with a mesonephric accessory part of the testis and large glandular oviducts. Fertilization is always internal, and the male has some form of copulatory organ. This is usually double, consisting of erectile and eversible half-tubes which can be inserted into the cloaca; that of tortoises and crocodiles is median, arising from the ventral wall of the cloaca. It foreshadows something of the structure of the more complicated mammalian penis, having two strands of erectile tissue, but it is not a complete tube.

With life on land and internal fertilization there is associated in Sauropsida the cleidoic egg. This has not only, like the egg of a dogfish, a large amount of yolk and an outer layer of albumen or white, but also a hard and relatively impermeable shell. Inside this the embryo develops with little interaction, other than the transfer of heat, with the outside world. Only a small amount of water, less than a third of the total required, enters the eggs of reptiles during their development, and in the birds, in

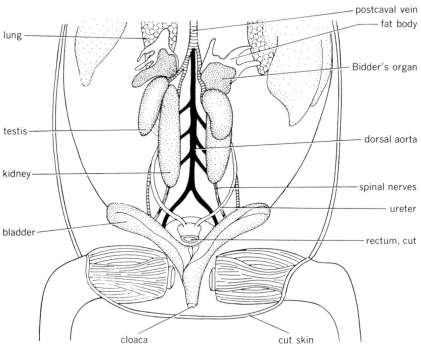

FIG. 12.4 Dissection of the reproductive organs of a male toad, *Bufo bufo*, to show the vestigial ovary, or Bidder's organ, x 2.

which the egg is even more cleidoic, what little passage there is goes on in the other direction, the eggs actually losing some water before they hatch.

A few lizards and snakes are viviparous, including the common lizard of Europe, *Lacerta vivipara*, and several of the swifts (*Sceloporus*) of western North America. To some extent viviparity can be correlated with habitat, since Squamata which possess it are found much further north and at greater altitudes than those that lay eggs. Chelonians and crocodiles, none of which is viviparous, are restricted to climates that are, at the coldest, warm and semi-tropical respectively. The advantage of the habit seems to be chiefly that it produces shelter and a slightly higher temperature for development. Most viviparous Squamata have no special structures, but a few have a yolk sac placenta and an allantoic placenta or both (Fig. 5.8). It is possible that these, especially the second, provide some nourishment for the embryo. Some pterodactyls and ichthyosaurs were viviparous.

The gonads of birds are built on the reptilian plan, but the right ovary and oviduct are usually absent, being developed in the raptors and only occasionally elsewhere. Birds are notable for the very marked seasonal variation that their gonads undergo. This occurs to some extent in all vertebrates, but it seldom affects the testes to any great extent. In birds, however, both testis and ovary shrivel almost to nothing after breeding is over, and then with the coming of spring undergo an expansion in size which may be 360-fold. This may perhaps have arisen because it is an advantage to a flying animal not to have to carry any more weight than is necessary.

In spite of their internal fertilization most birds are without a copulatory organ. Ducks and geese have one which is rather less well developed than that of crocodiles. Viviparity is unknown in birds.

In the mammals the reproductive organs are more complex, and have more accessory structures, than in any other vertebrates. Moreover, on account of their human and medical interest more is known about them.

The testes begin in the normal position and have the usual connection with the mesonephros which we have already described, but, as the embryo grows, they move backward toward the region of the cloaca. In most mammals they pass out of the body cavity by a normal rupture so that they lie or hang just in front of the anus. When this happens they are enclosed in the adult in a bag, the scrotum, but the visible part of this is not, as might appear at first sight, a pouch of the body wall. It is formed by the fusion of two lips of tissue that grow round the testes and enclose them, and the line of junction remains as a pigmented band on their ventral surface. The corresponding parts in the female remain separate as the labia majora surrounding the genital and urinary openings. Inside the scrotum there is a lining which is part of the body wall, and its cavity is an extension of the celom. To some extent the usual description of the movement of the testis is misleading, for much of what happens is caused by the fact that the testis is attached posteriorly to the body wall by a strand of connective tissue, the gubernaculum; as the embryo grows this does not lengthen, but holds the testis in place at the posterior end of the body. This does not, however, account for the actual descent of the testis into the scrotum. The cavity of the scrotum remains more or less open to the celom by a passage, the inguinal canal.

No convincing reason for the development of the mammalian scrotum has ever been given. If the testis is experimentally tied into the body cavity the sperms fail to develop, and this appears to be due to the resulting high temperature, for the testes in the scrotum are normally slightly cooler than the rest of the body. Experiments have shown that in a number of mammals the scrotum is a very efficient thermoregulator, maintaining the temperature inside it approximately constant with a wide range of surrounding air temperatures. It does this partly by muscular contraction of the coat, which produces wrinkles and reduces the over-all surface-area on the stimulus of cold, and partly by a reaction of the blood vessels. But this is a mechanism for keeping the testes warmer than their surroundings.

The sperms of birds develop quite well inside a body that is hotter than that of mammals, and elephants and whales have no scrotum and yet produce sperms. In many of the more primitive mammals, such as insectivores and some rodents, the scrotum is shallow, and in some the testes are withdrawn into the body cavity either seasonally or occasionally, by a muscle, the cremaster. The slight and unexplained asymmetry of the kidneys of many mammals, where the left is a little posterior to the right, is often shown by the testes also, the left hanging a little lower in the scrotum.

The backward movement of the testes of mammals, or perhaps to be more accurate the separation in space of the testes and kidneys, leads to a complication in their connections with the rest of the body. Each testis originally has a short artery, vein, and nerve, but these are forced to lengthen, and cross over the ureter (Fig. 12.5). The resulting bundle of blood vessels, nerve, and connective tissue is called the spermatic cord. The epididymis is divided into a distinct caput above the testis and a cauda below, and from the latter the vas deferens leads away, loops round the ureter, and opens into the median common duct for urine and sperms, the urethra. Into this open the prostate and Cowper's glands, which make much of the liquid part of the semen. In some mammals there is a small seminal vesicle, in which sperms are stored, on the lower ends of the vas deferens.

The urethra opens through a copulatory organ or penis which is a complete tube, and is stiffened and erected by the swelling within it of venous spaces when they become full of blood. This is brought about chiefly through the contraction of muscles which constrict the veins at the base of the organ and prevent the return of blood. In a few mammals, such as carnivores, the penis is supported by a bone. Semen is pumped out by contractions of muscles in the vas deferens.

Marsupials have a scrotum, but it is in front of the penis, which is itself peculiar in many species in being forked, with two exits for the sperms to fit the double uterus which will be described below. Monotremes have a penis but no scrotum.

The ovaries of mammals retain their original position and are always small, in relation to the fact that the eggs are yolkless and minute. Monotremes are exceptional in having large yolky eggs, a larger left ovary, and the right one much reduced.

The chief interest of the female organs lies in the ducts. Each oviduct begins as a funnel opening into the celom. This is always near the ovary and sometimes almost surrounds it, so that although the ova are shed into the body cavity, they do not have far to go before they enter the oviduct. This upper part of the oviduct, in which the sperms meet the egg and fertilization occurs, is called the Fallopian tube and is slightly coiled. It is much the same in all mammals.

Lower down, the oviduct widens and becomes glandular and highly

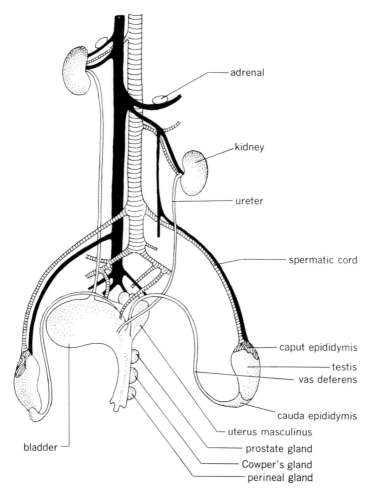

FIG. 12.5   Semi-diagrammatic drawing of the urogenital organs of a male rabbit, *Oryctolagus cuniculus*, x 2/3.

vascular, and is called the uterus or womb. When the mammal is pregnant processes grow out from it and become interlocked with similar processes from the allantois of the embryo, and so the complex structure, the placenta, is formed. This not only supplies food and oxygen to the developing young, but also carries away carbon dioxide and other waste products.

The uterus varies much in different orders of mammal, and has various degrees of fusion of the two sides. In the most primitive form, found in some insectivores, some bats, rodents, lagomorphs, and elephants, the uteri of the two sides remain separate, merely meeting in a common lower passage, the vagina, into which the penis is inserted in copulation. This condition is called duplex (Fig. 12.6). In a few bats, some rodents, most carnivores, pigs, and cattle the lower parts of the two uteri are themselves fused, a condition called bipartite (Fig. 12.6). When this fusion extends to most of the length of the uteri, as in some insectivores, most bats, sheep, whale, and dogs, the uterus is called bicornuate (Fig. 12.6). Finally, where, as in the higher primates, including man, the fusion is complete, so that the two Fallopian tubes open into a single uterus, the state is simplex

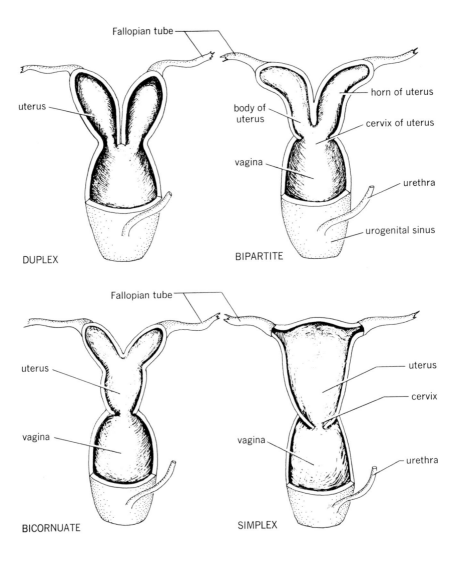

FIG. 12.6   Types of uterus in placental mammals.

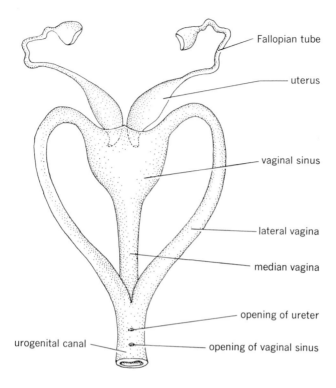

Fallopian tube

uterus

vaginal sinus

lateral vagina

median vagina

opening of ureter

urogenital canal

opening of vaginal sinus

FIG. 12.7   Uterus of a kangaroo, semi-diagrammatic.

(Fig. 12.6). No functional explanation of the fusion of the uteri seems possible, for although it has clearly gone on to an increasing degree as the
placentals evolved, it is connected neither with habit of life nor number
of young. Elephants, whales, and apes, all having only one or two young
at a birth, show the complete range from duplex to simplex.

The marsupials have, as one might expect from their generally primitive
condition, a duplex uterus, but they are peculiar in having the vagina divided as well. In the most primitive forms each uterus opens into a curved
lateral vagina which meets its fellow and the urinary passage in a urogenital canal. Into these vaginae the bifid head of the penis, in those species
which have it, fits. In others, the two uteri meet in a median vaginal sinus,
from which the lateral vaginae diverge, and in some, such as kangaroos, a
pouch from this sinus projects back on the dorsal surface of the urogenital
canal. When the young are about to be born the lower end of the pouch
ruptures into the canal, so that at parturition the young pass down what
is now called the median vagina, instead of using the lateral ones (Fig.
12.7).

In the placentals the vagina and the urinary passage open separately into a shallow vestibule, which is surrounded by lips, the labia majora, which are the homologue of the scrotum. On the front wall of the vestibule is a small clitoris, which is the homologue of the penis. Except that it is highly sensitive to touch and may therefore be of some value in stimulating the female to orgasm and ovulation, it is usually functionless; in a few, such as the hyenas, it is pierced by the urethral canal, and in copulation the penis is inserted into it. In the hyenas it is in fact so large, and so like a penis, that the external genitalia of the two sexes are very similar.

The sexes of all vertebrates are often distinguished from each other by size, color, or behavior, and sometimes by the development in one sex, usually the male, of special structures for display or sexual combat. Some of these, such as horns, antlers, and tusks, are dealt with in other places in this book. Female mammals are characterized by the possession of milk glands or mammae. These are formed in the skin, and resemble, and may perhaps be derived from, sweat glands. Each consists of a much-branched tube, and they develop along two lines running on the ventral surface of thorax and abdomen. The number of glands that are present depends on the species, and has a general relationship to the number of young. Thus in animals such as rats and pigs, where the litters are large, there are a dozen or so teats running the whole length of the body. Where the young are few, as in horses, cattle, elephants, and primates, the glands are reduced to two or four and are confined either to the inguinal region or to the thorax. The position of the human mammae is generally said to be related to the mother's habit of carrying the young in one forearm while climbing trees, which may be seen in some monkeys; this may be so, but elephants also have thoracic mammae, and there does not really seem to be any advantage to a quadruped in having mammae at one end of the body rather than another.

For most of the year the mammae are inactive, but when the young are about to be born the cells of the walls of the ducts divide rapidly and secrete the milk, a liquid containing varying amounts of fat, sugar, and protein. Activity is under the control of hormones from the anterior pituitary and the reproductive organs, and usually continues so long as may be necessary. It can be continued long after the usual time if the young continue to suck, and conversely it ceases prematurely if they are taken away early. In general, so long as the production of milk, or lactation, continues, no more ova are released from the ovary, so that another pregnancy is impossible.

The mammary glands of monotremes are of a different nature, and resemble sebaceous glands rather than sweat glands. They open by several small pores instead of by a few distinct nipples.

The milk glands of both monotremes and marsupials are enclosed in the pouch, a fold of skin which makes a bag with its opening usually forward but occasionally, as in the thylacine, backward. A few marsupials, such as the opossum *Didelphis* and the carnivorous Dasyuridae, are without it.

A peculiarity of the male mammal is the occurrence of rudimentary milk glands, and nipples which are sometimes quite large, and these are generally in the same position as the functional glands of the female—along the whole ventral surface (though difficult to find in the fur) in rabbits, on the chest in man, and beside the scrotum in bulls. They are enlarged in many intersexes. In both sexes of mammals that normally have only two or four mammae, supernumerary glands and nipples sometimes occur.

Excretory and Genital Ducts

We must now consider the homologies of the genital ducts and of the excretory ducts with which they are associated, bringing together the facts in this chapter and the previous one and adding others from embryology. It is customary to say that the oviduct, or Müllerian duct as it is sometimes called, is always the pronephric duct, while the vas deferens is a mesonephric duct, or in amniotes the only mesonephric duct that persists, but this, though useful for shorthand, is a simplification.

It is easier to begin with the most evolved forms, the amniotes. In them, as we have seen, a new duct grows forward from the base of the mesonephric duct; it drains the metanephros and becomes the only functional kidney duct in the adult of both sexes (p. 206). It is called the ureter, and some zoologists would restrict this name to a metanephric duct, though others use it more widely.

Where the mesonephros is the functional kidney, things are more complicated, especially in the male. When the anterior tubules of the mesonephros become associated with the testis they, as it were, tap this, so that the sperms pass through them and so into the backward-running duct, which may be called the Wolffian mesonephric duct. In nearly all amphibians and elasmobranchs there is some splitting of the duct, so that the anterior branches carry only sperms, the posterior, only urine; but in most there is a common basal portion, opening into the cloaca, which conveys both. In some, however, the lower few branches are completely separated, so that the urinary duct and the vas deferens open independently into the cloaca or into the urogenital sinus. The urodeles illustrate this (Fig. 12.8). If one then imagines the mesonephros suppressed as an excretory organ, and so naturally its duct also, one has the condition in amniotes (Fig. 12.9). The only mesonephric duct is now the vas deferens.

This does not, however, solve the problem of the homology of the ducts, for, although we have used the term mesonephric duct for one which drains a mesonephros, it is, in forms which have a pronephros, simply the posterior part of the duct of the latter. Where the channels for the sperm

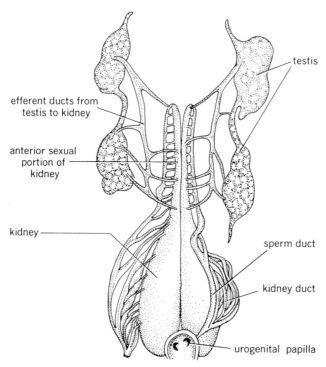

FIG. 12.8 Semi-diagrammatic drawing of the urogenital system of a male salamander, *Salamandra maculosa*, x 3/2.

and for the urine are separate, it is the former that is the original longitudinal duct, while the more posterior and excretory tubules of the mesonephros that make the functional kidney grow backward to make their own duct. This, if anything, is a true mesonephric duct, since it is in a sense a new one; but it can only be called new because it fails to reach the pre-existing duct.

Some parts at least of the main collecting ducts of the kidney are derived from the pre-existing Wolffian duct. In elasmobranchs they are split off from the dorsal part of this, while in the newt *Triton* they are outgrowths of it. Some authors would therefore say that they are homologous with the metanephric ducts of amniotes and may be called ureters. Others say that as they do not start from the extreme posterior end of the Wolffian duct and grow forward this is a bad usage. In any case it is inadvisable to call them metanephric ducts, since they never drain a metanephros.

In the females of nearly all vertebrates (Figs. 12.10 to 12.15) the oviduct is large and, except at the extreme posterior end, completely separated from the duct that drains the kidney. It is called the Müllerian duct, and in elasmobranchs and urodeles it is formed by division of the

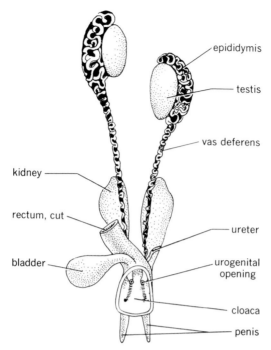

FIG. 12.9 Semi-diagrammatic drawing of the urogenital organs of a male lizard, *Lacerta viridis*, x 3.

pronephric duct, the other part forming the Wolffian duct from the kidney. In elasmobranchs the anterior funnel of the Müllerian duct is actually formed from a few pronephric tubules. For this reason it is usually said to be homologous with the pronephric duct throughout the vertebrates. Its origin in the amniotes and anurans is quite different, for in them it is formed independently of the excretory system, as a fold in the epithelium of the dorsal wall of the celom. Its true homology must therefore remain doubtful.

A tube develops in the same position in the embryo of male mammals, but it degenerates before birth. The fused lower ends of the two male Müllerian ducts can, however, perhaps be seen as a probably functionless pouch, the uterus masculinus, opening into the dorsal surface of the origin of the urethra (Fig. 12.5). According to some embryologists, however, this is a true seminal vesicle, formed from the lower ends of the Wolffian ducts. In the same way a mesonephric or Wolffian duct develops in the female embryo and then mostly disappears, leaving this time a remnant, the epo-ophoron, at the upper end near the ovary (Fig. 12.14). It has no known function. The relationships of the amniote ducts are shown in Plate V.

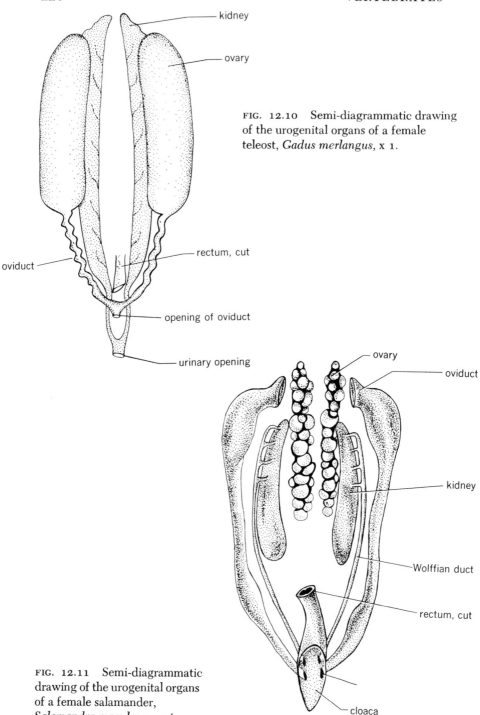

FIG. 12.10   Semi-diagrammatic drawing of the urogenital organs of a female teleost, *Gadus merlangus*, x 1.

FIG. 12.11   Semi-diagrammatic drawing of the urogenital organs of a female salamander, *Salamandra maculosa*, x 3/2.

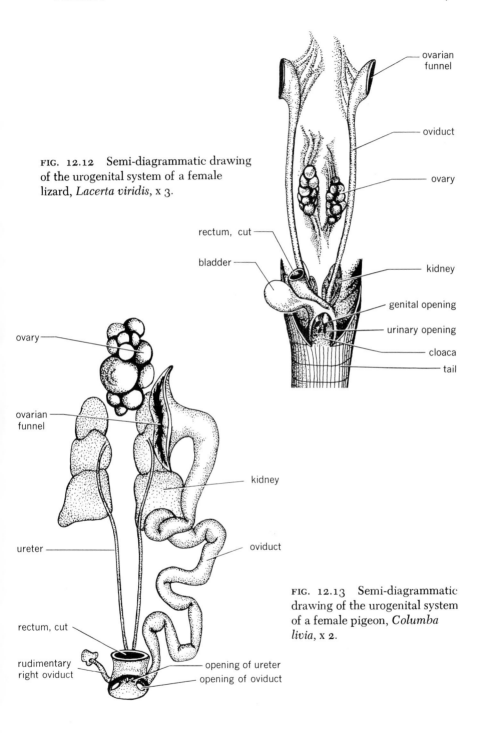

FIG. 12.12 Semi-diagrammatic drawing of the urogenital system of a female lizard, *Lacerta viridis*, x 3.

ovarian funnel

oviduct

ovary

rectum, cut

bladder

kidney

genital opening

urinary opening

cloaca

tail

ovary

ovarian funnel

ureter

kidney

oviduct

FIG. 12.13 Semi-diagrammatic drawing of the urogenital system of a female pigeon, *Columba livia*, x 2.

rectum, cut

rudimentary right oviduct

opening of ureter

opening of oviduct

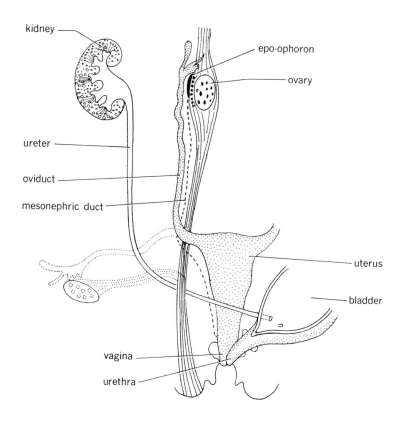

FIG. 12.14 Urogenital system of an embryo female mammal, semi-diagrammatic, to show the epo-ophoron and the vestigial mesonephric duct. The dotted outlines show the final position of the organs. (Redrawn from Young, *The Life of Mammals*, Clarendon Press, 1957)

The bony fish do not easily fit even into this somewhat confused story. In the sturgeons and Holostei the same duct carries sperms and urine, but in *Polypterus* there are separate ducts. Dipnoi show a range. In *Epiceratodus* there are common ducts, but in *Protopterus* and *Lepidosiren* there is some degree of separation, comparable to the condition in anurans such as the toad *Bufo*. This suggests that the development of an independent mesonephric urinary duct has occurred more than once. The teleosts have an entirely new and independent sperm duct leading directly back from the testis. Their oviduct is probably of the same nature.

We may now recapitulate by means of a table.

KIDNEYS

	CYCLOSTOMATA	ELASMOBRANCHII	ACTINOPTERYGII and CROSSOPTERYGII	AMPHIBIA	AMNIOTA
Pronephros	Functional in larvae, perhaps persists in hagfishes	Vestigial	Functional in larvae; then aborts except in a few teleosts		Vestigial
Mesonephros	Functional	Functional; anterior part sexual in male	Functional; anterior part sexual in male Dipnoi and Holostei	Functional; anterior part sexual in male	Functional in embryos; anterior part sexual and functional in male (vasa efferentia, epididymis), vestigial in female
Metanephros	←———————————— Absent ————————————→				Functional kidney

DUCTS

	CYCLOSTOMATA	ELASMOBRANCHII	ACTINOPTERYGII and CROSSOPTERYGII	AMPHIBIA	AMNIOTA
Male kidney	Duct which is at first pronephric and later mesonephric	←———— Wolffian "mesonephric" duct ————→			Metanephric duct or ureter
testis	None	Wolffian "mesonephric" duct, except teleosts, which have a new duct			Wolffian mesonephric duct
Female kidney	As male	←———— Wolffian "mesonephric" duct ————→			As male
ovary	None	Pronephric duct = Müllerian duct	Dipnoi—Müllerian duct, development unknown; Teleostei—new duct.	Urodela—pronephric Müllerian duct; Anura—new Müllerian duct from celomic wall	New Müllerian duct from celomic wall

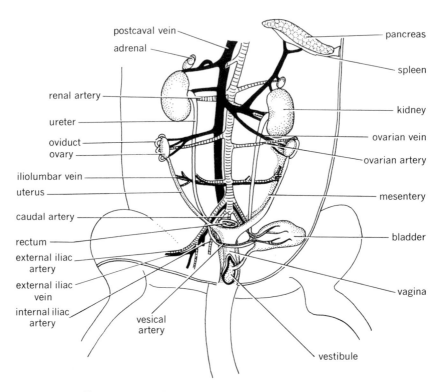

postcaval vein
adrenal
pancreas
spleen
renal artery
kidney
ureter
oviduct
ovary
ovarian vein
ovarian artery
iliolumbar vein
uterus
mesentery
caudal artery
rectum
bladder
external iliac
artery
external iliac
vein
internal iliac
artery
vagina
vesical
artery
vestibule

FIG. 12.15   Dissection of the urogenital system of a female kitten, x 1.

The cloaca, which is a terminal part of the alimentary canal into which
urinary and genital ducts open, has already been briefly dealt with above
(p. 169). It is formed partly of endoderm and partly of an ectodermal invagination, the proctodeum. If the excretory tubules are celomoducts, as
we have considered them to be above, they would primarily open through
the ectoderm, but, whatever may have been the original state of affairs,
they, as well as the genital ducts associated with them, now always open
into the endodermal part. A typical and well-developed cloaca is present
in cyclostomes, most elasmobranchs, dipnoans, amphibians, reptiles, and
birds; and in some of these, as we have seen, there is a degree of separation and specialization of parts.

The remaining fish have lost the cloaca. In the Holocephali the rectum
opens separately from the ducts, which combine in a shallow urogenital
sinus. The openings of sturgeons, *Polypterus*, *Lepidosteus*, and *Amia* are
similar. This condition is probably not primitive, but it may be looked on
as a reversion to a more primitive state. In most teleosts, urinary and genital pores and anus are all completely separate, but in a few there is some

association, the sperm ducts opening into the base of the mesonephric kidney ducts, or into the rectum; or all three may be associated. This variability fits with the supposition that the testis ducts are a new formation.

In mammals, though a cloaca is present in the embryo, it tends to disappear in the adult, by the formation of a partition which grows backward to divide it into a dorsal rectal portion and a ventral urogenital portion. There is very little of this in monotremes, and the penis, though partly tubular, is still in communication with the rectum. In marsupials and placentals the division is complete, and in the male a further rolling-up of an anterior groove froms a channel, the urethra, opening on the end of the penis. Through this both sperms and urine pass. In the female, urinary and genital apertures remain separate, opening into a shallow vestibule which is the representative of the urogenital portion of the original cloaca.

While the endodermal portion of the cloaca is completely divided, a shallow ectodermal depression, into which all the tubes open, may remain. It is distinct in marsupials, where a sphincter muscle surrounds anus and urogenital opening, and has been recognized in some insectivores and rodents. A similar ectodermal cloaca, probably a new formation, is present in whales.

It is only with the adoption of a terrestrial habitat that a bladder for storing urine becomes necessary. It first appears in the amphibians, as a thin-walled ventral expansion of the endodermal part of the cloaca. In amniotes a similar and presumably homologous outgrowth forms the allantois. This stores excretory products in the egg of reptiles and birds, and in mammals forms the embryonic half of the placenta. Its main part disappears in amniotes, but the urinary bladder of the adult is formed from its base.

The primitive hermaphroditism of the vertebrates, which has been mentioned above (p. 212), applies to the ducts, the external genitalia, and the secondary sexual characters, as well as to the gonads. It is clear that whatever their homologies as mesonephric or pronephric ducts, the Wolffian duct of the male and the Müllerian duct of the female are separate and parallel structures. Rudiments at least of both occur in most embryos, and it is only when the individual begins to develop toward functional testes or ovaries that the one develops and the other degenerates to become vestigial.

The general mechanism for the determination of sex in vertebrates is the same as that in other animals. One pair of chromosomes consists of two members which may be unequal. In one sex, called homogametic, or homozygous for sex, they are alike, and indistinguishable in behavior from the other chromosomes, which are also perfectly paired. In the other sex, the two sex chromosomes are unlike, and it is said to be heterogametic, or heterozygous for sex. In most vertebrates (and most other animals) the male is heterogametic, but in birds it is homogametic. It is obvious that with normal segregation in meiosis either system will lead to the production of equal numbers of males and females, and this is in general found to be true. Exceptions can be usually explained on special grounds, as, for example, in mammals, by a differential mortality of the two sexes in the uterus.

In general it may be taken as a rule that if the sex chromosomes are odd (except in birds, which are the other way round), the gonad of the animal possessing them will develop into a testis; if they are even, it will become an ovary. But experiments, particularly in fish, have shown that the other chromosomes, or autosomes, also have some effect in the determination of sex, and it is probably differences in their action, dependent on the genes which they carry, which lead to the production of intersexes. An intersex may usually be considered to be basically either male or female, according to its sex chromosomes, but to have been able to develop the features of the other sex to some degree.

The physiological control of sex is largely carried out by hormones, produced not by the sex cells themselves but under their influence in other parts of the gonad (the interstitial tissue) or elsewhere in the body, and their effects are largely inhibitory. Both sexes produce both male and female hormones, but in each the one set comes to predominate. The Müllerian duct develops to form an oviduct unless it is inhibited by the presence of male hormones. The Wolffian duct, on the contrary, disappears unless it is stabilized by male hormones. The same sort of control determines whether the folds of skin beside the urogenital sinus become labia majora or a scrotum. In marsupials the scrotum is homologous with the pouch, and if young males are castrated and then injected with female sex hormones (estrogens) they develop a pouch instead of a scrotum. The intersexes in man, in which the external genitalia have an intermediate form, are usually genetic males in which by an abnormality of function some development in a female direction has occurred. When this is extreme they may be classified at birth as girls, with unfortunate results when their true maleness becomes apparent as they grow older. They are presumably comparable to the experimental male kangaroos with a pouch.

The later sexual differences are also dependent on hormones. Thus the adjustments in the pubic symphysis and the sacro-iliac junction that allow birth to occur in female mammals are brought about by a hormone which, in different species, is produced by the ovaries, uterus, placenta, or vagina. The ovipositor that grows from the lower end of the oviduct in the teleost fish the European bitterling (*Rhodeus amarus*) does so under the influence of a hormone produced in the ovarian follicles after the ova have been shed. To come to a more superficial level, the antlers of male deer are produced only if male hormones from the testis are present. They can be induced to grow in both castrated males and castrated females of Virginian deer (*Odocoileus virginianus*) by the injection of testosterone.

The development of the sex cells themselves depends in part, as does that of other cells of the embryo, on their relationships to other parts of the body. We have seen that female cells tend to remain on the surface of the gonad, while those of the male sink in. If the formation of the middle part of the gonad, or medulla, which comes from the nephrotomic region, is delayed in anurans, as it can be by low temperatures, the sex cells cannot sink in; they become ova, and the animal is a female irrespective of its genetic sex. But if the medulla develops, in time spermatozoa may be formed and sex reversal may occur. It is presumably some such interference with the normal course of development that leads to the naturally occurring intersexes. The male toads with a rudimentary ovary become female if castrated, their Bidder's organ developing into an ovary. Presumably, without castration the original active testis is responsible for the production of a hormone that suppresses any further development of the ovary. In the special case of freemartins in cattle, there are twins of opposite sex; the arrangement of the placenta while the young are in the mother's womb is such that hormones from one of them can reach the blood of the other. The male hormones interfere with the development of the female fetus so that it becomes an intersex.

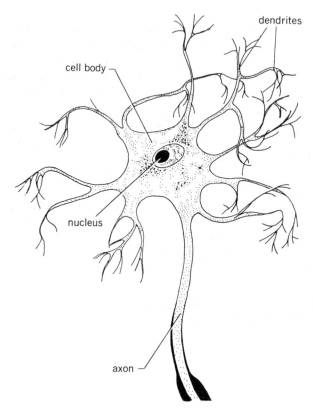

FIG. 13.1   Generalized drawing of a neuron, x 250.

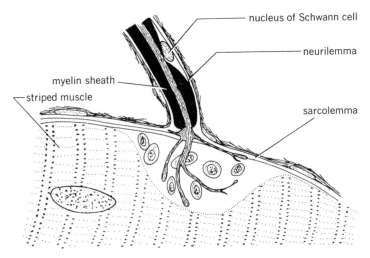

FIG. 13.2   Diagram of a nerve-muscle junction. (Based on Gutmann and Young, *J. Anat.*, Lond. 78, 1944)

13

Nervous System

THE NERVOUS system is unique among the parts into which the animal body has long been divided for study in that it is built almost entirely of one fundamental type of cell; nervous tissue is therefore almost synonymous and coterminous with the nervous system. All that has to be added to the tissue to make the system complete is a very little connective tissue, and enough arteries, veins, and capillaries to supply the necessary oxygen and food for its functioning. For this reason its morphology is of little interest apart from its cellular structure, and cannot be understood without it. Further, since all nerve cells behave in pretty much the same way, its structure and function are intimately connected.

The basis of the nervous system is the nerve cell or neuron. This develops from a part of the gastrula, or its equivalent in amniotes, which is on the outside and so is usually called epiblast, but in fact the cells that are going to form the nervous system are distinct in the blastula, so that to ascribe them to one of the three layers of the triploblastic theory is not very helpful.

Whatever its origin (and more will be said of this later) the neuron has a characteristic structure (Fig. 13.1). It is typically large (about 100 microns in diameter) and has a conspicuous nucleus. It appears stellate, or star-shaped, because it has many protoplasmic processes stretching out from it. These can be seen properly only in very careful preparations, which show that the end of each of the processes is finely branched. They are called dendrons or dendrites, from the Greek word for a tree. Most of them are relatively short, not more than a few diameters of the central body of the cell, but occasionally they are longer. Some nerves have, in addition to typical dendrons, one process which is very much longer indeed; it is called an axon, and the tuft of branches at its end, although no different in principle from that of a dendron, is given the special names of terminal arborization or telodendron.

It is characteristic of dendrons that they always come into contact with other dendrons, or with telodendrons, and of telodendrons that they either come into contact with dendrons or spread out on an organ as, for example, a nerve-muscle junction (Fig. 13.2), or end as a sensory spot. The contact between two processes is not one-to-one, but overlapping, so that

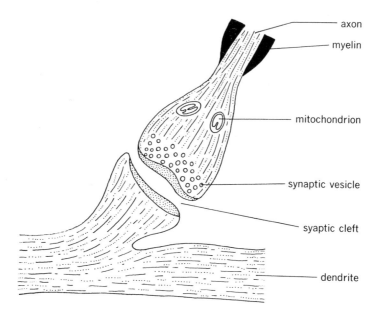

FIG. 13.3   Generalized diagram of a section through a synapse, as seen in electron micrographs.

each nerve cell touches several others. Such a contact is called a synapse (Fig. 13.3). There is no cytoplasmic continuity from cell to cell.

Since a neuron with an axon may have its body and nucleus within the backbone and the tip of its axon at the end of a toe, it is easily the longest type of cell known. The neurons of a giraffe's fore-legs may be about ten feet long; there is no reason to suppose that the neurons of a dinosaur were any different in their arrangement, and some of them must have been twice this length. In spite of this great length the volume of a neuron is small.

The general arrangement of nervous tissue in vertebrates is that there is a large concentration of it, the central nervous system, within the backbone and skull, and stretching out from this to all parts of the body are the nerves. At some points on the nerves are knots or swellings called ganglia. The nerves generally branch and become finer the further they go from the central nervous system. The central nervous system when cut across generally shows an inner gray matter surrounded by white matter.

Broadly speaking the gray matter and the ganglia consist of cell bodies with dendrons, and have many synapses. There are also in gray matter many packing cells, making the neuroglia. These have the same embryonic origin as nerve cells, and are usually regarded as such cells which have not fully developed. The nerves and the white matter consist of axons, with some additions.

The unit of a nerve is the nerve fiber, shown in longitudinal section in Fig. 13.4. The essential central part, the axon, is simply a long extension of a nerve cell. In most fibers it is surrounded by a layer of fatty substance, the myelin or medullary sheath, which gives the characteristic black appearance to nerves stained with osmium tetroxide. It is not continuous, but broken at intervals by the nodes of Ranvier. Outside the myelin can be seen a little cytoplasm and an occasional nucleus; in fact, one nucleus per internode. This and other evidence suggest that the cells to which these nuclei belong, called Schwann cells, secrete the myelin. Whether myelin is present or not is simply a matter of size, and so, to some extent, of age; when a fiber reaches about one micron in diameter, the myelin appears. The Schwann cells are derived from neuroglia, and these in turn from the original nervous epithelium, so that the Schwann cells may be looked on as nerve cells whose development has been deflected. Most of them come from the tissue on the edge of the rolled-up neural tube called the neural crest, which gives rise to some nerves (pp. 256-78) as well as to much tissue generally thought of as mesodermal. Electron micrographs suggest that the Schwann cells secrete a thin sheath around even the smallest fibers, but that this does not contain enough fat to give the characteristic appearance under the light microscope.

Outside the myelin sheath is another coating, the neurilemma; it is of protein, but its origin does not seem to be known. Finally, the fiber is surrounded by a tube of ordinary connective tissue, the endoneurium, with occasional nuclei. Those who know that 'endo' comes from a Greek word meaning 'inside,' will be surprised to find endoneurium on the outside of

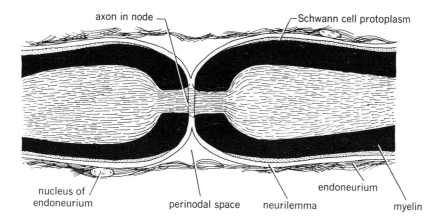

FIG. 13.4 Diagram of a nerve fiber at a node of Ranvier, x 1600. (Redrawn from Hess and Young, *Proc. Roy. Soc. B.* 140, 1952.)

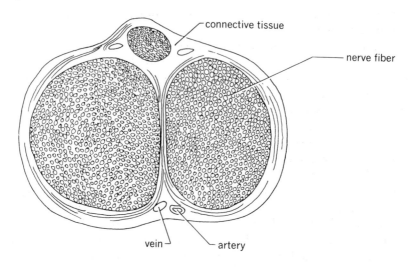

FIG. 13.5   Diagrammatic transverse section of a nerve.

the fiber. It gets its name from the fact that it is inside the nerve, which, as a transverse section shows (Fig. 13.5), consists of many fibers bound together by more connective tissue, the perineurium (peri- meaning around). A large nerve may have several bundles of fibers, each with its perineurium, the whole surrounded by another sheath of connective tissue, the epineurium ('epi-' meaning 'upon').

Cutting a nerve fiber causes degeneration of the part distal to the cell body. There is now ample experimental evidence that the cytoplasm of the fiber, like that of most cells, is dependent for its life on the nucleus, and that proteins made by or under the influence of this travel down the fiber at a speed of about 2.5 mm. per day.

Stimulating one part of a living cell will often cause a response in a distant part; this is well seen when the leading pseudopodia of a large amoeba are touched, and as a result new ones form to one side of them. Conduction is therefore a characteristic of living matter. Nerve cells have specialized in this, and moreover instead of conveying information merely from one part of a cell to another they work so as to convey it from one part of a complex body to another. No metazoan is without nerve cells, and their existence seems to have been a condition of the evolution of the animal kingdom. It is not entirely an exaggeration to say that the chief difference between the Metaphyta and the Metazoa is that the latter possess a nervous system.

Conduction in a nerve fiber depends on changes in the surface of the axon. At rest, this is polarized, with a layer of positively charged ions on the outside, and of negatively charged ions on the inside (Fig. 13.6).

Chemical analysis shows that the concentration of potassium ions is twenty to sixty times as much inside the fiber as it is outside, while that of sodium ions is three to ten times as much outside as it is inside. The absolute concentrations of sodium are very much higher than those of potassium, so that the net result is that there is an excess of metallic ions outside, enough to make it sixty to eighty millivolts positive to the inside.

The wall of the fiber is relatively impermeable, but differences of this order can only be maintained by continual transfer of ions across the membrane to replace those that leak through along the concentration gradient. Except that this is, as one would expect, dependent on a living cell and the use of oxygen, nothing is known of it. Since it consists largely of expelling sodium ions from the cell it is known as the sodium pump.

Stimulation of a nerve cell may consist of almost any type of physical action. Electrical change, pressure, heat, cold, acid, and other chemicals produce a response in almost all nerve cells under almost all conditions, and can be used for simple experiments. Other nerve cells, or cells under special circumstances, respond to light, sound, and a further range of chemicals. Whatever the stimulus, there is only one type of response in the nerve cell: an immediate and rapid movement of sodium ions into the fiber at the point of stimulation, so that the potential difference across the

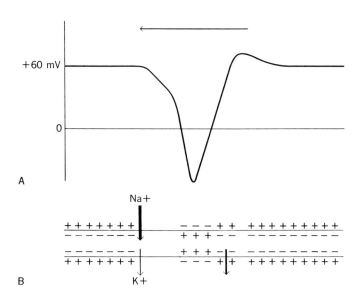

FIG. 13.6   Diagram of a nerous impulse traveling from right to left. (A) the electrical potential difference between the outside and the inside of the nerve fiber. (B) the passage of ions; the size of the arrows indicates approximately the magnitude of the flow.

wall is reversed, and the outside becomes thirty to fifty millivolts negative to the inside. Shortly afterwards potassium ions flow out, and then the former state is restored. These movements of ions are ascribed to changes in permeability of the cell surface.

The negativity produced at the point of stimulation appears to act as a stimulus for adjacent parts of the nerve fiber, so that they too become more permeable. The result of this is that a wave of negativity spreads along the fiber. This is the nervous impulse, and the voltage by which it is measured is the action potential.

It seems probable that the first change in the fiber must be chemical. It may be that the substance acetylcholine, which will be referred to again below, is first formed, and that this causes the change in permeability. The first movement of the ions is under a concentration gradient, so that it involves the use only of potential energy, but the restoration uses oxygen, and involves some of the ordinary reactions by which energy is supplied in the animal body, including glycolysis.

This account of the origin and passage of the nervous impulse suggests that it ought to travel in both directions along a nerve fiber which has been stimulated somewhere in the middle of its length. This is easily shown to be true. If, for example, the sciatic nerve of a frog in the usual preparation is stimulated in the middle, the action potential travels at equal rates in both directions. In nature, however, long axons are usually arranged so that only one of their ends can receive stimulation, the rest of their length being more or less sheltered. This means that in life the direction of passage of the nervous impulse is essentially one-way.

The speed of passage of the impulse depends on temperature (which points to its basically chemical nature), and also, more surprisingly, on the diameter of the fibers, the larger ones having the higher velocity. The speeds in mammals at body temperature range from 0.3 meter per second up to 100 m.p.s. In amphibians and reptiles they are somewhat less, and nothing seems to be known of the speed in fish or birds. Although the maxima of these rates appear high, they do clearly limit the size at which an animal can be efficiently co-ordinated. Consider, for example, a dinosaur with fore- and hind-legs fifteen feet apart and about ten feet long. At 100 m.p.s. an impulse would take one-ninth of a second to travel from the toe of one leg to that of the other. Impulses from the tip of the tail of a dinosaur such as *Diplodocus* would take one-third of a second to reach the brain. If, as is likely, the rate in these creatures was very much less, perhaps only 10 m.p.s., the times would be proportionately longer. It is presumably because of this that the dinosaurs, as shown by their skeleton, had a large expansion of nervous tissue in the spinal cord of the sacral region, suggesting that this to some extent took the place of the brain, which was relatively small.

The relationship between diameter and conduction velocity is not simple, but when nerves are myelinated the rate of increase with diameter is greater than when they are not. This suggests that the formation of the myelin sheath is partly responsible for the high rates in big nerve fibers, and that it has been evolved through the advantage that these give.

Sooner or later the impulse comes to the end of the cell in which it was initiated, and reaches a synapse. There is no cytoplasmic continuity, so that the impulse cannot continue. Instead, the wave of change, whatever it may be, leads to the build-up and liberation of a substance called acetyl-choline, a relatively simple nitrogen-containing organic compound, or, in certain nerves, of another comparable substance. Its liberation starts a new impulse in the cell across the synapse, and so the effect of the orig-inal stimulation is propagated. Investigations of systems where the num-ber of synapses can be known or guessed suggest that the time between the arrival of an impulse at the synapse and the accumulation of enough acetylcholine to start a new impulse is about four milliseconds in ganglia, and rather less in the brain.

The synapse acts as a valve, for acetylcholine is liberated only at that side of it at which impulses normally arrive. If an impulse is experimen-tally sent into a synapse from the other direction it ceases, and no new impulse is started in the adjoining cell. Where the synapse is between an axon and a dendron the effective direction is from the axon to the dendron.

The chemical and electrical mechanism of the nervous impulse explains the working of the reflex arc (Fig. 13.7). Nerve cells may be put broadly into three groups. Those which receive stimuli, either from the outside world or from inner parts of the body other than nerve cells, are called receptor or sensory cells, and their axons are sensory or afferent fibers. Those which carry impulses to structures such as muscles and glands which do things (collectively known as effectors, or effector organs) are efferent or motor neurons, and the same adjectives are used for the fibers formed from their axons. Between the two are one, two, or more inter-nuncial or association neurons, with many dendrons and either a short axon or none. The overlapping arrangement of the synapses means that with a few internuncial neurons an afferent fiber is put into touch with many efferents. The effect of drugs such as strychnine, which cause a light touch on any part of the body to produce a violent reaction everywhere else, suggests that in mammals every sensory fiber is in potential com-munication with every motor fiber.

Most of the central nervous system consists of internuncial neurons, its gray matter being the cell bodies and dendrons, while the white matter consists of the tracts, which are bundles of axons, not greatly different from the nerves which are made up of the axons of sensory and motor fibers. The cell bodies of the motor neurons are also in the central nervous system, but those of the sensory cells are collected together just outside it in blobs called dorsal root ganglia. This arises partly because in these

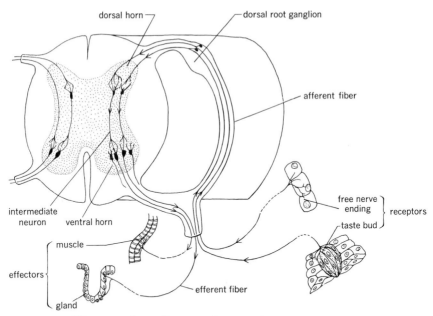

FIG. 13.7   Diagram of a reflex arc, showing the course of a nervous impulse from a receptor (free nerve ending or taste bud) through one intermediate neuron and two synapses to an effector (muscle or gland).

cells the body is on a side-line. A single process divides into a relatively short part going into the central nervous system, and a long one going to the sense organ. The body is thus by-passed when the impulse travels from the distal end to the central nervous system. More will be said of these ganglia shortly.

At its simplest the distal part of the afferent cell simply ends in the appropriate part of the body, skin or whatever it may be, as a free nerve ending. More often it connects by a snyapse with a short process from a specialized cell in a sense organ. We shall say more of these in Chapter 14. The distal end of the axon of a motor nerve cell ends in a terminal arborization which spreads out over the organ which it supplies. The best known of these connections is the nerve-muscle junction or motor end plate. (Fig. 13.2). The branches consist of the actual nerve cell only, without any of its sheaths, and as they penetrate the connective-tissue wall of the muscle fiber (sarcolemma) the cytoplasms of the two cells are brought close together, and are separated only by the two surfaces and perhaps a very small space between them. The nerve-muscle junction is in fact similar to a synapse, and it works in much the same way. The end of the nerve liberates acetylcholine, which, in ways with which we are not at present concerned, causes the contraction of the muscle.

The central nervous system of all vertebrates is in principle much the same. It consists of a tube which is formed by the rolling-up of a flat plate of cells on the dorsal surface of the gastrula. Sometimes longitudinal folds appear, grow, bend over, and meet, so forming a tube under the epidermis; sometimes a single line of cells on each side grows inward over the central flat plate, which afterward rolls up, but these can be looked upon as variants of one process, in which the time-relations of the movements of the different cells are slightly different. The result is the same. The shoulders of the ridges, which do not form the actual tube itself, make the neural crest. The part of the central nervous system within the skull does not differ in origin from the rest, but early becomes specialized and enlarged as the brain.

A transverse section of the spinal cord shows the same parts, differing only in their proportions, in all vertebrates (Fig. 13.8, 13.9). On the outside are one or more membranes or meninges, seen at their greatest development in mammals. In these the whole cord is surrounded with a relatively tough dura mater, which is made of connective tissue, and is fibrous and vascular. Inside it is a thin and vascular arachnoid membrane, beneath which is a small arachnoid space, containing cerebrospinal fluid. The innermost membrane is the pia mater, a thin wall of scattered cells. The pia mater and the arachnoid membrane are derived from cells of the neural crest. The meninges of birds are similar to those of mammals, but in the reptiles and amphibians the pia mater and the arachnoid membrane are not distinct. In the fishes they are hardly distinguishable from the dura mater, so that the cord is surrounded only with a single membrane.

In the nervous part of the section the white matter surrounds the gray matter. Except in the cyclostomes, where the gray matter appears as a simple thick plate, it is always more or less in the form of a Saint Andrew's Cross, or saltire, with two dorsal horns and two ventral horns. This arrangement is recognizable in the dogfish, only slightly marked in amphibians, but very pronounced in crocodiles, birds, and mammals. It is obvious from a consideration of the appearance of a transverse section that the horns in these must run as thick ribs the whole length of the spinal cord. The hollows between these ribs are filled with white matter, which consists of long nerve fibers of internuncial and sensory neurons. Clearly the more the animal uses its brain the more of these fibers there are likely to be, carrying impulses to it from other parts of the body. It is therefore not surprising that the horns or ribs of gray matter are well developed in the higher animals. The cross-shaped appearance of the gray matter in section is produced by the necessity for some part of it to come near the surface.

The dorsal horns contain chiefly the cell bodies of association neurons, the ventral horns, those of motor cells. The lighter color of the white matter is due to the myelin sheaths of the axons of which it is composed. Both

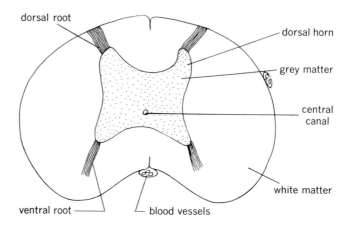

FIG. 13.8   Diagrammatic transverse section of the spinal cord of a dogfish.

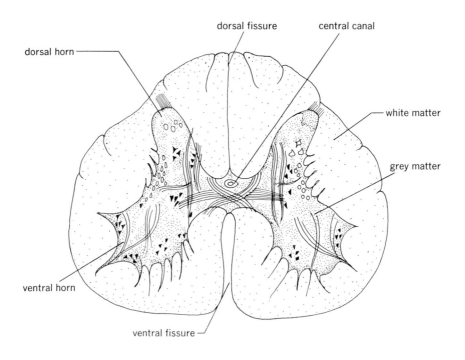

FIG. 13.9   Diagrammatic transverse section of the spinal cord of a mammal.

gray and white matter contain also glial cells, which are branched and look much like nerve cells, but are perhaps largely nutritive in function. At least, they contain many mitochondria, which generally indicates an active metabolizing cell. They possibly secrete the myelin of the axons in the white matter, for these do not have Schwann cells; they have, however, a different origin from the Schwann cells, coming from the nerve cord itself and not from the neural crest. There are also some smaller cells, called microcytes or microglia, which are mesodermal and are ordinary connective tissue cells.

In the center of the gray matter is a minute hole, the cerebrospinal canal, which is the descendant of the original large space made by the meeting of the medullary folds. It contains cerebrospinal fluid (p. 248). The white matter in mammals is almost divided into right and left halves by a dorsal and a ventral fissure.

There is little variation in form of the spinal cord throughout its length, though there may be some specialization of tracts of fibers, and some swelling at the levels of the limbs. These are well seen in birds, presumably in connection with the very high degree of co-ordination of which the wings and legs have to be capable in flight and on landing. In most vertebrates the spinal cord runs for almost the whole length of the backbone, but in mammals there is a tendency for it to be shortened in the abdominal region, so that the last few paired nerves run together as a bundle alongside a small functionless remnant of the cord. Something of the same sort has happened in the frog, presumably in connection with the general shortening of the body that characterizes the anurans.

Brain

The brain is primarily and in origin simply an anterior expansion of the spinal cord. There is a general constancy in its development. After an initial swelling, which is largely an increase in the size of the internal hollow space with no increase in the thickness of its walls, the brain bends ventralward, so that two flexures or kinks divide it into a fore-brain or prosencephalon, a mid-brain or mesencephalon, and a hind-brain or rhombencephalon which is continuous with and merges into the spinal cord. These three parts do not correspond with the mesoblastic segmentation of the head, although they bear a fairly constant spatial relationship to it, which will be mentioned in Chapter 19. There is also a general relationship between these three divisions and the three chief distant senses of the head; the fore-brain is concerned with smell (or the distant chemical sense), the mid-brain with vision, and the hind-brain with hearing and its forerunners. In higher vertebrates vision is largely transferred to the fore-brain.

The fore-brain soon becomes double, by the growth of two lateral out-pushings near its anterior end; these make the olfactory lobes and cere-brum or cerebral hemispheres (so called from their shape in man), and as these grow forward as well as laterally the original anterior wall of the prosencephalon remains between them as the lamina terminalis. These three (or five) parts—olfactory lobes, cerebral hemispheres, and lamina terminalis—are now called the end-brain, or telencephalon, while the re-mainder of the fore-brain is the tween-brain, or diencephalon or thala-mencephalon.

The anterior part of the hind-brain grows dorsally to make the cere-bellum. This, and a few other parts at the sides and below, are called the metencephalon and retain the name of hind-brain, while the remainder of the rhombencephalon is called the after-brain or myelencephalon.

While these changes have been going on there have been alterations in the size and proportions of the hollows inside the brain, which are now, if well developed, called ventricles. Each side of the end-brain has a fairly large space, which is a lateral ventricle, opening by a pore, the foramen of Monro, into another large hollow, the third ventricle, in the tween-brain. Another large space, the fourth ventricle, extends through the meten-cephalon and myelencephalon. The lateral ventricles are called also the first and second ventricles.

In fishes and amphibians there is little difference in the diameter of the ventricles from the lamina terminalis back to the beginning of the spinal cord, so that third and fourth ventricles cannot be distinguished except by their position, and the hollow of the mid-brain is widely continuous with them. In amniotes it is constricted to a narrow passage, known in human anatomy as the *iter a tertio ad quartum ventriculum* (the way from the third to the fourth ventricle), or aqueduct of Sylvius. These silly names, which are all that are available for the space of the mid-brain, may be reduced to iter for short.

With the growth of the embryo the original flexures usually become straightened out, so that a typical adult vertebrate brain may be repre-sented in longitudinal section by Fig. 13.10. It will be clear from the above description that in a sagittal section the cerebral hemispheres and olfactory lobes will not be cut. Strictly, neither they nor their openings into the tween-brain (the foramina of Monro) will appear in the section, but both are shown for clarity, the right hemisphere in solid and the foramen as a hole opening from it toward the reader.

As would be expected, and as will be shown by examples shortly, the parts of the brain that are most developed in any animal are those that are most used. This raises the difficult question of localization of function in the brain. There is no doubt that in the lower vertebrates there is much of this; that is to say, a particular function, such as olfaction, is mediated by one particular part—in this example the olfactory lobes. Removal of

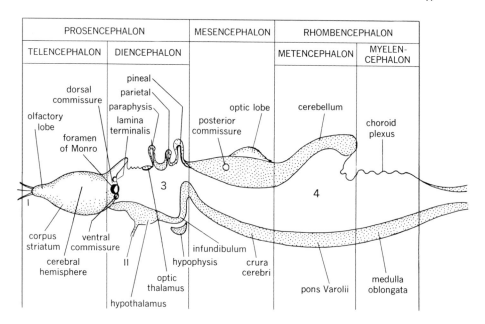

PROSENCEPHALON		MESENCEPHALON	RHOMBENCEPHALON	
TELENCEPHALON	DIENCEPHALON		METENCEPHALON	MYELEN-CEPHALON

FIG. 13.10   Diagram of the right half of a generalized vertebrate brain, cut sagittally. In this and other sections of brains (Figs. 13.12 to 13.15) the right cerebral hemispheres and the right olfactory and optic lobes, and the olfactory and optic nerves, the shown in solid, the other parts in section. I and II, cranial nerves; 3 and 4, ventricles.

them interferes with the distant chemical sense, removal of other parts either has no effect on it, or, if it does, it is clearly not acting directly. (An animal whose heart has been removed will not respond to smell, or anything else; this does not mean that it smells with its heart, but a supply of oxygen, and hence a circulatory system, and so a heart, are necessary for the working of all parts of the brain.) In the higher vertebrates there is much less localization, and although removal of a part may interfere with a function, the power may gradually come back, showing that other parts of the brain have taken over the job of that which was removed. Nevertheless there is a general correspondence of functions and parts, and this is represented in their relative size. The result of this is that any single diagram can represent the relative proportions of parts only in few animals, but it will show the relative positions of the parts for the whole phylum.

The olfactory lobes are closely associated in their size with the use that the animal makes of the distant chemical sense, and tend to become reduced as, with land life and greater activity, vision becomes the dominant sense. The striate body (corpus striatum or basal nucleus) is the main part of the gray matter of the cerebral hemispheres. The commissures are transverse bands of fibers. Since the general direction of the tracts in the white matter runs fore-and-aft it is obvious that without these there would be little co-ordination between the right and left sides, and yet without such co-ordination swimming and walking would be impossible. The cerebral hemispheres increase greatly in size through the vertebrate classes. In the cyclostomes they remain small lateral expansions of the fore-brain, in man they are larger than the whole of the rest of the brain, and are almost all that is visible when it is viewed from above.

The roof of the tween-brain is a choroid plexus, a thin folded membrane rich in blood vessels. Its folds hang down into the third ventricle, usually much more than is shown in the diagram, and in some animals such as mammals go through the foramina of Monro into the lateral ventricles. Its chief, and perhaps its only function, is to secrete the cerebrospinal fluid. This extends throughout the cavities of the brain and spinal cord, but some of it escapes into the arachnoid space through three foramina, a median called of Magendie and two lateral called of Luschka, in the roof of the medulla. From there it leaks back into the veins, so that there is a definite but slow circulation.

The nervous parts of the tween-brain make up the various parts of the thalamus, of which the optic thalami lying at the sides receive fibers from the eyes and send others forward to the cerebral hemispheres, while the thickened floor, or hypothalamus, receives fibers from several sense organs. Beneath it is the optic chiasma. In the lowest forms this is little more than a simple crossing of the optic nerves from the eyes, so that the right eye is connected to the left side of the brain, and vice versa, but in the mammals there gradually develops a more complicated arrangement in which fibers go from each eye to both sides of the brain. This is most marked in the primates with their binocular vision.

The roof of the tween-brain has a number of non-nervous projections, of doubtful function and various degrees of development. The paraphysis, the most anterior of these, has no known function. Behind it come the parietal (or parapineal) and pineal bodies. When one of these is well developed the other is usually not, and in spite of their present position one behind the other there is evidence that they are really a pair of structures. In some animals one or other of them shows unmistakable signs of being a degenerate eye with traces of retina and lens, and there is little doubt that their original function was vision. The implication of this is that the first vertebrates had two pairs of eyes, one pair looking sideways and one upward. In view of the obvious convenience of this arrangement it is difficult to see why the upper pair have been lost. The parapineal or pineal body, if present at all, has slight endocrine functions, as described in Chapter 20.

On the floor of the tween-brain, behind the hypothalamus, is an outpushing, the infundibulum. It always meets an upgrowth from the pharynx, the hypophysis, and the two together make the pituitary, an endocrine gland described in Chapter 20.

The mid-brain is often relatively small. Its roof is somewhat expanded to make the optic lobes, which in lower vertebrates are the final points reached by the fibers from the eyes.

The distinction between metencephalon and myelencephalon is not very marked in the lower vertebrates, and is shown only by the myelencephalon having a thin roof, which is the posterior choroid plexus. This is similar to the anterior choroid plexus of the tween-brain, and secretes some of the cerebrospinal fluid, but it is not well developed. The floor and sides of the after-brain make the medulla oblongata (usually called simply medulla), which is a relatively unspecialized part, and merges gradually into the spinal cord with which it is continuous. The roof and sides of the metencephalon are the cerebellum, which is not always well developed. Equally the pons on its floor, which consists of transverse fibers, is only fully developed in mammals. The cerebellum is in origin closely connected with the lateral line system and labyrinth (Chapter 14).

All the cranial nerves except the first four have their origin in the medulla.

The brain of an elasmobranch (Fig. 13.11) is very similar to the generalized diagram. The olfactory lobes are well developed, in accordance with the fact that the animal is carnivorous and finds its prey by the distant chemical sense, but the cerebral hemispheres, though distinct, are small, and the olfactory lobes are not clearly separated from them; it is probable that the cerebral hemispheres are here concerned with little else

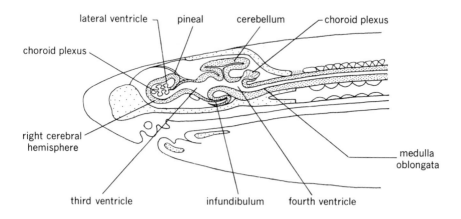

FIG. 13.11 Diagram of a sagittal section of the head of a dogfish to show the brain.

than the chemical sense mediated by the lobes. The pineal is well developed and is extended on to the end of a long stalk. The roof of the mid-brain is thick and appears to be the chief association center, since it receives fibers from most other parts of the brain.

The hypothalamus has a large expansion or saccus vasculosus; its function is not known, but since it is present also in the teleosts, which are not very closely related to the elasmobranchs, it is likely to have something to do with swimming. One suggestion is that it is concerned with the perception of pressure.

The cerebellum is relatively large and consists of a central and dorsal body and two lateral wings. The body extends forward over part of the mid-brain and back over part of the posterior choroid plexus. Its roof is smooth in small species, but it has furrows in the large ones; it is a general observation that furrows on the surface of the brain are connected with greater and better use, perhaps because in this way more connections can be made, so that it seems that the body of the cerebellum is more important in the large fish. This fits with the fact that it is well supplied with fibers from the eyes and the proprioceptors. The wings of the cerebellum are connected chiefly with the lateral line system and the labyrinth. The large development of the wings fits the great importance of these sense organs in swimming.

The brains of other fish are on rather the same pattern as that of the dogfish, reflecting a generally similar mode of life. The cerebral hemispheres of teleosts are somewhat expanded, with a thin roof and most of the gray matter on the floor. The olfactory lobes are relatively smaller, and removed to some distance from the hemispheres on long, thin stalks. A saccus vasculosus is present and the mid-brain is well developed, being, as in sharks, the chief association center. The cerebellum is perhaps relatively smaller than in elasmobranchs, particularly in the wings. But in some, the mormyrids, it has a huge extension both fore and aft; this is connected with a great development of the lateral line in these fish.

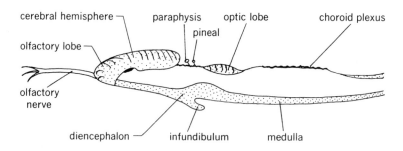

FIG. 13.12   Diagram of the right half of the brain of *Necturus maculosus*, cut sagittally, x 3.

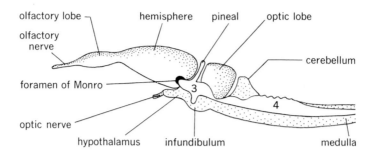

olfactory lobe ⌐ hemisphere pineal optic lobe

olfactory
nerve

cerebellum

foramen of Monro

3

4

optic nerve

hypothalamus infundibulum medulla

FIG. 13.13 Diagram of the right half of the brain of a lizard, *Lacerta agilis*, cut sagittally, x 8.

In some respects the brain of an amphibian (Fig. 13.12) is less well developed than that of a fish. This is because, whatever may be the case with its reasoning power or intelligence, its mode of movement, by creeping or slow swimming or blind leaping, does not require the same degree of rapid co-ordination or adjustment to the outside world as does the fast swimming of a typical fish. The olfactory lobes are small and hardly distinguishable from the cerebral hemispheres, which are themselves not well developed. They do, however, show the beginning of the concentration of the gray matter on the outside to form the cerebral cortex or pallium (or archipallium), a tendency which goes much further in other tetrapods. The pineal is small and there is no parapineal. The mid-brain of anurans is large, with two big optic lobes, reflecting the increasing importance of sight in land animals, but in urodeles its roof is undivided. The cerebellum is very much reduced, matching the absence or reduction of the lateral line system.

The reptiles show further development of several parts of the brain (Fig. 13.13). The olfactory lobes, though not large, are distinct from the cerebral hemispheres, except in chelonians. The hemispheres themselves are large and beginning to show the shape and twin form so characteristic of the higher vertebrates. The cortex is enlarged, so that it covers the corpus striatum lying below it, which is no longer visible in a dorsal view. There are bands of fibers connecting the cerebrum to the thalamencephalon, and where these enter they make the beginning of the neopallium, which becomes important in mammals.

The tween-brain of reptiles is notable because in *Sphenodon* and some lizards the parapineal body is well enough developed to be visible on the outer surface and to be recognizable as an eye in section. It was first discovered by Moseley as the result of a chance observation of something odd on the head of *Sphenodon* in a practical class at Oxford. The pineal body also is well developed, except in crocodiles. The dorsal part of the thalamus is much more strongly developed than in amphibians and fish, and sends fibers forward, as we have seen, to the hemispheres.

The mid-brain has two large and well-marked optic lobes which meet the hemispheres so that the tween-brain is hardly visible in a dorsal view.

The cerebellum varies considerably. In lizards and *Sphenodon* the body is a small transverse band scarcely larger than that of amphibians, but in snakes it is larger, and in crocodiles and chelonians it is large and prominent. In the crocodiles especially, where it has two transverse furrows on its surface, it foreshadows the condition in birds. One cannot easily account for the difference between the various reptile brains, for although crocodiles may be, as large carnivorous animals, in need of good co-ordination, the lizards as a group are at least as active as the tortoises. In all reptiles the wings of the cerebellum are represented by a small flocculus on each side. Unlike the lower vertebrates, the reptiles have a layer of white matter inside the gray in the cerebellum.

The brain of the pterodactyls has some remarkable resemblances to that of birds. As in them the markings inside the skull show that it fitted closely to the brain and the size of the various parts is thus known. The olfactory lobes were small and the optic lobes large, their ratio in size being about 1:25, whereas in *Sphenodon* it is 1:1. The cerebellum is enlarged and extends forward, sometimes meeting the fore-brain, so pushing the optic lobes to one side. These features are more marked in the later fossils, suggesting that the pterodactyls were becoming more highly adapted to flight before they became extinct.

The birds have relatively large brains (Fig. 13.14), and the great development of the eyes, which as they enlarge grow inward and constrict the front part of the skull so that they almost meet, means that the cranial cavity is much more nearly spherical, instead of being elongated as in fish, amphibians, and reptiles, and the brain has to be adjusted in shape to fit it. The tendency to width at the expense of length is encouraged also by the increase in the size of the cerebral hemispheres and the cerebellum, both in proportion to the rest of the brain and in proportion to the size of the body. The mass of the brain of a bird is about ten times that of a reptile of equal size.

The olfactory lobes are not very clearly marked off from the hemispheres and are always small; in some passerine birds they are hardly recognizable at all. This accords with the general experimental evidence that birds are very insensitive to smell, and that some of them may not be able to smell at all. Only a few, such as ducks and especially the kiwi, seem to use the sense for any practical purpose, and these have the largest olfactory lobes. Since they are also, on other grounds, regarded as relatively primitive types, they may be looked on as not having gone so far as most

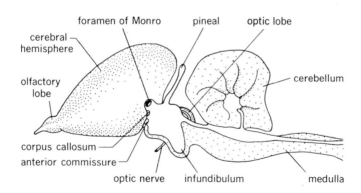

FIG. 13.14 Diagram of the right half of the brain of a pigeon, *Columba livia*, cut sagittally, x 2. The cerebellum has been displaced slightly backward to expose the optic lobe, which it covers in the natural position.

birds in losing both the sense and the nervous equipment that goes with it.

The cerebral hemispheres are large, and their ventricles are practically obliterated. Much of their bulk consists of the corpus striatum, but dorsally there is a thick cortex which is mainly derived from the neopallium, of which only a trace is found in reptiles. The paleopallium, which was largely concerned with smell, is reduced to a small patch on the outer edge, and the archipallium is not much larger. Pigeons from which the cerebral hemispheres have been removed lose their conditioned reflexes and cannot form new ones, but they can see and fly, and although they do not eat they can be kept alive by forced feeding. The hemispheres are not therefore necessary for basic co-ordination, but they are needed for everything beyond this.

The pineal body is large and knobbed, but the diencephalon is small. The optic lobes, which are pushed sideways by the great development of the hemispheres, are large. Moreover, they have a complicated internal structure, more so even than in mammals. This agrees with the extremely good vision of birds and their reliance on this for food gathering, finding a mate, and many other activities. The optic lobes are especially well developed in those birds, such as hawks, that find their prey by sight at a distance.

The cerebellum is large and has several deep transverse fissures with a correspondingly increased cortex. It is concerned largely with the control of movement and balance that is so important in flight. The fourth ventricle is much reduced.

With the mammals we come to the most highly developed of all brains, for while the cerebellum is not so large as in birds the cerebral hemispheres may be even larger and more complicated, and in the primates very much so (Fig. 13.15).

The olfactory lobes are distinct, and larger than in birds. Most mammals find much of their food by smell, and recognize their mates and enemies in the same way. While some have the lobe well developed in accordance with the use that they make of the sense, others have a smaller lobe and use the sense of smell little. That of whales is very small or absent, and they appear to be entirely without a sense of smell.

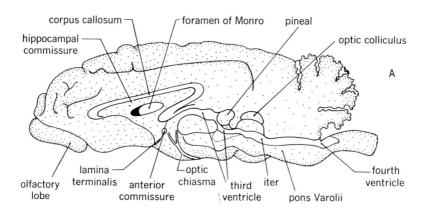

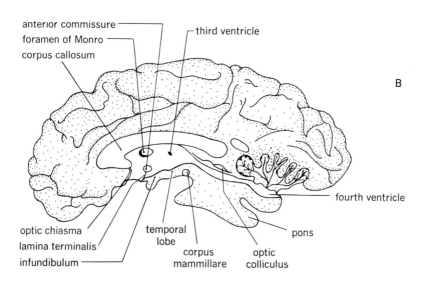

FIG. 13.15   (A) Diagram of the right half of a sheep's brain, cut sagittally, x 1. (B) Diagram of the right half of a human brain, cut sagittally, x 1/2.

The cerebral hemispheres are greatly expanded, and stretch back to cover most of the brain except some of the cerebellum and the medulla. They are almost smooth in what may be called the less intelligent mammals, such as rabbits, rodents, insectivores, and marsupials, but are highly convoluted in the primates, and especially in man. Other orders are intermediate, the most convoluted after the primates being, perhaps surprisingly, the whales. In all mammals a great part of the large hemispheres is made up of an expansion of the middle of their upper part, the neopallium, and its two halves are connected together by a new band of transverse fibers, the callous body (corpus callosum). The neopallium is connected by fibers to all other parts of the brain and to the spinal cord, and is therefore a well-developed association center. Its important part is its surface, and it is the expansion of this to a greater extent than the rest of the brain that leads to the furrows. To some extent particular senses, sight, hearing, and so on, can be assigned to particular parts of the cortex, and another part is concerned with the motor outflow. This part can itself be divided up into regions concerned with particular muscles. There is, however, much overlap, and experiments on a series of rats in turn has shown that no single part of the cortex is either essential to life or connected exclusively with one particular activity. The whole area co-ordinates the impulses that arrive in it and selects appropriately for the right response. In primates an anterior part of the brain, the prefrontal lobe or silent areas (so called because electrical stimulation of them produces no obvious response), seems to be concerned with general attitude, or what is called in man personality or character. Hence comes the partial success of prefrontal leucotomy—cutting the fibers that connect these areas to the rest of the brain—in treating some types of insanity. The areas that can be associated with particular senses show a relationship to the importance of each sense in the life of the animal. That for sight is very large in man, that for the lips, in horses.

The cortex is an extremely complicated three-dimensional network of interconnected neurons. Some idea of its complexity is given by the fact that into each cubic millimeter of that part of the cat's cortex concerned with vision there lead 25,000 afferent fibers, while three times that number of efferent fibers leave it. Reaction to any particular stimulus or input is a matter of selection (not necessarily conscious) from this wide range of possibilities.

In the tween-brain the walls are greatly developed and meet across the middle of the third ventricle, dividing it into upper and lower portions. Its fibers run both forward to the cortex and backward to the rest of the brain, suggesting that it is an important relay station, but little is known of its function. The hypothalamus is highly vascular, and its activities are influenced in various ways by the composition of the blood that flows through it. Much of its action is to send impulses to the pituitary body, which lies below it. The pineal body is present, but the paraphysis disappears in the adult. Among the faculties with which the thalamus is chiefly concerned are temperature regulation and sleep.

The mid-brain of mammals is relatively small, but the optic lobes are now divided so that there are four of them. Only the anterior pair are apparently connected with the eyes, and for the purpose of controlling their movements only. The faculty of vision has been transferred to the cerebral cortex.

The cerebellum of mammals is large and, like that of birds, deeply fissured. It differs from the condition in birds, however, in having two large side pieces, the cerebellar hemispheres, which represent new structures not present in any other animals. Its fibers go through the pons direct to the neopallium of the cerebral cortex, and the two new structures have presumably evolved in parallel. The wings of the primitive cerebellum, which receive the fibers concerned with balance, are represented by the ventral and flattened flocculi. They are relatively large, reflecting the fact that mammals, with their long jointed legs, can stand only by a continual process of adjusting the tensions in the muscles. A real horse has more resemblance than might be supposed to the toys made of hollow pieces of wood through which is threaded string. Just as the model will stand only if the string is under tension, so the horse can stand only if its muscles are in a state of tonus, and the degree of this in antagonistic muscles must be finely balanced. All this is mediated by the cerebellum. As an extension of this function it also smooths out all movements, preventing their going in jerks or passing into oscillation.

Nerves

The central nervous system is useless without the nerves, or peripheral nervous system, to supply it with information and carry away its instructions. (The use of these words, used here metaphorically, must not be taken to imply that the brain is conscious, or knows what it is doing.) These nerves are paired, and primitively at least the series stretches from one end of the body to the other. The central nervous system is formed from a continuous flat plate of cells and is never segmented; the nerves, however, have a segmental pattern impressed on them by the arrangement of the mesoderm. If they are motor, and going to the muscles, they must go individually to the separate myotomes, and so be the same in number and arrangement as those; if they are sensory, and bringing information from the skin, they have to find their way past the muscles, and the easiest way is between the myotomes.

The nerves appear somewhat differently according to whether one looks at the adult animal or follows their development in the embryo. They can be understood much better in the latter way. In the embryo there are at least four bundles of nerve fibers per segment, but as these bundles do not correspond to the nerves of the adult they are called by the descriptive and non-committal name of roots. The simplest are the ventral roots, which grow out as the axons of nerve cells from the ventral horns of the gray matter. The cell body remains within the central nervous system, and the fiber grows to whatever point it has to reach. The fiber is motor, sending impulses out of the brain or spinal cord.

The dorsal roots are different. Nerve cells are formed in the neural crest and never become part of the central system. They grow two processes, and so are called bipolar. One process grows into the dorsal horn of the gray matter, the other grows out into the animal's body, to become a sensory ending. The fiber is therefore afferent. As the cell develops the two processes slide round the cell body until they meet, so that the body is, as it were, left on a side-path. The cell bodies remain outside the central nervous system, and those of one root become aggregated together in a clump to form the dorsal root ganglion.

This simple arrangement is seen, with only slight modifications, in amphioxus. In each segment there is a group of ventral rootlets which go chiefly to the muscles, and a dorsal root which passes between the muscles and chiefly spreads out into the skin. The fact that the myotomes of the two sides are not directly opposite each other, but alternate, means that the nerve roots also alternate. In cyclostomes also, especially lampreys, much of the embryonic arrangement persists in the adults. Each ventral root comes out opposite a myotome, and most of its fibers go direct to this, forming a motor nerve, while the dorsal root comes out opposite a myocomma and goes between the myotomes as a sensory nerve.

In all vertebrates, including the cyclostomes, the segmentation is obscured in the head, and will be left for consideration until Chapter 19. In the rest of the body the segmentation remains, although the farther the nerves go from the central nervous system the less obvious it becomes. The pattern of exit of nerves from the spinal cord is imposed by the vertebrae, for the nerves necessarily go between these.

In gnathostomes the dorsal and ventral roots of one side of a segment join just outside the vertebra to form a single nerve. This almost immediately breaks up into three main branches, which are the nerves as normally dissected. All of these are at first mixed, that is to say, they contain fibers from both dorsal and ventral roots, so that the nerves do not correspond to the roots. It is unfortunate that the two largest branches are known, from their position, as dorsal and ventral.

The fibers of a nerve are classified, according to their function, into four groups, depending on whether they are sensory or motor and on whether they deal with the inner or outer parts of the body. The inner parts of the body are the viscera, the organs that hang or project into the celom, and structures connected with them; the outer parts are the skeletal muscles and the skin. There are then four functional types of fiber.

Somatic sensory fibers receive stimuli and convey messages from the outside world, which may be called the exteroceptive field, and from some parts of the animal's own body, the proprioceptive field. This includes the skeletal muscles and structures such as tendons associated with them. The senses that they mediate are thus touch, temperature, and the unnamed sense of position, by which we can tell approximately (and in the case of the index finger very accurately) where our limbs are in relation to the rest of the body. They are concerned also with pain, and the special or highly developed sense of hearing, when it is present, and the other senses connected with the labyrinth of the ear and the lateral line.

Visceral sensory fibers carry impulses from the viscera and blood vessels, the interoceptive field. There are no sensations connected with most of these, but their importance is shown by the way in which the gut, heart, and bladder respond to various internal conditions. Like the somatic sensory fibers, the visceral sensory fibers carry impulses which give rise to the sensation of pain, while the chemical senses, which in higher animals are confined to surfaces connected with the gut, are also considered as interoceptive.

Somatic motor fibers supply skeletal muscle. They are the fibers whose impulses in man are (or appear to be) under the control of the will. Why we should be able to initiate impulses in this set of fibers and, generally speaking, not in the others, is unknown. The distinction is not, however, absolute, for it is, under certain circumstances, possible for man to initiate impulses in other motor nerve fibers, for example, those that go to the sweat glands.

The visceral motor fibers go to the smooth muscles of the gut, arteries, excretory ducts, bladder, and so on, and to glands. They supply also the skeletal muscles of the jaws, which are derived from the lateral plate mesoblast, which may be regarded as originally part of the gut wall. They have now, however, come to resemble other skeletal muscles.

The distribution of these fibers is shown in diagrammatic form in Fig. 13.16. Although sensory fibers generally come from the dorsal root and motor fibers from the ventral root, this distinction is not absolute, and there appears to have been a change as the vertebrates have evolved. In lampreys all the visceral motor fibers are in the dorsal root, and in fishes and amphibians many are. In amniotes only a few are left, most now coming from the ventral root.

In the head the dorsal and ventral roots do not join to form a mixed nerve, but there is rather more mixture of fibers in the roots. In both these points the head of gnathostomes, in spite of its specialization, appears to retain the state of affairs that was general in primitive vertebrates. The

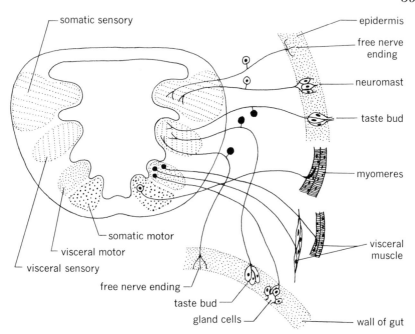

FIG. 13.16 Diagrammatic transverse section of a vertebrate spinal cord to show the composition of the spinal nerves.

skeletal muscles of the head are formed from the myotomes, and are assimilated to them. In the same way the visceral motor fibers that supply them do not seem to differ from the somatic motor fibers, and, like them, in man are under the control of the will. The typical visceral motor fibers differ from the others in that they do not go direct to the structure that their impulses will stimulate. Instead, they end in ganglia, where their telodendrons come into synapse with dendrons of a new set of nerve cells. These constitute the sympathetic or autonomic system, which will be described below. The relationship of the visceral motor fibers to this has led to them being called preganglionic fibers.

The segmental pattern of the nerves means that they vary in number with the number of segments that go to make up the body. Within the skull they are specialized as the cranial nerves; in the tail they are degenerate or non-existent. The typical spinal nerves supply the trunk, and their number ranges from ten in frogs to about a hundred in snakes. It is impossible to make exact homologies between numbered segments in vertebrates except in the anterior part of the head, but there is evidence that in amniotes segments that were originally in the trunk have to some extent been incorporated in the head. Amniotes have more intracranial nerves than fishes, and it seems that the first two or three pairs of spinal nerves have been engulfed by the skull, presumably as a result of the growth of the brain. The relationship of head to trunk is not, however, simple, for the neck, which in its dorsal part can be assimilated to the trunk and has spinal nerves, in its ventral part contains structures, derived from the pharynx, which in fishes are in the head. Segmentation in the vertebrates is no easy guide to understanding structure.

In the tetrapods all trace of segmentation is lost, except in the vertebrae and a few structures close to them. In particular the muscles, even where they begin as segmental myotomes, show no segmentation whatsoever. The result is that soon after they leave the vertebrae the nerves also lose much or all of their segmental pattern. It is clear from the development of limbs, in fish as well as in tetrapods, that each of them is formed in the first place from the unsegmented lateral plate, but that it is soon invaded by tissue from the myotomes. More than one segment contributes to a limb, and so more than one nerve goes to it. Generally these continue either to form a single nerve or to make a network or plexus which sorts itself out into two or three main nerves in a limb. The limb nerves, like all others, branch and become smaller as fibers leave them to go to the parts that they pass.

The pattern of these plexuses, though it may appear arbitrary, is often highly characteristic for a species. In fishes there is little in the way of a true plexus, but several nerves run together to form the brachial nerve. In *Squalus* there are nine (nos. 3-11), and in skates, with their greatly expanded pectoral fin, there may be as many as twenty-five (Fig. 13.18). The brachial plexus supplying the fore-limb in the frog is formed chiefly from the second and third spinal nerves, with a small branch from the first (Fig. 13.17). In mammals only a few nerves go into the fore-limb, but they form a complex plexus; it is made of four nerves in the rabbit, five in the cat (Fig. 13.19) and man, where it comes from the last four cervical segments and the first thoracic.

The sciatic plexus, supplying the hind-limb, is similar in general to the brachial plexus. That of the frog includes branches from the seventh, eighth, ninth, and tenth nerves, so that in this short-bodied animal only three segments are not involved in the limbs. In mammals about seven nerves usually take part, branches from the last few lumbar segments joining with those from the sacral region. In the cat, which has seven lumbar vertebrae and three sacral, the plexus is formed from branches of the fourth to seventh lumbar and first and second sacral nerves, while in man, with only five lumbar vertebrae and five sacral, the plexus comes from the last two lumbar nerves and the first four sacral. This suggests that in man, possibly as an adaptation to his upright stance, the two posterior lumbar vertebrae of other mammals have become incorporated in the sacrum.

There may be other plexuses, particularly in the neck and going from the lumbar region to the genital organs, all of which emphasize the essen-

FIG. 13.17   Brachial plexus of a frog *Rana temporaria*, x 2. Spinal nerves I, II, and III contribute to the brachial nerve.

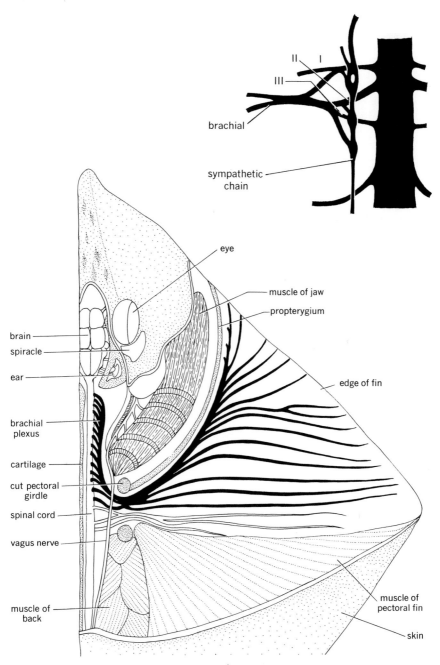

FIG. 13.18   Brachial plexus of a skate, *Raia batis*, x 1/2.

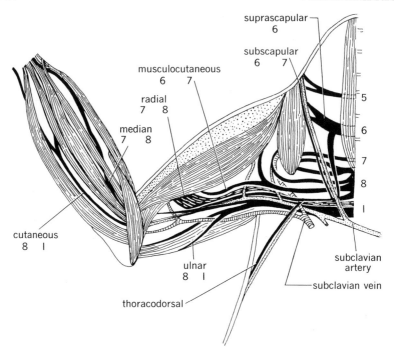

suprascapular
6

subscapular
6   7

musculocutaneous
6   7

radial
7   8

median
7   8

cutaneous
8   I

5

6

7

8

I

subclavian
artery

subclavian vein

ulnar
8   I

thoracodorsal

FIG. 13.19   Brachial plexus of a kitten, x1. 5-8: cervical nerves; I: the first spinal nerve.

tial loss of segmentation. In mammals a plexus is formed from two or three nerves in the neck (numbers four, five, and six in the rabbit, three, four, and five in man, five and six in the cat) to form the phrenic nerve, which runs back through the thorax to supply the diaphragm.

In the head of adult vertebrates no segmentation can be seen, except in fish in the pharyngeal region, where it is marked by the gill slits and their skeleton, musculature, and blood supply, but by embryological studies some of the cranial nerves can be recognized as the dorsal or ventral roots of segmental nerves. That is to say, they have the same type of origin as the spinal nerves described above; they have the same sort of relationship to the myotomes; and the ventral roots have the same relationship to the autonomic system. Dorsal and ventral roots, however, remain separate. Other cranial nerves do not fit into this pattern, and their origin is different. Since all are seen together and look alike, except for their size and position, in dissection, it is still convenient to consider them as a group; discussion of their segmental arrangement will be left until later. The standard nomenclature is derived, as usual, from the anatomy of mammals, and is not entirely appropriate to fish, but is too well established to be changed. Moreover, one nerve, the terminal, was unknown when the standard numbering was laid down, and two other nerves are found only in fish and amphibians. Roman numerals are customary.

A bare list, with the place of origin and main distribution, is as follows:

I   OLFACTORY   From the anterior (originally lateral) end of the olfactory lobe to the nasal epithelium

I A   TERMINAL   From the medial surface of the olfactory lobe to the nasal epithelium, especially Jacobson's organ

II   OPTIC   From the diencaphalon through the optic chiasma to the eye

III   OCULOMOTOR   From the mid-brain to the eyeball

IV   TROCHLEAR (= PATHETIC)   From the mid-brain to the eyeball

V   TRIGEMINAL   From the medulla to the mandibular segment

V A   DEEP OPHTHALMIC BRANCH OF THE TRIGEMINAL   From the medulla to the snout

VI   ABDUCENT   From the medulla to the eyeball

VII   FACIAL   From the medulla to the hyoidean segment

VIII   AUDITORY   From the medulla to the labyrinth

VIII A ANTERIOR LATERAL   From the medulla to the anterior lateral line canals

IX   GLOSSOPHARYNGEAL   From the medulla to the region of the first gill slit

X   VAGUS (= PNEUMOGASTRIC)   By several roots to the region of the remaining gill slits, with a long, caudally running visceral branch

X A   POSTERIOR LATERAL   From the medulla to the posterior lateral line canals

XI   ACCESSORY (= SPINAL ACCESSORY)   From the medulla to the occiput

XII   HYPOGLOSSAL   From the medulla to the tongue

The olfactory nerve is sometimes said not to be a nerve at all, but this is playing with words. It is not, however, a segmental nerve, and does not originate in either of the ways that we have described for the dorsal and the ventral roots. It consists of fibers whose cell bodies are in the nasal epithelium, and constitute in fact its sensitive part. They are sense cells which are formed from epithelium and are never part of the central nervous system or of the neural folds. Their axons grow back until they meet the fore-brain, where they form synapses; they remain unmedullated. This type of sensory nerve, with the cell body far from the central nervous system and in the sense organ, is the normal thing for all types of sense organ in invertebrates, but is unusual in vertebrates. Except for varying in diameter with the importance of the distant chemical sense in the life of the animal, and in length with the shape of the head, the olfactory nerve does not differ much throughout the vertebrates. It is notable in mammals, where smell is very important, for being multiple, so that it goes through the skull to reach the brain not by a single foramen but by a whole sieve of them, which give a characteristic appearance to the mesethmoid bone that makes the front wall of the skull.

The terminal nerve was for long unknown (hence its lack of a number) and was first described in elasmobranchs. Here it enters the olfactory lobe on its medial surface; it has since been found in all vertebrates except birds. There are always near its entry into the brain or on its length cell bodies which may make a ganglion. It seems that these are sense cells which have moved toward the brain from their original position, which, like that of the cells of the olfactory nerve, was in the nasal epithelium. No physiological work on the terminal nerve seems to have been done, but its peripheral ends are among those of the olfactory nerve, and it presumably subserves the distant chemical sense. In mammals, reptiles, and to some degree in Amphibia, it is closely associated with Jacobson's organ, which is anatomically a specialization of the nose. It seems therefore as if the terminal nerve has taken on the special function of picking up stimuli and conveying impulses from this organ. Whether it is concerned with any particular type of smell is unknown. The absence, or at least the very small size, of the terminal nerve in birds is presumably connected with the poor sense of smell in these creatures.

The second or optic nerve is even less of a nerve than is the olfactory. As the brain grows, two bulges grow out laterally from the tween-brain, and in a somewhat complicated way (see Chapter 14) make most of the eyes except the cornea and humors. In particular, the layers of cells that in the brain become nerve cells become in the eye the retina or sensitive part, which may thus be looked on as a part of the brain that has removed to near the surface of the body. From the originally innermost cells of the retina (in fact they are now on that surface of this which lies against the vitreous humor) axons grow back to make the fibers of the optic nerve, until they meet the brain in the floor of the thalamencephalon. In the lower vertebrates they run on to the optic lobes, where they make synapses in the usual way. In amniotes they have synapses in the diencephalon, from which relays go to the cerebral hemispheres. The optic nerves are therefore similar in origin to the tracts of fibers that run from one part of the brain to another, for example, from the thalamus to the cerebral hemispheres. They are, as it were, lengths of white matter of the central nervous system which are physically outside that system.

The optic chiasma has already been mentioned in the description of the brain. Where it is complete, as it is in nearly all vertebrates, the fibers of one side may go through a hole made by the separation of the fibers of the other, or the bundles of fibers of the two sides may interpenetrate each other.

Nerves III, IV, and VI, the oculomotor, trochlear, and abducent, are conveniently taken together. All are motor, and all supply chiefly the small striped muscles that move the eyeball. Study of the development of these, especially in elasmobranchs, has shown that they are derived from the myotomes of the head; or rather, of the only myotomes in the head that give rise to anything recognizable. The most posterior myotome forms the posterior rectus muscle; the middle one forms the superior oblique; and the anterior one the other four that complete the normal set—superior, inferior, and anterior rectus, and inferior oblique. Nerves VI, IV, and III supply these muscles in the same pattern, as is easily seen in a dissection of the dogfish. The mode of origin of the nerves is normal, and it is therefore obvious that they are the ventral or motor roots of the three segments.

Almost all vertebrates have the standard pattern of four rectus and two oblique eyeball muscles, and they are always innervated in the same way. A few vertebrates have extra muscles, such as the retractor bulbi of frogs, which pulls the eye back into its socket. These are usually supplied by a special branch of the oculomotor nerve.

Nerves V, VII, IX, and XI also form a natural group, since they all supply the region of the gill slits and are called branchial nerves. They include both sensory and visceral motor fibers, and may be regarded as dorsal roots; their allocation to segments is a little difficult. The standard pattern is for each nerve to run toward a gill slit, and then to divide into a pretrematic branch in front of it and a posttrematic behind it, but many have other branches as well. The posttrematic branch is taken as running to the region of the segment to which the nerve belongs, the pretrematic branch to the one in front, but it must be remembered that the lateral plate musculature, in which the gill slits are formed, is not strictly segmented. There is a general tendency for the branchial nerves to form plexuses with one another. As dorsal roots, consisting mainly of efferent fibers, the branchial nerves have ganglia outside the brain, corresponding to the dorsal root ganglia of the spinal nerves.

The fifth nerve, or trigeminal, is, in terms of segmentation, double. Its deep ophthalmic branch, which runs forward through the orbit to the region of the face in front of the eye, is in origin separate from the other branches and has its own ganglion. In adults this is usually fused with the ganglion of the rest of the trigeminal, but two distinct, though joined, ganglia persist in birds. The deep ophthalmic is purely sensory, and is the dorsal root of the premandibular segment whose ventral root is the oculomotor. It is small in dogfish and was for long said to be absent from *Scyliorhinus*; it is, however, present in some individuals. Throughout the vertebrates there is a tendency for it to join the superficial ophthalmic branch of the trigeminal, and in mammals the two are fused.

The trigeminal proper is the dorsal root of the mandibular segment, and its ganglion is the Gasserian; its pretrematic and posttrematic branches run to the upper and lower jaws respectively, so giving support to the suggestion that the mouth represents two fused gill slits. This first branch, called maxillary, innervates the skin between the mouth and the eye, and is somatic sensory. In tetrapods it becomes associated with a branch of the seventh nerve and innervates also the palate, so taking on a visceral sensory function. The posttrematic branch, called the mandibular, is chiefly visceral motor and goes to the muscles of the jaw; these are, however, skeletal muscles, and, in man, voluntary. It has also somatic sensory fibers, and innervates the region of the chin and cheek. In tetrapods it runs also into the mouth and especially to the tongue.

The superficial ophthalmic runs through the orbit higher up than the deep ophthalmic. It supplies the same part of the head and has the same function.

The seventh or facial is a typical branchial nerve, and its ganglion is called geniculate. Its posttrematic branch runs behind the spiracle (when that is present) so that it is the dorsal root of the hyoidean segment. The visceral motor fibers run in a branch of the posttrematic (or postspiracular) called the hyoidean or external mandibular, and supply the muscles of the hyoid arch. These muscles are replaced in tetrapods, as the hyoid ceases to be used in breathing, by some muscles of the face, which continue to be innervated by this nerve. It contains also visceral sensory fibers.

Another branch of the posttrematic of the seventh nerve, the internal mandibular, is visceral sensory and goes to the mucous surface of the lower jaw and buccal cavity, where it is largely concerned with taste. In amniotes it is a large nerve, sometimes called the chorda tympani because of its relationship to the tympanum or eardrum, and is associated with the maxillary branch of the trigeminal to innervate the tongue. In mammals the two nerves join to form a lingual.

There is some confusion in the nomenclature of other branches of the facial nerve. A small prespiracular branch leaves the main trunk of the nerve in dogfish and runs just in front of the spiracle; it is visceral sensory and seems to be in the position of a pretrematic branch. But some authors give this name to a more superficial branch, also visceral sensory, which runs to the roof of the buccal cavity and is better known as the palatine. These sensory fibers become few, or perhaps entirely disappear, in amniotes.

In many teleosts a new branch of the facial (Weber's nerve) runs to the skin of the body to one side of the backbone. It is visceral-sensory, and supplies the taste buds which in these fish are scattered over the whole body.

The ninth nerve, or glossopharyngeal, is relatively simple, with a petrosal ganglion which may be divided into proximal and distal parts. Its main or posttrematic branch goes behind the first gill slit and has sensory and motor fibers. Some of the former run within the buccal cavity, and in mammals supply the posterior third of the tongue, hence the name of the nerve. The pretrematic branch, and its sub-branch the dorsal pharyngeal, are sensory only.

The tenth nerve, or pneumogastric or vagus, has several roots, and since in fishes it goes to all the gill slits except the first it is obviously a compound nerve. Its ganglion, the vagus, may be divided into a proximal jugular ganglion and a distal nodosum. In dogfish the branches correspond to the number of gill slits, and each subdivides into a pretrematic and a posttrematic branch in the usual way. Much of this is lost in amniotes, but there are then generally four branches, supplying the muscles of the tongue (which are largely derived from those of the branchial skeleton) by visceral motor fibers and having largely lost their sensory fibers. There are also, however, two important sensory branches of the tenth nerve, the anterior laryngeal and the recurrent laryngeal. Both supply the larynx, but while the former goes there directly from the vagus ganglion, the latter runs down the neck almost to the heart, loops round a blood vessel, and then runs forward to the larynx. This happens because it is formed in such a position that as the heart moves relatively backward in development the nerve is dragged with it.

In all vertebrates a branch of the tenth nerve runs backward into the thorax and abdomen, and it is this alone that should strictly be called the vagus. It is visceral sensory, and supplies heart, stomach, intestine, and viscera generally. In tetrapods it supplies the lungs, and so gets its name of pneumogastric. It is unfortunate that the tenth nerve has no descriptive name that is appropriate for it in fish.

In mammals a conspicuous sensory branch of the tenth nerve, the auricular, or great auricular, supplies the pinna of the ear.

The eleventh nerve, or spinal accessory, found only in mammals, is a detached motor branch, presumably the last, of the vagus, which becomes associated with the first spinal nerve. Since the number of segments within the skull is not fixed, no strict homology is possible in this region.

Similarly, the twelfth nerve, or hypoglossal, is not represented inside the head in fishes, and is taken to represent a cervical spinal nerve that has become included in the head, or since it usually has four roots it may represent more of these. It is somatic motor and supplies the tongue, and corresponds, in position at least, to the ventral roots of the posterior branchial segments, of which the vagus and spinal accessory are the dorsal roots.

We broke the numerical series so as to take all the branchial nerves together, and must now return to the last numbered nerve, the eighth, or auditory or acoustic. It is a sensory nerve, but is concerned with much more than hearing, since it supplies all the parts of the labyrinth, whether they are concerned with appreciation of position, movement, balance, or acceleration. It has an anterior branch running to the anterior portion of the labyrinth, including the utriculus, and a posterior branch, running to the posterior part of the labyrinth, including the sacculus and its derivatives the lagena and cochlea. In amniotes the posterior branch has two distinct sub-branches, a cochlear which is auditory in function and a vestibular which goes to the parts of the labyrinth that are not concerned with hearing.

The ganglia of the eighth nerve are originally within the cranium, but may move out into the ear.

In the ordinary dissection of a dogfish one sees some branches of the branchial nerves which have not been mentioned above. These are the ones which supply the sense organs of the lateral line and associated organs, and hence are now often called lateral nerves. They are reducible to two main trunks, an anterior lateral nerve associated with the facial nerve, and a posterior lateral which appears as a branch of the vagus. The anterior lateral nerve appears as two main branches. One runs forward close to the superficial ophthalmic branch of the trigeminal and supplies the ampullae of the lateral line organs on the snout; it is known as the superficial ophthalmic branch of the facial. The other runs across the orbit with the maxillary branch of the trigeminal and supplies the organs on the side of the head; it is called the buccal branch of the facial. The posterior lateral nerve, or lateral line branch of the vagus, supplies the lateral line organs of the branchial region, and its main trunk runs backward down the body even to the tail, and is the nerve of the lateral line itself.

The actual branching and pattern of these nerves depend on the presence and distribution of the lateral line organs. In teleosts additional lateral fibers run in Weber's nerve, and in amphibians, where there are three more or less parallel lateral lines, the posterior lateral nerve branches accordingly. They are not present where the lateral line organs have been lost, as in most adult anurans and in all amniotes.

On some of the extinct cephalaspids it is possible to see the imprints of the cranial nerves in the fossils, and it appears that in some there were lateral line branches for all the branchial nerves. This seems a logical arrangement, and it is simplest to think of the lateral line system as an organ of special sense in the head, supplied by special branches of the appropriate dorsal roots, that is, the fifth, seventh, ninth, and tenth nerves. Of these, only those of the seventh and tenth nerves now usually remain, but *Petromyzon* has lateral fibers in the deep ophthalmic. If, as is generally held, the labyrinth is a specialization of the lateral line system which has sunk into the head, the eighth nerve can also be looked on as a special sensory branch of the dorsal root of the appropriate segment, that is, of the facial nerve, with which it is in origin closely associated.

The sympathetic or autonomic system has been briefly defined above (p. 259). All spinal nerves of mammals have preganglionic fibers that run to sympathetic ganglia from which the autonomic system starts, but, as might be expected from the simple nature of the cranial nerves, preganglionic fibers are present only in some of them, namely, the oculomotor, facial, glossopharyngeal, and vagus—that is, chiefly in the branchial nerves, or those which can be regarded as dorsal roots. The preganglionic or visceral motor fibers are present only in the posttrematic branches; since they are present in the vagus branch of the tenth nerve this must be considered as posttrematic. Fibers from the maxillary branch of the trigeminal which run to the sympathetic ganglion supplied by the facial do not end there, but run through it and continue as sensory nerves. The presence of visceral motor fibers in the oculomotor nerve, which is a ventral root, is an unexplained anomaly.

The condition of the trigeminal nerve is anomalous in the opposite way, for although a dorsal root it has no preganglionic fibers. The status of the deep ophthalmic is doubtful. It sends a branch to the ganglion of the oculomotor, but the classical view is that its fibers do not enter any synapses. They have been described as doing so, however, in the chick, and if this is so, this first branchial nerve has preganglionic fibers like the other dorsal cranial nerves.

The autonomic system gets its name from the fact that it is a law unto itself; man cannot (or can very seldom) control the contraction of his intestine, the beating of his heart, and the secretion of his glands, by taking thought. All these things are, however, under very fine automatic control, and they are all easily influenced by the emotions—by fear, hate, love, temper, and so on. This suggests that they have a relationship to the endocrine system, and in fact many of them are controlled both by hormones and by nerves. Fine anatomical investigations show that most of the viscera have a double innervation, and that stimulation of the one set of nerves induces activity, of the other inactivity. This has led to the division of the autonomic or sympathetic system into the sympathetic system proper (or orthosympathetic) and the parasympathetic. The original division was worked out largely on the basis of the response of the nerves to drugs, but a more rational distinction can now be made. While the ends of the parasympathetic nerves act on the muscles and glands by liberating acetylcholine, just as the ordinary motor nerves do at their motor end plates, the ends of the sympathetic nerves act by liberating a substance called sympathin. The nature of this has been elusive, but it is, at least in some mammals, identical with noradrenaline, a compound closely similar to the adrenaline fromed by the adrenal glands. The different mode of mediation

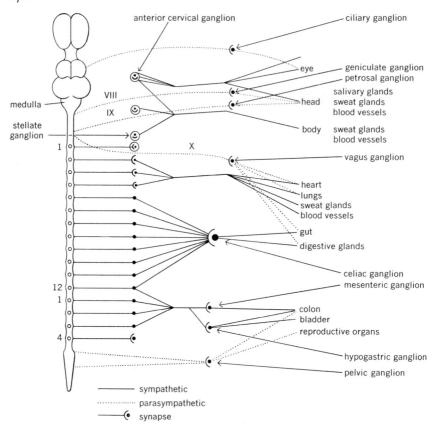

FIG. 13.20   Diagram of the autonomic system of a mammal; only the chief
connections are shown. The first and twelfth thoracic nerves and the first and
fourth lumbars are shown.

of their effects would account for the different actions of drugs on the two
sets of nerves. There are a few exceptions to this rule; the orthosympathetic
nerves to the sweat gland, for example, produce sympathin in some mammals, but acetylocholine in others.

A single diagram (Fig. 13.20) shows the arrangement of both systems
in the mammal; other vertebrates approximate to this, and the differences
will be considered later. The sympathetic system originates from the spinal
nerves of the thoracic and lumbar regions. Each of these has a preganglionic branch, or white ramus communicans or connecting branch, which
runs to a ganglion in the same segment. These ganglia are usually on each
side of the dorsal aorta, and are connected by longitudinally-running

fibers, which are continuations of those of the white connecting branches. There are also fibers running across from the ganglion on one side to its fellow on the other. Fibers also run forward to ganglia in the neck, which have lost their direct connection with their own spinal nerves.

The sum of all this is a double series of connected ganglia running most of the length of the body; they are well seen in the dissection of a mud puppy or a frog, since they become visible, lying on each side of the dorsal aorta, when the viscera have been carefully removed. In other vertebrates they take rather more skill in their finding.

It is easy to see under the microscope that the ganglia contain large numbers of nerve cells, which give them their bulk, but it is more difficult to see whether they contain synapses that are interpolated on any particular nervous pathway. This is investigated by applying to the ganglion the drug nicotine, which blocks the transmission of a nervous impulse across a synapse. If this abolishes the response that an organ previously gave to stimulation of a preganglionic fiber, one may assume that a synapse is present on that path. Experiments of this sort have shown that all the sympathetic ganglia in mammals have synapses between the preganglionic fibers and the postganglionic fibers (or gray rami communicantes, because they are non-medullated) that run from the ganglia back to the spinal nerves. They run in these and are distributed to various parts of the body, but especially to the skin. Excitation of a gray ramus causes, for example, erection of the hairs of a cat on a narrow band of the body corresponding to one segment, but excitation of a white connecting nerve causes erection over a wider area, showing that its fibers have synapses with gray fibers of several segments.

Some of the ganglia also contain synapses from which nerves pass direct to other structures. These are the ganglia in the neck (superior and inferior cervical), and the anterior three or four thoracic ganglia, usually condensed into a single stellate ganglion. From these, nerves go to the eye (through the ciliary ganglion, see below), salivary glands, sweat glands, blood vessels, heart, and lungs. Where it is appropriate, as on the way to the blood vessels of the limbs, these fibers run with the nerves, such as the brachial, derived from spinal roots.

White preganglionic fibers continue through most of the thoracic and lumbar ganglia without synapses, and run to join together in the abdomen to form two or three splanchnic nerves. Each of these runs to a ganglion in the abdominal cavity close to the dorsal wall. In each ganglion are synapses, from which non-medullated fibers run to all the abdominal viscera, including the urogenital organs. The most conspicuous of these ganglia is the most anterior, called celiac or semilunar, or, with its associated network of nerves, the solar plexus. It is easily seen in the dissection of a

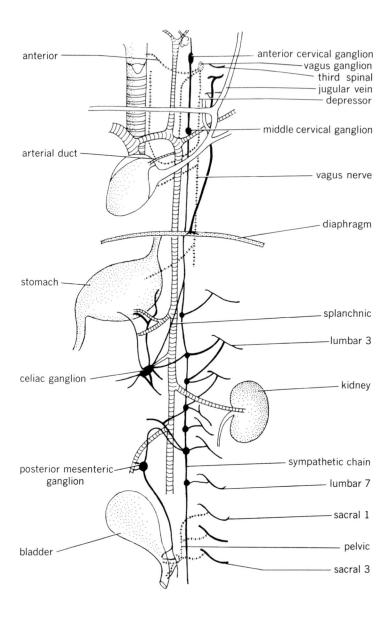

anterior

anterior cervical ganglion
vagus ganglion
third spinal
jugular vein
depressor

middle cervical ganglion

arterial duct

vagus nerve

diaphragm

stomach

splanchnic

lumbar 3

celiac ganglion

kidney

posterior mesenteric
ganglion

sympathetic chain

lumbar 7

sacral 1

pelvic

bladder

sacral 3

FIG. 13.21 Semi-diagrammatic drawing of the orthosympathetic system and
the parasympathetic system of the neck and sacral region of a rabbit, *Oryctolagus cuniculus*, x 1/2. Only the chief trunks are shown and the sympathetic
cord is shown on the left side only.

mammal below the dorsal aorta, near the origin of the anterior mesenteric artery. The postganglionic fibers form the plexus of Meissner and the plexus of Auerbach in the wall of the small intestine.

We have defined the parasympathetic system physiologically, and this is the only meaningful way of doing so, but it is also distinct anatomically (Fig. 13.21). Its preganglionic fibers arise from the cranial nerves, the third, seventh, ninth, and tenth, as discussed above, and from a short group of spinal nerves in the sacral region. The fibers run to ganglia, as do those of the sympathetic outflow, and after synapses in the ganglia postganglionic fibers run as nerves to various structures.

From the ganglion of the oculomotor nerve, which is called ciliary, they go to the moving parts within the eye—the iris and ciliary muscles. From the geniculate ganglion of the facial nerve they run in the tympanic nerve to the submaxillary and sublingual salivary glands, and to the lacrimal gland and to the blood vessels and mucous surfaces of the same region. From the petrosal ganglion of the glossopharyngeal nerve they run to the parotid salivary gland and to the blood vessels and mucous surfaces of the corresponding region, including the posterior part of the tongue.

The vagus outflow is the most important of the sources of parasympathetic fibers. From its ganglion they run in the vagus nerve to almost all the viscera except the bladder and the reproductive organs: lungs, liver, pancreas, kidney, and the gut as far back as the colon. A special large nerve, the cardiac depressor, takes them to the heart.

The function of the autonomic system is to control what may be called the visceral functions of the body, those that go on whether the animal is sleeping or waking, doing something active or nothing in particular. The secretion and movements of the intestine, the beating of the heart, the maintenance of tone in the arteries, are examples. It covers also some things which are by nature intermittent, such as sweating, micturition, and the contraction of the involuntary muscles of the sexual parts. Many of the structures concerned have a double innervation, and are supplied by fibers of both the sympathetic and the parasympathetic systems. When this is so, the two usually act antagonistically, stimulation of one set of nerves having the opposite effect to stimulation of the other. Examples are that the pupil of the eye is dilated by the sympathetic, constricted by the parasympathetic; the sympathetic quickens the heart beat, the parasympathetic slows it; the sympathetic stops movement of the small intestine, the parasympathetic increases it; the sympathetic inhibits erection of the penis, the parasympathetic induces it. In other cases the actions of the two systems, though not antagonistic, are different; for example, while that of the sympathetic produces a small amount of sticky saliva, that of the parasympathetic produces large quantities of a watery secretion.

The distribution and properties of the two systems in mammals may be summed up as follows:

SYMPATHETIC	PARASYMPATHETIC
From most spinal nerves	From selected cranial nerves and a few sacral spinal nerves
White connector neurons (preganglionic fibers) to sympathetic ganglia near vertebrae or to ganglia in mesenteries (celiac, anterior, and posterior mesenteric)	Long nerves to distant ganglia or plexuses, in or near effectors
Ganglia joined by longitudinal cords made of branches of preganglionic fibers	Ganglia discrete

Gray postganglionic fibers join spinal nerves and supply
    sweat glands
    muscles of hairs
    larynx
    heart
	Postganglionic fibers from oculomotor to intrinsic eye muscles;
	from facial and glossopharyngeal to tongue and salivary glands;
	from vagus to heart
	    lungs

Long postganglionic fibers sometimes running with spinal nerves, to
    arteries
    viscera
    urethra
    bladder
    copulatory organs
	alimentary canal as far as colon;
	from sacral nerves to
	    rectum
	    bladder
	    copulatory organs

Accelerates cardiac muscle	Slows cardiac muscle
Contracts arteries, hence produces pallor	Dilates arteries, hence produces flushing and erection
Dilates pupil	Contracts pupil
Inhibits peristalsis	Increases peristalsis
Relaxes bladder and contracts its sphincter	Contracts bladder and relaxes its sphincter, hence produces micturition
Causes secretion of mucus in saliva	Causes secretion of watery saliva
Causes erection of hairs (gooseflesh)	No effect on hairs
Causes secretion of adrenal medulla	No effect on adrenal gland
Liberates sympathin = noradrenaline	Liberates acetylcholine

The autonomic system thus plays an important part in the life of the animal, and it is perhaps surprising that it is found at its full development, in the form in which we have described it, only in the mammals. Perhaps its selective value has been that it has freed the rest of the peripheral nervous system, the spinal and cranial nerves as generally understood, and their connecting tracts in the spinal cord and brain, for the more special functions, especially associated with learned actions, in which the higher vertebrates excel the lower.

Nothing that really corresponds to the autonomic system has been found in the protochordates, and although a sympathetic system is usually said to be present in lampreys, the equivalence of most of it to that of gnathostomes seems doubtful. Stimulation of the vagus accelerates the heart beat, instead of depressing it, and acceleration is produced also by acetylcholine, while adrenaline has no clear effect. Whatever the normal mechanism of its control of the heart, therefore, it is not the same as in other vertebrates. It may be that this is a degenerate condition, for *Myxine* has no known nerve supply to its heart and acetylcholine produces no effect. But just as probably the condition may be primitive, for it must be remembered that the hearts of embryos beat satisfactorily long before any nerves reach them. The vagus of lampreys goes also to the intestine, which has practically no other nerve supply. Something like a sacral parasympathetic out-flow goes to the cloaca, rectum, and ureters, but the nerve cells are scattered, so that there are no true ganglia and the so-called postganglionic fibers are such only in name. They do, however, supply the viscera after the nervous impulse has passed a synapse, and to that extent agree with the autonomic system of mammals.

Similar scattered secondary neurons are interpolated between fibers from both the dorsal and the ventral roots of the trunk nerves, and so make something of a sympathetic system, but the majority of the visceral motor fibers run directly to their organs without a relay. They cannot therefore be considered as similar to the sympathetic fibers of gnathostomes.

The sympathetic ganglia of elasmobranchs (Fig. 13.22) are irregular, and only approximately segmental, presumably showing that some fusion has taken place. They lie above the posterior cardinal sinus and above the kidneys and are connected irregularly by longitudinal connectives. They do not send nerves forward into the head and they do not have gray rami running to the spinal nerves. Hence the skin appears to be without sympathetic nerves, and in correspondence with this its chromatophores appear to be under endocrine control only. The parasympathetic is formally present in the head, since the ganglia are visible on the cranial nerves and the vagus runs back to the viscera as usual. Little, however, is known of how they act; obviously there cannot be antagonistic control of the intrinsic muscles of the eye, for the sympathetic system does not reach them. The stomach is the only organ that certainly possesses motor fibers from both the vagus and the spinal nerves, and they are additive, not antagonis-

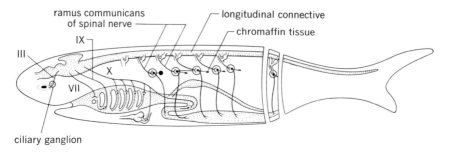

ramus communicans
of spinal nerve

longitudinal connective

chromaffin tissue

IX

III

X

VII

ciliary ganglion

FIG. 13.22   The sympathetic system of a dogfish. (Modified from Young, *Quart. J. Micr. Sci. 75*, 1933)

tic, in their action. There seems to be no nervous control of the digestive glands. Nothing is known of any sacral parasympathetic outflow.

It is impossible to say how far the autonomic system of the dogfish, with its obvious deficiencies, is primitive, and how far it is degenerate.

The autonomic system of teleosts approaches that of tetrapods. There is a chain of sympathetic ganglia, of which the three most anterior are associated with the vagus, the glossopharyngeal, facial, and trigeminal nerves. They do not, however, receive preganglionic fibers from these, but, as do the cervical ganglia of mammals, from forward-running branches from the trunk. A branch also goes to the ciliary ganglion. There are gray rami, and the chromatophores in the skin are under nervous control.

There are fibers from the oculomotor nerve to the iris, and a well-developed vagus which does not, however, reach the intestine, and apparently no other nerves that could be called parasympathetic. The antagonism of the two systems is not clear, and it is probably best not to use the terms sympathetic and parasympathetic. In the iris, where there is an antagonism, it is in the reverse sense to that in mammals, for stimulation of the spinal nerves produces contraction of the pupil, stimulation of the oculomotor causes dilatation. In some viscera, innervation is by one or the other type only—the heart from the vagus, the intestine from the spinal nerves, the stomach sometimes from both, sometimes from the vagus only. The swim bladder has double innervation, the vagus probably inducing secretion of gas and the spinal nerves absorption. Nothing seems to be known of the control of the digestive glands.

The Amphibia show an autonomic system comparable to that of mammals, and with some development of the antagonistic action of sympathetic and parasympathetic systems. The preganglionic spinal fibers run forward into the head, but, since there is no neck, there are no detached ganglia corresponding to the cervical ganglia of mammals. *Necturus* is peculiar in having an accessory line of sympathetic nerves outside and parallel to the normal sympathetic trunk. There is no concentration of the anterior thoracic ganglia into a single stellate ganglion, but in anurans the synapses of the abdominal outflow of nerves four to seven are partly removed to a celiac ganglion on the celiacomesenteric artery. Most of the postganglionic fibers that return to the spinal nerves are medullated and so as white as the preganglionic fibers, instead of being, like those of mammals, gray. The system is much simpler than in the mammal, though in principle the same. The parasympathetic outflow in the head goes through the oculomotor and branchial nerves, and for the first time there is, in anurans but not in urodeles, a sacral parasympathetic outflow as well.

There is much double innervation of the viscera—of the esophagus, stomach, rectum and bladder, and heart—but the experiments on these are confused and to some extent contradictory. The only organ in which there is an undoubted antagonistic effect is the heart, and this behaves just like the heart of mammals. Adrenaline, or stimulation of the sympathetic nerves, causes increased frequency and amplitude of contraction, acetylcholine and stimulation of the vagus the reverse. To this extent at least then the amphibians have a proper sympathetic-parasympathetic arrangement. It may be that this is true also of the other viscera, the contradictory results being explained as due to inadequate separation of the fibers in the experiments. On the other hand, the antagonistic system might well have evolved first in the heart, in which it is clearly of great use, and may later have been taken up by the other viscera. A third possibility is that the Amphibia once possessed a complete system and that the modern forms have, in their general degeneration, lost some of it. The absence of a sacral parasympathetic outflow from the urodeles seems most likely to be secondary. Unfortunately, nothing is known of the working of the autonomic system in the Dipnoi which might help us to decide this problem, but it is anatomically inconspicuous and, except for the ciliary fibers, a parasympathetic system does not seem to have been described.

The autonomic system of the Apoda is on the same pattern as that of the urodeles, but there is some fusion of ganglia in the trunk.

Reptiles have the usual double trunk which runs from the head to the tail. Crocodiles, like *Necturus*, have a second trunk on each side, which runs with the arteries through the vertebrarterial canal formed between the heads of the ribs and the vertebrae. The gray rami are important, as in teleosts, in the control of color change in lizards such as the chameleon.

The system in birds closely resembles that of mammals. A peculiarity is that the last pair of ganglia is sometimes fused. The cord is double in the neck, the deeper part running through the arterial canals of the vertebrae,

14

Sense Organs

WHEN WE consider the human body, the presence in it of special parts, or organs, concerned with the senses is obvious enough; clearly the eyes and ears are used for seeing and hearing. There are also senses to which, at first glance, it is impossible to assign any special structures; temperature and touch can be felt all over the body, though with different degrees of sensitivity in different parts, and seem to be general properties of the skin and of such parts of the internal surfaces as can be reached for testing. Pain is even more widely diffused, as anyone who has suffered from rheumatism knows. Anatomically, we must distinguish between a sense organ and a receptor. The organ is a complex structure, built up of connective tissue, skeletal material, and muscles, with all the services of blood supply and nerves that such a structure needs, but always including a collection of cells which are sensitive to stimuli. These are the receptors, and they are probably always nerve cells, or parts of them. The receptors for many senses are scattered in appropriate parts of the body and not associated with special structures. For them the term organ is inappropriate.

The study of the senses is necessarily in large part subjective, though, as we shall see, there are cases where anatomical investigation of an animal has led to the discovery of a sense undreamed of by man. If we begin by listing the sort of stimuli to which man can respond we find that there are many more than the traditional five senses of sight, hearing, smell, taste, and touch. We can soon add pressure (which is felt quite differently from a light touch), tension, temperature, with its two opposites of hot and cold, and pain. A little more thought will add the common chemical sense, which appreciates the impact of, say, ammonia, on the eyes, and an electric sense. Another mysterious one is that which enables us to determine the position of our limbs in space, so that we can unerringly touch any part of our body that we can reach.

These senses, many of them associated with the skin, have long fascinated anatomists, and many attempts have been made to associate a particular sense with a particular type of nerve ending. Unfortunately there has been little success in this. Histologically, the skin is usually said to show free nerve endings of many different types, and it would be logical to expect that each type corresponds to a particular sense. This does not appear to be so, since more than one sense may be present in a patch of skin that has only one type of ending, or there may be more types of nerve ending than there are senses. Moreover, the validity of many of the classical types of nerve-ending is now questioned, and it is said that they are artifacts, produced by the particular methods of fixation and staining. There is, however, no doubt that afferent nerve fibers, whose cell bodies are in the dorsal root ganglia, do end in the skin and that they respond to stimulation. There appear, in fact, to be only three main types of ending (Fig. 14.1). The commonest is an arborization of fine naked axoplasmic filaments less than one micron in diameter, which occur at all levels in the skin and probably end freely. Some such endings are closely associated with hairs. In glabrous (hairless) skin such as that of the lips, anus, and glans penis, and in mucous membranes, there are encapsulated nerve endings, where similar naked fibers arborize among a lemon-shaped mass or capsule of special cells. All that we know of nervous physiology suggests that nerve fibers respond pretty easily, and always in the same way, to a wide range of stimuli. It is easy to show, for example, by turning the eye inward and then pressing the outer edge of the sclerotic, that the cells of the retina respond to mechanical deformation by giving the sensation of light. ('Seeing stars' as a result of high intra-ocular blood pressure shows the same thing.) The eyes normally respond to light, and to nothing else, because they are sheltered from other types of stimuli. Something of the same sort probably applies in the skin; nerve endings at the base of the hairs, for instance, are liable to a large deformation when the hair is touched, so that if they have a high threshold they might respond to touch but not to things, such as temperature, that do not move the hairs.

This is certainly not the whole story, and much of these surface senses remains a mystery. It does seem certain, however, that one type of ending can respond to more than one sort of stimulus, and that therefore the distinction between one sense and another must be made, not, as it is with senses such as sight and hearing, by the part of the brain that receives the afferent impulses, but by the pattern of impulses that the receptor sends in. In other words, the same receptor, responding at one time to touch and at another to warmth, sends a different code of electrical changes along the fiber. Little physiological investigation has been done on this point, but it is known that while light touch causes a brief discharge of electrical impulses, steady pressure produces a continued discharge.

Very little is known about these general senses in lower vertebrates. That fish are sensitive to touch is shown by the old trick of catching trout by tickling them—gently stroking a stationary fish's abdomen and so hypnotizing it until it can be thrown out of the water. But ordinary touch is not likely to play a great part in their lives, and animals living in water are hardly ever subject to rapid changes of temperature. It may well be

that nerve endings sensitive to touch and pressure first became important
in land animals, when the contact of the feet with the ground began to be
a source of valuable information about the environment and the animal's
relation to it. Temperature, except at harmful extremes which must be
avoided, is perhaps even narrower in its incidence, for only warm-blooded
animals, which must set their thermostat so that it responds to warning
surface changes, need to be finely responsive to it.

A peculiar sense organ which has no homologies elsewhere is the facial
pit of snakes of the subfamily Crotalinae. It is a depression alongside the
eye lined with a membrane rich in nerve endings. It is sensitive to
warmth, especially radiant heat, and by it even in the dark the snake can
detect the presence of warm-blooded animals on which it feeds.

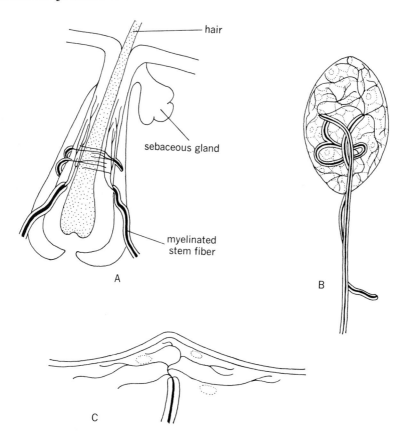

FIG. 14.1   (A) Diagram of free nerve endings in a hair follicle of a rabbit ear,
x 700. (B) Diagram of an encapsulated nerve ending, x 700. (C) Diagram of
free nerve endings in human skin, x 700. (All based on Weddell, Palmer, &
Pallie *Biol. Rev.* 30, 1955)

Histologically, birds show as wide a range of cutaneous nerve endings as do mammals, and many of the same types have been described. That some parts of the body respond to touch and temperature is obvious, and when the feet of some birds are cooled a reflex is initiated by which the blood circulation in the legs is restricted and their temperature falls. This enables birds such as gulls to conserve heat while standing on ice. Peculiar encapsulated nerve endings are present in the soft bills of birds such as waders and ducks that feed by probing in mud, but whether they are receptors for taste or touch is unknown.

Sensory nerve endings in the skeletomuscular system are known as proprioceptors. Some of these are as vague in their properties as those of the skin, but one, the stretch receptor, has a precise relationship to both stimulus and response. Its association with a modified muscle cell, the muscle spindle, means that there is a simple sense organ (Fig. 14.2). The spindle contains non-contractile fibers round which the sensory nerve endings coil, and in series with these are other fibers, called intrafusal, which have small motor nerves and are contractile.

In spite of the simplicity of this as a sense organ, its operation is a little complicated, since it is directed toward automatic control, both of smooth contraction of the muscle and of the maintenance of a certain degree of contraction, or tonus, of the muscle as a whole. The basic point is that the sensory nerve endings respond when they are stretched. This can happen in two ways. Contraction of an antagonistic muscle will stretch the fibers, and they then respond by starting a reflex which causes contraction of the main muscle fibers around them, so reducing the tension on the spindle. Secondly, contraction of the intrafusal fibers stretches the nerve endings of the same spindle. When they respond in the same way as before, the ordinary (or extrafusal) fibers of the same muscle contract; in this way tone is maintained. An extension of this mechanism can lead to the rhythmical alternation of contraction in antagonistic muscles such as is required in walking.

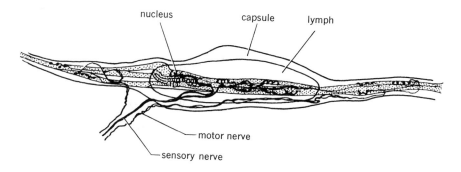

nucleus   capsule   lymph

motor nerve

sensory nerve

FIG. 14.2   Mammalian muscle spindle, semi-diagrammatic, x 70.

Almost nothing is known of proprioceptors in fish, but there is evidence that the eel can swim, provided the brain and spinal cord are intact, under conditions where proprioceptors could not act; hence, even if they are present, they are not necessary. This proves little, for alternations of contraction can obviously be produced voluntarily, if not so smoothly as by an automatic mechanism, in man. Nerve endings described as proprioceptors have been found in the muscles of rays, and since stretch receptors have been found in annelids, crustaceans, and insects, it seems likely that, in some form, they are present in all vertebrates.

Muscle spindles are present in Amphibia, but they seem to be not well developed. Nothing seems to be known of them in birds, in spite of the fact that they would seem to be of great value in some forms of flight, especially hovering. The balancing function may, however, be adequately served by the well-developed eyes and labyrinths acting through the central nervous system.

Lateral Line Organs

Fish have a special system of sense organs, the lateral line system, which to a great extent serves in water the same ends as the touch, pressure, and perhaps temperature receptors in the skin of tetrapods. Of touch in the ordinary sense the fish has little need, but it is subject to currents and turbulence in the water in which it lives, and it is these stimuli with which the lateral line organs are chiefly concerned.

The lateral line organs are rows of sensory endings found on the outer surface. Generally in fish they make a pattern over the head, running especially round the eye and on the lower jaw. One long line runs down the flank of the body, and is often easily recognized by being pigmented (Fig. 4.20). It is the lateral line in the strict sense, which has come to give its name to the whole system. The lines are innervated, as has been said in the last chapter, by the seventh, ninth, and tenth cranial nerves, and their distribution corresponds closely to the parts to which these nerves belong, except that the lines innervated by the facial nerve run forward over the snout, which is territory really belonging to the fifth nerve, and the tenth runs back the whole length of the body, just as does the internal branch of it known as the vagus.

A roughly similar pattern of lines is found in cyclostomes, elasmobranchs, dipnoans, and teleosts. Similar lines are present in the larvae of amphibians, and persist in the adults when these are permanently aquatic, The posterior line is here generally split into three (Fig. 14.3).

The primary sense organs of these lines are free-standing structures called neuromasts, which may be sunk into a slight pit. A neuromast has a characteristic structure (Fig. 14.4). Embedded in a group of epidermal cells is a knob of flask-shaped nerve cells, each with an axon running in-

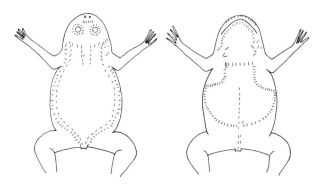

FIG. 14.3   Adult female clawed toad, (*Xenopus laevis*) in dorsal view (left) and ventral view (right) to show the lateral line canals, x 2/5. (Redrawn from Murray, *Quart. J. Micr. Sci.* 96, 1955)

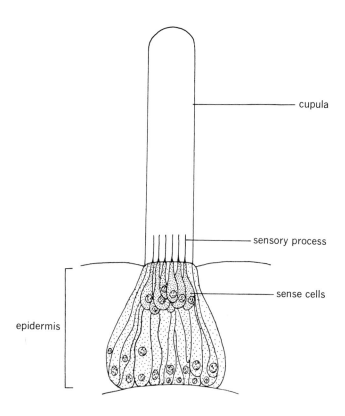

FIG. 14.4   Diagram of a neuromast. (Redrawn from Dijkgraaf, *Biol. Rev.* 38, 1958)

ward and a hair-like process projecting outward. The group of these hair-like processes is embedded in a secreted mass of jelly-like material called the cupula. Sections in the electron microscope show that each process consists of a tuft of about twenty to fifty organelles which have a very similar structure to that of cilia, with a system of nine internal filaments but without the central pair; they are therefore known as stereocilia. There is also a single ordinary cilium, or kinocilium, in each process (Fig. 14.5).

In elasmobranchs and most teleosts some of the neuromasts are sunk in tubes which run just below the surface and have occasional openings (Fig. 14.6). The neuromasts remain for the most part unchanged, but the cupula is rather more squat, as befits its covered position. It is these tubes or canals that largely make the visible lateral lines. The canals contain a fluid, which is in contact with the external medium. Canals seem to be formed in relation to fast swimming or life in swift currents, so that they are probably arrangements for reducing and damping the effect of rapid

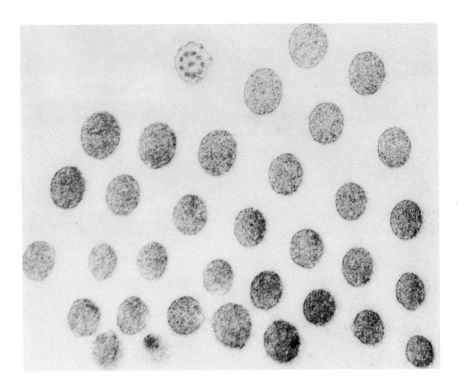

FIG. 14.5   Electron micrograph of a transverse section of a sensory process from the lagena of the skate *Raia clavata*, x 54,000. The kinocilium is at the top. The same essential structure is found in the other parts of the labyrinth and in the neuromasts. (From Lowenstein, Osborn and Wersäll, *Proc. Roy. Soc. B.* 160, 1964, 1)

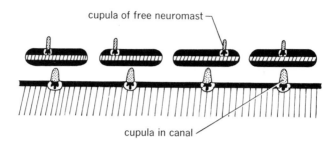

cupula of free neuromast

cupula in canal

FIG. 14.6 Diagrammatic longitudinal section through a lateral line canal. Black represents epidermis. (Redrawn from Dijkgraaf, *Biol. Rev.* 38, 1958)

movement of the water over the fish's body. Thus in the salmonids, which grow up in swift rocky streams, the canals close over early in development and come to contain about 50 per cent of the total number of neuromasts, while in cyprinids (carp-like fish) in stagnant waters the canals close later and contain only about 10 per cent of the neuromasts. Such fish, however, have about five times as many neuromasts altogether as the salmon. There are, however, exceptions to this rule. All fish, even dogfish, retain some free neuromasts.

Cyclostomes and amphibians have only free neuromasts. They are present in amphibian larvae, even in the young of viviparous salamanders, where they can hardly have any function, and persist in most aquatic adults, such as the urodeles *Necturus* and *Proteus* and the anurans *Xenopus* and *Pipa*. They disappear in terrestrial adults, such as the urodele *Salamandra* and the anurans *Rana* and *Bufo*. When the mainly aquatic forms leave the water their neuromasts sink below the skin and presumably become functionless, and re-emerge when the animal returns to the water. This can happen after an interval of as much as two years in some species. Some Stegocephalia, such as *Mastodonsaurus*, have patterns of grooves in the bones of the skull which can only be ascribed to lateral lines; their presence in what are certainly adult skeletons strongly suggests that these early amphibians never left the water. This raises the interesting problem of the connection of these creatures to the first land animals. It can hardly be supposed that the changes in the limb skeleton to be described in Chapter 17 could have been brought about in an animal that was never really terrestrial, so that it seems likely that many of the Stegocephalia known to us as fossils were a degenerate side line that had given up the land-living habits of their ancestors. This agrees with the fact that many of them were huge; for large size, as in the dinosaurs and elephants, often goes with extreme specialization and generally indicates that a line is on the road to extinction.

The structure of the neuromast looks as if it were designed to be bent, when it would give like an ordinary cilium, and then recoil. This does in fact appear to be how it works, and the nerves from the lateral line organs respond when anything happens which bends the sterocilia in this way. The passage of fluid over the surface will do this to the free neuromasts, and a current in the canals will do it to the enclosed ones.

Much experimental work has been done on lateral line organs, and it is now fairly certain that they respond, as their structure suggests, to movements of water over the body. They belong to a class of receptors that send signals to the central nervous system even when not stimulated, so that continuous electrical activity is recorded from the lateral line nerves. Movement of water over a neuromast in one direction increases the frequency of the signals, in the other direction decreases it. This is well seen in the canals, where currents of water driven toward the head and toward the tail, for example, have opposite effects. The effects are related to an asymmetry in the ultramicroscopic structure of the sensory process, which has a group of sterocilia with one kinocilium at one side; the receptor responds only when it is bent in a plane that goes through the kinocilium. In the canals the asymmetry is such that response takes place when water moves along them, not when it moves across them. Apart from the individual's own movements, the chief sources of such currents are other animals, whether of the same or different species, and it is probable that the main value of the lateral line is to act as an organ of distant touch, giving the creature information of the presence of others in its neighborhood. It does not seem likely that any very precise information about the nature of the second animal can be received. There may be minor functions in obstacle avoidance and rheotactic response, where reflected currents from solid objects may stimulate the neuromasts.

Elasmobranchs possess, in addition to their lateral lines, groups of similar receptors sunk in flask-shaped pits on the head. These are the ampullae of Lorenzini (Fig. 14.7), and the whole pit is filled with jelly, which apparently takes the place of the separate cupulae of the ordinary neuromasts, since these are now absent. Similar organs occur in a number of families of teleost, in *Polypterus* and other primitive bony fish, and in dipnoans. The ampullae of Lorenzini and similar organs in teleosts have now been shown to be chiefly organs for detecting electrical changes. These may be produced by almost any biological activity, but are also produced especially by the electric organs of a large number of fish. The similar electric receptors in elasmobranchs and different families of teleost must be presumed to have been independently evolved, just as the organs that produce the current must have been derived from muscles several times over (p. 484).

Ampullae of the lateral line system have been described as responding also to changes in pressure and temperature, but these do not appear to be

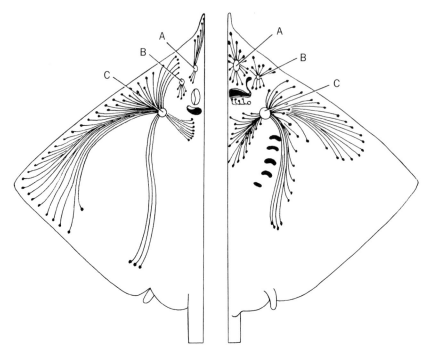

FIG. 14.7 Diagram of the ampullae of Lorenzini and their tubes in the skate *Raia clavata*; dorsal surface on the left, ventral on the right. The largest three capsules (A, B, C) have tubes opening on both dorsal and ventral surfaces, the small capsule behind the mouth has tubes opening on the ventral surface only. (Redrawn from Murray, *J. Exp. Biol.* 37, 1960)

important in life. Dogfish are not likely to be subject to the sudden changes of temperature to which their ampullae of Lorenzini respond.

The organs of the lateral line system are formed in the embryo from thickenings of the ectoderm called placodes. These, like the nerves to which they become connected (p. 268), are more or less segmental in arrangement. In selachians there are three pairs, supra-orbital, infra-orbital, and postorbital, in front of the ears, and one over the glossopharyngeal nerve and each branch of the vagus. There is some fusion of these posterior placodes, and tissue grows back down the body, chiefly from the two posterior vagal placodes, to form the lateral line in the narrow sense. In addition to the fusion of the posterior placodes, there seems to have been capture of the anterior lines by the facial nerve, since the embryonic arrangement of the placodes is much more clearly segmental than that of the nerves which supply the adult organs.

The senory cells of the neuromasts are formed from these placodes, their axons growing inward to the appropriate ganglion. Some part of the ganglion of the facial nerve is also formed by cells from the placode that move inward, the rest coming, in the normal way, from the neural crest.

The Labyrinth

A very similar placode forms at the side of the head behind the eye. It sinks in and makes the inner ear, or, to use what is perhaps a better term, the labyrinth, or membranous labyrinth. Some of the cells of the placode form the sensory cells of the organ, others move inward to make the ganglion of the eighth nerve. None of this comes from the neural crest. The similarity with the lateral line system is obvious.

Most of the placode forms, in one way or another, a hollow sac (Fig. 14.8). The method of formation is different in different classes, but in general the end, or rather the halfway result, is the same. A hollow, the utricle or

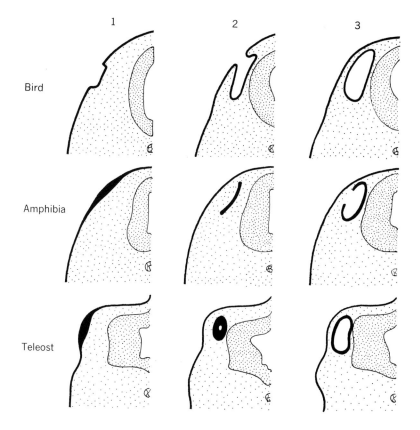

FIG. 14.8 Diagrams of the mode of formation of ear placodes in vertebrates.

utriculus, has running out of it three tubes; they are called semicircular canals, but in fact each makes considerably more than a semicircle. Two are vertical, one horizontal. Opening out of the utricle below is a more or less spherical swelling, the saccule or sacculus. These structures are made of membranous connective tissue, and come to be surrounded by cartilage formed in a special part of the skull called the auditory capsule; later, in most animals, the cartilage is replaced by bone. In elasmobranchs the skeleton is not closely applied to the contained sacs and tubes, but follows their shape, so that there is a cartilaginous as well as a membranous labyrinth. In the higher forms the bony labyrinth becomes more and more closely applied to the membranous labyrinth, and in mammals the two are practically inseparable. A dorsal outgrowth from the original hollow, called the endolymphatic duct, ends blindly under the skin except in elasmobranchs, where it is open to the exterior. It is usually said to represent the original neck by which the utricle was connected to the exterior, but in fact it normally forms separately after the placode has become completely separated from the surface. The membranous labyrinth contains a fluid called endolymph, the bony labyrinth another called perilymph.

This general structure is found in all gnathostomes (Figs. 14.9 to 14.12), though tetrapods, and especially birds and mammals, have specializations which will be dealt with below. In lampreys there are only two semicircular canals, while *Myxine* has only one. The cephalaspids also had only two semicircular canals, but as the two present in lampreys are vertical while that of *Myxine* is horizontal, it does not look as if any less number than three were primitive. Alternatively, if, as is said by some authors, the

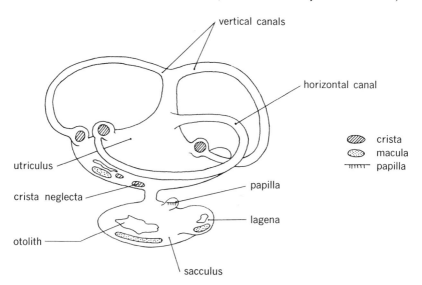

FIG. 14.9   Diagram of the labyrinth of a teleost.

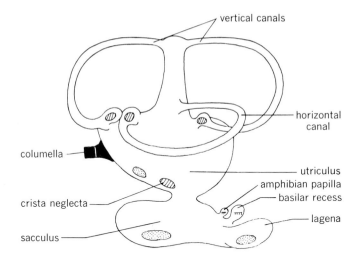

FIG. 14.10   Diagram of the labyrinth of a frog.

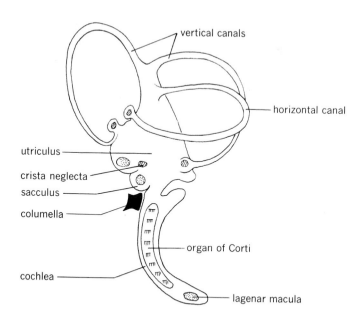

FIG. 14.11   Diagram of the labyrinth of a bird.

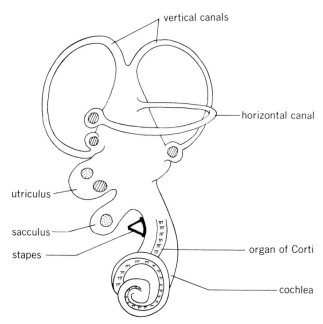

vertical canals

horizontal canal

utriculus

sacculus

stapes

organ of Corti

cochlea

FIG. 14.12   Diagram of the labyrinth of a mammal.

single canal of *Myxine* corresponds to the posterior vertical canal of others, this state may be primitive, the condition in lampreys and cephalaspids may be an intermediate stage, and the set of three was perhaps achieved only by the gnathostomes or their immediate ancestors.

The arrangement of the three canals is characteristic, the horizontal one being lateral to the others, and the two vertical ones at right angles to each other and each at about 45 degrees to the long axis of the body. One end of each canal has a swelling, or ampoule; those of the anterior and horizontal canals are at the anterior ends, and so close together, that of the posterior canal is posterior. Each ampoule opens into the utricle, as do the other, unswollen, ends of the canals, except that the unswollen ends of the two vertical canals have a short common branch which opens by a single hole. Inside the utricle, and on its lower surface, is a patch of sensory cells, the macula, and another patch, the crista (or, less correctly, the papilla or macula) neglecta, is sometimes present in a variable position. It is present in some teleosts, amphibians, reptiles, birds, and mammals. A patch of sensory cells, called a crista, is inside each ampoule. There is no important variation in the pattern of the utricle and canals in any gnathostome, but the canals of rays are to a great extent free of each other and of the utricle.

The saccule is more variable. It is basically a diverticulum of the utricle, bearing on its floor its own patch of sense cells, or macula. It usually has one or more extensions or expansions. Chief of these are a basilar recess and the lagena, each with its own patch of sensory cells, the papilla and the macula of the lagena respectively. In teleosts the hollows are distinct, but in the reptiles the macula and the papilla are situated in a single extension of the sacculus. This extension is enlarged in crocodiles and birds, and although it is not coiled, is called, by analogy with that of mammals, the cochlea. The papilla is developed into a more complicated sensory structure, the organ of Corti, running (in birds) the length of the finger-like cochlea, at the end of which is the macula of the lagena. In mammals the diverticulum is not only long but helically coiled, so that the name of cochlea is appropriate, since it is a Greek word meaning snail. The macula of the lagena has disappeared in marsupials and placentals, but is present in monotremes.

Amphibia have, in addition to basilar recess and lagena, a small extra dorsal pocket, with its own patch of sense cells, the amphibian papilla. The anurans are peculiar also in that the endolymphatic ducts are much enlarged. They extend inside the skull so that those of the two sides meet both dorsally and ventrally around the brain, and run down the trunk inside the vertebrae. Where the spinal nerves emerge from between these the ducts also bulge out, and are covered with calcium carbonate, thus making the little white patches so visible in dissection. The calcium in the ducts is much reduced during metamorphosis, so that it appears to be in some way a reserve for the formation of the bony skeleton. Why this function should have been taken over by a sense organ is unexplained.

A somewhat similar expansion of the ducts occurs in dipnoans, and in lizards the ducts of the two sides are swollen and meet above the fourth ventricle, but they do not join. Birds are peculiar in that the common base of the anterior and posterior canals is twisted, but this does not affect the general spatial arrangements of the three. The cochlea, and the parts of the middle and outer ear connected with it, will be considered below.

There is every reason to believe that the labyrinth that we have considered so far—utricle, saccule, and semicircular canals—is a primitive sense organ which was present in the very early vertebrates, and out of which the ear of higher forms has developed. Basically all the sensory patches are built on the same plan, which is that of a neuromast. A group of supporting cells surround a group of nerve cells, and each of these has several cilia projecting into the endolymph. These cilia are covered with non-cellular material, and it is on the nature of this that the naming of the patches is based. Maculae are covered with a membrane with many grains of calcium carbonate, called otoliths or statoliths. In the teleosts, instead of a membrane, there is a single large otolith covering each macula. These are of characteristic form, and have some value in taxonomy, particularly of fossils. They increase in size with time, and, as they show annual growth lines, they can be used to determine the age of the animal.

A crista has a jelly-like covering similar to that of neuromasts, so that it may be called a cupule or cupula. A papilla has a non-calcareous membrane attached to the bordering cells and stretching over the sensory cells, so that it lies on the tips of their cilia, like a roof; it is hence called a tectorial membrane, from a Latin word meaning 'a roof.'

A large amount of experimental investigation, both electrical and behavioral, has been made into the functions of these sensory endings, and though many details are still obscure it is now clear that all the sensory cells of the utricle and canals (the pars superior of the labyrinth) respond in one way or another to the position or acceleration of the body. In elasmobranchs the maculae and papilla of the saccule and its appendages (the pars inferior of the labyrinth) respond in the same way, and if, as is possible but not proved, this response is not present in the higher forms, it has probably been lost. Satisfactory experiments on acceleration have not been made on reptiles, but there is no reason to think that they are in principle different from other animals.

All vertebrates are able to a very great extent to maintain the body in a natural position. A fish tilted to one side bends its fins in such a way that when it swims forward it rights itself; a frog sitting on a board which is tilted through a sagittal plane stretches or bends its fore-limbs so as to maintain a constant angle between the body and the horizontal; a duck held by the feet bends its neck up so that its head is in the natural position relative to the ground; and a cat thrown into the air twists its body back and forward so that, by using the principle of rotational inertia, it falls on its feet. All these responses are mediated by the labyrinth. So too are eye movements. When we move our head to the right our eyes remain fixed on what we were looking at before, then jerk into a new position, where they again stop, and, if the head goes on turning, do another jerk a little later. The co-ordination of hand and eye so important to a baseball player or cricketer depends on the labyrinth, and a dog whose labyrinth is damaged can no longer catch meat in its mouth.

It is very difficult to carry out experiments to distribute these various responses among the parts of the labyrinth, and it may be that the distribution is not the same in all vertebrate classes. In general, however, it seems that the utricular macula, and in elasmobranchs the saccular and lagenar maculae, are the parts that respond to tilting and linear accelerations, while the cristae of the semicircular canals respond to angular accelerations. The importance of the placing of the canals in three planes at right angles is thus obvious, for in this way, and only in this way, there is response to angular acceleration in any plane. Although experimental proof is lacking, it is probable that the acceleration causes movement of the endolymph which bends the cilia of the sensory cells, while tilting causes displacement of the otoliths. These correspond to the types of structure called maculae and cristae respectively.

All these organs are physiologically similar to the lateral line system in that they are continually sending signals to the central nervous system. On stimulation the frequency of the impulses is increased or decreased. All are supplied by the eighth nerve.

It seems physically necessary that anything that shakes the otoliths, and perhaps the endolymph in general, must move the cilia and so act as a stimulus. Such shaking could be brought about by sounds, and there is good evidence that electrical responses can be produced in the auditory nerves of fishes, both teleost and selachian, by sounds. Hearing, however, in the sense of making use of the stimuli which are physically perceived, seems to be well developed only in a limited number of fish. These are chiefly the Ostariophysi which have a chain of modified vertebrae (Weber's ossicles) connecting the swim bladder with the saccule (p. 154). In these the saccules are enlarged and joined, and from the junction a median chamber stretches back within the skull. The perilymphatic space that surrounds it bulges out of the skull by two foramina to make contact with the anterior ossicle. The otolith of the saccule has a long process. Such fish not only respond to higher frequencies than other fish (up to 7000 cycles per second in some species), but have a much finer discrimination of pitch, some being able to recognize a change of a quarter of a tone, which is better than most men can do. Moreover, many of them produce sounds of various sorts. Sound production is not, however, confined to the Ostariophysi, and since all fish seem to be very bad at localizing sound, its value, like that of hearing, is doubtful.

In the herrings (Clupeidae) an anterior extension of the swim bladder makes contact with the utricle, but there are no Weber's ossicles. It thus seems that, as we might expect, any part of the labyrinth can take on an auditory function, and that this has been achieved more than once. There is no reason to think that the system found in the teleosts has anything to do with the evolution of the ear of the tetrapods, to which we must now turn.

All tetrapods differ from all fish in that a bone called the columella auris has some connection with the labyrinth. Its development and its relation to blood vessels and nerves suggest that in most vertebrates it is homologous with the hyomandibular bone or cartilage of fish, and that when its function of anchoring the upper jaw to the skull (see Chapter 16) became no longer necessary as the jaw and cranium were firmly fused together, it became free to be used for conducting sound from the surface to the labyrinth. This is probably true, but only with qualifications.

In what may be considered its standard position the columella runs from a stretched piece of skin, the tympanum, across a space, the tympanic cavity, which is derived from the first gill slit, to fit against a gap, the oval window (fenestra ovalis) in the bony labyrinth. This is seen in an amphibian such as the frog (Fig. 14.13), a lizard or crocodile, and a bird. The

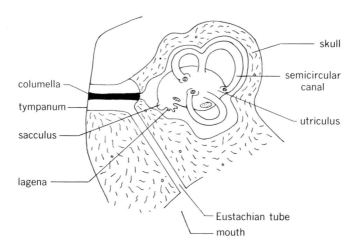

FIG. 14.13   Ear of a frog, diagrammatic.

condition in mammals is not different in principle, but has important differences of detail and will be considered below. The derivation of the
tympanic cavity from a gill slit means that it is lined with endoderm. Its
connection with the gut is maintained through a narrow elongated opening, the Eustachian tube. The tympanum, or ear drum, is formed by the
contact of endoderm with ectoderm, and represents the place where the
gill slit primitively opened to the exterior.

   The usual story is that this was the primitive condition, and was evolved
as soon as the tetrapod ancestors left the water, but other explanations are
possible. Different types of ear exist in various present-day vertebrates. In
snakes there is no tympanic cavity, and the outer end of the columella
comes into contact with the quadrate bone. They have no ear drum, and
are deaf to air-borne sounds, but can hear sounds transmitted through the
ground, which get to the inner ear by bone conduction, a method well
known to human otology as a means of dealing with deafness caused by a
defective middle ear. Such hearing is obviously suitable to a creature that
goes on its belly and has its ear even closer to the ground than the Indians
of story-books. Chelonians have another variation. The tympanic cavity
exists, but is apparently functionless, since the columella does not cross it
and there is no ear-drum; a space filled with fluid separates the tympanic
cavity from the inner ear, and the columella runs across this from the oval
window to end externally in the thick skin of the head. The animals are,
not surprisingly, nearly or quite deaf, although sounds of frequency up to
about 300 cycles per second can cause impulses in the auditory nerve. In
spite of the possibly primitive condition of the skull, the tortoises are in
this respect clearly degenerate.

The urodeles have an ear similar in principle to that of snakes. There is no tympanic cavity or membrane, and the columella runs from the oval window to the squamosal. In many species it is more or less degenerate.

It is clearly possible that something like the system used by snakes (and presumably urodeles) might have been the primitive state of the tetrapod ear, and that hearing of air-borne sounds by their transmission across a drum and an air-filled cavity came later. Since the embryos even of mammals have gill slits, the evolution of a tympanic cavity could presumably take place at any time, even though the slits had been previously lost in the adults. It used to be said that the early stegocephalians, such as *Eogyrinus*, must have had a tympanum to fill the notch in the back of the skull (Fig. 16.9), but this does not seem necessary. Similarly shaped skulls are found in some modern lizards and chelonians even though no ear-drum is present. The earliest amphibians had short legs that stuck out sideways; their bodies were in contact with the ground when they came out of water, and hearing by bone conduction would have been adequate for them. Something like the condition in the urodeles may therefore have been primitive. Relics of another connection between the labyrinth and hearing are also present in anurans, and those urodeles which metamorphose, in the shape of a small cartilage, the operculum; it rests, like the columella to which it is attached, against the oval window, but is connected by muscle to the shoulder girdle. This apparatus may be used for a simple form of hearing, or it may be concerned with balance as the animal walks. The operculum of Stegocephalia, if it had been present, is unlikely to have been preserved since it would have been small and cartilaginous.

There is also good reason for thinking that neither the cotylosaurs nor the therapsids had a tympanum. In the latter the stapes, the bone that corresponds to the columella auris, is well known; it is large, and calculations suggest that it was much too big and heavy to be used for hearing, since the energy of any ordinary sound would not be enough to set it in motion.

If this argument is accepted, it follows that hearing of air-borne sounds by transmission across the middle ear was evolved separately in the lines leading to the mammals, birds, and anurans, and perhaps in the lizards. Nothing is known of the columella in dinosaurs, so that we cannot tell how far back in the diapsid ancestry of birds such hearing appeared. This is perhaps a surprising and untidy conclusion, but no more so than many others to which comparisons of structure compel us; we have already seen that the use of the swim bladder in hearing must have evolved at least twice in the teleosts. If our story is true, the difficulties in homologizing the columella and tympanum of anurans with those of amniotes disappear. Different authors have given different accounts of the origin of the columella in frogs, but none has been able to find any connection with a branchial arch. It is always made of at least two parts, of independent origin. The tympanum is always behind the internal mandibular branch of the facial nerve, whereas in amniotes it is in front of it. This can be explained away as of no importance (though such apparently trivial points are often remarkably constant in a wide range of the animal kingdom), but if the ear drums of the two groups have been independently evolved this is just the sort of small difference that might be expected.

However many times hearing may have been evolved, good functional ears are present only in birds and mammals.

In birds the tympanum is sunk a little way below the surface, so that there is a simple external ear, or external auditory meatus, which in most species is covered with feathers. The beginnings of such a depression of the tympanum can be seen in crocodiles. The outer branched end of the columella auris rests against the tympanum, the other fits into the oval window, in which it is held by a strong flexible auricular ligament, so that it can move slightly in and out. The oval window is near the beginning of the cochlea (Fig. 14.11). The parts of the cochlea are given the same names as the corresponding parts of the cochlea of mammals, but if the ears of the two classes have been evolved independently they are not strictly homologous.

The central part of the cochlea, the scala media, is an outgrowth of the sacculus, and contains endolymph. It is surrounded by a bony cochlea of the same shape, which, however does not fit closely to it, except that along the length of the cochlea the scala media is held in position by two shelves of cartilage. The result is that the bony cochlea encloses two cavities, a scala vestibuli above the scala media, and a scala tympani below, both containing perilymph, although the scala vestibuli is largely filled up with processes from the membrane below it. The oval window opens into the scala vestibuli, and another gap, the round window, which is filled up with membrane, opens from the scala tympani to the middle ear. Obviously the arrangement is such that if, for example, by the arrival of a sound wave, the columella and oval window are pushed in, pressure will be transmitted through the perilymph, the scala media will move down, and the membrane of the round window will bulge outward. There need be no change in volume of the relatively incompressible liquid of the perilymph. A short canal leading from the scala tympani to near the oval window acts as a damper.

The upper wall of the scala media is the vascular tegmental membrane, its floor the basilar membrane. This includes transverse fibers which are anchored to the cartilaginous shelf. They vary in number from one to two thousand, and increase slightly but regularly in length as one goes toward the apex of the cochlea. Above the fibers are sensory cells of the usual type, covered by a tectorial membrane. The whole sensory arrangement is called the organ of Corti. Inside the scala media, at its apex, is a macula, which is the representative of the lagena.

In general it seems likely that the cochlea acts in some way as a detector of pitch, notes of different frequency activating sensory cells at different parts along it according to their length, but there are many difficulties. The cochlea of birds is simpler than that of mammals, and zoologists have argued that they should be unable to distinguish such a wide range of frequency. In view of their complicated songs, far surpassing in range of pitch any but selected human voices, this seems extremely unlikely, at least for the songbirds (Oscines). One of the puzzles in the study of the ear is that in general both mammals and birds seem to have a more versatile structure than they ever use, but such a structure could hardly have been produced by natural selection.

The lagenar macula is not known to have any function. It may be simply a relic.

General observation, and such experiments as have been carried out, suggest that in most respects the ears of birds are as efficient as those of man, for example, in pitch discrimination and direction finding. At detecting rapid variations in pitch they are probably much better. Some birds have special adaptations. Owls, for example, find their prey, such as mice, by detecting their whereabouts from the high-pitched squeaks that they emit. They have good discrimination for pitch, and can hear sounds up to 20,000 cycles per second; the excellent direction finding is presumably connected with their long and asymmetrical external ears.

The cochlea of a mammal is by contrast difficult to understand and quite impossible to draw in any way that will convey any useful informa-

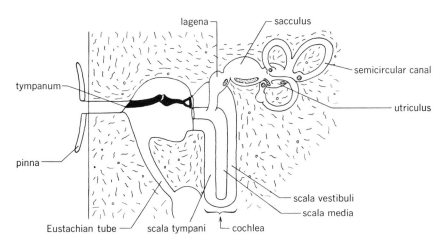

FIG. 14.14 Ear of a mammal, diagrammatic.

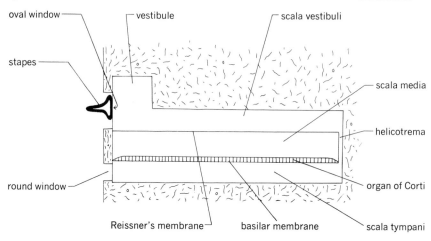

FIG. 14.15 Diagram of the mammalian cochlea, unwound. Shading indicates bone. The stapes is in the middle ear, and the round window also looks into this space. (Redrawn from Yapp, *Animal Physiology*, Clarendon Press, 1960)

tion to a student. It is tightly twisted on itself, bone and all, for two to four turns, but if one imagines the spiral unwound and diagrammatized the result can be represented by Fig. 14.15. There are the same three chambers as in birds, but this time the scala vestibuli and scala tympani are connected by a narrow passage, the helicotrema, at the apex. The roof of the scala media (Fig. 14.16), instead of being a thick vascular membrane, is very thin, and known as Reissner's membrane; the scala vestibuli is well marked and unobstructed. The tectorial membrane is for the most part not in contact with the sensory cells of the basilar membrane, which can move freely beneath it. Round and oval windows are much as they are in birds.

There are important differences in the middle and outer ear (Fig. 14.14). The columella is present, and is characteristically stirrup-shaped (hence its name of stapes), but it is only one of three bones that stretch across the tympanic cavity. It articulates with the incus (or anvil) which in turn articulates with the malleus (or hammer), whose outer end rests on the ear-drum. All three are held in position by small muscles. The homologies of these bones, or ear ossicles, are considered in Chapter 16.

All the evidence is that the organ of Corti acts in much the same way as in a bird, different parts of it probably acting as resonators for sounds of different pitch. Destruction of different points along its length can cause deafness for a narrow range of tones. One cannot say whether birds or mammals have the better ears unless one knows what they are used for, but all the evidence is that some birds (such as owls) can do more with their ears than any mammals except bats, which are a very special case.

The strict Darwinian will say that the coiled and long cochlea of the mammal must have advantages, or it would not have been selected. (Such a structure could hardly be explained as due to linkage, or the multiple effects of a single gene.) The fact that birds do just as well with a shorter and simpler cochlea is therefore a difficulty. It is extremely unlikely that the one could have been converted to the other, so that, whatever the case with air-hearing in general, the cochlea must have been evolved independently twice over, another example of the remarkable parallelism between mammals and birds.

The normal upper limit of pitch that either birds or mammals can hear is about 20,000 cycles per second or less, although there is some evidence that small rodents can respond to sounds much higher than this. Bats certainly can, and have evolved a very efficient system of echolocation or sonar. When flying they constantly emit ultrasonic squeaks with frequencies of up to 100,000 cycles per second or more, and by listening to the reflection of these they can not only avoid obstacles, even quite fine wires, but can find and catch the insects on which they feed. The much less well-documented ultrasonic hearing of mice has a different purpose. Presumably, those mice with the highest pitched notes were less easily detected by owls, and so more successful in the struggle for existence. But it is useless making noises that your companions cannot hear, and the upper hearing limit of mice, as well as of the owls, would gradually be pushed up.

The oil birds (*Steatornis*) that live in caves in South America also find their way in darkness by echolocation, but the clicks that they emit have a frequency of only about 20,000 cycles per second.

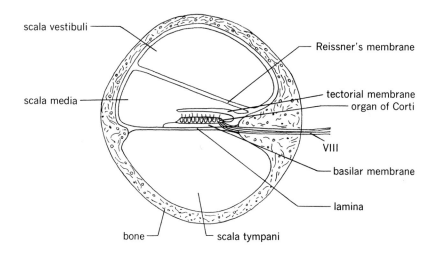

FIG. 14.16   Diagrammatic transverse section of the mammalian cochlea.

Chemical Senses

We must now return to the surface of the body and deal with that other group of sensory cells which respond especially to chemical substances. The study of these is handicapped because there is no worthwhile physical chemistry that can be used. Light and sound can both be measured in terms of frequency, amplitude, energy, duration, and so on, but there is no system by which the taste and smell of a peach, for example, can be numerically compared with those of a chocolate, yet the two stimulate the same, or adjacent, nerve endings very differently. The result is that much of the study of the chemical senses is based on man's subjective responses, and animals can only be investigated in a very crude way.

The chemical senses are usually divided into three: the common chemical sense, taste, and smell.

The first is rather a wastepaper basket, and is applied to all those cases in man where a chemical substance produces a sensation which is neither smell nor taste. It includes therefore such things as the appreciation of mustard or mustard gas on the skin, of 'lacrimators' such as ammonia and tear-gas on the eyes, of 'sternutators' such as arsenical smokes on the nose, and of 'suffocants' such as chlorine on the respiratory tract. Some authors would include also the sensation of 'hot' tastes, such as those of pepper and ginger, in the mouth. While many of the substances which are stimuli of this sort, especially the gases that have been developed for warfare, are artificial and can have played no part in the evolution of the sense, many others are natural products, occurring especially in plants. It is clear that while in large quantities they are all unpleasant irritants, in small quantities man, or some men, find many of them very pleasant.

It has been suggested that they affect free nerve endings by destroying their cytoplasm, and are thus akin to the stimuli of cutting and burning, which cause pain. They are felt especially by the mucous membranes of the mouth and respiratory tract, so that they must affect the trigeminal and facial nerves. The other mucous membranes that are more or less exposed to the exterior, such as those of the anus and genital tracts, are also sensitive. Other vertebrates give responses to the same kinds of substances as does man, but in fishes and amphibians there is a much wider distribution of the sensitive nerve-endings, the skin responding to stimulation that in man would affect only the mouth or nose. There is evidence that in frogs general chemical stimuli received by the skin from the surrounding water are necessary for the maintenance of muscle tone, just as pressure on the feet may be in higher animals.

The distinction between taste and smell is difficult. The fact that man smells with his nose and tastes with his tongue has led most authors to class as smell anything that stimulates the first cranial nerve, and as taste anything that stimulates the seventh. But for man there are two more important distinctions: smell is air-borne and taste is water-borne, and this means that while smell is a distant sense, taste can occur only with something in the mouth. The first of these distinctions cannot apply to an aquatic animal, and the latter need not. Clearly if a fish is sensitive to, say, sugar, the sugar need not be placed in its mouth, but can diffuse to it from a distance through the surrounding water. Although then there is an anatomical distinction between the olfactory and gustatory organs of fish, all the sensations that they mediate must be, in human terms, taste, and when the vertebrates left the water for the land their olfactory nerves must have acquired a sensitivity to a new range of air-borne chemical substances. Only then did smell, in the true sense, come into existence.

That the sense mediated by the first cranial nerve in fishes is neither, in the ordinary sense of words, smell nor taste, but is perhaps closer to the former, is suggested by a neglected experiment on the catfish *Ameiurus*. It was found that the olfactory stalk transmitted continuous impulses, and that these increased when material such as crushed earthworm or alligator was place in the nostril; but the increase was much less when the same material was applied after it had been filtered, and no substance that dissolves completely in water stimulated the olfactory organ without causing damage. This suggested that contact of a solid material with the epithelium was important, and it was found that stroking it with a paintbrush or pressing it also produced a discharge. Some substances that man considers strong smelling, such as oil of cloves and a suspension of cheese, caused no discharge. Other experiments showed that the reaction of the dogfish *Mustelus* to strong-tasting substances such as cloves and thyme placed in the nostrils was not abolished when the olfactory stalks were cut, but was abolished by cutting the facial nerve. Clearly then, this was in no sense smell, but either taste or the common chemical sense.

The bodies of the sensory cells of the first cranial nerve are, as we have seen, in the olfactory epithelium, and they send short processes toward the surface as well as the long axons that run back to the olfactory lobe of the brain. Their general structure is remarkably constant throughout the vertebrates, from the cyclostomes up. The processes, usually about eight to twelve per cell, are mostly short, but in fishes and amphibians some of them are long and project through the layer of mucus on the surface. The similarity of these cells to the receptor cells of the lateral line and ear is obvious, and they seem well adapted to be moved by, and so respond to, small solid particles. The loss of these long processes in reptiles and mammals may be connected with the terrestrial environment, since such thin strands of cytoplasm could hardly exist in air. A peculiarity of the olfactory epithelium is that it is usually, perhaps always, yellow, and it appears probable that the pigment is in some way concerned in the detection

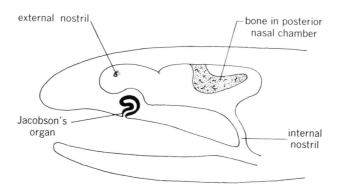

FIG. 14.17   Diagrammatic longitudinal section of the head of a lizard to show Jacobson's organ.

of odors. Many strongly odoriferous substances have a marked Raman spectrum, that is, they scatter monochromatic light to give a range of wave-lengths, and there is plenty of evidence that white, and especially albino, varieties of animals are less sensitive to smell than colored ones. The morphology of the nostrils and nasal cavities, with their gradual increase in complexity, has been described in Chapter 9. It is only in the land vertebrates that the cavities have specialized parts of any note, and this agrees with the suggestion that smell is essentially a function of terrestrial life. On the other hand, the relative importance of the olfactory lobes decreases, as these make up a decreasing proportion of the brain. They are, as we have seen, practically non-existent in most birds and in whales, which have almost no sense of smell.

In reptiles there is an accessory olfactory organ, or vomeronasal organ, or Jacobson's organ (Fig. 14.17), in the shape of a curved blind tube opening through the roof of the buccal cavity well in front of the internal nares on each side. In lizards and snakes these pits are especially well developed, and the forked tip of the tongue fits into them. The continued darting of the tongue in and out of the mouth is for testing the air, odoriferous particles being picked up and carried into Jacobson's organ. The pits are not present in adult crocodiles or chelonians. An organ which is considered to be homologous is present in most mammals, though well developed only in monotremes, marsupials, and some primitive placentals such as insectivores and rodents; here it is a tube above the palate which is blind posteriorly but opens into the nasal cavity in front. A blind sac on the medial side of the nasal passage in anurans, and some separation of the olfactory epithelium into two parts in elasmobranchs, dipnoans, and most urodeles (not *Necturus*) are also considered homologous. The organ is absent from birds, even its embryonic rudiment being doubtful. All these structures are supplied by a distinct branch of the olfactory nerve and by the terminal nerve. The sensory cells are similar to those of the ordinary nasal epithelium, but in reptiles and mammals it seems that they do not bear the projecting hair-like processes. Except for its use in the Squamata, little is known of the function of Jacobson's organ. It is presumably concerned with some sort of distant chemical reception, and in lizards it seems to be specially concerned in feeding and with recognizing other members of the species. But these are the chief uses of all the chemical senses.

A sense of smell in the strict sense, that is, appreciation of air-borne chemicals, is present in amphibians, especially frogs and toads, and in many reptiles. Chelonia have proportionately larger olfactory lobes than other orders, and some lizards apparently have very little sense of smell, a state called microsmatic. Birds also are mostly microsmatic, and among mammals the higher primates, including man, have little sense of smell, and whales probably none. Perennibranchiate urodeles, birds, and the higher primates have no Jacobson's organ.

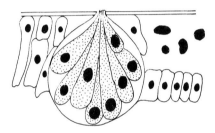

FIG. 14.18   Taste bud of a rabbit, slightly diagrammatic, x 350. The figure showes the pore, and the surrounding stratified epithelium.

Taste, which in man is usually tacitly defined as the perception of chemical stimuli in the mouth, is generally associated with the branchial nerves and with a particular type of sensory ending, the taste bud (Fig. 14.18). This is a lemon-shaped mass of cells embedded in the stratified epithelium, and consists of a cortex surrounding a medulla of thin cells each of which has a short process. All the processes from one bud project together through a fine hole onto the surface of the epithelium. The terminal arborizations of the axons of the facial or other appropriate nerve spread among the cells of the medulla. These taste buds are found in man chiefly on the tongue (though not all over it), but there are a few of them on the hard palate, inside the cheeks, and elsewhere in the mouth and pharynx. Similar buds are found in the buccal cavity of all other vertebrates, and in other places as well. Many fishes have them over part or the whole of the body. They are especially well known in the catfish *Ameiurus*, which will turn and snap at food, or extract of food, brought against almost any part of its outer surface. The possibility for the wide diffusion of the sense of taste over the skin is obviously present when the wide distribution of the tenth nerve is remembered, but in many fish there is also a branch of the facial which extends some distance back on the flank to supply the taste buds.

Most authors say that there are only four basic tastes in man: sweet, sour (or acid), bitter, and salt, and some add to these a metallic and an alkaline taste. There is some evidence that each of these is perceived by a separate group of taste buds, for adjacent spots on the tongue may give different sensations to the same substance, and drugs may inhibit one taste but not another. The whole subject is, however, extremely difficult and in an unsatisfactory state. Most of the complex 'tastes,' such as those of peaches, strawberries, salmon, and wine, are said to depend on smell, vapors from the food or drink passing up from the mouth to stimulate the olfactory nerve endings.

Obviously all vertebrates have some sense of taste, and in fish and Amphibia it is very much more refined than anything we can understand. Many fish react to water that has passed over other fish. By this means a minnow (*Phoxinus*) can recognize the proximity of a predator such as a pike (*Esox lucius*), and can even distinguish between a member of its own shoal and another minnow. It seems that some anurans have receptors that respond specifically to distilled water, and the same has been claimed for a number of mammals. The value of such a response is doubtful, although an ability to distinguish between fresh and brackish water, which need depend only on the ability to detect salt, could have survival value. Birds have relatively few taste buds, situated on the back of the tongue and on the soft palate.

Touch, temperature, and the chemical senses are generally connected with the outside world, but there is clearly the possibility that such senses might be present inside the body, and there might be advantages in their existence. They have, in fact, developed here and there, but in no very systematic way.

Wherever an animal, or a part of its body, reacts to the composition of the blood, whether it be the oxygen or carbon dioxide content or the presence of some specific hormone, there must be a chemical sense. Such reactions occur throughout the vertebrates, but no special sensory structures are, for the most part, concerned with them. The responding organs are independent effectors. Tetrapods have developed one rather peculiar organ for this sort of purpose. The gill capillaries of the first gill remain, as a tangle of capillaries called the carotid body, at the point where the common carotid artery divides into internal and external carotid, and at the base of the internal carotid is a slight expansion, the carotid sinus.

Both body and sinus are supplied by the ninth and tenth cranial nerves and while the body acts as a chemoreceptor the sinus is a pressure receptor. According to the degree of oxygenation and pressure of the blood flowing through them they initiate reflexes that affect the heart beat and respiratory rate, so as to maintain the system working efficiently. Similar tissue to that of the carotid body occurs in various parts of the body of birds and mammals, and so may also be sensitive to oxygenation.

In the hypothalamus of mammals there are neurons which apparently react directly to the osmotic pressure of the blood passing round them, and so initiate secretion of a hormone from the posterior pituitary which controls the formation of urine, and so the osmotic pressure of the blood.

Eyes

The last, the most complicated, and for many vertebrates the most important sense organ is the eye. Vertebrates seem very early to have discovered a versatile and efficient structure for seeing with, for eyes were present in the earliest ostracoderms known, and the imprints of muscles suggest that externally they were similar to those of the present day. Of their origin nothing is known; Darwin realized the difficulty of conceiving how natural selection could produce an eye by small steps, and despite much sophistry the problem is not solved. An eye is much more than an organ that is sensitive to light: it is something that produces an image, by which is meant a representation in the body, without undue distortion, of a shape or pattern in the external world. It is conceivable that a vertebrate could tell whether it is night or day by using simple nerve endings in the skin, just as an earthworm can, but this is not vision. So far as is known, an image can be produced in three ways only: by a small hole in an opaque screen, the principle of the pin-hole camera; by a lens; and by a mosaic of tubes. The first two produce an image that is inverted with respect to the object, the third gives one that is the right way up, or erect. A mosaic image is produced, under certain circumstances, by the compound eye of insects and other arthropods. The eyes of vertebrates and cephalopods have lenses. They work, that is, on the principle of the ordinary camera.

It is easy to state certain principles that must be satisfied if such an eye is to be satisfactory. While the lens must be transparent, the rest of the eye must be opaque to prevent unwanted light entering, and in order to minimize the effect of light that does accidentally enter, the internal surfaces should, so far as possible, be black, so as to reduce reflections. The dimensions must be such that rays from objects placed in positions where the animal needs to see them must come to a focus on the sensitive surface (the retina); if it is necessary for the animal to see objects at more than one distance from its body there must be a mechanism for dealing with this—what is called in the camera focusing, in the eye accommodation.

There are three possible ways of doing this: to alter the distance between lens and retina (the mechanism of the camera); to alter the curvature of the lens; or to alter its refractive index. There must be some means of reducing both spherical and chromatic aberration, the first being caused by the fact that all lenses produce a curved image, and the second by the fact that light of different wave-lengths is bent to different degrees by the same lens. These errors become more important with a short image-distance (that is, a small eye), which means a thick lens. Finally, if the eye is to be sensitive over a wide range of light intensities, there must either be an equally wide range of response in the sensitive element, or some means of reducing the quantity of light that enters the eye as its intensity increases.

All these principles are satisfied in the eyes of vertebrates, although not always in the same way. The same basic design has in fact been modified to work in various ways according to the needs of the animal.

The functional eyes of present-day vertebrates are sometimes called lateral eyes, to distinguish them from the dorsal or pineal and parapineal eyes which grow out from the roof of the diencephalon. These are still a mystery. It is now generally agreed that they represent a pair of structures, which have secondarily come to lie one behind the other; both are present in lampreys, but in other vertebrates only one is well developed. In lampreys they are sensitive to light but have no lens. In *Sphenodon* and many lizards a lens-like structure is present in the parapineal; the organ is sensitive to light, or perhaps more generally to solar radiation, but there is no evidence that an image is formed. A gap in the skull above the organ is called the pineal foramen, and can be recognized in many extinct reptiles and in some ostracoderms. The pineal, therefore, whatever its original function, is an ancient organ.

The lateral eyes, or briefly eyes, of vertebrates have a characteristic structure which can be represented by the best-known example, that of man (Fig. 14.19). It is roughly spherical, but toward the front is somewhat flattened, and then in the flattened part there is a raised bulge. This is the part that looks outward (the cornea); the reader should be able to feel the change in curvature by pressing a finger gently over the front of his own eye with the lids shut, and moving the eyes. The outer wall of the sphere is the sclerotic, made of a tough connective tissue consisting mostly of white fibers with some cartilage. The white fibers are continuous with those of the tendons of the extrinsic muscles that move the eye. In the anterior bulge the same tissue becomes transparent and is the cornea. Sclerotic and cornea are mesodermal. On the outer surface of the cornea is a thin layer of epidermis, which is continuous at the edges with the general epidermis. It is called the conjunctiva, and is also transparent. The front surface of the conjunctiva is kept moist by the secretion of glands. In most mammals there are two, a Harderian gland in the anterior part of the orbit and a lacrimal gland posteriorly, but the former is not present in man. When the two glands are present there is no recognizable difference between them, and they would be better and more simply called anterior and posterior lacrimal glands, especially since the anterior gland was not discovered by Harder, whose name it bears. The watery liquid that they secrete runs away into the nasal cavity by the lacrimal duct, which pierces the lacrimal bone on the front edge of the orbit and so gives it its name. Only when the glands are unusually active does the secretion run over the edge of the lower eyelid as tears.

Within the sclerotic, and closely applied to it, is the choroid coat, which is richly vascular and highly pigmented, so that it makes a black and non-reflecting wall. In many mammals it has also a highly reflecting layer, the tapetum, which makes the eyes of such animals as cats shine when illuminated in the dark. Near where the sclerotic merges into the cornea the choroid thickens to form the ciliary body, and from this an annular projection, the iris, stretches across the eye. The hollow of the eye is thus incompletely divided into two parts, the anterior and posterior chambers. The former contains a watery liquid, the aqueous humor, and the latter a much more gelatinous fluid, the vitreous humor, or vitreous body, or simply, in the jargon of ophthalmologists, the vitreous. Much of the ciliary body consists of smooth muscle, which will be referred to later. The iris

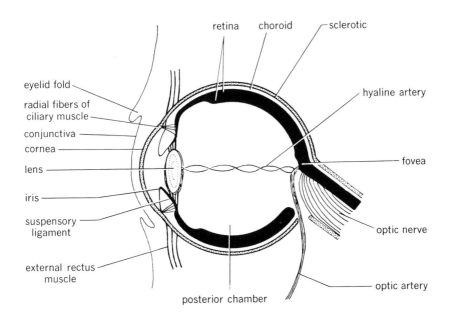

FIG. 14.19 Diagrammatic vertical section of a mammalian eye. In this diagram, and in Figs. 14.21 to 14.25, only the major features are shown.

also contains smooth muscle fibers, both radial and in the form of a sphincter, and by the antagonistic contraction of these the size of the hole in the
center of the iris, or pupil, can be increased or diminished. In many mammals, such as cats, the muscles are so arranged that as the large circular
pupil decreases in size it forms not, as in man, a smaller circle, but a vertical slit. A thin epithelial layer, continuous in front with that of the inside
of the cornea, behind with that of the choroid, covers both surfaces of the
iris, but most of its bulk is made up of connective tissue with blood vessels and many pigment cells. If there are few of these, the dark color of
the posterior epithelium, which is pigmented like that of the choroid,
showing through the white muscles, makes the iris appear blue; if there is
much pigment the iris appears dark brown. Intermediate quantities and
different distributions within the iris give shades of gray, green, and
lighter brown; probably also two separate pigments, black and yellow, are
involved. Except for its possible value in sexual selection in man (and that,
in more ways than one, must be a matter of opinion), and in some fishes
and snakes where it contributes to the general color pattern of the head,
the color of the iris has no known use in animals.

In the very front of the vitreous humor, and so immediately behind the
iris, is the lens, or, as the older books call it, the crystalline lens, where
the adjective has its original meaning of ice-like or transparent. It has a
basically fibrous structure, but this can be seen only with special treatment. Its outer surface is an elastic capsule, and from this radial fibers
run outward to make the suspensory ligament, and converge to be attached on the ciliary body as the zonule of Zinn.

Finally, lining the posterior chamber and making the sensitive surface
of the eye is the retina. On its outside this has a pigmented epithelial
layer, and then come three layers of nerve cells, with two layers of
synapses separating them. The actual light-sensitive cells, the rods and
cones, are immediately within the pigment layer, and the axons of the
inner layer run away over the internal surface of the eye to make the
optic nerve. Where this leaves the eye there can be no rods and cones,
and a blind spot is formed. Over its front portion the retina loses its nerve
cells, and runs forward to cover the posterior surface of the ciliary body
and iris as a pigmented layer. The line of transition is called the ora ser-
rata. The retina is supplied with blood through an artery which enters by
the optic nerve, and whose branches spread in a network in the outer
layer. Other arteries enter the eye at various points.

In spite of their position on or near the surface of the body, most of
these structures in the eye are formed from the brain, or, perhaps more
accurately, from the same part of the neural tube as forms the brain. As
the tube rolls up, in the region of the future tween brain there grows out
of it on each side a projection, which itself rolls up to form a cup
(Fig. 14.20). The hollow in the walls, which will shortly disappear, is

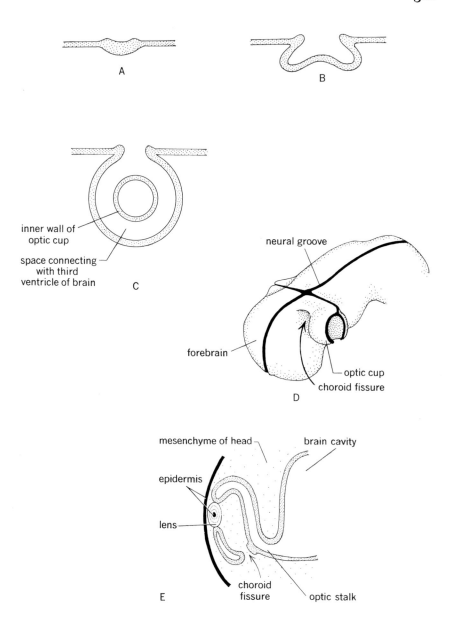

FIG. 14.20 Stages in the development of the mammalian eye. A, B, C show the formation of the optic cup in section as an outpushing of the wall of the tween brain; D shows the same stage as C. in solid; E is a section of a later stage in which the lens has been formed; the dead ectodermal evocator is seen at its center.

continuous with the third ventricle of the brain. Where the cup does not quite close a chink is left, the choroid fissure. As the cup is being formed, it comes very close to the surface of the body, and a small portion of the ectoderm above it sinks in and forms a sort of plug in the mouth of the cup. It used to be said to form the lens, but that appears not always to be true. Instead, it dies, and in dying, induces the nearby edge of the optic cup to form a lens around it. The cup produces also the ciliary body and the iris as an ingrowing flange. Around the outer wall of the cup, cells from the mesenchyme form the sclerotic and cornea and choroid, the last of which is comparable with the dura mater and arachnoid and pia mater of the brain. The cup itself, continuous with the wall of the brain, produces the retina. The axons of the inner layer of this grow inward to the brain to make the optic nerve. The cornea, although continuous with the sclerotic, appears to be formed from ectoderm, which also closes over the eye to make the conjunctiva. The humors are probably formed from mesenchyme.

Anyone who knows how a camera works knows, for the most part, how the eye works. Rays of light are bent and brought to a focus on the retina, but whereas in the camera all the bending is done by the lens, in the mammalian eye most of it—about two-thirds—is brought about by the cornea. There are in fact four refracting surfaces, air-cornea, cornea-aqueous humor, aqueous humor-lens, lens-vitreous humor, so that in effect the eye has a complex optical system comparable to that of a camera with a telephoto lens. The refractive index of the lens is not uniform throughout, so that there is some correction for aberration, and spherical aberration is also dealt with to some extent by the fact that the retina is curved, so that it accommodates a curved image. At rest, the optical system of the eye brings rays of light from distant objects (theoretically, those infinitely far away, such as a star, but in practice there is little difference between these and objects at a distance of a few hundred yards) to focus on the retina. Accommodation for nearer vision is brought about by altering the shape of the lens. Ciliary muscles, which have their origin on the inside of the sclerotic near the cornea and are inserted on the ciliary body, contract and so pull the body inward and forward. The result is a decrease in the tension in the suspensory ligament which holds the lens. The elasticity of the capsule of the lens then squeezes it into a more nearly spherical shape, chiefly by causing it to bulge forward. The resulting thicker lens bends the rays of light more than before, which is what is wanted for looking at near objects.

The pupil acts like the stop of a camera in reducing the amount of light that enters when its intensity is increased. Also like the camera-stop, it makes for a greater depth of focus by confining the part of the lens that is used to the central part. Hence in the eye defect of middle age called presbyopia, in which accommodation becomes inadequate through loss of the elasticity of the capsule, small print can be read in a bright light but becomes a complete blur in a dim one.

The ciliary muscles, and the circular muscles of the iris, are contracted by impulses from the parasympathetic fibers of the third cranial nerve, so that stimulation of this causes decrease in the size of the pupil and accommodation for near vision. They have also sympathetic innervation from the cervical ganglia, activity of which causes the opposite effect. The iris, at least in fish and amphibians, can act also as an independent effector, contracting automatically without nervous control, when light falls on it.

The sensitive elements in the eye that initiate a nervous impulse when light falls on them are the rods and cones, and their stimulation is connected in some way with the reduction of pigment in the retina. One, called chlorolabe, is bleached by green light, and another, erythrolabe, by red. A third, sensitive to blue, has recently been found, so that there is a basis for the old trichromatic theory, according to which all colors are derived from varying degrees of stimulation of receptors sensitive to the three primary colors of red, green, and blue.

On physical grounds one can be certain that an animal can discriminate two adjacent points only if their images fall on separate cells, so that the smaller the cells the better. But this is strictly true only if each sensory cell has its own independent fiber to the brain, and for most of the retina (at least in mammals) this appears not to be so; only in a special part, the fovea, is there one cell to a fiber, and this is the area of greatest discrimination. It is seen as a pit in the retina, because in it the lines of neurons are fanned out so that light falls directly on the cones instead of having to pass first through two other layers of cells. The fovea is the region on which we focus an object when we look directly at it. It contains no rods, and this suggests different functions for rods and cones. So too do the facts that the periphery of the retina contains only rods, and that in this region we can detect a faint star which is invisible if we look directly at it and make its image on the fovea. Unfortunately the distribution of rods and cones in other animals does not always agree with this distinction, and there appears to be no fundamental difference in the properties of the two types of sensory cell, in spite of their difference in shape.

There are also some external parts of the eye that are important in its working. The extrinsic muscles are six in number: a pair, superior and inferior, called oblique, which are attached toward the anterior half of the sclerotic (the inner or medial half in man), and four rectus muscles, superior, inferior, anterior (or internal), and posterior (or external), attached to the posterior half in the form of a cross. Various contractions of these can move the eye in all directions like a universal joint. The eyelids are muscular folds of skin which can meet over the cornea. The eyelashes with which they are fringed are ordinary hairs except in stiffness and length. A third eyelid, or nictitating membrane, which is vestigial in

man, starts from the anterior corner of the exposed part of the eye in
many animals. The socket of the skull which surrounds three-quarters of
the eye is the orbit.

The variations on this general plan in the various classes of vertebrate
affect chiefly the relative size of the lens, the method of accommodation,
the cellular structure of the retina, the number and function of the eye
muscles, and the state of the lids.

The eyes of cyclostomes, though built on the general vertebrate plan,
are peculiar in some important respects. Those of lampreys and hagfishes
are somewhat different; while those of the hagfishes are certainly degenerate, there is at least a suspicion that those of the lampreys are also.

The lamprey's lens, like that of most primitive vertebrates, is much
more nearly spherical than that of mammals. The cornea in front of it is
of normal construction, but in front of this there is a transparent covering of a multilayered skin which may be called a dermal cornea. Accommodation is carried out in a unique way, by the contraction of a special
muscle attached to the dermal cornea. This both flattens the cornea and
pulls the lens nearer to the retina. Both of these actions will adjust the
optical system for more distant objects, the reverse of what happens in
human accommodation, so that presumably the lamprey at rest is near-
sighted. The iris is rudimentary and the pupil probably does not change
in diameter. There are no lids, and no glands to produce a secretion to
protect the cornea. The eyes of the larvae are functionless and buried beneath the skin.

The eyes of hagfishes have no extrinsic muscles and are more or less
deeply buried, with normal pigmented skin overlying them. The eyes of
Myxine are without a lens.

The eyes of most elasmobranchs, which can be well seen by the student
when he dissects the dogfish, are complete, and remarkably similar, considering the differences in the modes of life, to those of mammals (Fig.
14.21). The sclerotic contains some cartilage. The lens is nearly spherical,
hard, and not easily deformable, and the cornea is thin. Accommodation
is by the contraction of a protractor muscle which pulls the lens forward,
so adjusting for the sight of near objects. There is a well-developed and
active iris, the sphincter of which has no innervation and acts as an independent effector, contracting, rather slowly, when light falls on it. The
radial muscles have the usual parasympathetic innervation from the oculomotor nerve. The retina consists mostly of rods, and there is no color
vision. Most dogfish have eyelids, which are, however, immovable. Those
of *Squalus* make a horizontal slit. A few, such as *Mustelus*, have also a
nictitating membrane.

Most teleosts (Fig. 14.22) have a normal cornea, which has, however,
some yellow pigment; others, such as eels, have a dermal cornea like that
of lampreys. The refractive index of the cornea, as in elasmobranchs, is

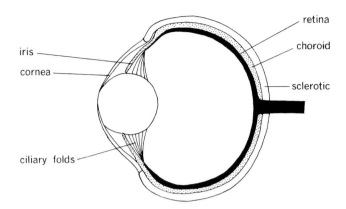

FIG. 14.21 Diagrammatic vertical section of the eye of a dogfish.

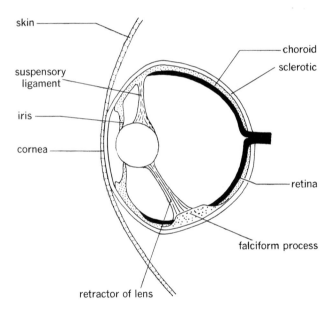

FIG. 14.22 Diagrammatic vertical section of the eye of a teleost.

almost the same as that of water, so that almost all the refraction of the eye is produced by the lens. This also is similar to that of elasmobranchs, but in some, such as the trout (*Salmo fario*), it is ellipsoid, which has the peculiar optical result that objects straight in front of the eye are in focus if close to, while those behind or to one side of the eye are in focus at distances from about one yard to infinity. There is some dispute about the method of accommodation. The usual view is that the eye at rest is adjusted for near vision, and that a retractor muscle pulls the lens back in accommodation. This muscle enters the eye through the choroid fissure, which does not completely close, and whose position is marked in many fish on the inside of the eye by the falciform process. According to some workers the retractor is not in fact muscular; they say that accommodation is brought about by contraction of the ciliary muscles, which does not, as in mammals, alter the shape of the lens, but reduces the diameter of the eyeball at the points where they are attached. Since its liquid contents are incompressible, this leads to a compensating increase in the diameter from retina to cornea. This, if it occurs, would adjust the eye for near vision. If the retractor is not muscular, and not used for accommodation, its function is unexplained.

Some fish have an active iris, others do not. Generally the sphincter is supplied from the sympathetic system, the radial fibers from the parasympathetic of the oculomotor nerve, the opposite arrangement to that of mammals, but the sphincter of the eel is largely an independent effector. There are more rods than cones in the retina, and some species have color vision. Most teleosts have no eyelids, but a few, such as herrings, have fatty lids that make a vertical slit.

The teleosts show a very wide range of adaptive radiation in their eyes, according to their habitat. In many deep-sea forms the eyes are very large, presumably to pick up the faint light of luminescent organisms. Some fish can form an image both in air and water, and the tropical *Anableps* has almost divided each eye into two for this purpose, having two pupils, a lens so placed that its curvature is different for each pupil, and a divided retina. It swims with its eyes awash, so that it can presumably see both up and down.

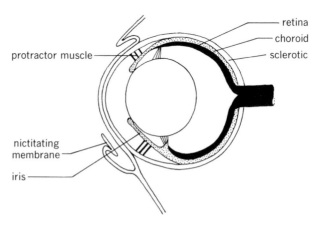

protractor muscle

retina
choroid
sclerotic

nictitating
membrane
iris

FIG. 14.23   Diagrammatic vertical section of the eye of a frog.

The skin of amphibians seems to be generally sensitive to light, for many species can detect the direction of illumination after the eyes have been removed. The eyes (Fig. 14.23) of tadpoles have cartilage in the sclerotic, and this sometimes persists in the adult. There is a persistent choroid fissure, which allows the passage of the protractor muscle of the lens, and through it in anurans there pass also hyaloid blood vessels to supply the inner parts of the eye. Accommodation is by the contraction of the protractor muscle of the lens, which pulls it forward and so adjusts for near vision. There is an iris which has double autonomic control and is also an independent effector. The retina has both rods and cones, and in frogs and toads there is some concentration of the latter to form a fovea. Within the four rectus muscles is another, the retractor of the eye, which can pull the whole eyeball back into its socket. Beyond these general points there are considerable differences between the eyes of anurans and urodeles, and between aquatic and terrestrial species in each order. A change in the eyes must have been one of the results of (or perhaps a prerequisite for) life on land, for the refractive index of air is very different from that of water. The result is that the cornea, as well as the lens, becomes an important source of refraction. Further, the removal of the eyes from water requires that they shall be lubricated (if they are mobile) and protected from dust and drying. We may expect that, allowing for any possible specializations, the eyes of the terrestrial present-day species will best show the typical amphibian eye.

The typical frogs have a fixed upper eyelid, and a lower lid which can be extended upward to cover the whole eye with a thin transparent sheet; when retracted it looks like an ordinary lower lid. It is called, from its use, a nictitating membrane, but it has a different point of origin from that of birds and mammals and may not be homologous. Lubrication for the movement of the lid is provided by an anterior lacrimal gland, and there is a lacrimal duct. Lids, glands, and duct are not present in the tadpole, and their formation takes place as part of the metamorphosis. In aquatic forms, such as *Pipa americana*, they are all lost, and instead of a thin conjuctiva there is a dermal cornea comparable to that of fishes.

The terrestrial urodeles, such as the salamanders, have a somewhat similar eye to the frogs, but both lids are fixed and there are both anterior and posterior lacrimal glands. Perennibranchiates such as *Necturus* have no lids or glands, and have a dermal cornea. *Proteus* and other species that live in caves are blind and have degenerate eyes. There is no cornea, the skin over the eye having the normal structure of other parts of the body, even to the presence of mucous and other glands, and there are no extrinsic muscles.

The Apoda have a small eye with a dermal cornea.

Rather surprisingly, it has been reported that while frogs and toads have

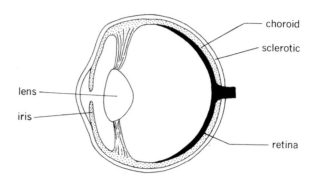

FIG. 14.24   Diagrammatic vertical section of the eye of a lizard.

very little power of discriminating colors, salamanders and newts have good color vision.

The typical reptilian eye (Fig. 14.24) is generally similar to that of mammals, except that accommodation is carried out by the contraction of ciliary muscles which press the ciliary body against the periphery of the lens and so make its surfaces, especially the anterior one, more rounded. This muscle, as well as that of the iris, is unusual in being striated. Both rods and cones are generally present, and in some reptiles there is a fovea. The vitreous is supplied with blood, not, as in rays, by hyaloid blood vessels, but by a papillary cone on the retina, which is, however, not present in turtles. A few have a retractor muscle of the eyeball. The sclerotic is generally cartilaginous, and in many it contains, near the junction with the cornea, a ring of bony plates, the scleral ossicles. These are well preserved in many fossils, such as ichthyosaurs. Their presence is not correlated with any particular habitat, and their function is unknown; they will presumably resist changes in curvature of the cornea. Both anterior and posterior lacrimal glands are present, and there are upper and lower eyelids and an anterior nictitating membrane.

There is much adaptive radiation within the class. The distribution of rods and cones in the Squamata generally follows the habit of life, diurnal forms tending to have only cones, nocturnal species, such as geckoes, only rods. Most lizards and a few snakes have a fovea, and also an area where, although there is not one-to-one connection of retinal elements to nerve fibres, each cone is thinner than normal, so that acuity is improved. Since the cones are also taller than normal, the area appears as a slight bump on the surface of the retina. Diurnal snakes and lizards have a round pupil and a yellow lens, nocturnal species have a vertical pupil and a colorless lens, and no fovea. The eyelids of many snakes are modified in a peculiar way to form the 'spectacles.' A sheet of transparent skin grows over the eye to form what is in effect a fixed eyelid, since between it and the cornea is a space filled with the secretion of the lacrimal glands. The normal eye-lids and the nictitating membranes are absent. Snakes have a special method of accommodation, in which contraction of the iris puts pressure on the vitreous, which moves the lens forward. *Sphenodon*, which is noc-turnal, has an eye very similar to that of nocturnal lizards, but with a shallow fovea.

The posterior lacrimal gland has become very large in marine turtles, and has acquired the new function of osmotic regulation, getting rid of sodium chloride absorbed by the tissues from the sea. There are probably no lacrimal ducts, so that the traditional picture of the weeping turtle is a correct one. Crocodiles, not so fully aquatic, retain the duct.

Both lizards and tortoises have good color discrimination.

The eyes of birds (Fig. 14.25), like so much else in their body, are fun-damentally reptilian, but are developed to a very high degree of efficiency. They are large, both relatively and absolutely, and are clearly important sense organs. The shape of the eye varies with the species. It is usually flattened from back to front, or it may be extended in the same dimension so as to approach the cylindrical, as in owls. The curvature of the retina is such that spherical aberration is almost completely eliminated, the im-age being bent to exactly the same degree. The cornea protrudes so that there is a ring-shaped groove behind it. Accommodation is brought about chiefly by the contraction of the ciliary muscle, which is striped as in liz-ards, squeezing the lens from its normal shape, something between a sphere and an ordinary biconvex lens, into a more or less pear-shaped form, with greatly increased curvature of the anterior surface. Another part of the ciliary muscle is so situated that its contraction must increase the curvature of the cornea, although it seems that this has not been proved to take place. This extra muscle is well developed in hawks, of lit-tle importance in nocturnal birds, and absent from aquatic birds, in which,

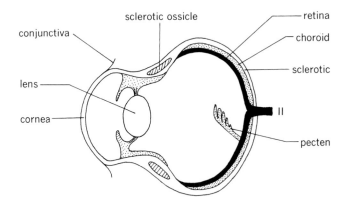

FIG. 14.25   Diagrammatic vertical section of the eye of a bird.

when they are under water, the cornea presumably plays little part in refraction. The iris is active, and can contract very quickly. It contains many pigments, giving rise in some birds to brilliant colors.

Both rods and cones may be present in the retina, but while in general diurnal birds have very few rods, nocturnal species have very few cones. The density of cones of passerine birds over most of the retina is about the same as that in the fovea of man, and the density of nerve fibers is nearly as great, so that there is presumably one-to-one correspondence. The cones are about the same size as those of man, so that the visual acuity is about the same, but birds can apparently see as clearly over the whole field of view as can man in the narrow line that he sees directly ahead. They can therefore see detail over a wide arc (virtually all around them) which man can find out only by scanning. In view of this it is surprising that birds not only have a fovea, in the sense of a region where the retinal cells are sloped outward so as to make a pit, but that this is often large, deep, or otherwise specialized. The foveas are at the centers of areas, in which the cone-density is higher than normal and the cones thinner and taller. The area may be central, as in man, that is, on the optic axis; it may run horizontally around the eye as a band; or there may be one central area and another on the temporal side of the retina. This last arrangement is found in many different sorts of birds that catch moving objects: falcons, kingfishers, swifts, swallows, and hummingbirds. Probably the temporal areas are used for binocular vision, which most birds do not possess. The value of the fovea is speculative; it may help in fixation.

The retina is completely free from blood vessels. Projecting into the vitreous humor from the optic nerve is a structure called the pecten, or comb. It has various shapes, but is usually corrugated and always highly vascular. It is presumably derived from the papilla of the eye of reptiles, and is assumed to convey food and oxygen to the vitreous and so to the retina. The pecten must cast a shadow on the retina, and as the form of the pecten bears some relation to the habits of the bird, and none to the size of the eye, it may have also an optical function. The suggestion that it helps in the detection of moving objects has been made, but this has not been proved.

Birds have sclerotic ossicles round the cornea, and some, such as the woodpeckers and passerines, have another ring round the entry of the optic nerve. The former possibly stiffen the eye to control the change of shape of the lens in accommodation. There are movable upper and lower eyelids, and a nictitating membrane which is drawn backward across the eye by a muscle which is apparently homologous with the rectractor of the eyeball of frogs and reptiles.

Birds have good color vision, which may, in some species, be superior to that of man.

The mammals show relatively little adaptive radiation in the eyes. Only the primates have good color vision, although rats appear to be able to distinguish red from other colors. The distinction of function between rods (for twilight vision) and cones (for acuity and color) that holds in man and birds, and to some extent in lizards, does not always apply. Mice, which are nocturnal and color-blind, follow the rule and have no cones, but squirrels, with an all-cone eye, are color-blind. Whales and seals retain their lacrimal glands, but have lost the duct. The secretion has become fatty, and presumably protects the cornea from irritation by the water. Most mammals have a retractor muscle of the eyeball.

It is impossible to make a neat consistent story of the comparative anatomy of the eye. Within the same basic pattern there are many variations, some closely connected with habit and function, others less so. Accommodation, since it is carried out in at least five different ways, has presumably been invented that number of times. Color vision has been acquired by teleosts, urodeles, lizards, chelonians, birds, and primates, probably all independently. Its mechanism is still obscure, but experience suggests that it need not always be the same. The relationship of rods and cones is still a mystery, and there are difficulties in understanding the chemistry of the retinal pigments. The eye is indeed even more of an evolutionary wonder than Darwin suspected.

15

The Axial Skeleton

THERE IS no formally agreed definition of the word 'skeleton' in zoology. Some books define it as a supporting or protecting structure, but when one considers individual pieces of skeleton in various animals it is often difficult to decide what it is that they support or protect. The ribs of man, for example, appear to protect the heart and lungs, but the abdomen is just as dangerous a place for a stab wound as the chest, as every infantryman of the First World War knew, yet it is quite unprotected. Nor do the ribs support anything, for they hang from the backbone and are rather themselves supported by the body wall. Moreover, some vertebrates, such as frogs, get on perfectly well without them. Ribs in fact appear to have become important as part of the mechanism for expanding the thorax so that the lungs could be filled with air. In other words, they are part of the joint mechanism, hard structures being necessary to give a steady movement of one part of the body or another. This brings us to what is probably the only characteristic that is common to all the many and various things to which the name skeleton has been applied. All are relatively hard and stiff. Their functions are not always the common ones of support and protection, and indeed are not always easy to determine. This is especially true of some of the odd structures that appear on the surface of the body.

The skeleton of vertebrates can be divided in various ways for the purposes of study and classification. The best division to begin with is one which applies to all animals, that is, into the part which is on the surface of the body, or is external, which may be called the exoskeleton, and into the part which is deep-seated and surrounded by other tissues, or is internal, which is called the endoskeleton. This, though convenient and practical, is not, however, an absolute division, for parts that are internal in one animal may come to the surface of others. Even less does it correspond to a possible embryological classification, into skeletons derived from ectoderm, mesoderm, and endoderm.

The main endoskeleton of vertebrates is unusual, as we have seen in Chapter 2, in being mesodermal, and unique in being made either of cartilage or bone or both. Most of this chapter and the next two will be concerned with it. Vertebrates do, however, possess other types of endoskeleton, which they share, to a greater or lesser degree, with other animals. First, there is the notochord, present in protochordates as well as in vertebrates. It is very unusual among skeletal structures in being derived, at least in some animals, from the wall of the archenteron, and so in being endodermal. Its stiffness arises not in any hard material of which it is made, but in the fact that its cells contain large vacuoles containing water under pressure. Water being only slightly compressible, such a structure will bend only a little without rupture, and when released will spring back elastically. We are familiar with this type of structure in the stems of herbaceous plants. They will bend to the wind and recoil, but if bent through too great an arc at one point they collapse irrecoverably; the cells have been broken. The same principle, though a different form of construction, is found in a number of animals, including vertebrates, where blood under pressure from the heart is prevented from escaping from venous spaces. Examples are found in the erection of the comb of the cock and of the mammalian penis.

The yellow and white fibers of connective tissue, made of elastin and collagen respectively, both substances being proteins, are stiffer than their surrounding fluids or cells, and so must be counted as skeletal material. When they are condensed to form ligaments and tendons this becomes very obvious; the difficulty of cutting tough meat is due to the white fibers that it contains.

The characteristic histological structure of bone and cartilage has been described in Chapter 2. In the development of the individual, cartilage appears before there is any bone, and many bones are formed in cartilage, which is dissolved as the bone spreads. This leads to the distinction between cartilage bones and the others, not preceded by cartilage, called membrane bones, but there is no other difference betwen the two types. One may assume that the history of the race has followed the same course, and that there were once vertebrates, or protovertebrates, that possessed cartilage but not bone, but there is no evidence of this. The earliest vertebrates known, as we have seen in Chapter 3, had a bony skeleton. An alternative view is that cartilage was developed as an embryonic tissue, and that its persistence in the adults of elasmobranchs and sturgeons is an example of neoteny, the survival into sexual adulthood of features of a larva. There is no evidence for this view either, and the student may make his choice. What is certain is that cartilage and bone have different physical properties of elasticity, hardness, breaking stress, and so on; from this one may deduce that if they have been produced by natural selection different environmental pressures must have been at work in the two cases. What these pressures were, however, we do not know. Dogfish and teleosts live side by side in the same seas, one with cartilage, the other with bone, and although the elasmobranchs are apparently unable to live in rivers, the sturgeons, which also have a cartilaginous skeleton, do. It hardly seems likely that the heterocercal tail, possessed by both sharks and sturgeons, necessitates cartilage rather than bone. We shall, in the account that follows, take cartilage before bone, without making any decision about which came first in evolution.

The bony or cartilaginous skeleton is customarily divided, not very satisfactorily, into the axial skeleton which runs the length of the body, and the appendicular skeleton which supports the limbs and is hung from the first. In what follows we shall use this division as a frame of reference rather than as a formal classification.

The head of vertebrates, however it may be defined, contains the skull; running back from this is a chain of separate skeletal elements, the vertebrae, making up the vertebral column or backbone and usually running to the tip of the tail. These two parts make up the strict axial skeleton. Both surround, and in a fully developed vertebrate replace, the notochord.

The notochord itself has a characteristic structure of large vacuolated cells in all vertebrates. On its outer surface is a condensation of cells making an endothelium and outside this the notochordal sheath. This always has at least two layers, an inner consisting mainly of white fibers, and an outer consisting mainly of yellow fibers. In elasmobranchs, dipnoans, and sturgeons a third layer, also of yellow fibers, occurs inside the white fibrous layer. The origin of the notochordal sheath is disputed, some workers saying that the fibers are secreted by the cells of the notochord itself, others that it is mesoblastic, and formed by cells that belong to the sclerotomes. Yet another view is that the white fibrous sheath is made by the notochord and the elastic sheath by the mesoblast. In all adult vertebrates the notochord and its sheaths are partially or entirely lost. We shall mention the degree to which this takes place in the accounts of the vertebrae below.

Vertebrae

The adult vertebra is formally divided into a middle piece or centrum, a neural arch above this enclosing the nerve cord, and a hemal arch below, which is often incomplete, but which, when it is present, encloses an artery and vein. Sometimes the centrum itself is missing, and then the notochord persists, the neural arch sitting on top of it and the hemal arch projecting below.

The embryology of the vertebrae is difficult, and so, consequently, is their homology. Sense can be made of both if one adopts the scheme developed by Gadow about the beginning of this century. According to this the sclerotome of each side formed originally four skeletal pieces, cartilaginous or bony, called arcualia (Plate VI.1). There are the interdorsal and interventral in front, the basidorsal and basiventral behind. The elements 'ventral' and 'dorsal' in these four words describe their position. Cells from the myotome grow between the interarcualia and the basiarcualia of each sclerotome, so that the skeletal segment becomes divided into two. The posterior pair of elements (basi-) from one side of segment n then join with the anterior pair (inter-) from the same side of segment $n + 1$ to make half a vertebra, and the cartilages formed from the four arcualia of each side join together around the notochord, so that each vertebra is made up from eight elements. The degree to which each of the four contributes to the adult vertebra differs in different groups, and leads to an embryological classification of the vertebrae. The arcualia are so called because they form primarily the arches, and only later grow upward, downward, and inward to constrict the notochord and make the centrum. Some part of the centrum may also be formed from the notochordal sheath or from the unsegmented mesenchyme around the notochord. In some animals this gives rise directly to bone, without the previous formation of cartilage. The arcualia generally first become cartilage, which is then replaced by bone in the ordinary way. In most animals they fuse to form a single piece in the adult, but in some, such as the dogfish, separate pieces persist. These are even more obvious in the bony vertebrae of some extinct tetrapods.

The supporting axis of the cyclostomes is still the notochord, which has the double sheath thick and well developed, and more or less continuous with a layer of connective tissue that surrounds both notochord and central nervous system, and is itself continuous with the myocommata separating the somites. There are no centra, but pieces of cartilage lie on each side of the nerve cord. They are best developed in *Petromyzon*, where there are two per segment on each side, so that they perhaps represent the basidorsal and interdorsal elements. In *Myxine* they are present only in the tail. There are also ventral elements in the tail of lampreys, which perhaps represent the basiventral and interventral elements. There is no reason to think that the persistent notochord and rudimentary vertebrae of cyclostomes are necessarily primitive, since these creatures have lost most of the skeleton of their ostracoderm ancestors. Unfortunately, since these all had a bony exoskeleton, their backbone, if they had one, is not preserved. We therefore know nothing of the vertebral column of the earliest vertebrates.

In elasmobranchs the sclerotomes become joined with those in front and behind and on the other side to form a continuous cylinder surrounding the notochord and the nerve cord. In this the four dorsal arcualia develop in each original segment, the position of which is marked by intersegmental blood vessels. They grow, and the basidorsals meet over the nerve cord to form the neural arch. The interdorsals are smaller, and remain as separate pieces behind the arch. Basiventral elements form in a similar way, but do not fuse to form a hemal arch except in the tail. Smaller interventrals sometimes fuse with the basiventrals of the same segment, sometimes with those of the segment behind, so that there is some irregularity in the segmentation of the vertebral column. The inner pieces of the basidorsals and basiventrals, which lie close to the noto-chord, form part of the centrum, but most of this comes from two other sources. Most of it is formed from a calcification in the fibrous notochordal sheath, and some of it from a calcification in the mesoblast surrounding the notochord separate from that of the arcualia. Since the cells of the arcualia invade the sheath, and since the arcualia are themselves formed in the continuous tube of mesoblast surrounding the notochord, the dis-tinction between these three types of origin is not very clear. The result of the invasion and chondrification in the notochordal sheath is that in the region of the arcualia the notochord is constricted and all but obliter-ated. A transverse section of the mass of cartilage so formed is shaped like a circle with a hole in the middle, while its longitudinal section ap-pears as two triangles not quite meeting at their points. To these simple shapes are added the neural and hemal regions (Plates VI.2-5, VII.1, VII.2).

The proportions of the centrum formed from the various sources, and the disposition of the interarcualia, vary in different species. *Squalus* has one of the simplest arrangements, with a centrum which is amphicelous, that is, shaped like a double-ended cup; it is formed largely of the noto-chordal sheath and the basalia, the basidorsals being fused above the nerve cord to make the neural arch, and the interdorsals also fused, to complete the tunnel in which the nerve cord runs. In *Scyliorhinus* the interdorsals barely meet, and the spaces between them and the neural arch are filled up with extra cartilages called supradorsals (Plate VI.5). In both the basiventrals form short processes bearing ribs in the trunk region, and meet to form a hemal arch in the tail (Plate VII.2).

In the tail each vertebra becomes double, a condition known as diplo-spondyly. It apparently arises by a longitudinal growth and subsequent transverse division of the basidorsal and basiventral, followed by the for-mation of a new interdorsal. The result is that for each pair of myomeres and spinal nerves there are two complete vertebrae.

The early elasmobranchs (Pleuracanthodii and Acanthodii) had an un-constricted notochord without centra, but in at least some of them the four types of arcualia appear to have been present.

The centra of teleosts are bony and well developed. They are formed mostly from the mesoderm outside the notochord, with some contribution from the inner parts of the basidorsals and basiventrals. They grow in-ward and obliterate the notochord without invading it, so that although the centrum is slightly amphicelous (hollow at both ends), it has not the double cone form of that of the dogfish. Basidorsals and basiventrals form neural and hemal arches, but the interarcualia are probably absent, and certainly not well developed. Supradorsals are usually present between the neural arches. In the sturgeons the notochord persists and is unconstricted; there are no centra, but basidorsals and basiventrals, and smaller interdorsals and interventrals, are present.

Dipnoi also have an unconstricted notochord, but the interarcualia are fused with the basals except in the tail, where separate interdorsals are present. *Latimeria*, too, has an unconstricted notochord.

The cartilaginous skeleton of the elasmobranchs has the same sort of properties as the notochord. It is tough, flexible, and elastic, and presumably less easily broken. The bony vertebrae of the teleosts make a clear advance in that they allow the formation of sliding joints. These take the form chiefly of processes from the neural and hemal arches, but there may in addition, or instead, be processes from the dorsal part of the centrum. These seem not to be homologous with the corresponding processes in tetrapods, for they are not regular, and articulate so that the posterior process of one vertebra is below the anterior process of the next.

It is difficult to associate the different forms of fish vertebrae with their mode of life. Though articulations may appear to be mechanically better than a bending rod, there is no evidence that bony fishes, as a class, swim any better than the cartilaginous groups. Some of them, such as the tunny (*Thynnus vulgaris*) are faster, and as this species has large articulating processes one may assume that they are connected with its speed, but many others, which yet retain the bony backbone, are more sluggish than any shark. The sturgeons have lost, presumably, the bony vertebrae that they once possessed, and support the swimming tail entirely by the notochord and its sheath. Yet they are active enough to swim up fast-flowing rivers to spawn, living in this respect a very similar life to the salmon, one of the most active families of teleost. The bony vertebrae of teleosts give us no help in understanding the evolution of those of tetrapods.

While in general all four arcualia can be recognized in fishes, in tetrapods there is always more or less of a reduction, and it is not always easy to say which pieces contribute to the adult vertebra and which are missing. The scheme most generally accepted is shown in Plate VII.3. We may assume that the earliest, unknown, tetrapods already showed some reduction of the interarcualia, especially of the interventral. From this it is easy to derive the condition in the earliest amphibians, the Rhachitomi of the Carboniferous, in which the interventral was missing and the interdorsal small. This is the condition in crossopterygian fishes also. Other early amphibians, the Stereospondyli, have lost the interdorsal as well.

From the rhachitomous condition can be derived that of all the modern Amphibia. In the Anura and Gymnophiona the centrum is formed from the basidorsal with a small contribution from the interdorsal, and the basidorsal is fused on top to make the neural arch. The vertebra of urodeles is similar except that the interdorsal remains separate as an intervertebral disc.

It is impossible to derive the amniote condition from any of these, and one must suppose that in some unknown early amphibian the interarcualia began to grow in importance. The stegocephalians known as Embolomeri show something of this condition, but appear to have lost the interventral completely. From a hypothetical form one can derive the amniote vertebra, in which the centrum is made mainly of the interdorsal, with the neural arch formed from the basidorsal rising above it. A small posterior part of the centrum is made from the interventral, and the basiventral persists as the intervertebral disc. According to some authors the interventral makes the bulk of the centrum.

Another series of names, such as notocentrum (for the Anura) and pleurocentrum or gastrocentrum (for the amniotes), is also in use. The names were mostly invented by paleontologists, who have not always agreed about their meaning. Moreover, they are sometimes applied as descriptions of the vertebra as a whole, sometimes to the elements of which it is supposed to be built. In view of these confusions, and of the fact that the etymology of the words gives no clue to their meanings, they will not be used here. In general, authors use the word intercentrum as the equivalent of basiventral; pleurocentrum for interdorsal, and hypocentrum for interventral or basiventral.

The vertebrae of modern amphibians show all the essential features of those of tetrapods, and can be functionally interpreted as suited to a life on land. They are bony, each centrum articulates with the one in front of it and with the one behind, and the joint is strengthened (though restricted in its movements) by paired processes from the dorsal part of the centrum. The anterior process is a prezygapophysis, the posterior a postzygapophysis, and the former can be recognized by the fact that its articular surface looks upward. In other words the prezygapophysis is below the postzygapophysis in the joint. This is a general rule that applies throughout the tetrapods, and enables one to orientate any vertebra. The neural arch is above the centrum, the prezygapophysis is anterior, and when these are known the third axis is fixed. Fortunately, tetrapods rarely have a hemal arch, so that there is seldom any difficulty in deciding which is centrum and which neural arch.

The Amphibia show a beginning of regionalization in the vertebrae, so that it is impossible to take any one and say that it is completely typical. This division into different forms at different levels is carried further in the amniotes, where vertebrae of neck, thorax, and so on, must to a great extent be described separately.

Most urodele vertebrae are opisthocelous, that is, they are hollow behind. It may be taken for granted that, if they articulate with the adjacent ones, they must also be convex in front. Most anuran vertebrae are the reverse, procelous, or hollow in front. In both groups the first vertebra, which articulates with the skull and is called the atlas, is different. It has two hollows on the front of the centrum, to articulate with two knobs, or

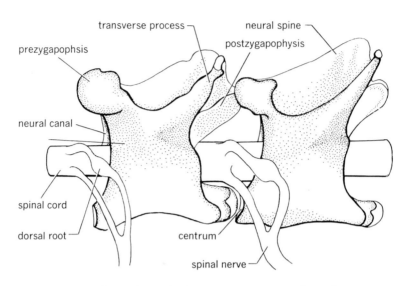

FIG. 15.1   Two trunk vertebrae of a frog, *Rana temporaria*, lateral, x 5.

occipital condyles, on the skull. Posteriorly, it is normal, to fit into the series. Each vertebra (Fig. 15.1) has also two transverse processes. In the
urodeles these are much the same all down the trunk, but in the frog
they are slightly different in each vertebra and enable one to recognize
which is which.

Urodeles have many vertebrae, the usual range being from about thirty
to about a hundred. About half or less of these are trunk vertebrae, and
one articulates with the pelvic girdle and is called sacral. The remainder,
which are in the tail, are called caudal, and are unusual among tetrapod
vertebrae in having a hemal arch, formed from the basiventrals, which
encloses the caudal artery and vein just as does that of the dogfish. The
number of vertebrae in the Anura is greatly reduced, usually to nine, of
which the last is the sacral. Frogs have no tail, but behind the sacral vertebrae and articulating with it is a pointed, partly hollow, unsegmented
bony rod, the urostyle, which consists of several vertebrae fused. No vertebrae are present in the tadpole's tail, which is stiffened only by the notochord. The urostyle has two hollows at its anterior end, which means that
the sacral vertebra must have two bulges. It is also convex anteriorly,
which puts the eighth vertebra in front of it out of step, since it has to be
hollow both fore and aft.

The Apoda have up to 250 vertebrae, which are amphicelous. Obviously,
centra which are all of this shape cannot articulate, and in fact, except in the
centers of the vertebrae, the notochord persists. There has been a return to a
fish-like condition, presumably in association with the loss of the limbs and

of the normal tetrapod habit. The same amphicelous condition and persistent notochord are found in some urodeles, especially those, such as *Necturus,* that never leave the water.

The development of the vertebrae of the Amphibia can be made to fit into the scheme shown in Plate VI.1, but there is a much earlier fusion of the cartilaginous blocks, and if the clearer state of affairs in fishes had not been known to us it is very unlikely that it would have been discovered in the amphibians. This is especially true of the anurans, where the accounts of different investigators do not agree and where some have failed to find any basiventrals except in the urostyle. Much of the vertebra comes from the notochordal sheath, and since the degree to which this is so differs within a genus, and even between vertebrae in the same species, ontogeny does not seem here to be a very helpful guide.

The interarcualia in urodeles usually become split vertically, each half becoming attached to the vertebra next to it to form its articular surface, convex or concave as the case may be.

The reptiles vary widely in form and habit, and so it is not surprising that they have many different types and arrangements of vertebrae. Some generalizations are, however, possible. The regionalization, incipient in the Amphibia, is more marked. In particular there is a distinct neck, with cervical vertebrae which have short ribs or none. Those of the trunk are sometimes divided into an anterior thoracic set which bear ribs and a posterior lumbar set which do not. Lizards have only one or two lumbar vertebrae, but crocodiles have more. Many extinct reptiles have no distinction in the trunk vertebrae, and in early tetrapods such as *Seymouria* and *Paracyclotosaurus* (Fig. 17.35) even the caudal vertebrae have ribs, a sobering thought for those who tell us that ribs were evolved for thoracic respiration. In living reptiles there are usually two sacral vertebrae, but in many extinct forms there were more, up to six. Small chevron bones on each side of the caudal vertebrae probably represent the basiventrals, and if so are homologous with the hemal arches of fish and amphibians.

The centra are generally procelous, but there are many exceptions. Those of *Sphenodon* and the geckoes are amphicelous, with a persistent notochord. Some of those of chelonians are opisthocelous. In the crocodile's tail they are convex at both ends, a condition so rare that it does not seem to have been given a name. When the vertebra articulates, pre- and postzygapophyses of the usual form are present.

The vertebra that supports the head is modified as the atlas, and the vertebra immediately behind this is also modified as the axis. The modifications are much more than a mere change in form, for there is a characteristic rearrangement of the elements from which the vertebrae are formed (Plate VIII.1). The atlas consists almost entirely of the basidorsals, with a small contribution from the basiventrals. The basidorsals make a neural arch and the basiventrals join to form a small hypocentrum below the nerve cord. Its interdorsals remain separate, and later join with the centrum of the axis to make a forwardly projecting peg or odontoid process. The effect of this is that the atlas functions as a split washer between the axis and the skull. The single hollow formed by the base of the neural arch and the hypocentrum articulates with a single large occipital condyle on the skull.

In some reptiles, such as crocodiles, a small bone called a pro-atlas occurs in front of the atlas. Its homology is not clear; it may be part of the atlas, or the remains of an occipital segment of which the rest has been included in the skull, or it may be a sesamoid bone, that is, a small bone formed in a tendon.

Reptiles of specialized habits have various peculiarities in the backbone. In snakes, apart from the atlas and axis, the only distinction is into trunk and caudal vertebrae, the difference being that the former have ribs. The centra are strongly procelous, and in addition to the zygapophyses there are extra paired articulating processes, zygosphene in front and zygantrum behind, at the base of the neural arch (Fig. 15.2). The effect of this is that the body is very flexible in the horizontal plane, but can move hardly at all in the vertical plane. This agrees with the usual method of locomotion of snakes.

The vertebrae of ichthyosaurs were amphicelous, one of many features in which they had reverted to a fish-like condition.

More than once processes from the vertebrae have become associated with an armored exoskeleton. In the turtles expanded neural spines become fused with a row of dermal bones to form the neural plates that make the dorsal axis of the shell (Fig. 18.14). In the Pelycosauria the neural spines were huge, up to three feet long, and some of them such as *Edaphosaurus* had cross-pieces (Fig. 15.3). These spines must have supported something, presumably a web of skin, but what its function was is anyone's guess.

The birds show the division of the backbone into cervical, thoracic, lumbar, sacral, and caudal regions very clearly. The neck is long, with the number of vertebrae varying from nine to twenty-five (Fig. 15.4). They have short double-headed ribs, which except in the last few become fused onto the centra to enclose a small space, the vertebrarterial canal, through which runs the vertebral artery. Their most characteristic feature is the shape of the articulating surface of the centrum, which is hollow in one direction, convex in the other, giving a form known as saddle-shaped or heterocelous. The hollow runs from side to side on the front surface. This arrangement, combined with the large flat zygapophyses makes a neck which is extremely flexible. Most birds can turn their heads through 180° to look at their tails, and some, such as the wryneck (*Jynx*), can go the whole circle through 360°.

The thoracic vertebrae, usually few in number, bear ribs, and are

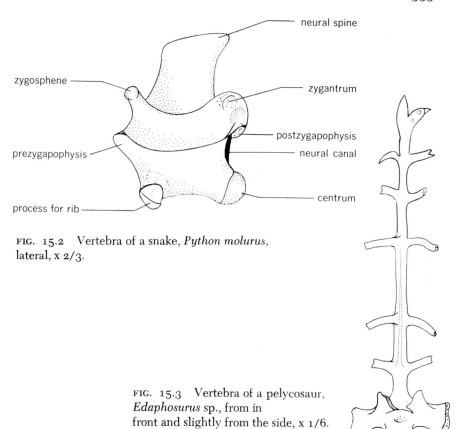

FIG. 15.2 Vertebra of a snake, *Python molurus*, lateral, x 2/3.

FIG. 15.3 Vertebra of a pelycosaur, *Edaphosurus* sp., from in front and slightly from the side, x 1/6.

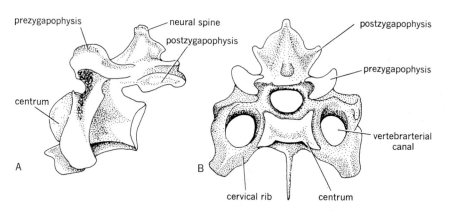

FIG. 15.4 Cervical vertebra of a turkey, *Meleagris gallopavo*, (A) Lateral, x 3/2. (B) Anterior x 3/2.

locked together by the sternum, described below, so they have little move-ment. Some of them become fused to each other. When separate they are either heterocelous or procelous, and can often be recognized by the rather large neural spines, which are elongated into flat longitudinal plates. The lumbars, distinguished only by the absence of ribs, are also immovable, and may be fused to the thoracics in front of them and the sacrals behind. The true sacrals, that is those which actually touch the ilia of the pelvic girdle, are two, but several caudal vertebrae are fused on behind. The result is that there is a long solid mass of bone made from lumbar, sacral, and caudal vertebrae to the total number of about twenty; the pelvic girdle is also firmly fused on to this, and the whole complex makes a single bony structure called the synsacrum (Fig. 6.8). Behind it are a few free but degenerate caudal vertebrae, and then a few more which are fused together to form a single bone. This is usually called the pygostyle, but it is formed in the same way as the urostyle of frogs, and there seems no reason why it should not have the same name. It is, how-ever, free to move, and supports the tail feathers.

The atlas and axis are formed in the same way as in reptiles, but the hypocentrum of the atlas is joined on to the neural arch to form a ring. This is another example of how the birds have independently attained the same state as the mammals.

Archaeopteryx has a backbone that is more reptilian than avian in form. The centra are flat or slightly biconcave, and have no trace of the heterocelous shape. There are eight sacral vertebrae but no synsacrum, and there is a long tail of twenty separate vertebrae.

The mammals have the same sort of regionalization as the birds, but it differs much in detail. The neck has an extraordinary constancy in having seven vertebrae (Fig. 7.1), in strong contrast to that of birds. As in birds, short ribs fused on to the centrum form a vertebrarterial canal. The cervical vertebrae are mostly flat on both surfaces, or amphiplatyan, so that most of the articulation depends on the zygapophyses. In Perisso-dactyla and Probiscidea they are opisthocelous.

The thoracic vertebrae, from nine to twenty-five in number, are also mostly amphiplatyan, or nearly so, and are perhaps the most character-istic mammalian vertebrae (Fig. 15.5A). Most of their ribs are double-headed, and to take the upper limb of this articulation each vertebra has a slight hollow on its transverse process. The lower limb articulates not with a single vertebra but with the centra of two, fitting against the crack between them. Each centrum thus has two half-facets, one anterior and one posterior, on each side.

The lumbar vertebrae (Fig. 15.5B) are usually four to seven in number, but may be as few as two or as many as twenty-four. There is a rough constancy of about twenty thoracic and lumbar vertebrae taken together, a deficiency in one region being balanced by an excess in the other. Big

deviations from this number are found only in the Cetacea, some of which
have twenty or more lumbar vertebrae. The other fully aquatic order, the
Sirenia, have nineteen to twenty-four in all, but not more than five lumbars. There is in many mammals slight variation within a species. The
lumbar vertebrae have large transverse processes, sometimes called pleur-
apophyses, and many of them have other long processes as well; a hyp-
apophysis below, balancing the neural spine, and a pair of metapophyses
rising up above the prezygapophyses. These are not for articulation, but
for attachment of muscles, and are developed in connection with the
great bending of the back in a vertical plane that takes place in the running of most mammals. This is in strong contrast to the running or hopping of birds, where all the bending takes place in the legs and the body
is rigid. Man, with his bipedal gait, uses his back muscles less in walking,
but they are still some of the most powerful in the body, and are used in
such activities as lifting or the artificial one of rowing.

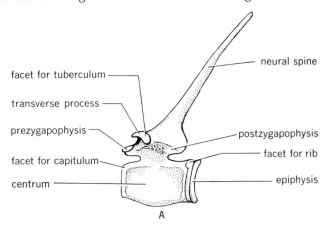

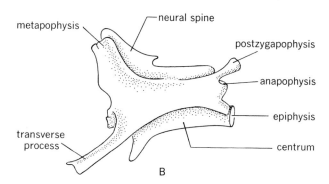

FIG. 15.5   (A) Thoracic vertebra of a rabbit, *Oryctolagus cuniculus*, lateral,
x 2. (B) Lumbar vertebra of a rabbit, *Oryctolagus cuniculus*, lateral, x 1.

The sacral vertebrae are fused together, and it is sometimes difficult to determine the exact number that touch the girdle. It seems to be generally from three to five. The limits of separate vertebrae in the fused tube are marked by the foramina for the exit of the spinal nerves.

The number of caudal vertebrae varies much, according to the length of the tail. In the false vampire bat *Megaderma frons,* there are none. Man has three or four, which are fused together to form a short coccyx or uro-style, which is presumably functionless. The peculiar tail-less Manx cat also has three. The highest numbers are found in the rodents, carnivores, whales, monkeys, and, rather surprisingly, the elephants, many of which have over twenty. All caudal vertebrae show some degree of degenera-tion, with reduction of the processes, and toward the tip of the tail they become mere beads of bone without even a passage for the nerve cord, which does not extend that far.

Chevron bones are present in the tails of some mammals, of several orders.

The atlas and axis are formed as in reptiles, but the atlas is a complete ring. The odontoid process of artiodactyls is notable for being spoon-shaped (Fig. 15.6).

The assignment of the vertebrae of amniotes to the scheme shown in Plate VII.3 can only be made in the most general terms and with a certain amount of faith. Accounts of the development of the vertebrae of reptiles are contradictory, but it is doubtful if the interdorsals exist at all, and in-terventrals almost certainly do not. Basiventrals remain separate in the tail and form chevron bones, but elsewhere they contribute to the cen-trum. As we have seen, in the atlas they remain distinct as a hypocentrum. The ontogeny is rather clearer in birds, and basidorsal and interdorsal form the vertebra, with small contributions from the basiventral and in-terventral, and of course from the ossification of the notochordal sheath.

In some mammals also the eight theoretical blocks have been made out, but in others it is said that there is a continuous mass of mesenchyme, which merely varies in its density from place to place. The cartilaginous epiphyses, or intervertebral discs, which are attached to the bony verte-brae, and make the actual articulating surface, are apparently formed from the mesenchyme surrounding the notochord, which grows in be-tween the vertebrae.

Ribs

Most authors avoid the difficult problem of defining such apparently simple things as ribs. They are certainly paired lateral structures, and they usually articulate with the vertebrae. We have seen, however, that in birds and mammals structures called ribs fuse onto the centra of the cervi-cal vertebrae. They appear to be serially homologous with the undoubted

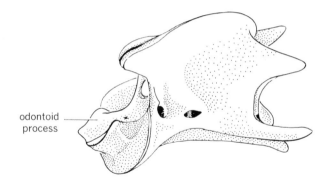

odontoid
process

FIG. 15.6 Axis vertebra of a fallow deer, *Dama dama*, lateral, x 1, to show the shovel-shaped odontoid process characteristic of artiodactyls.

ribs of the thorax, but they make definition difficult, because ribs are, in common conception, distinct from vertebrae. Another source of confusion could arise if some of the arcualia became ossified and extended laterally without joining the centrum. This has indeed happened, and has led to the expected confusion, for some books apply the term rib to the chevron bones and hemal arches, which are formed in this way. If one regards the ribs as outgrowths of the vertebrae (of the basiventrals, in fact) definition is impossible. One may, however, consider them as independent pieces of skeleton, developed not as strictly part of the axial skeleton but as lateral structures secondarily becoming connected with it, and so more properly called appendicular. A rib may then be defined as an intersegmental lateral skeletal structure articulating with the vertebra, or, if attached to it, clearly by a secondary union. This excludes the hemal arches from the definition, which is in accordance with common usage, and is supported by the fact that in no known case, except the Chelonia, does cartilage grow out centrifugally from a vertebra to form anything that looks like a rib.

The elasmobranchs have well-formed ribs in all the trunk segments except the first few, and sometimes there are vestiges in the first few caudal segments as well. They are formed where the myocomma dividing the successive muscle blocks cuts the horizontal septum that separates the dorsal series of muscles from the ventral, and are distinguished as dorsal ribs. The tissue from which they are formed has grown out from the posterior part of each somite. This is the region which forms also the basiventral, and sometimes cartilage appears simultaneously all along, separation into rib and vertebra coming later. In other cases the cartilage forms in two separate blocks. There is no means of telling which is the more primitive condition.

Teleosts have thin bony ribs in the same position as the cartilaginous ribs of the elasmobranchs (Fig. 15.7), but they have also a longer pair, which are called pleural, or ventral, which run down the abdominal wall where it comes against the muscle, that is on the inner surface of the somatopleure. These ventral ribs sometimes almost surround the abdominal cavity. Both ribs may articulate with the basiventral region of the vertebra, or the dorsal ribs may come against the bases of the ventral ones. Both types of rib may be present in the anterior part of the tail. The hemal arches are formed from outgrowths of the basiventrals and are independent of the ribs.

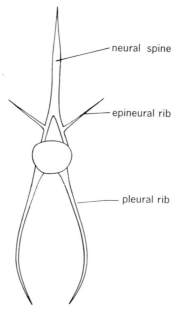

FIG. 15.7   Trunk vertebra and ribs of a salmon, *Salmo salar*, anterior, x 2/3.

The condition in some of the more primitive bony fish is rather different. In *Polypterus*, for example, the ventral ribs pass gradually into the hemal arches, with which they appear to be serially homologous. It would seem more logical not to regard them as ribs at all, but as mere processes from the vertebrae. There is support for this view in the fact that they develop from different blocks of cartilage from those that form the dorsal ribs.

Dipnoi have ventral ribs only. They are peculiar in that the ribs of the occipital segments that become incorporated in the brain-box persist, so that there are cranial ribs attached to the skull in the adult.

The ribs of tetrapods are dorsal in origin, but often extend ventralward until they meet. They are developed in relation to the basiventral (hypocentrum), with which they primitively have articulation through a knob

called the head or capitulum. Most of them have also a second articulation, with the transverse process of the vertebra, through a second knob
or tuberculum. Such ribs are called two-headed or bicipital. The vertebral
artery and vein run between capitulum and tuberculum, and so are enclosed in an incomplete tunnel. One would expect the simple-headed rib
to be primitive, but there is no paleontological evidence that this is so.
Eogyrinus, one of the earliest amphibians, and *Seymouria,* one of the most
primitive of reptiles, already had bicipital ribs. The ventral articulation
may shift to make contact with other parts of the centrum, especially when
the basiventral is not well developed, as in amniotes. Other shifts, of both
capitulum and tuberculum, also occur.

The ribs of tetrapods always, except in chelonians, chondrify separately
from the vertebrae, so that they scarcely belong to the axial skeleton.

Of the early phylogeny of ribs nothing is known, since they do not
occur in Agnatha, and nothing can usefully be said. It remains possible
that the ribs of fishes and tetrapods are not homologous.

The Stegocephalia had a complete series of ribs, with no distinction between thorax and abdomen, and caudal ribs continued behind the sacrum
(Fig. 17.35). The earliest forms had typically double-headed ribs, but in
some later species they were single-headed. In all modern amphibians they
are more or less reduced. In urodeles they are generally two-headed and
very short, as in *Necturus.* Most of the Anura have lost them altogether.

Reptiles often have abdominal and caudal ribs. The earliest species also
had typical two-headed ribs, but most modern forms—*Sphenodon,* snakes,
and most lizards—have ribs with only one head. The reduction seems to
have been achieved by the fusion of capitulum and tuberculum to form a
single knob that articulates with the centrum. Single-headed ribs were also
present in cotylosaurs and many theromorphs.

The Chelonia are peculiar in several ways. Their ribs are double-headed,
and in the trunk are greatly expanded to support the shell. Short ribs are
present in the sacral region and in the tail, and in the latter they may be
fused to the vertebrae. Their unusual centrifugal development of the cartilage from the vertebrae has already been mentioned, and is presumably
secondary.

Both *Sphenodon* and the crocodiles have on their ribs backwardly-di-
rected cartilaginous spurs, known as uncinate processes (Fig. 15.8). Since
they chondrify separately from the ribs, and join up later, it has been suggested that these are relics of the dorsal ribs of elasmobranchs which are not
otherwise known in tetrapods, but it seems more likely that they are new
structures developed in connection with some function of the thorax. They
occur also in birds (Fig. 15.9), where they are fully ossified, and one is often
told that they are an adaptation to flight in that they help to lock the thorax
into a rigid box which is not deformed by the beating of the wings. This
could be so, but their presence in the relatively sluggish crocodiles and

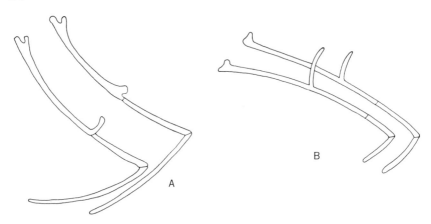

FIG. 15.8   (A) Sixth and seventh thoracic ribs of a young crocodile, *Crocodilus niloticus*, x 2/3. (B) Sixth and seventh thoracic ribs of *Sphenodon punctatus*, x 2/3. (Figs 15.8 to 15.10 all show uncinate processes.)

FIG. 15.9   Fourth and fifth thoracic ribs of a barn owl, *Tyto alba*, x 2/3.

FIG. 15.10   Two thoracic ribs of *Eryops megacephalus*, x 1/4.

tuatara is unexplained. Both these types of reptile are diapsids, and to that extent related to the birds, but uncinate processes are not known in dinosaurs, which are much nearer the avian ancestry, nor were they present in *Archaeopteryx*. But if they were only cartilaginous in these extinct creatures they might not have been preserved. Most surprisingly, uncinate processes were present in the stegocephalian *Eryops* (Fig. 15.10).

Apart from the uncinate processes, the ribs of birds are typical and double-headed. In the neck, except for a few of the posterior segments, the ribs are fused onto the vertebrae to form the vertebrarterial canal.

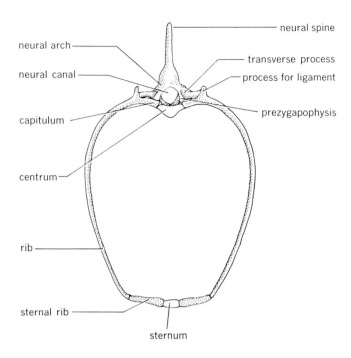

FIG. 15.11   Cervical vertebra of a rabbit from in front, with its ribs fused onto the centrum to make the vertebrarterial canals, x 2.

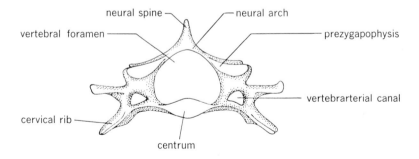

FIG. 15.12   Thoracic vertebra of a rabbit *Oryctolagus cuniculus*, with its ribs, from in front, x 2/3.

Posterior to the thorax they are missing, and abdominal ribs such as occur in reptiles are present only in *Archaeopteryx*.

The cervical ribs of mammals (Fig. 15.11) are fused onto the vertebrae and form a similar vertebrarterial canal to that of birds. The thoracic ribs (Fig. 15.12) are for the most part quite typical, but posteriorly the two heads approach one another, and in the last few there is only one articulation. Generally the tuberculum has been lost, but occasionally the capitulum has gone and sometimes the two knobs appear to be fused, as in lizards. All the ribs of the monotremes have a capitulum only. There are no abdominal or caudal ribs in mammals.

Sternum

The main axial skeleton of the vertebrates is dorsal, but some have also a subsidiary axial skeleton, which is ventral. This is the sternum. It varies much in the different classes, and often has connections with the shoulder girdle that make its delimitation in the adult animal somewhat difficult. More regularly it has connections, by articulations or fusion, with some of the thoracic ribs. Earlier authors thought that it was formed either from the girdle, or, more probably, from the ventral ends of the ribs, but wherever the development has been clearly worked out this is not the case. It is formed from paired cartilaginous rudiments, but that need not prevent us from calling it axial, since the vertebrae themselves are formed in the same way. The development is clearest in birds, where the original paired strips of cartilage fuse from before backward. A small piece of the appropriate mesoderm cut out of an embryo and allowed to grow on its own will form a sternum which is almost perfect, even to details of shape, but mesoderm from the region of the ribs never forms anything approaching a sternum. This is as good a proof as one is likely to get that the sternum is not a structure formed from the ribs, but stands on its own as an independent part of the skeleton. The mesoderm in which the cartilages form is the unsegmented lateral plate, and they seem always to be continuous through several segments of the body; the subsequent ossification may take place from several centers, making separate bones or sternebrae, which correspond to the ribs and so to the segments. Like the ribs, they are strictly intersegmental in position.

No sternum strictly so called occurs in fishes, but a few have a median piece of cartilage between the coracoids. There is such a piece in *Squalus*. In this and other fish it is formed by a fusion of cartilages from the ventral tips of the coracoids. It is therefore not homologous with the sternum of tetrapods.

It is characteristic of amniotes that their anterior thoracic ribs articulate with the sternum, although the ventral portion which does so is often

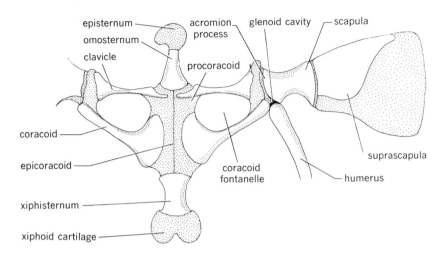

FIG. 15.13 Sternum and pectoral girdle of a frog, *Rana temporaria*, ventral, x2. The scapula has been brought into the same plane as the coracoid.

cartilaginous. Cartilage does not fossilize as well as bone, and the absence of a sternum, or of ribs which extend to the ventral surface of the thoracic wall, does not necessarily mean that an extinct animal, known only as a fossil, was without them. Some authors have thought, from the general disposition of the bony ribs of the Stegocephalia, that they probably did have cartilaginous extensions and that there was a cartilaginous sternum. This would explain the presence of a sternum, in spite of the reduction of ribs, in the modern Amphibia. There is, however, no paleontological history.

Adult urodeles have a small sternum, which is a cartilaginous plate with which the coracoids articulate. It develops from cartilages that have processes running in the myocommata and so are intersegmental in position to match the ribs. It is evidently a true sternum, though much reduced. The sternum of anurans develops in the same way, but in the frogs (Firmisternia), especially the genus *Rana*, it is more complicated. A large median sternum joins the median or cartilaginous portion of the coracoids behind (Fig. 15.13). Its anterior part is ossified and is known as the xiphisternum, while posteriorly it swells out into a flat plate, the xiphoid cartilage. In front of the coracoids is another median element, with a short posterior bony rod, and an anterior cartilaginous knob. These are called omosternum and episternum respectively, but their homology is obscure. The simplest explanation is that they are parts of the originally undivided sternum which have been separated from the xiphisternum by the growth of the coracoids, and that this growth took place in relation to the peculiar leaping mode of progression.

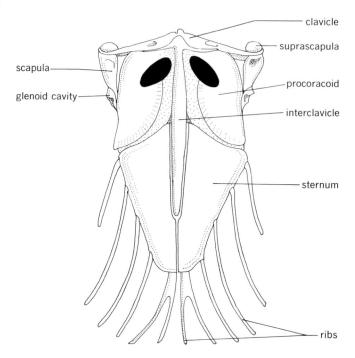

FIG. 15.14   Sternum and pectoral girdle of a lizard, *Iguana iguana*, ventral x 1.

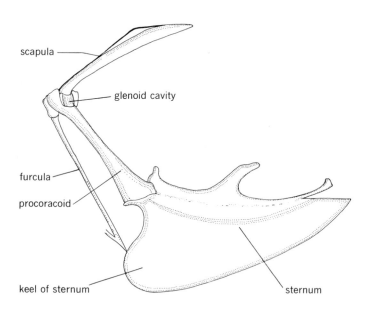

FIG. 15.15   Sternum and pectoral girdle of a pigeon, *Columa livia*, lateral, x 1.

The sternum of reptiles (Fig. 15.14) is usually large, and has ribs attached to it. It is a simple cartilaginous plate, sometimes with a little calcification in modern forms, but in many extinct groups, such as the therapsids and dinosaurs, it was ossified. It was ossified and large in the pterodactyls, and in some of them it had a similar central keel to that of birds, presumably for the same purpose of forming a base of attachment for the muscles used in flight.

In birds (Fig. 15.15) the sternum, though basically reptilian in form, is large and completely ossified. Typically it has a ventral vertical extension, the keel or carina, on which both the pectoralis major muscle, which lowers the wings, and the pectoralis minor which raises them, have their origin. The size of the keel bears a general relation to the size and use of these muscles. There is none in *Archaeopteryx*, and it is missing also, presumably by secondary loss, in the modern flightless birds, the ratites. Penguins however, though flightless, use their wings for swimming, and have a keel. The sternum has various lateral processes, and sometimes also foramina, to some extent according to the attachments of the muscles. The anterior thoracic ribs join it, and are divided into an upper vertebral and a lower sternal part, with an angle of less than a right angle separating them. Both parts are bony.

The sternum of mammals is divided into segments or sternebrae, corresponding in number anteriorly to the ribs, but posteriorly several ribs

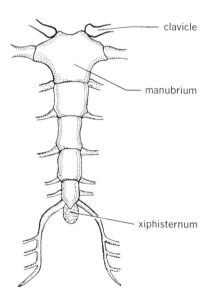

FIG. 15.16 Young human sternum, ventral, x 1/4. In an older skeleton the sternebrae are fused.

come onto one. The first pair of ribs fairly meet the first sternebra, or manubrium, but the second pair are against both the second and first sternebrae, and so on. The clavicles also meet the manubrium (Fig. 15.16). The posterior sternebra is known as the xiphisternum. The sternal parts of the ribs of mammals are cartilaginous. In monotremes a small piece of the sternum in front of the first stenebra to articulate with ribs, called the episternum, fuses with the interclavicle (Fig. 17.34). According to some authors the manubrium should be regarded as the equivalent of the inter-clavicle. The objection to this view is that in most animals the interclavicle, like the clavicles that it connects, is a membrane bone, while the sternum is preformed in cartilage.

Unpaired Fins

In a swimming fish the unpaired fins, and especially the caudal fin, in-crease the surface that can be pushed against the water, and so the effect that can be produced. The muscles work by deflecting the backbone, and so it might be expected that these fins might be supported by processes from the vertebrae. In a general way this is what has happened, but the homologies of the skeletal elements that they contain are by no means clear. In *Amia* each basidorsal is prolonged into a spine that runs out into the fin so that there is a double row of them, which would not seem to be very efficient. In others they fuse and form a single neural spine, and a similar hemal spine may be found in the tail. In some elasmobranchs these spines may become secondarily detached.

More generally, the unpaired fins are mainly supported by cartilages or bones which are not continuous with the vertebrae, called radials. Primi-tively, they appear to have corresponded in number to the segments, and to have articulated with the neural spines, as they do in the Dipnoi and did in some fossil sharks. More often the strict segmentation is lost, and there is concentration of the radials, several either occurring very close together or being fused to form large pieces, in both cases without contact with the spines. Generally, as in the elasmobranchs (Fig. 15.17) and tele-osts, each radial is divided into two or three pieces. In many teleosts there are two radials per segment, apart from any crowding together that may have taken place during the growth of a fin. These radials can be distinguished from mere displaced neural and hemal spines by the fact that each has a pair of muscles attached to it, which run parallel to them to be inserted on the skin or on to skeletal elements distal to the radials. These are the dermal fin rays or dermotrichia, which are formed in the skin. In the elasmobranchs they are generally described as being 'horny', but are in fact made of elastin, the protein of which the yellow fibers of connective tissue is made. Those of the teleosts are chiefly bony, and are formed from scales. In the more advanced teleosts, with a fin con-

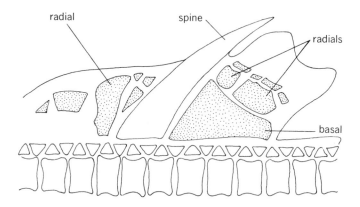

FIG. 15.17 Skeleton of one of the dorsal fins of *Squalus acanthias*, x 2/3.

sisting almost entirely of web and hardly at all of flesh, these rays form almost the sole support for the fin.

One of the difficulties in deciding the homologies of the skeleton of the unpaired fins is that it is extremely similar, in any given form, to that of the paired fins. The radials of these cannot be derived from vertebrae, so, it may be said, those of the unpaired fins must not be. On the other hand, it is formally difficult to separate a radial of an unpaired fin from a neural or a hemal spine, especially when the spine is detached from the body of its vertebra. The solution is perhaps that too much stress is being put on homology. In terms of natural selection, any supporting structure that strengthens the fin is likely to be valuable. In some cases this has probably been a growth of a vertebral spine, in others, and in all the paired fins, a new cartilage or bone has been formed. Similarity of function has impressed similarity of form on all of them.

It certainly seems that the dermotrichia of elasmobranchs and of teleosts are independent structures. So long as the former were called horny they could be assimilated to the bony and scaly rays of the teleosts, for both could be regarded as derived from the exoskeleton, but the discovery that the dermotrichia of elasmobranchs are made of elastin marks them out as things on their own. Elastic fibers occur widely in skin, but they do not, so far as is known, enter into the exoskeleton. Their use in this way must be regarded as an example of the sort of opportunism that makes nonsense of apparent homologies.

In front of each of the dorsal fins of *Squalus* and some other sharks is a long spine, which appears to be a greatly expanded placoid scale. Somewhat similar spines are found in many fossil fishes, notably the Acanthodii, where they occur also as ventrilateral pairs. Their function remains unknown. No doubt they could be defensive against such predators as the toothed whales, many of which swallow fish as large as dogfish whole, but other small sharks seem to get on perfectly well without them and this explanation could not apply to the fossils.

The tails and caudal fins need special mention. One would expect that the primitive form would be the simpler one, with a straight backbone surrounded by a symmetrical fin. This is the sort of tail found in amphioxus (where it is supported by a straight notochord), but although symmetrical tails are found in cyclostomes and a number of fishes, there is always evidence, paleontological or embryological or both, that the symmetry is secondary, and that the ancestors of the fish had a backbone which did not run straight to the tail's tip. One can therefore only show a primitive symmetrical tail in vertebrates as belonging to a hypothetical ancestor. Such a tail is called protocercal (Fig. 15.18).

The fossil evidence is that the type of tail from which all others derive, in both Agnatha and gnathostomes, is the heterocercal (Fig. 15.18), in which the vertebral column bends upward. Such a tail is found in the cephalaspids, in placoderms, and in many of the more primitive fish of the present day, such as elasmobranchs and sturgeons. It is possible that more than one type of tail is concealed under the one name, for in general in elasmobranchs the cartilaginous supports (hemal spines and radials) of the lower or hypochordal lobe tend to be short or to disappear, while in sturgeons and other Osteichthyes they are elongated.

Much confusion has been caused in writings about heterocercal tails in referring to relative sizes of the upper or lower lobes of the tail. In the first place, it depends on what is meant by 'upper' and 'lower.' If these simply mean above and below the notochordal axis respectively, then the lower or hypochordal lobe is nearly always larger than the upper or epichordal. But 'lobe of the tail' implies something that you can see without dissection, and when the word is taken in this way, as I shall use it below, to apply to the visible finny parts of the tail, then the upper lobe is often, and probably usually, much the larger, as in *Squalus* and *Scyliorhinus*. It includes the whole of the epichordal and part of the hypochordal lobe. Another difficulty is that we seldom know what the actual shape of the fins was in fossil forms, since although impressions of the fins are sometimes left in the rocks this is not always so, and the dermotrichia are not likely to leave remains. It appears probable, however, from the length and position of the lower radials, that the heterocercal tail of *Cladoselache* was externally perfectly symmetrical, with lobes, in the sense in which we have just used the word, of equal size.

The explanation of the heterocercal tail usually given is that its beat raises the tail, and as the body of the fish must tend to turn about the center of pressure this means that the head is lowered and the fish tends to swim downward. This is counter-balanced, when the fish is swimming in a horizontal plane, by the set of the pectoral fins, which act like the wing

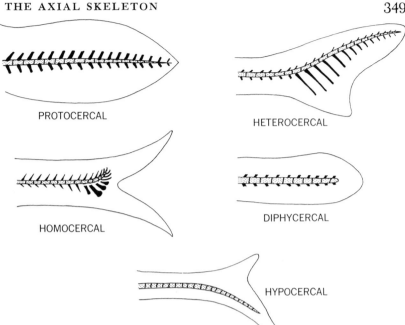

PROTOCERCAL

HETEROCERCAL

HOMOCERCAL

DIPHYCERCAL

HYPOCERCAL

FIG. 15.18 Skeletons of the tails of fish, diagrammatic. The radials and dermal fin rays, which variously support the caudal fin, are not shown.

flaps of an aircraft, and prevent the fish from sinking. These conclusions are drawn from experiments with models and on amputation of the fins in *Mustelus canis*, a species with a relatively small upper lobe. A number of comments may be made on this conclusion. First, it seems a long way around to reach a simple result; if the pectoral fins can be used to produce positive pitch (raising of the head) they might equally well produce negative pitch. Secondly, heterocercal tails occurred in many extinct Agnatha which, so far as is known, had no pectoral fins. Thirdly, the conclusion is not entirely justified by the results of the experiments, since the fish's equilibrating organs were intact, and it may have compensated for the results of the operation; indeed the author assumes that it did when it suits his explanation. Lastly, while the effect of the beating of a heterocercal tail must depend on the relative sizes of the two lobes, and on the type of beating, the shape of a well-developed heterocercal fin such as that of *Squalus* is incompatible with the explanation. Here the upper lobe is much larger, and if the beat of the tail is from side to side, it must depress the tail. The advantage of the heterocercal tail is probably much simpler. A fish without a swim bladder is denser than water and so sinks. The heterocercal tail gives positive pitch and so keeps the fish swimming off the bottom. This accounts, as the usual explanation does not, for its evolution before there were pectoral fins, and is in accordance with the physical facts.

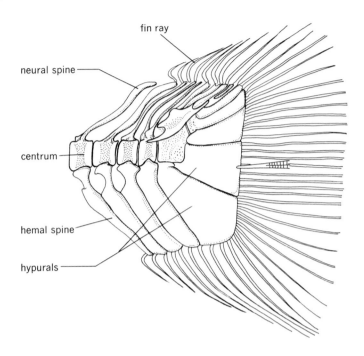

FIG. 15.19   Skeleton of the homocercal tail of a salmon, *Salmo salar*, x 1/2.

What is not accounted for is the peculiar reversed heterocercal or hypo-cercal tail (Fig. 15.18) found in the anaspids. No details of these tails are known, but a recent interpretation of the animals suggests that they up-ended to feed by standing on their heads in the mud, and that the hypo-cercal tail assisted in this, as it would do if it produced negative pitch. This explanation would mean that the anaspids never left the bottom because unable to swim upward.

The majority of bony fish have a tail called homocercal. It is externally symmetrical, usually with large upper and lower lobes, but internally the bony part of the skeleton shows a greater or lesser degree of asymmetry (Fig. 15.18). The vertebral axis shows a slight upward kink, while the hemal parts of the vertebra are expanded to produce an apparent sym-metry. The embryos of many teleosts show a quite distinct heterocercal stage, in which the notochord and developing vertebrae are bent markedly upward, and there are epichordal and hypochordal lobes supported by dermotrichia. As the embryo grows, the notochord and epichordal lobe shrink, the hemal arches of the last few vertebrae expand and move up-ward. In the typical homocercal tail, two of them, now known as hypural bones, fuse with the last centrum to form an almost symmetrical structure (Fig. 15.19). The membranous part of the fin in such a tail corresponds completely to the hypochordal lobe of the dogfish.

In many teleosts the caudal fin is much reduced, and it may become continuous with dorsal and ventral fins, as in the eels. Such a condition is called isocercal.

The cyclostomes and dipnoans have tails which are symmetrical both internally and externally, and are therefore indistinguishable from the hypothetical protocercal condition. No trace of heterocercy has been found in the embryos, but in view of the heterocercal tails of most Agnatha and of many fossil Dipnoi those of their modern descendants are assumed to have passed through such a condition, just as did the homocercal tails of the teleosts. They are called diphycercal (Fig. 15.18).

It is characteristic of the tetrapods that, even if they have unpaired fins, there are no specially developed fin rays, bony or otherwise, in them. The tail of the tadpole is supported solely by the notochord, and though there are vertebrae in the tails of urodeles they are smaller and without spines. The caudal fin has therefore no skeletal support beyond the bony axis.

The external forms of the acquired tails of secondarily aquatic tetrapods vary considerably. The backbone of the ichthyosaurs turned downward, so that the fin could be described as hypocercal, though of course having no relationship to that of the anaspids. In a few fossils the impression of a large nearly symmetrical fin has been found, so that the external appearance of the tail was almost like that of a herring or salmon. What advantage there was in the downturned backbone no one knows, but it was present also, though to a lesser extent, in the extinct swimming crocodiles, such as the Jurassic *Geosaurus*.

Almost the only point in which the two fully aquatic groups of mammals, the Cetacea and Sirenia, agree, is that their tail fins are expanded horizontally.

16

The Skull

AT THE ANTERIOR end of the axial skeleton of all vertebrates there is a special part, which is the skull, however that word may be defined in detail. The skull may be considered in several ways. From one point of view, it is simply a part of that specialization and concentration of nervous tissue, sense organs, feeding apparatus, and their ancillary structures, which occurs at the leading end of all the higher animals and is known as cephalization. From another, it is fundamentally the brain box, surrounding and enclosing the brain. Thirdly, one may search, in terms of paleontology and embryology, for clues to the serial homology of the skull, in an effort to assimilate it to the rest of the axial skeleton. In this chapter we shall take the first viewpoint, leaving what can be said on the third for Chapter 19.

If the skeleton of a dogfish is examined it will be seen that at the anterior end there are three distinct functional parts. Dorsally, a continuous mass of cartilage almost completely surrounds the brain, covers most of the ears and nasal organs, and makes sockets for the eyes. Below this, and attached to it by ligaments, are the jaws, each consisting of two pieces joined to each other in front by ligaments. Behind the jaws is the series of cartilages which together make the branchial basket (Fig. 4.4) and which support the region of the gill slits. The hyoid arch has a somewhat equivocal look. Its appearance suggests that it is part of the series of gill arches, but it has no gills near it, and it is connected to the jaws and to the main part of the skull by ligaments.

If we take the view which is suggested by the distribution of the cranial nerves, that the mouth was formed by the coalescence of two anterior gill slits, or at least is serially homologous with the slits behind it, the jaws and branchial arches belong to the same series, so that we can distinguish a dorsal skull, surrounding the brain and main sense organs, from a ventral skull concerned with the more vegetative functions of feeding and breathing. This is broadly in accordance with the facts in all fish, but, as we shall see later, there is a progressive tendency in the tetrapods for pieces from the ventral skull to become attached to, or even to move up into, the dorsal part.

While the dorsal skull is clearly axial in any ordinary sense of the word, the ventral skull remains clearly paired for the most part, and would be

353

better described as appendicular. It is perhaps best to abandon these terms in connection with the skull, and to think of all the parts simply as the skeleton of the head. We shall begin with the dorsal skull, taking with it those parts of the ventral skull, especially the upper jaw, that often become incorporated in it, and then go on to the remaining parts of the ventral skull.

The skull of the elasmobranchs and modern cyclostomes remains cartilaginous throughout life. In all other vertebrates it is to a greater or lesser degree ossified, and always in two ways: partly by centers of bone formation appearing within the cartilage and partly by bones which are formed outside the original cartilaginous skull and are afterward closely applied to or incorporated in it. To some extent, and especially in the more primitive skulls, these two types, cartilage bones and membrane bones, make two layers in the adult skull, but on the whole, and always in the higher types, they fit together to form a continuous bony covering in which all trace of their different modes of origin is lost.

It would make the story of the evolution of the skull neat and simple if one could say that first there was a cartilaginous skull, then one in which some or all of the cartilage was replaced by bone, and that only in the third and last stage were the membrane bones applied from the outside, but unfortunately there is no evidence whatsoever from paleontology that this is what happened. The earliest vertebrate fossils, as we have seen in Chapter 3, have bony skulls which have all the appearance of being made of dermal and membrane bones that are merely specializations of the plates or scales present elsewhere on the body. The succession of cartilage, then cartilage bone, then membrane bone, is on the whole followed in ontogeny, but ontogeny unchecked by paleontology can be a deceitful guide. Some authors have even suggested that cartilage is an embryonic tissue, evolved for the special conditions of the life of immature forms, or to allow growth in the larvae of ostracoderms, whose completely armored condition in the adult stage made it impossible. We shall describe the skull in terms of the three stages, because that is a convenient way of stating and learning the facts, but in doing so shall make no implication that it has any evolutionary value.

The cartilaginous box that surrounds the brain and sense capsules is called the chondrocranium. It is seen in an almost diagrammatic form in the skull of the dogfish (Fig. 4.3), but may be represented more formally (Fig. 16.2A). The brain box, or cranium proper, is shaped rather like a wooden seventeenth-century cradle. It has a complete floor, sides, and ends, but the roof is mostly missing, the gap, which is sometimes divided, being known as the fontanelle. The wall of the cranium is pierced by a number of holes or foramina for the passage of nerves and blood vessels, and in particular there is a specially large one in the back wall, the foramen magnum, for the passage of the spinal cord. About the middle of the floor, and marking the anterior limit of the notochord, is another gap, the hypophysial fenestra, through which the hypophysis and the infundibulum make contact to form the pituitary. Where it persists in the adult, and in all but the earliest stages of embryos, the chondrocranium is a single piece of cartilage, but it is made by the joining together of a number of separate pieces, all of which are paired. In this respect the skull agrees with the rest of the axial skeleton. More is said about the nature of these paired pieces in Chapter 19 (Fig. 19.3).

Firmly fused to the brain box at each side, but not joining it until after it has become a single cartilage, are two pairs of sense capsules, nasal in front and auditory at the posterior corners. The nasal capsules tend almost to meet each other across the front of the brain box, in accordance with the anterior position of the nasal organ; they are separated only by a vertical plate, the nasal septum, which is formed from the brain box; the auditory capsules remain lateral. Each capsule is formed from its own cartilage, which develops along with the sense organ to which it belongs. Similar skeletal pieces that appear in the walls of the optic cups do not become attached to the skull, but may persist as cartilage or bone in the sclerotic. It is necessary for the eyes, as directional sense organs, to be free to move, so that they would be unduly restricted if they were enclosed in fixed capsules.

Such a chondrocranium can be seen in the appropriate stage of all embryos. It persists also, with only little modification, in the adults of sturgeons and modern Anura. These have some ossification, but the membrane bones can be picked off, and an underlying chondrocranium, in which only a few cartilage bones are left, can be seen (Fig. 16.1). The chondrocranium of urodeles is greatly reduced, and has a large fontanelle in the floor as well as the roof.

The points within the chondrocranium where ossification takes place are remarkably constant, so that on the whole there is no difficulty in the view that bones that correspond in position in different classes are homologous. Some may be missing, and ossifications that start from two or three centers meet in some animals and form a single bone, which can be regarded as the equivalent of the separate bones in other groups, but there is generally no difficulty in homologizing a bone in one animal with one or more in others. The membrane bones are not so clear. In the fish and early tetrapods there are more of them than in modern tetrapods, and some of them run in series in particular parts of the head. In this case it may be difficult or impossible to say which of the series have been lost in the later groups. This is to be expected if the dermal bones are derived, as is usually held, from the bony armor of the early Agnatha, whether this began as a continuous shield, as it is in the cephalaspids, where it covers the head like the carapace of a crab, or whether it began as a skin containing an indeterminate number of small scales. The comparison with

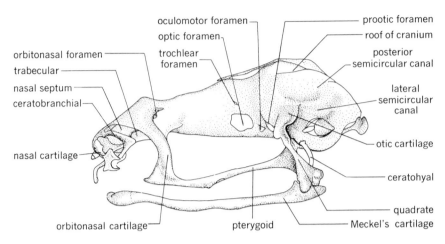

oculomotor foramen — prootic foramen
optic foramen — roof of cranium
orbitonasal foramen — trochlear posterior
foramen semicircular canal
trabecular —
nasal septum — posterior
ceratobranchial — lateral
semicircular
canal
otic cartilage
nasal cartilage —
ceratohyal
orbitonasal cartilage — pterygoid — quadrate
Meckel's cartilage
lateral
semicircular
canal

FIG. 16.1 Cartilaginous skull of an adult frog, *Rana* sp., x 13. (Redrawn from De Beer, *The Development of the Vertebrate Skull*, Clarendon Press, Oxford, 1937)

placoid scales and teeth is apt; where these are many and indeterminate in number, as in fishes and reptiles, no one thinks of naming or homologizing any individual tooth, but when, as in mammals, there is a limited number, having special and constant relationships to particular bones, each tooth can be given a name and homologized with the corresponding tooth in other orders.

Figure 16.3 and Plate VIII.2 show what may be regarded as the normal maximum number of bones in the skull. Additional membrane bones occur in many fish, and may be looked on as pieces of exoskeleton brought in for special purposes. That the membrane bones of the skulls of fishes are derived in this way is suggested by the fact that they sometimes bear on their outside a layer of ganoin or cosmine according to the type of scale that the animal carries on its body (Chapter 18).

The cartilage bones are relatively constant in number and position and may be learned from the position in the chondrocranium in which they form. The cartilaginous nasal septum forms a single bone, the mesethmoid (Fig. 16.2 B and C). From its position it is primarily a vertical plate of bone, but at its posterior end it spreads laterally to make the front wall of the cranial cavity, so that in frontal section it is typically T-shaped. Behind it the side walls form paired orbitosphenoids, which, as their name implies, make most of the orbits which hold the eyes. In teleosts and some amniotes the eyes are large, and almost meet each other in the middle line. This leads to a compression of the cranium in the orbital region. The paired cartilages of which the floor of the cranium in this region is composed (trabeculae, p. 446) meet and grow up to form a cartilaginous interorbital septum, continuing the line of the nasal septum backward, with consequent adjustments in the orbitosphenoids. The cranial cavity is then confined to the posterior part of the skull. This condition is called tropybasic. The opposite condition, where the trabeculae remain widely separate, is called platybasic. The orbitosphenoid can nearly always be recognized by the fact that it is pierced by a hole through which passes the optic nerve. With the exception of the foramen magnum this is generally the largest foramen in the skull.

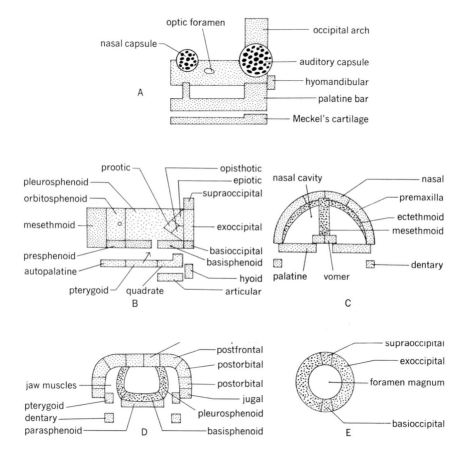

FIG. 16.2 (A) Diagram of the cartilaginous skull, lateral. (B) Diagram of the cartilage bones of the skull, lateral. The arrow shows how the pterygoid grows up in mammals to form the side wall of the cranium. (C) Diagrammatic transverse section through a skull in the ethmoid region. (D) The same, in the sphenoid region. (E) The same in the occipital region. (Cartilage bones are shown by heavier shading.)

Continuing the side walls of the cranium behind the orbits are paired pleurosphenoids (Fig. 16.2D). There has been much confusion in the naming of these bones, arising from the fact that in mammals, from which all anatomical nomenclature is primarily derived, cartilage in this position does not ossify. The bone which is immediately behind the orbitosphenoid in an adult mammalian skull is called the alisphenoid, but, as we shall see later, it does not originally belong to the brain box at all, and its name should therefore not be used for the bone in the same position in lower animals. The bone in this position in fishes is sometimes, and perhaps generally, known as the pterosphenoid, on the grounds that its center of ossification is behind, and not in front of, the exit of the profundus and abducent nerves, as is that of the pleurosphenoid of reptiles. In view of the very varying degrees of formation of cartilage in this region this view seems to carry the concept of homology to an unnecessary degree of refinement, and we shall here regard the pterosphenoid and pleurosphenoid as fundamentally the same bone.

The base of the skull between the pleurosphenoids ossifies as a single bone, the basisphenoid. It is the region of cartilage (just in front of the notochord), which originally surrounded the hypophysial fenestra. This usually closes, but its position is marked by a pit on the upper surface of the basisphenoid which holds the pituitary body.

The posterior part of the cranium, where the skull has roof, sides, and floor, ossifies from four centers to form a supra-occipital bone above, a basi-occipital below, and a pair of exoccipitals to make the sides, the four of them surrounding the foramen magnum (Fig. 16.2E). The basi-occipital is continuous with the basisphenoid, but there is a space between each exoccipital and the pleurosphenoid, which is filled by the auditory capsule. This ossifies from three centers, to form pro-otic, opisthotic, and epi-otic.

The details of these bones differ much between the classes. Most bony fishes are strongly tropybasic, so that the eyes almost meet and the orbital septum and orbitosphenoid are largely membraneous (Fig. 16.6). The displacement of the pleurosphenoid (pterosphenoid) to the rear may be considered as associated with this. The basisphenoid in most teleosts is entirely in front of the hypophysial fenestra. In *Amia* it arises from two ossifications in the paired cartilages, and this may be its original condition. The supra-occipital is not formed in *Amia* and *Lepidosteus*. The usual three bones are present in the auditory capsule, but in teleosts there are two others, the sphenotic and pterotic. These appear to be invasions of the capsule by the postfrontal and supratemporal, which are membrane bones from the roof of the skull (p. 363). A similar invasion of the nasal capsule by the prefrontal may form an ectethmoid.

In the sturgeons all the ossifications are greatly reduced, and in the modern *Acipenser* only the orbitosphenoids, pro-otics, and opisthotics are left. The skull of the modern Dipnoi also is almost completely cartilaginous, with one pair of bones which may be exoccipitals.

The cartilage bones of crossopterygians show a good deal of fusion, occipital and otic bones combining to form one massive ring. It was deduced from the appearance of these bones in the fossils that the front part was probably movable on the posterior part, a condition called kinetism, which has developed, in a different way, in some amniotes. Such a movement of the skull has now been found in *Latimeria*, where there are large muscles for the purpose. One may presume that this ability to raise the upper jaw is helpful for catching the other fish which *Latimeria* eats and swallows whole.

The early stegocephalians had a fairly complete set of cartilage bones, but they already begin to show traces of the reduction so characteristic of their modern descendants. In front there was a single large bone, which may be called sphenethmoid, since from its position it appears to represent a fusion of the mesethmoid and the two orbitosphenoids. Nothing is known of its development. Its posterior part is a low vertical interorbital septum, suggesting that the platybasic condition characteristic of the modern amphibians is secondary. There were no pleurosphenoids. The epi-otic was not present, but otherwise all the cartilage bones of the cranium have been recognized. Later stegocephalians had lost supra-occipital and basi-occipital.

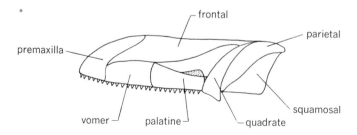

FIG. 16.3   Skull of the mud puppy, *Necturus maculosus*, lateral, x 1.

Modern amphibians (Fig. 16.3) have taken the reduction even further. Urodeles and the Apoda have paired orbitosphenoids, but the Anura have a sphenethmoid which is shaped rather like two paper cups placed bottom to bottom. The auditory capsule has usually only one bone, which is regarded as the pro-otic, but *Necturus* has two, the second presumably being the opisthotic. There is neither supra-occipital nor basi-occipital, the condyles of the skull being formed entirely by the exoccipitals.

The cotylosaurs seem to have had a skull which closely resembled that of the early amphibians, with a sphenethmoid, which is present also in some later reptiles. Most reptiles have a skull which is tropybasic; not only is there no sphenethmoid but the orbitosphenoids are much reduced and difficult to retain in dried skulls. Their absence from fossils does not mean, therefore, that they were necessarily completely missing. The basisphenoid retains the hypophysial fenestra. The other bones are usually present, but the epi-otic may unite with the supra-occipital and the opisthotic with the exoccipital. In the early reptiles and in the Chelonia there are three condyles, formed by the exoccipitals and the basi-occipitals, but in other modern reptiles the two exoccipital condyles have been lost, so that the skull articulates with the atlas by a single knob.

The cartilage bones of birds do not differ significantly from those of reptiles. Although the skull is tropybasic there is usually a well-developed bony orbital septum, made of orbitosphenoids, but it is thin and is often incomplete in dried skulls. There is a hypophysial fenestra. The otic bones fuse to form a single peri-otic, and in adults there is much general fusion.

Mammals, or many of them, have all the bones we have named in their embryos, but there is always some, and often much, fusion. In some, including the monotremes, marsupials, and some placental orders such as the Artiodactyla, Perissodactyla, and Sirenia, there is a sphenethmoid, but in most placentals there are separate mesethmoid and orbitosphenoids. In this case the orbitosphenoids meet ventrally to form the floor of the brain case, for the mammals are only moderately tropybasic, and a small cavity extends forward between the orbits to be bounded in front by the posterior part of the mesethmoid, which is pierced by several foramina for the olfactory nerve and so is called the cribriform plate. It happens that because of the presence of other bones the two orbitosphenoids cannot be seen to be continuous in the intact skull; their ventral fused portion, which can be seen only when the skull is looked at from below, was therefore given a name of its own, the presphenoid (Figs. 7.6 to 7.8). This bone, however, has no separate existence. There is only a single bone enclosing the ear, called the peri-otic or petrosal. In some mammals it is formed from three ossifications, which may be considered as homologues of the three bones of reptiles and fishes, but sometimes there are four, five, or six centers, and in man at least the number appears not to be constant. In these circumstances it seems foolish to try to make exact homologies. What matters is that the auditory capsule is fully ossified, and that as a whole it corresponds to the three bones of other animals.

There are two occipital condyles, formed chiefly from the exoccipitals. Stages in the loss of the median basi-occipital condyle can be seen in the synapsid reptiles.

The line where two bones meet is called a suture, and is generally somewhat wavy or irregular. In many mammals it is very wavy indeed, and in some, such as man, small irregular or Wormian bones are formed in the sutures. If the two bones join, so that the suture is obliterated, there is an ankylosis.

In all adult mammals there is a considerable degree of fusion of adjacent bones, no distinction in this being made between cartilage and membrane bones. The peri-otic usually remains distinct (though in man it joins two membrane bones, the squamosal and tympanic, to form the temporal), but in an old dog, for example, hardly any other separate bones can be made out. In man (Fig. 16.19) all the sphenoid bones, with some others, early join together, and so do the four occipital bones. Later the sphenoid and occipital bones combine.

Before we can consider the membrane bones of the skull we must digress to deal with the upper jaw. This is the upper limb of the supposed branchial arch which bears the same relationship to the mouth that the other branchial arches do to the gill slits. We may suppose that it originally had nothing to do with the cranium, but in all existing vertebrates it has at least some connection by ligament or through the hyoid, and in many it becomes so intimately joined up that it is unrecognizable as a separate part of the skull. This has led to a considerable study of what is called jaw suspension. This refers to the upper jaw only; the lower articulates with the upper (or, as we shall see later, occasionally directly with the cranium) but is not in the same sense suspended.

The upper jaw begins as a single bar of cartilage on each side. In this, in most vertebrates, ossification takes place from two or three centers, so that three bones are formed, the palatine or autopalatine in front, then the pterygoid or metapterygoid or epipterygoid, and the quadrate at the posterior end. At points corresponding roughly to these three parts the jaw may touch the skull, and may have processes that grow into the skull. Unfortunately, perhaps, these processes are generally known not by the names of the parts of the cartilage from which they come, but from the parts of the cranium with which, if they reach it, they make contact. Their names are, then, ethmoid, basal, and otic processes. There may also be a fourth, the pterygoid or ascending process (a silly name, for they all go upward), more or less alongside the basal process, but placed more laterally.

The upper jaw may, then, be attached or fused to the cranium at one or more of these four points. In addition, its posterior end may also be joined through the hyomandibula, the upper piece of cartilage in the hyoid arch, the branchial skeleton that is in front of the spiracle.

There is a very large number of ways within this general scheme, in which the jaw is fastened to the cranium, but they can, for simplicity, be reduced to the few shown in Fig. 16.4. Hyostyly is attachment by the hyoid alone; autostyly is attachment through the processes; amphistyly by both. Autodiastyly means that the junctions are mere articulations,

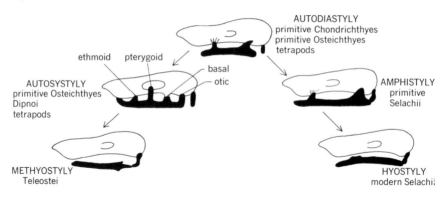

AUTODIASTYLY
primitive Chondrichthyes
primitive Osteichthyes
tetrapods

ethmoid   pterygoid

basal

AUTOSYSTYLY   otic   AMPHISTYLY
primitive Osteichthyes   primitive
Dipnoi   Selachii
tetrapods

METHYOSTYLY   HYOSTYLY
Teleostei   modern Selachii

FIG. 16.4 Diagrams of the main types of suspension of the upper jaw. Auto-diastyly, in which there is only apposition of the palatoquadrate bar and the cranium, is perhaps primitive. Amongst tetrapods it is found in Apoda, most reptiles, and birds. Autosystyly, in which there is fusion of the bar and the cranium at one or more points, is found in urodeles, anurans, and mammals, and probably arose more than once.

autosystyly that they are fusions. It is probable that the same type of con-nection has been evolved more than once.

Most modern elasmobranchs are hyostylic, as in the dogfish, with no junction of jaws and cranium, but in primitive forms the hyoid took no part, so that they were autodiastylic, and others were amphistylic. The peculiar cartilaginous fish called Holocephali have the upper jaw com-pletely fused into the skull, but this must have been derived independently of the autostyly of the tetrapods. Bony fishes have some degree of auto-styly, and the Dipnoi and many tetrapods are autosystylic. This condition may have been achieved once only in their ancestors, but the way in which the connection is formed varies widely.

In urodeles the ethmoid connection is often missing, and in anurans and apodans there is no basal. In amniotes the ethmoid is missing and the whole anterior region of the jaw is defective. The pterygoid process is usually important, and in many reptiles and in mammals it grows so far upwards as to make the side wall of the skull in the region between the orbitosphenoid and the auditory capsule. It is then called the epipterygoid (in reptiles) or alisphenoid (in mammals). There is, however, a difference between mammals and all modern reptiles. The pterygoid process is placed as far laterally as it can be, and it grows up, therefore, some little distance away from the cranial wall. In reptiles the cartilaginous wall of the cranium in this region persists, so that there is formed a space, through which run the internal juglar vein, arteries running forward to the face, and the profundus, trigeminal, and facial nerves. In the mammals, pre-sumably because of the expanding brain, the side wall of the cranium does not chondrify and is reduced to a membrane, which is pushed out into contact with the pterygoid process, which is now called the alisphenoid bone. The space is thus obliterated. It could be regarded as being originally the posterior part of the orbit, and its connection with this remains in the mammal as a small crack, the anterior lacerate foramen, between the anterior edge of the alisphenoid and the orbitosphenoid, through which the profundus and eyeball nerves leave the skull. The pterygoid connection is not present in birds, and is reduced in the Chelonia and crocodiles.

The quadrate of amniotes is always more or less associated with the cranium, but in different ways in different groups. In the Chelonia and Crocodilia the quadrate becomes so closely applied to the auditory capsule that it becomes in effect part of the dorsal skull. This condition is called monimostyly. The lower jaw articulates with the quadrate as usual, so that it now swings firmly on the cranium.

In other reptiles there is a condition called streptostyly, in which the quadrate is relatively free, not meeting the epipterygoid, and connected with the main part of the pterygoid and with the auditory capsule only by ligament or not at all. The name covers a condition which has been reached more than once in the Squamata, in the dinosaurs and birds, and in the therapsids and mammals. In the snakes the quadrate is kept away from the capsule by the squamosal, and in the mammals it has moved within the capsule, as will be described below.

Where there is streptostyly there may also be kinetism, the ability to move the facial region of the skull forward and upward on the posterior part. This occurs to some extent in *Sphenodon* and dinosaurs, but is most developed in snakes and some birds, such as parrots (Fig. 16.5). In these the quadrate, which is lengthened, swings forward when the pterygoid muscles contract, and a joint allows the upper jaw to be raised. In snakes this joint is between the maxilla and the prefrontal (for the nature of these bones see below), while in birds it is further forward and is usually formed within the premaxilla and nasal bones. The nasal septum and interorbital septum are not continuous. The same arrangement in a different form occurs in the woodcocks (Scolopacidae), where the joint is halfway down the beak, so that the closed beak can be thrust into the mud and then opened at the tip.

We can now return to the cranium and consider the membrane bones. These cover almost all parts of the original cartilaginous skull except the occipital region. They are developed in the skin and are probably, in some way or other, derived from scales. Since the buccal cavity is lined with ectoderm they can be, and are, applied below the palate as well as above the cranium. We will begin with a reference list of the normal maximum number of membrane bones, starting from the front and referring the bones to the parts of the chondrocranium that they cover. Obviously

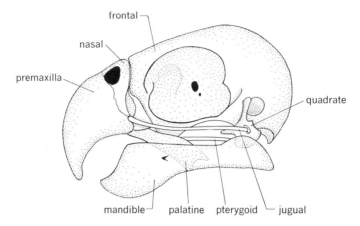

FIG. 16.5 Skull of a macaw, *Ara* sp., x 4/5, to show streptostyly. When the jaws open the quadrate swings forward, pushing the jugal and pterygoid and raising the maxilla and nasal.

where a dermal bone is applied to a fontanelle it will form part of the definitive wall of the cranium. In other places there will be a double wall, the dermal bones sometimes standing away from the cartilage bones to leave a space except at certain points of contact. This is shown in the diagrammatic sections (Fig. 16.2C, 16.2D).

Above each nasal capsule, and usually closely applied to it, is a nasal. Below, and formed from the skin of the roof of the mouth, is a vomer, which often bears teeth.

In the orbital region an incomplete ring nearly surrounds the eye. There may be a lacrimal (often unnecessarily spelled lacrymal or lachrymal), prefrontal, frontal, one or two postfrontals, and one or two postorbitals. Of these the frontal is the largest; it is in the position of the anterior part of the dorsal fontanelle, and makes the dorsal roof of the cranium. The lacrimal is on the front edge of the orbit and gets its name from the tear duct that pierces it in tetrapods. The others make the anterior and posterior edges of the orbit, the postfrontals and postorbitals standing out from the side of the cranium and joined to it only by their connection with the frontal.

Below the cranium in the orbital region, and covering the ventral fontanelle if there is one, but otherwise closely applied to the cartilage, is a single bone, the parasphenoid. Like the vomer, it is formed in the skin of the roof of the mouth, but it does not bear teeth.

Behind the frontals the fontanelle is filled up by a pair of parietals, behind which may be a pair of smaller dermosupra-occipitals, which as their name implies are above the cartilaginous supra-occipital. They are also

called postparietals, or, where the two are fused into one bone, the inter-
parietal. Below them may be a number of small bones which have been
given several names; intertemporal, supratemporal, posttemporal, and tabular. These stand away from the side wall of the cranium.

Outside the auditory capsule, and often closely applied to it, is the
squamosal.

The upper jaw has two series of membrane bones. On its outside are
four bones, premaxilla, maxilla, jugal (or malar or zygomatic), and quadratojugal, the first two of which usually bear teeth. The sizes and limits of
the four vary considerably, but usually premaxilla and maxilla are in front
of the orbit, forming part of the face, the jugal is below the eye, and the
quadratojugal behind the orbit. The name of this last bone should be
noted. Usually, when a bone has a compound name made up of those of
two other bones, the implication is that it is a compound bone, formed by
the fusion of the two. (The radio-ulna and tibiofibula in the limbs are
well-known examples.) But here all that the double name means is that
the bone stretches from the quadrate to the jugal. While the premaxilla
and maxilla are often closely applied to the nasal capsule, and make contact with the nasal bone, the other two lie well away from the cranium,
making a bar, the zygoma or zygomatic arch, below the eye. The dermal
bones of the temporal region (postfrontals, postorbitals, intertemporal,
supratemporal, tabular, and quadratojugal) primitively meet, so that,
with a part of the squamosal, they form a continuous more or less vertical wall which is attached to the cranium through the parietal and frontal
above, but is free behind and below. The result is that there is a large
space roofed above by the frontal and parietal, bounded on the medial
side by the cranial wall and on the lateral side by the temporal series of
bones just mentioned, blocked in front by the postorbitals and postfrontals,
but open below and behind. In it are the jaw muscles, which pass down
to be inserted on the lower jaw. We shall return to this point shortly.

Inside and below the jaw, and formed from the roof of the mouth, are
the palatine and the dermal pterygoids (or ectopterygoid and endopterygoid). These may bear teeth. In bony fish there is another series of bones
which may be listed here; they are developed in connection with the operculum which grows back to cover the gill slits, and are called the opercular, preopercular, subopercular, and interopercular.

Many of the dermal bones of the head of fish have canals in them containing organs of the lateral line system, and some authors think that the
bones were developed in connection with them. This may be so, but as
dermal bones develop also where there are not lateral lines the conception
does not seem very helpful.

Unfortunately, the skull of the only sort of bony fish that is generally
available for the student to study, a teleost such as a cod or salmon, is ex-

tremely difficult to make out—practically, because the brain case is very small and the rest of the bones stand out from it in a framework that, in the dried skull, does not make sense; theoretically, because the homologies of the bones with those of tetrapods are not always clear. It is generally best studied after that of the early reptiles, but will be dealt with here for convenience (Fig. 16.6).

The skull roof is made of an anterior pair of large bones, and a smaller posterior pair, which look like frontals and parietals respectively, but their paleontological history suggests that they are in fact parietals and post-parietals, these having enlarged and moved forward while the frontals are lost. In the orbit there is usually a crescent of orbital bones, derived from the optic capsule and running around behind the eye. The premaxilla (with teeth) and the maxilla (without) are attached to the rest of the skull only at their anterior ends. The side view of the temporal region is largely obscured by a large bony hyomandibula which joins the quadrate and is the chief support of the upper jaw. Its lower end has a separate ossification and is called the symplectic.

An ectopterygoid and an endopterygoid are present in addition to the cartilage bone called pterygoid or metapterygoid. The paired vomers are replaced by a single median bone, which shows traces of a double origin in some embryos.

The posttemporals are joined to the supracleithrum, a membrane bone of the shoulder girdle (p. 416).

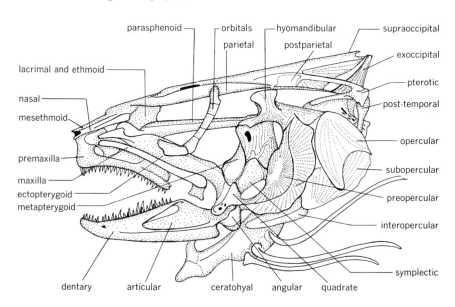

FIG. 16.6   Skull of a cod, *Gadus morrhua*, x 1/2.

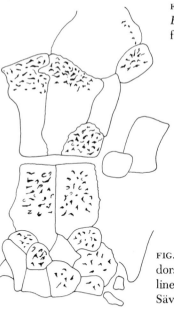

FIG. 16.7 Skull of a crossopterygian, *Ectosteorhachis* (=*Megalichthys*) *nitidus*, from the Lower Permian, x 1/2, dorsal.

FIG. 16.8 Diagram of the crossopterygian skull, dorsal. The dotted lines show the course of the lateral line canals. (Based on the restorations of Säve-Soderbergh, Westoll, and Romer.)

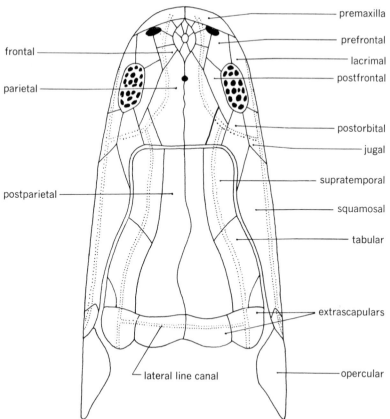

We can now return to the more typical, or completely roofed, bony skull. This is found, with few fundamental differences, in the earliest bony fish (Crossopterygii), in the early amphibians (Stegocephalia), and in the earliest reptiles (Cotylosauria). No tetrapod has any opercular bones, but traces of lateral line canals can be found in the appropriate bones of some Stegocephalia. From this central condition it is possible to derive the skulls of later bony fish as well as all the tetrapod descendants.

The primitive *Amia* and *Polypterus* have skulls not very different from the basic type, but that of the Dipnoi has lost most of the bones. The sturgeons, too, although they have a complete roof, lack many of the bones of the jaw, presumably in connection with their peculiar habit of feeding by sucking up mud to extract the organic matter from it.

The modern amphibians also have lost many bones. *Necturus* (Fig. 16.3) has large frontals and parietals, but no bones in the temporal region, which is therefore open and confluent with the orbit; and there are no nasals, prefrontals, or lacrimals, although all of these are present in some urodeles. Its vomers bear teeth, and there is a large parasphenoid. A single bone running from the vomer back to the quadrate is some sort of pterygoid, and is usually called the palatopterygoid. In most urodeles it is short and does not reach the vomer. There are premaxillae with teeth, but *Necturus* has no maxillae, although most urodeles have them.

The Anura also have lost many bones, and the interpretation of those that remain is sometimes difficult, because the skull is very much flattened and spread from side to side, with the maxillae and pterygoids standing out well away from the brain case to make a relatively large orbit. The roof is made by a single pair of bones, which used to be called frontoparietals, from the belief that they represented the frontals and parietals fused together. They are now considered to be expanded frontals, the parietals, as well as the temporal series, having been lost. There is a small pair of nasals, although most of the nasal capsule has the cartilage exposed, and vomers, premaxillae, and maxillae (all three with teeth), and a short quadratojugal but no jugal. The squamosal is a large bone of very characteristic form, shaped like an italicized T with the stem extending downward and slightly backward. The palatine runs transversely behind the nasal capsule, and its outer end (which is morphologically posterior) abuts on a large membrane bone called pterygoid. This is forked at its hind end, and joins the auditory capsule and the quadrate. The parasphenoid is a large bone, and one of the easiest of all animal bones to recognize, since it is shaped like a dagger with a wide cross-piece on the hilt.

The Apoda have a skull of more normal shape, but they too have lost many bones.

The reptiles have evolved from the completely roofed condition not so much by loss of bones, though this does happen, as by forming gaps in the temporal wall that is outside the jaw muscles. Although these gaps are

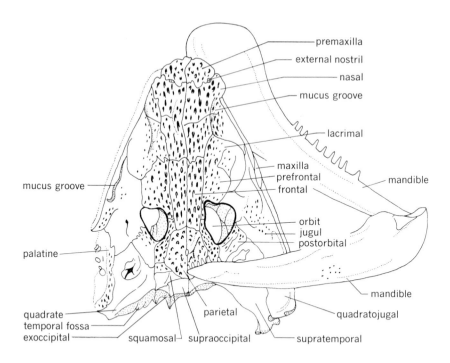

premaxilla
external nostril
nasal
mucus groove
lacrimal
mucus groove
maxilla
prefrontal
frontal
mandible
orbit
jugul
postorbital
palatine
mandible
quadrate
temporal fossa
exoccipital
parietal
quadratojugal
squamosal
supraoccipital
supratemporal

FIG. 16.9 Skull of *Eogyrinus attheyi*, dorsal, x 1/5. (Drawn from the type specimen in the Hancock Museum, Newcastle upon Tyne)

probably not so helpful or important in the classification of the reptiles as was thought thirty years ago, they are still of much interest. There are four main types of skull (Plate VIII.2-5). The completely roofed skull which we have already described is called anapsid (Plate VIII.2). Apart from small foramina for nerves the only gaps in the sides and roof of the skull are the external nares, the orbits, and in the Stegocephalia and the earliest reptiles (Figs. 16.9, 16.10) a hole on the top between the parietals which is presumed to have been for the pineal body, possibly still functioning as an eye. Except that the skulls of the Stegocephalia may show lateral line canals, there is little difference between them and those of the Cotylosauria; on the other hand, skulls of the crossopterygian fishes are also very similar. Whatever the skull of the ancestral bony gnathostomes may have been like (and of this we have no knowledge whatsoever), it is evident that the first tetrapods and their immediate ancestors had a uniformly anapsid skull. Such differences as there are lie in the proportions of the parts of the skull rather than in number or arrangement of the bones. In general, as the animals become more terrestrial in habit, the face becomes relatively longer. This means that the orbits are relatively shifted backward,

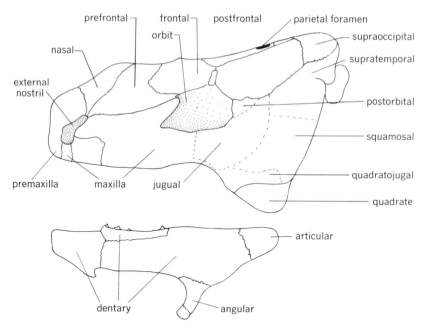

FIG. 16.10 Skull and lower jaw of *Pareiasaurus baini* (Cotylosauria), Permian, x 1/6. There are no sutures in the temporal region of this specimen; they have been inserted as dotted lines in approximate positions from a specimen of *P.bombidens*.

the jaws increase in length, and the parietals (marked by the pineal foramen) and postparietals shrink and move backward. In an early crossopterygian (Figs. 16.7, 16.8) these two together are more than half the length of the skull, so that the small frontals are entirely in the front half of the skull. In the therapsid reptiles, the parietals were small bones, broader than they were long, at the extreme posterior end of the skull, and the postparietals had disappeared. The anapsid reptiles are intermediate.

No reptile exists today which has a skull like that of a cotylosaur. The Chelonia are anapsid in form, but they have lost many bones (Fig. 16.11A). The only bone in the temporal region is a postfrontal. There has been much difference of opinion as to whether the Chelonia have always been anapsid, merely losing bones by shrinkage until they gradually disappeared, or whether their ancestors had gaps in the side wall of the temporal region which were afterward filled up. There is practically no fossil history, but the present fashionable view is that they are primitively anapsid. Whether this is so or not, a turtle skull can conveniently be used to demonstrate the anapsid condition in the laboratory, and the disposition of the muscles. A view from behind (Fig. 16.11B) shows the large space which these occupy between the cranium and the temporal wall, and the

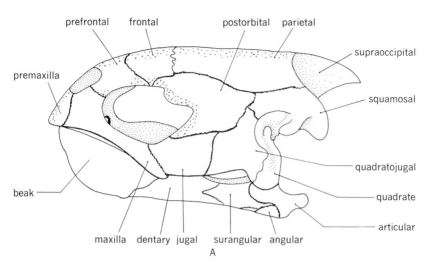

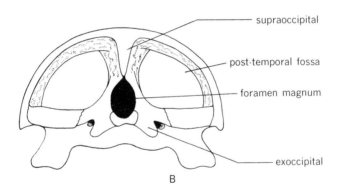

FIG. 16.11 Skull of Kemp's loggerhead turtle, *Lepidochelys kempi*, x 2/3. (A) Lateral view. (B) Posterior view.

way in which the latter is attached to the roof. The entry into this space from the back is called the posttemporal fossa.

Before the end of the Carboniferous there appeared a group of reptiles called Pelycosauria, which differed from the contemporary anapsid cotylosaurs in having a gap, a lateral temporal fossa, in the temporal wall. They are called synapsid, the name being derived from an early mistaken view that their single fossa was formed by the fusion of two. In the early

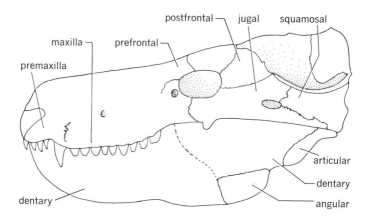

FIG. 16.12   Skull of *Cynognathus crateronotus* (Therapsida), Triassic, x 1/4.

synapsids the fossa was quite clearly low down on the skull. The jugal and quadratojugal made a bar below it, and it was bordered above by the postfrontal, which met the squamosal. In later reptiles, and especially in the therapsids, it became much larger, and the postorbitals and postfrontals were reduced and did not meet the squamosal (Fig. 16.12). The first advantage of the lateral fossae was presumably that they allowed the jaw muscles to expand sideways and so to contract more vigorously. (It is characteristic of muscle that it changes little in volume when it con-

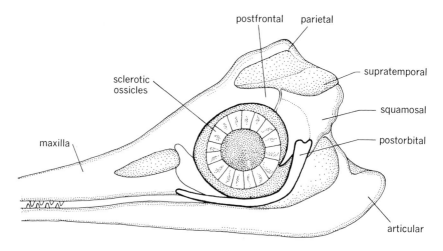

FIG. 16.13   Skull of *Ichthyosaurus* sp. (Ichthyosauria), x 1/3. The anterior part is missing.

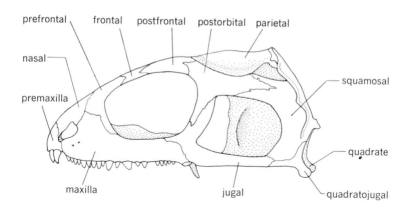

FIG. 16.14   Skull of *Sphenodon punctatus*, x 3/2.

tracts, a shortening in length of each fiber being compensated by an increase in diameter. If therefore the muscle is to contract a great deal, as it must if it is to move the jaw a long way without a very low mechanical advantage, it must have room to expand laterally.) A later benefit, as the fossae expanded, was that there was much freedom in the positioning of the origins of the muscles, and a third, which became very important in the mammals and birds, was that they allowed the brain to expand.

Found in the lower Permian of Texas, alongside cotylosaurs and pelycosaurs, is a small lizard-like creature called *Araeoscelis*, which differed from all its contemporaries in having a single lateral temporal fossa which was above the postorbital and postfrontal, a condition called parapsid (Plate VIII.4). *Araeoscelis* is isolated, and left no obvious descendants, but skulls with a similar upper vacuity are found in the ichthyosaurs (Fig. 16.13) and plesiosaurs. These groups were both aquatic, and both lived from the Triassic to the Cretaceous, but their method of swimming and other features of their skeleton were so different that they do not appear to have been closely related, and the prevailing opinion is that the two groups acquired their temporal openings independently of each other. It seems possible to derive the plesiosaurs from *Araeoscelis*—it was early enough, and they still retain four limbs—but the earliest ichthyosaurs were already so highly modified for swimming that their ancestry can only be guesswork. Some of the guesses that have been made seem rather unlikely.

Most of the remaining reptiles differ from all that we have considered so far in having two gaps in the temporal wall, and so are called diapsid (Plate VIII.5). This condition is found in dinosaurs and pterodactyls, and among living reptiles in *Sphenodon* (Fig. 16.14) and the crocodiles. The

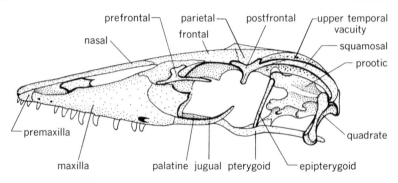

FIG. 16.15   Skull of a lizard, *Varanus salvator*, x 1.

postorbitals and postfrontals are often reduced to a single bone, the exact homology of which is doubtful, but, whatever it is, it joins the squamosal and separates the two lateral fossae. The jugal and quadratojugal make a complete bar along the lower edge of the skull.

The lateral fossae do not in themselves alter the appearance of the skull from behind, but their enlargement, accompanied by alterations in the shape of the skull, makes most diapsids less useful than turtles for demonstrating the posttemporal fossa. The crocodile's skull is dorsoventrally flattened, so that the upper lateral fossa looks upward instead of to the side.

We are left with the Squamata. The temporal wall of their skull is very open, and the identification of some of the bones is difficult, but everyone is agreed that, in principle, there is an upper temporal fossa. In most lizards (Fig. 16.15) this is clear enough, but in snakes the postorbital does not meet the squamosal, and so the vacuity is open below and hardly recognizable. Most authors now generally agree that the quadratojugal is missing.

This type of skull is clearly parapsid in form, and some of the most learned paleontologists have thought that the Squamata are descended from creatures like *Araeoscelis*. But there is another possibility—that the ancestors of the lizards were diapsid and that by loss of the quadratojugal the lower vacuity was opened out. This view became more popular after the discovery of *Prolacerta* in 1935. This was a small creature in the lower Trias, and it had an upper temporal vacuity and below it, on the quadrate, a small quadratojugal which did not reach the jugal. The form of the skull suggested that perhaps the lower temporal vacuity was bounded below, where the quadratojugal ought to have been, by ligament. In other respects *Prolacerta* resembles the early diapsids such as *Youngina* from the upper Permian, and it is placed with them in the Eosuchia. All that this really shows is that the diapsids could have given rise to a skull of parapsid type by loss of the quadratojugal, which no one ever doubted. It is not really relevant to the problem of the origin of the Squamata, for the first lizards appear in the upper Trias and are unlikely to have been descended from *Prolacerta*, which is only a little earlier.

If the Squamata are descended from the Eosuchia, the diapsid condition has probably appeared more than once. Part of the evidence for this comes from the condition of the heart and arterial arches, which we have discussed in Chapter 10. The birds seem to be descended from the dinosaurs, and since their heart is similar to that of crocodiles but different in structure from that of the lizards, it is argued that dinosaurs and crocodiles on the one hand must have diverged very early from the ancestors of the lizards, probably having separate origins in the cotylosaurs. The diapsids are, on this view, an unnatural diphyletic assemblage. The fact that the heart of the lizards is nearer to that of the tortoises than to that of the crocodiles suggests that, whether the Chelonia are primitively anapsid or not, their cotylosaur ancestors may have been the same as or near to those of lizards.

Anyone who wants to reject this argument must assume *either* that the crocodiles, birds, and lizards retained a completely undivided ventricle until after they had developed a skeleton which was purely crocodilian, avian, or lacertilian, as the case may be, *or* that a heart having started along one line of division reversed and went back to diverge along another. If the argument is accepted, it should be a warning against making too positive statements about the relationships of animals when we know only their skeletons and such few facts about other systems as can be deduced from the bones. We know nothing about the circulatory system of the pterodactyls, but since they appeared late, in the Jurassic, after the anapsid cotylosaurs had disappeared, they may well have come from some already diapsid dinosaur-like group.

The earliest known diapsids come from the upper Permian, whereas synapsids were well established before the end of the Carboniferous and are contemporary with most of the anapsids. It has recently been suggested that a group of small apparently insectivorous reptiles of the Permian, called Millerosauria, were the ancestors of all the diapsids—Pseudosuchia, dinosaurs, crocodiles, pterodactyls, Eosuchia, *Sphenodon*, and Squamata. The Millerosauria had a single temporal vacuity, which was bounded by the postorbital, squamosal, and jugal. They were therefore synapsid in type, but the other parts of the skull suggest that they did not give rise to the therapsids.

The skull of a bird (Fig. 16.16) is one of the most difficult of all for the student to interpret, partly because in the adult almost all sutures are completely obliterated and the surface of the cranium is quite smooth. There are no obvious temporal vacuities, either lateral or posterior, but if

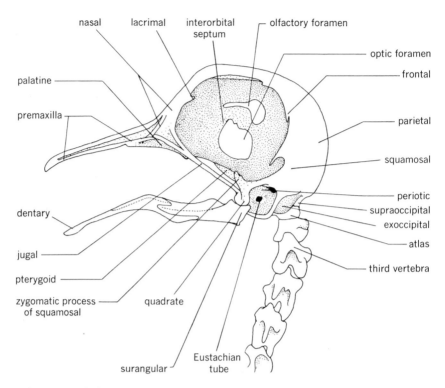

FIG. 16.16   Skull of a pigeon, *Columba livia*, x 2.

the birds are descended from dinosaurs the skull ought to be diapsid. The quadrate can be recognized as the bone with which the lower jaw articulates, and running forward from this is a slender rod. This is the jugal, or jugal plus quadratojugal; it makes the lower border of the temporal wall, but above it there is only a large space which is of one piece with the orbit. The interpretation is that the postorbital and postfrontal bones have been lost, so that the two lateral temporal fossae have become confluent not only with each other but with the orbit. At the same time the brain case has expanded greatly, and the frontal and parietal have grown down in contact with it and inside the jaw muscles. The posttemporal fossa has thus been eliminated. The only relic of the reptilian temporal wall, standing away from the cranium, is the narrow quadratojugal bar. The student can understand how these changes have come about, if he will look at a lizard or crocodile skull from behind and imagine the alterations in the position, shape, and size of the bones taking place as in a cinematograph film.

    There is also some spread of the squamosal over the cranium and inside the jaw muscles, with the result that much of the side of the brain cavity

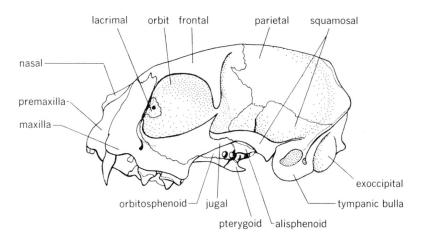

lacrimal orbit frontal parietal squamosal

nasal

premaxilla

maxilla

orbitosphenoid — jugal

exoccipital

tympanic bulla

pterygoid — alisphenoid

FIG. 16.17 Skull of a cat, *Felis catus*, x 2/3.

is bounded by this bone, the parietal, and the frontal. The limits of the three are usually quite unrecognizable. Most of the other membrane bones of the skull can be identified in birds. The beak is borne on the premaxilla, which has a small maxilla lying inside it.

Archaeopteryx had a typically diapsid skull (though the fossae were small) with a posttemporal separating the two gaps from each other and from the orbit. The mammals have achieved a very similar condition to the birds from a different starting point. Their ancestors were synapsid, but they too have lost the postorbitals and postfrontals, and a reference to Plates VIII.3 and VIII.5 will show that this will produce the same results as in a diapsid skull. There is also the same swelling of the cranium, and growth of frontal, parietal, and squamosal over it to form its upper side wall. Mammals have lost the quadratojugal, but the squamosal has a long zygomatic process going forward, while the jugal extends back, so that the two bones overlap one another and together make the characteristic zygomatic arch or zygoma (Fig. 16.17) running outside most of the jaw muscles. In the Hyracoidea and in some rodents the jugal extends so far back as to take part in the articulation of the jaw, which in mammals is made not by the quadrate but by the squamosal (see below).

In *Ornithorhynchus* there is a small gap between the squamosal and the cranium, which probably represents the posttemporal fossa (Fig. 16.21). The orbit and temporal fossa are confluent, but a small postfrontal and a small postorbital bone are present.

The membrane bones of the palate are less important in mammals than in reptiles. The palatines are the largest, and grow down and inward to meet each other and so to form the hard and bony false palate, above which lie backward extensions of the nasal passages (p. 144). The dermal pterygoid is a small bone attached outside the presphenoid. Below and in front of the presphenoid is a small bone, the vomer. There has been much speculation on its homology; it has been thought to represent the parasphenoid, but since in some mammals it is formed by the fusion of two bones it probably represents the fused vomers of reptiles. If this is so, the parasphenoid has been lost (Figs. 7.6, 7.7, 7.8).

The further evolution of the mammalian skull is largely a matter of adaptive radiation. This shows itself especially in the length and form of the jaw and the nature of its articulation, in the position of the external nostrils, and in the size of the brain. The teeth have been dealt with in Chapter 9. The general picture is that insectivores (e.g. shrews), and herbivores (e.g. cattle) tend to have a long jaw; carnivores (e.g. cats), a short one. Herbivores have a flat articulation, so that the lower jaw can move sideways and backward and forward, as well as up and down; this is seen at its extreme in rodents. Carnivores tend to have a roller joint, so that all sideways movement is prevented; in extreme cases it may be impossible to detach the lower jaw from the skull without breaking the squamosal. Omnivores such as man are intermediate. In the whales and Sirenia the external nares are high on the skull, just anterior to the frontals, so that the animal can breathe while its mouth is under water.

It is obvious that if the brain increases in size without a corresponding increase in the length of the jaw, the proportions of the cranial and facial portions of the skull must change. This is seen best in the primates and especially in man (Fig. 16.19), where the jaw almost fits under the cranium.

There is another change, which has occurred more than once, and which does not seem explicable as a simple adaptation. This is a resepara-

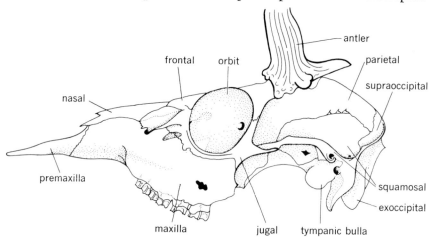

FIG. 16.18   Skull of a fallow deer, *Dama dama*, x 2/5.

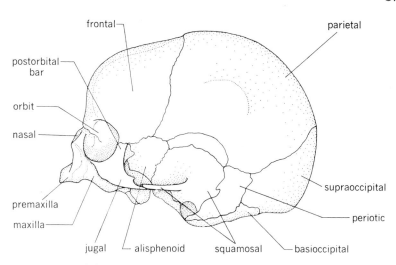

FIG. 16.19   Fetal human skull, x 4/5. In the adult there is much fusion of bones.

tion of the orbit and the lateral temporal fossa. It is incipient in the cat (Fig. 16.17), where a spur from the frontal curves behind the eye. In the artiodactyls, such as the sheep or deer (Fig. 16.18) this postorbital proc-ess is extended and meets a similar one that projects upward from the jugal, so that the eye is surrounded by a complete ring of bone, and in a lateral view the orbit and the temporal fossa appear to be separated. They are, however, still in open communication beneath the postorbital bar. Similar processes nearly, and occasionally completely, meet in the skull of the Sirenia. In the primates (Fig. 16.19) there are similar processes from frontal and jugal, but they grow in a medial direction as well, so as to meet the alisphenoid, thus separating the orbit completely from the temporal fossa. There is no evidence of any close relationship between artiodactyls and primates, so that this new bony orbit must have been evolved at least twice over. Other animals have produced a postorbital bar by different means. In horses it is made up by extensions from the frontal, jugal, and squamosal, but this is not the general condition in the Perissodactyla, for the rhinoceroses and tapirs do not have a closed orbit. The hyraxes have long processes from the jugal and parietal, which sometimes meet. In the whales a process from the frontal nearly meets the squamosal. The inter-esting points about these modifications are that an arrangement possessed and lost by the therapsids has come back into existence, presumably be-cause it was, after all, advantageous, some half a dozen times, and that, various though the means of producing it are, none of them is the same as that present in the ancestors. The separate postorbital bones, once lost, are

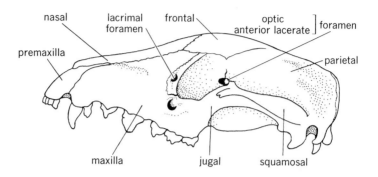

FIG. 16.20   Skull of a carnivorous marsupial, *Thylacinus cynocephalus*, x 2/3.

not regained. This is an example of the irreversibility of evolution, which is sometimes raised to the status of a law.

The skull of a marsupial differs in a number of points from that of a typical placental, although, as we have seen in Chapter 7, it shares many of these points with the insectivores. One of the most interesting is perhaps that the optic foramen, instead of piercing the orbitosphenoid, is on its posterior edge, so that it is confluent with the anterior lacerate foramen, which is simply the gap between the ascending process of the pterygoid (now become the alisphenoid) and the orbitosphenoid, where the side wall of the skull is not ossified. Another is that the tympanic is never inflated to form a flask-shaped bulla round the middle ear, although a similar structure may be formed from the alisphenoid. All these special points are called primitive, which means that they are present in the early mammals but not in most living ones. Since we can seldom point to any particular advantage in either state this is little more than a name for our ignorance, and they are perhaps more important to those who have to identify skulls than to anyone else.

More interesting are the many adaptations of marsupial skulls. These parallel almost all those of placental mammals except that there are no marsupials so completely aquatic as the whales and Sirenia, or even the seals. Superficially the skulls of carnivorous marsupials (Fig. 16.20) and placentals are very similar, and so are those of the herbivorous species of the two subclasses. Similar habits have selected similar modifications.

The foramina through which blood vessels or nerves enter or leave the skull, which in the dogfish are merely holes in the cartilage placed at appropriate points, have come in the mammals to have relatively fixed positions, with usually constant relationships to both cartilage and membrane bones. Since the nerves and blood vessels have little variation their foramina must also be much the same in all groups, but there are occasional slight variations, such as the fusion of the foramina for the optic and eye-ball nerves which we have already mentioned as distinguishing the marsupials and the insectivores. The list of the foramina which pierce the cranial wall in a typical mammal such as a dog or a cat is as follows:

NAME	POSITION	STRUCTURES TRANSMITTED
Lacunae of cribriform plate	Mesethmoid	Olfactory nerve
Optic	Orbitosphenoid	Optic nerve
Anterior lacerate, or sphenoidal or orbital fissure	Between orbitosphenoid and alisphenoid	Oculomotor, pathetic, and abducent nerves, and ophthalmic branch of trigeminal
Round or rotundum	Alisphenoid	Maxillary branch of trigeminal
Oval or ovale	Alisphenoid, behind and outside rotundum	Mandibular branch of trigeminal
Middle lacerate	Between alisphenoid and peri-otic	Internal carotid artery
Internal auditory meatus	Peri-otic	Facial and auditory nerves
Stylomastoid	Between bulla and mastoid	Facial nerve
Posterior lacerate	Between peri-otic and exoccipital	Glossopharyngeal, vagus and spinal accessory nerves, and internal jugular vein
Condylar	Exoccipital	Hypoglossal nerve
Magnum	Posterior end of skull	Spinal cord

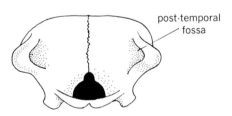

post-temporal fossa

FIG. 16.21   Skull of *Ornithorhynchus paradoxus*, posterior, x 1, to show the post-temporal fossa, Cf. Fig. 16.11.B.

There are also foramina which pierce or lie between other bones in the skull, and do not lead directly into or out of the brain cavity. Some carry blood vessels and nerves further on their way, while others carry ducts. The chief of them are:

NAME	POSITION	STRUCTURES TRANSMITTED
Incisive	Lower surface of premaxilla	Blood vessels and nerves (maxillary branch of trigeminal) to palate, and nerve to vomero-nasal organ
Palatine	Two or more pairs in horizontal portion of palatine	Branches of maxillary branch of trigeminal nerve
Infra-orbital	Maxilla, on edge of orbit	Maxillary branch of trigeminal
Lacrimal	Lacrimal	Lacrimal duct
Sphenopalatine	Ascending plate of palatine	Entry of maxillary branch of trigeminal to face
Ethmoid	Orbit, between maxilla and palatine	Maxillary branch of trigeminal nerve and ethmoid artery
Alisphenoid canal	Horizontal tunnel in alisphenoid	External carotid artery

Lower Jaw

The second element of the first arch of the ventral skull is the lower jaw or mandible. In the elasmobranchs (and in embryos) there is a single cartilage, known as Meckel's, on each side. The shape varies, showing a certain amount of adaptive radiation, but there is always an articular region toward the posterior end, which enables the jaw to move on the quadrate. The front end, for which the descriptive adjective is 'mental,' from the Latin word for the chin, is joined to its fellow by ligament. Other points of the mandible (not recognizable as namable structures in the dogfish) are the angle, which is the corner below the articulation, and a coronoid process which rises up for the attachment of muscles in front of the articulation.

When Meckel's cartilage ossifies it usually does so to form a single bone, which, since it forms the surface for the joint, is called the articular, and is usually more or less confined to the posterior half of the jaw. In many

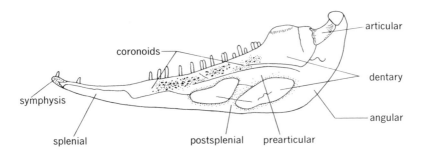

FIG. 16.22   Lower jaw of *Eogyrinus attheyi*, inner aspect, x 1/5, drawn from the type specimen. Watson thinks there are three coronoids, but only one possible suture is visible.

frogs, including *Rana,* the front tip of the cartilage ossifies as a small mentomeckelian bone, but the articular part in anurans remains wholly cartilaginous. In urodeles such as *Necturus* there is only slight ossification.

In all gnathostomes except the elasmobranchs the jaw is clothed, inside and out, in membrane bones, and, as with the dorsal skull, the more primitive forms have the most of these. The maximum is found in such a stegocephalian as *Eogyrinus* (Fig. 16.22), where there can be made out on the inner surface a splenial in front, followed by a postsplenial and a large angular, making the angle of the jaw, which is not yet, however, very marked. Above the postsplenial is a row of perhaps three coronoids, a prearticular and a surangular. Most of the outside of the jaw, except the angle, is covered by a large dentary, which, as its name implies, bears teeth. It is usually visible from the inside also, where the other membrane bones do not meet each other and the cartilage has disappeared.

Except that there is only one coronoid, the primitive bony fish, such as a crossopterygian or *Amia,* and the primitive reptiles are all very similar to this, but other vertebrates show various degrees of reduction. Meckel's cartilage persists in the teleosts, but the functional lower jaw is a large dentary, which ensheaths the cartilage inside and out and bears the teeth (Fig. 16.6). There may be a small posterior angular, and the articular is ossified. *Necturus* (Fig. 16.23A) has, in addition to the partly ossified articular, only three bones. There is a large dentary with teeth, but different authors give different names to the other two. A small splenial or coronoid bears teeth behind those of the dentary, and a large bone extends from the angle forward on the median surface nearly to where the two dentaries join in a symphysis. It is called both angular and pre-articular, and it occupies the position held by both these bones in the primitive amphibians.

Meckel's cartilage persists in the frog and is ensheathed by only two bones, a dentary on the outside and a bone usually called angulosplenial within. This probably represents either the pre-articular or that bone fused with the angular. Since the frog has no teeth in its lower jaw the name dentary is misleading.

The extant reptiles have more bones in the lower jaw than any other living vertebrates. Both crocodile (Fig. 16.23B) and lizard have the articular and five membrane bones, only the pre-articular being absent. The coronoid of the lizard is extended dorsally into a well-marked process. In snakes the two dentaries can be widely separated, to allow the swallowing of large prey. The dermal bones of turtles have partly fused into a single piece, and the two dentaries are also fused at the symphysis.

The lower jaw of a bird (Fig. 16.23C), like the skull, loses its sutures in the adult, and it is difficult or impossible to make out the separate bones. A young jaw, however, shows that articular, angular, surangular, dentary, and splenial bones are present, and in some birds there is a pre-articular as well. The two dentaries are fused at their front ends. The whole jaw is very slender, and the projecting part, which is mainly supported by the dentary, is covered by the horny beak. There are no teeth in any modern birds, and while they were present, in a somewhat reptilian jaw, in *Archaeopteryx*, the long, toothed, lower jaws usually appearing in books as belonging to the Cretaceous avian fossils appear more likely to be those of swimming reptiles, mosasaurs, accidentally associated with the birds' skulls.

Only one bone can be seen in each side of the lower jaw of a mammal (Fig. 16.23D) and all embryological studies show that this is a single structure, not formed by fusion. It necessarily bears all the teeth, and is called the dentary. The two are usually associated in front in a symphysis, which varies in its firmness but is never as complete as in birds. In the whalebone whales its connection is only by fibers, so that in a preserved skeleton the dentaries of the two sides appear as quite separate bones, and in the rodents also there is some degree of movement of the two sides.

A typical mammalian dentary shows three posterior processes, an upper coronoid, a middle articular process or condyle, and a lower angle, the shape and disposition of which often enable a lower jaw to be assigned to its order. The coronoid is the place of insertion of the temporal muscle, which has its origin on the temporal wall of the cranium and on contraction closes the jaw and pulls it backward. The articular process, which must not be confused with the articular bone of other tetrapods, makes contact with the squamosal, and forms the articulation of the jaw. The angle, together with the part of the jaw just in front of it, is the region of insertion of the masseter, the main muscle for closing the jaw. It has its origin on the zygomatic arch (the remains, it will be remembered, of the

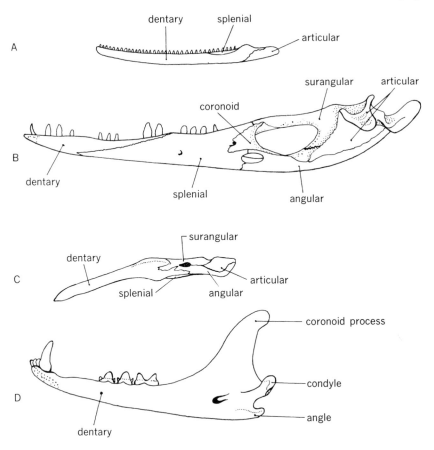

FIG. 16.23   Lower jaw of (A) Mud puppy, *Necturus maculosus*, inner aspect, x 2. (B) *Alligator* sp., inner aspect, x 1/3. (C) Barn owl, *Tyto alba*, outer aspect, x 1. (D) Cat, inner aspect, x 2/3.

old dermal temporal wall of the skull), and runs down the outside of the jaw to be inserted at its base.

The dentary has two conspicuous foramina. The inferior dental, on its medial surface, just in front of and below the condyle, takes the mandibular branch of the trigeminal nerve and the dental artery, while the mental, on the lateral surface near the chin, allows a branch of the same nerve to come out to supply the region of the lower lip.

In some embryos other bones can be seen in the mammalian lower jaw, and their fate is interesting. One of the clearest is the marsupial *Perameles* (Fig. 16.24A). In the pouch young of this animal the posterior end of Meckel's cartilage can be seen to be ossified, and the bone that it forms

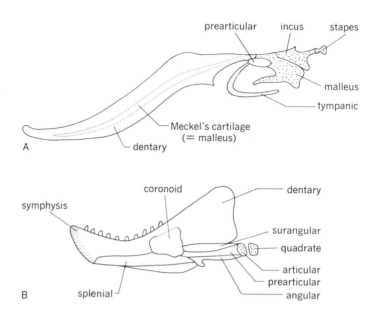

FIG. 16.24   (A) Diagram of the lower jaw of an embryo of *Perameles nasuta*, Marsupialia. Cartilage bones are shaded. (Based on Esdaile) (B) Diagram of the lower jaw of *Cynognathus crateronotus* (Therapsida), inner aspect. (Based on the restoration of Watson)

must be the articular. The rest of Meckel's cartilage is sheathed by a membrane bone, which is the dentary. At the posterior end are two small bones which, from their position, look like the pre-articular and the angular. The former is pierced by the chorda tympani branch of the seventh nerve, as is the pre-articular of reptiles. The whole lay-out of the jaw at this stage is very similar to that of a therapsid reptile such as *Cynognathus* (Fig. 16.24B). When the fate of these bones is followed through it is seen that the articular becomes the malleus of the middle ear, and the angular grows dorsally and becomes the ring-shaped tympanic which supports the ear-drum. The pre-articular is functionally lost as a separate bone, but may form splints on the malleus.

The second of the three ear ossicles, the incus, is from its first appearance in contact with the articular, and since this bone in vertebrates generally articulates with the quadrate, the obvious conclusion is that the incus *is* the quadrate. Its general position agrees with this. The third ossicle, the stapes, is not so easy to identify. In *Perameles* it is from the first in the foramen ovale, and only later comes into contact with the incus. At one time it was thought to be a detached piece of the auditory capsule, but the prevalent opinion has for a long time been that it represents the columella auris of reptiles, which is taken to be part of the hyoid arch.

The loss of the quadrate-articular joint as that on which the movement of the lower jaw depends, and its replacement by the new squamosal-dentary joint, raise the interesting problem of how the change came about. Clearly it did not happen all at once, and it is easy to suggest that there must have been an intermediate stage in which both joints were functional side by side, the new one probably lying outside the old. We are fortunate in having a number of fossils which show possible steps in the transition. In *Cynognathus* the articular makes contact with both the quadrate and the squamosal, and although the dentary does not quite reach the joint it is greatly extended backward and its tip reaches to within one-tenth of an inch of the articulation in a jaw about sixteen inches long. *Diarthrognathus*, which is placed in a group called Ictidosauria, which some paleontologists regard as reptiles, other as mammals, has both a quadrate-articular and a squamosal-dentary joint, and so fulfills the prediction that the two must have existed together.

As we have seen in Chapter 7, it is only on the criterion of the lower jaw, its articulation, and the middle ear, that one can decide whether many of these fossils are best called reptiles or mammals, and the decision must be largely arbitrary. The experts agree that the change in the joint took place more than once, since it is found in skulls which, on other grounds, could not have been derived from each other. It seems therefore that during the Mesozoic there was a general tendency among the therapsid reptiles toward what might be called mammalization. According to a recent view there have been at least four and perhaps as many as nine crossings of the line. We do not know how many of these led to mammals with hair and milk glands, but as monotremes seem to be on a different line from marsupials and placentals, hair at least has probably been produced at least twice—unless, indeed, the therapsids themselves had hair, in which case they would presumably be regarded, if they were alive today, as mammals, in spite of their reptilian skeleton.

Although at first sight simpler, the problem of the replacement of the one bone of the middle ear, the columella auris, by three, is really more difficult. If such a bone or chain of bones is to be of any use as a system for the transmission of sound, its outer end must be in contact with something that vibrates in response to the original sound—an ear-drum for airborne sounds, the ground or a bone in contact with the ground if hearing is to be by what is misleadingly called bone-conduction.

The usual assumption is that the therapsids had an ear-drum in the skin, from which the columella ran to the oval window. What has to be explained, therefore, is how, without loss of hearing, a new drum came into existence supported by the tympanic (the angular) at the bottom of the external auditory meatus, while at the same time the malleus and incus (that is to say, the articular and quadrate) inserted themselves between this and the columella, which, it must be emphasized, was in contact with the skin. The only possible way for this to have happened would seem to be for the columella to have become forked, so that while one limb reached the skin another shorter one met the incus; in this way both drums could be active at once. Since a sound would not reach the two drums simultaneously, and the columella could only vibrate as a whole, this would seem to be an extremely inefficient and unlikely arrangement. As we have seen in Chapter 14, there is another explanation, which gets over this difficulty by assuming that the therapsids had no ear-drum, a hypothesis which is supported by the clumsy size of the columella in many of them. It seems unlikely that creatures that stood high on their legs, as the therapsids did, would have been able to make much use of ground-borne sounds, but they may have been deaf. If this were so, the great success of the incipient mammals may have been due as much to their acquisition of hearing through the chain of ossicles in the middle ear as to anything else. The development of the tympanic-supported tympanum, as well as the formation of two of the ossicles from articular and quadrate, necessitated the reduction of the bones in the lower jaw, which does not, in itself, seem to have much functional advantage, and certainly none that could not be achieved equally well by fusion of bones early in development.

Branchial Skeleton

The branchial arches of the dogfish (Fig. 4.4) illustrate well enough a probably primitive state. It seems impossible to connect these with the continuous shield of the cephalaspids, which is scooped out into gill pouches on its under surface, and one can only assume that if the continuous skeleton was primitive it became fragmented, perhaps first into separate arches, and then into jointed ones. It looks as if in the elasmobranchs the primitive number of pieces of cartilage was four on each side. Their names are, beginning dorsally, pharyngo-, epi-, cerato-, hypo-, and basibranchial. This number is found in the third and fourth functional gill arches, the fourth and fifth of the series not counting the jaws, of *Squalus* and *Scyliorhinus*, but in the other arches there are reductions. The first arch, or hyoid, has a dorsal epihyal, called the hyomandibula, a ventral ceratohyal, and a single median basihyal. The hyomandibula joins the upper jaw to the auditory capsule, as we have seen above (p. 361).

In bony fishes there is generally a branchial skeleton which is recognizably similar to that of dogfish, but made of bones instead of cartilage. In many, including the cod (Fig. 16.6), the hyomandibula ossifies to form two bones, in which case the lower is called the symplectic. The epi- and

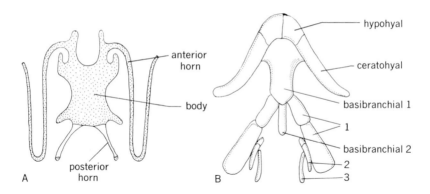

FIG. 16.25   (A) Hyoid skeleton of a frog, *Rana temporaria*, ventral, x 3/2.
(B) Branchial skeleton of *Necturus*, ventral, x 3/4. 2 and 3, the second and
third branchial arches.

cerato-elements often bear long bony gill rays supporting the gills. Gill
rakers are shorter rods projecting between the gills.

In tetrapods, with the loss of lungs, the branchial skeleton is much reduced. The hyomandibula becomes the columella auris, and other parts
of the hyoid combine to form a plate supporting the tongue. In mammals
this hyoid plate is also the insertion of the digastric muscle, contraction of
which opens the mouth. The other branchial arches contribute in various
degrees to sundry cartilages that support the bronchi and larynx.

The hyoid varies much in form, largely in connection with the mode of
use of the tongue. In frogs there is a flat cartilaginous plate with two
long and double-curved anterior horns (Fig. 16.25A). The only bony parts
are the two short posterior horns. The anterior horns are derived from the
ceratohyals, the plate from the basihyal (or fused hypohyals) and fused
basibranchials. In *Necturus* (Fig. 16.25B), as befits its larval condition,
there are remains of the separate arches.

Reptiles have a hyoid apparatus similar in general form to that of the
frog. In birds (Fig. 16.26) there are several distinct bones and a long pair
of posterior horns derived from the first functional branchial arch. In
woodpeckers they are extremely long and curve around the top of the
head like a watch-spring when the tongue is withdrawn (Fig. 9.6C).

The development of these cartilages is best known in mammals. In an
embryo, e.g. an early pouch young of *Perameles,* they show remnants
of three distinct arches, and their fate shows that the narrow median
body of the hyoid bone (Fig. 16.27) is derived from the median basibranchial, its anterior horn from the ceratohyal, and its posterior horn
from the first branchial arch. On the horns are inserted the stylohyoid

muscles, which have their origin on the occiput, and on contraction raise the floor of the mouth, as in the act of swallowing. The names sometimes given to the separate pieces of the anterior horn do not correspond to their embryological origin. The other cartilages move backward and form the thyroid, cricoid, and arytenoid cartilages which support the larynx. A similar development possibly happens in birds, but the facts are obscure.

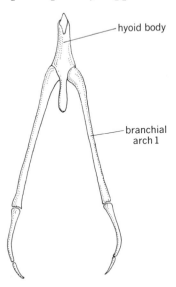

FIG. 16.26   Hyoid apparatus of a bird, the chaffinch, *Fringilla coelebs*, ventral, x 3.

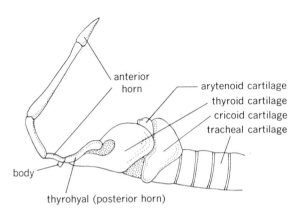

FIG. 16.27   Hyoid apparatus of a cat, lateral, x 1. (Modified from Mivart, *The Cat*, 1881)

17

Limbs and Girdles

LIMBS, in the sense of jointed appendages sticking out from the trunk and used for locomotion, or sometimes for handling and manipulating objects, are things which man, as a vertebrate, is inclined to take for granted, just as he assumes that eyes are normal sense organs. Limbs are, in fact, even rarer than eyes, for they are found only in the vertebrates and arthropods. The limbs of fishes have joints only at their base, so that fully developed limbs, capable of relative movement at points along their length, have been evolved only twice—unless, indeed, as some zoologists think, the 'arthropods' make an unnatural group and represent three separate lines. The tetrapod limb has such a standard pattern that it is unlikely to have arisen more than once.

Vertebrate limbs consist of little but skin, bone, and muscle, with what in the language of economics would be called the necessary services or facilities—blood vessels and nerves—to allow them to function. A little will be said about muscles in Chapter 21; here we are concerned with the skeleton, which is part of that called appendicular.

The modern cyclostomes have no paired limbs, and this condition used to be considered primitive; we cannot now be so sure. Of the four generally accepted groups of Devonian Agnatha, one, the cephalaspids, possessed lobed structures in the pectoral region which are generally regarded as fins, but nothing corresponding to these has been found in the other groups, nor is there any trace of a pelvic fin in any of them. Whether the cephalaspids were ancestral to the modern cyclostomes we do not know, nor whether these structures, if they really were limbs, were in any way ancestral to those of gnathostomes; it seems on the whole unlikely, for their bony skeleton, like that of the rest of the body, is external.

All true fish, in the sense of primarily aquatic gnathostomes, have at least two pairs of lateral fins, except for the few, like the eels, which can reasonably be supposed to have lost them. In no gnathostome which is fully known are there more than two pairs, except that monsters, in which development has obviously gone wrong, occasionally occur, even in mammals. It is, however, commonly said that the placoderms (p. 66) had more than two pairs. This is based on the fact that the fossils show a

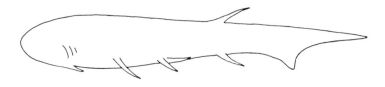

FIG. 17.1   *Mesacanthus mitchelli* (Acanthodii), Devonian, x 1/3.

row of spines, of varying length, along the flanks (Fig. 17.1). *Climatius,*
the genus usually pictured, may have had as many as seven. The assumption that these spines supported fins seems to be based on a comparison
with the dorsal spines and fins of modern sharks such as *Squalus.* But the
spines of *Squalus* do not support the fins in the way in which those of
Climatius are shown to do in the common restorations, and, since the
placoderms had a bony exoskeleton, their spines may have been mere
specializations of this. In any case, they seem to have nothing to do with
the fins of other fishes, supported, as these are, by an endoskeleton.

Much ingenuity has been devoted to inventing origins for the paired
fins. At one time some zoologists thought that they could be derived from
gill arches, the general idea being that as the continuous series of arches
of the protovertebrate (as in amphioxus) became reduced to the half-
dozen or so in the head region only, some of the more posterior ones, with
skeletal bars already in them, grew out to become limbs. There is no
paleontological evidence for this, and the fact that most fins show, by
their innervation and muscles, that they come from several segments, is
against it. The theory of the origin of the limbs from gill arches is not now
seriously held. Moreover, while the skeleton of the gill arches is formed
chiefly from the neural crest, that of the limbs comes from lateral plate
mesoderm.

The other chief explanation, and the one now generally given, is that
the paired fins were derived from two continuous folds developed ventro-
laterally along the body from head to anus, which afterward split up to
give two separate pairs only. The evidence for this, such as it is, is of three
sorts. First comes the fact that the skeleton of the paired fins is in general
similar to that of the unpaired fins. This does not really show more than
that this type of skeleton is suitable for both purposes. Just as the dorsal
and ventral fins have as their chief function the control of rolling and
yawing, so lateral folds are conceived as being developed to prevent pitching. But this function can be, and is, served by the pectoral fins alone, so
that, though it is not impossible that there was once a continuous lateral
fin fold, nothing in this argument compels us to believe in it. Secondly, it
is said that the form of the pectoral fin in a shark such as *Cladoselache*
from the Devonian (Fig. 17.2) suggests that the fin was a reduction from

a once-continuous fold. The fin is wider at the base than elsewhere (the fossils show impressions of what was presumably the actual outline of the fin), and the skeleton consists of a series of rods at right angles to the axis of the body and almost parallel and straight except at their distal ends, where they curve away from the axis of the fin. Clearly, a fin of this sort could have had practically no movement except in an up-and-down direction. It does not look, however, as if, as is sometimes said, it merges into the body fore and aft. What it does look like is a primitive fin that occupies more than one somite without concentration at the base.

Lastly, comes the argument from the rows of spines in the placoderms. If these did not support fins, and that they did is pure guesswork, they give no support for the hypothesis either. And since they could not have been ancestral to the fins of other fishes they are at best only oblique evidence for what was possible and not for what happened.

A modification of the lateral fin-fold theory suggests that only the pectoral fins were derived in this way, from a fold of limited length. This really means nothing more than that the fin was once broader at the base than it is now, a supposition which seems likely from its origin from several somites in ontogeny. The pelvic fins are on this view supposed to be developed as copulatory organs. This is what they are in modern sharks, their function in swimming being minimal. Those of the females are then regarded as functionless vestiges, like the nipples of male mammals. It is indeed striking that in nearly all fish the pelvic fins are of relatively small importance.

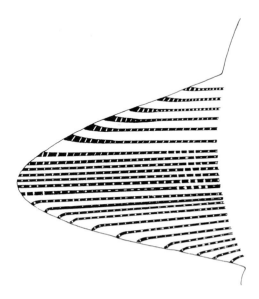

FIG. 17.2   Pectoral fin of a Devonian elasmobranch, *Cladoselache clarki*, x 1/3.

The general plan of the skeleton of paired fins is that there are one or more rows of cartilages (or bones) called radials, and distal to these there are thin supports called dermal rays, made of elastin (or bone), just as in the unpaired fins. The proximal row of radials is often concentrated into one or a few pieces called basals.

Within this general pattern there is much variation, and it is almost impossible to say which is the primitive type and what are the lines of descent. The student will not go far wrong if he takes the familiar dogfish skeleton as his starting point. Here there are three large basals, called propterygium, mesopterygium, and metapterygium, in the pectoral fin (Fig. 4.5), and one large basal and a smaller one in the pelvic fin (Fig. 4.6). *Scyliorhinus* has only a single pelvic basal. From the basals the radials radiate outward. Both these patterns could easily have been derived from the skeleton of a *Cladoselache* fin, by concentration of some cartilages and division of others, although *Cladoselache* is not generally regarded as being itself ancestral to modern sharks. The region of the basals and radials is fleshy, with muscle, that beyond, supported by the dermal rays, is membranous.

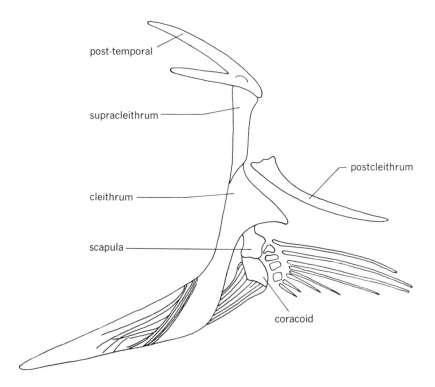

FIG. 17.3   Left shoulder girdle and skeleton of the pectoral fin of a cod, *Gadus morrhua*, outer aspect, x 1.

The other type of fish fin that the student can easily see, that of the teleost, is obviously specialized (Fig. 17.3). The basals are reduced to about three bones, which are closely applied to the shoulder girdle and sunk into the flesh of the body. There is practically no muscular part to the fin, and the membranous flap is supported entirely by the dermal rays, which are fine, slightly radiating needles of bone. This type of structure could be formed from that of the dogfish by a concentration and sinking in of the basals, with loss of the radials. The bony rays must be a new formation.

A rather different type of fin skeleton has the basals arranged as an axis, running from the girdle toward the more or less pointed tip of the fin, with radials branching from it both on the cephalic and the caudal side, or, to put it more simply, both pre-axially and postaxially. This type of fin was unfortunately named the archipterygium, because it was thought to be ancestral to the other types. It is found in the dipnoans (Fig. 17.4), and was also present in some extinct elasmobranchs such as *Pleuracanthus*, and in the other crossopterygians called Rhipidistia. Some of these, such as *Eusthenopteron* from the upper Devonian, had a very much shortened axis (Fig. 17.5) to which reference will be made below.

Peculiar types of fin skeleton are found in other fish. In the pectoral fin of *Polypterus* there are two straight diverging basals between which is a third, large and triangular and not touching the girdle. The pelvic fin has a single basal and then four straight radials. The sturgeons have a reduced skeleton, with only a few basal cartilages and the dermal rays. The extreme diversity of the patterns of these skeletons means that they are very labile, and it is possible, by small steps, to transform any one into any other by an infinity of routes.

Those who like long words may call the fish fin an ichthyopterygium. It is clearly useful as a stabilizing organ, and as an elevator converting the forward motion produced by the tail into an upward or downward motion when it is inclined to the horizontal. For this it needs to be jointed at the base, which it usually is, but it does not need to have joints within its length, which it usually has not. If the basal joint allows it to be moved backward and forward as well as to be rotated it can be used for swimming, although rather clumsily—it stands rather lower in efficiency in relation to the tail than the paddles of a nineteenth-century steamer do to a screw. Like side-paddles, it makes for easy maneuverability. Use of the pectoral fins in this way for swimming was probably never achieved by the elasmobranchs, but is common in the bony fishes, and can be watched in any good aquarium. Fish with a swim bladder have less need of external elevators than do dogfish, and the pectoral fins of teleosts have for the most part rotated so that their plane is nearly vertical. In this position they are better suited to swimming, but have a smaller effect on lift. They can also be used as brakes, simply by being pulled out at right angles to

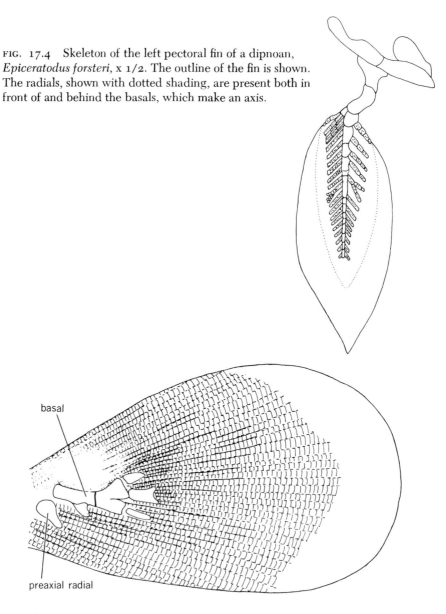

FIG. 17.4 Skeleton of the left pectoral fin of a dipnoan, *Epiceratodus forsteri*, x 1/2. The outline of the fin is shown. The radials, shown with dotted shading, are present both in front of and behind the basals, which make an axis.

basal

preaxial radial

FIG. 17.5 Skeleton of the left pectoral fin of a Devonian rhipidistian, *Eusthenopteron fordii*, dorsal, x 1. The postaxial region, just above the basal in the drawing, is crushed in the specimen, and probably contained one or two radials.

the body. When this happens their slight lifting force tends to make the fish rise in the water. This is counteracted in some fish by the pelvic fins, which are set at a different angle so as to depress the body when they are extended. This appears to be the functional explanation of the fact that the pelvics have in many teleosts shifted forward to lie below the pectorals. By this means the fish avoids rotation round the center of pressure when both fins are extended. It must be added that some of the most active fishes, such as salmon and trout, retain the pelvic fins in the normal position, and yet seem to be able to stop perfectly well. A similar forward shift of the pelvic fins had occurred in the later crossopterygians (Fig. 4.24).

The fish fin is not, by its structure, very suited for walking locomotion, but a few fish have managed to make use of it in this way. Gurnards (*Trigla*) have three rays of the pectoral fin extended so that they frequently make contact with the bottom of the pool in which the fish is lying. They are probably primarily sensory, but they can also push the body slightly forward, and they show how the fins might be developed for a cruder sort of walking, similar to the way in which a boat can be pushed with a pole. *Anabas*, the climbing perch, apparently moves on land not by its paired fins but by spines extending from the pre-opercular and anal fins. *Periophthalmus*, the other strikingly terrestrial fish, hops by means of its pectoral fins, which are turned outward, rather like the flippers of a seal. Its body is supported also by the pelvic fins and tail.

The Tetrapod Limb

All these walking uses of fins are side-lines, which have led to no great development, but it may be believed that the paired limbs of tetrapods were derived from fins of a fish which successfully took to using them in some such way as do the gurnard and mud skippers. On other grounds (the structure of the skull and presence of lungs) the ancestors of the tetrapods are generally looked for among the crossopterygians, and so it is from these that zoologists generally try to derive the tetrapod limb.

As with so many parts of the body, the earlier tetrapods had on the whole more complex skeletons in their limbs than have those alive now. On grounds of general comparative anatomy, with which paleontology and embryology, so far as they go, are in agreement, the tetrapod limb can be considered to have the basic plan shown in Fig. 17.6. Such a limb, or any that can reasonably be derived from it, is called a chiropterygium, or, since there are five digits, a pentadactyl limb. Fore- and hind-limbs are built on the same plan, but for the most part corresponding parts have different names, mostly derived from the obvious differences between arm and leg in man. The word digit, though belonging in Latin only to fingers, is used in zoology to include both fingers and toes.

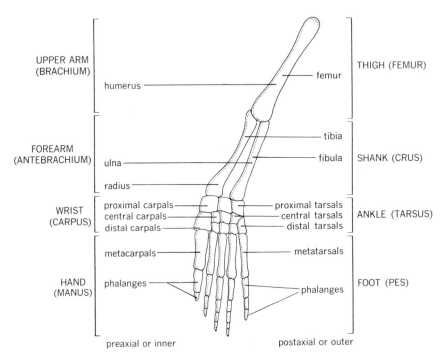

FIG. 17.6 Diagram of the chiropterygium. Names of the parts of the fore-limb are on the left, of the hind-limb on the right.

There has been much confusion in the naming of the small bones of the wrist (carpus) and ankle (tarsus). The chief names, with those of the pre-axial border on the left, are as follows; those not recommended are italicized.

PROXIMAL ROW	Carpus	radiale *scaphoid*	intermedium *lunate* *lunar*	ulnare *triquetral* *cuneiform*	
	Tarsus	tibiale *talus* *astragalus*		fibulare *calcaneum*	
MIDDLE ROW	Carpus	centralia, numbered from pre-axial border			
	Tarsus	centralia, numbered from pre-axial border			
		In man, *navicular*			
DISTAL ROW	Carpus	trapezium	trapezoid	magnum *capitate*	unciform 1,2 *hamate*
	Tarsus	entocuneiform *medial, intermediate,* and *lateral cuneiform*	mesocuneiform	ectocuneiform	cuboid

The bones of the distal now may be called simply first, second, third, fourth, and fifth, numbered from the pre-axial border.

If one looks only at the radials and the proximal bones, the skeleton of the fin of a crossopterygian such as *Eusthenopteron* (Fig. 17.5) is not vastly different from the diagram of the pentadactyl limb, or the limb of a primitive amphibian such as *Eryops* (Fig. 17.7). It is possible to imagine that each of the bones in the former became transformed into a bone in the latter, the largest basal becoming the humerus, and so on. Beyond this one cannot go, since the crossopterygians have no distal bones that could become the phalanges of hand and foot. The digits and the wrist and ankle are then generally thought of as a new formation. The trouble with this sort of explanation is that it weakens the former argument. If one set of bones can arise anew there is no reason why the others should not, so that although the student may, if he chooses, homologize humerus, radius, and ulna with bones visible in *Eusthenopteron*, he is not compelled to do so.

Whatever the origin of the bones of the pentadactyl limb, they would be useless without joints and muscles with which to move them. The

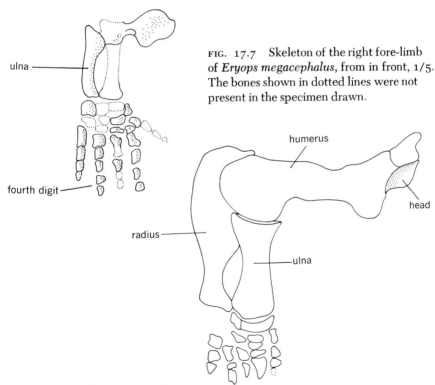

FIG. 17.7   Skeleton of the right fore-limb of *Eryops megacephalus*, from in front, 1/5. The bones shown in dotted lines were not present in the specimen drawn.

FIG. 17.8   Right fore-limb of *Pareiasaurus baini* (Cotylosauria), Permian, anterior, x 1/9.

tetrapod limb is a structure of a different kind from the fish fin, used in general for a different purpose. We have seen in Chapter 5 (Fig. 5.7) how the first land animals went on their bellies, and how only gradually did limbs develop so as to raise their bodies off the ground and enable rapid running and leaping to take place. Such a primitive reptile as the cotylo-saur *Pareiasaurus* (Fig. 17.8) shows the original position of the limbs, with the body suspended between them and touching the ground.

The number of bones in the pentadactyl limb is hardly ever that shown in the diagram, but the arrangements of the segments of the limb (upper arm, forearm, wrist, palm, digits, and corresponding parts in the hind-limb) is remarkably constant. This in itself suggests that the limb evolved only once, and, having come into existence, kept much of its original ar-rangement because this was both efficient and versatile. The chief change is a reduction in the number of bones. Only occasionally is there an in-crease, associated with a loss of functional joints and a general regression to a fin-like form.

Reduction in the number of bones can take place in two ways, by loss and by fusion. Sometimes a bone disappears without leaving a trace. A majority of tetrapods have fewer than five digits, and generally where this is so there is no sign of those that are missing. Sometimes, as in the artiodactyls and kangeroos, there are functionless or near-functionless splint bones representing some digits, and this may be taken to show how bones may be lost by gradually becoming smaller and smaller until they

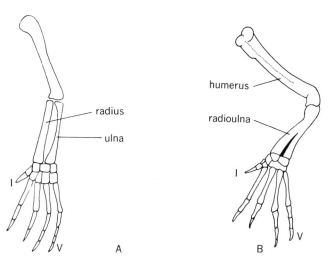

FIG. 17.9   (A) Skeleton of the left fore-limb of a tadpole of *Rana temporaria*, dorsal, x 10. Drawn from an alizarin transparency. The radius and ulna have not yet fused. (B) Skeleton of the left fore-limb of a full-grown *Rana tem-poraria*, dorsal, x 3/2.

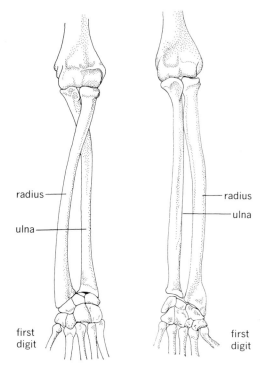

radius

ulna

radius

ulna

first
digit

first
digit

FIG. 17.10 Skeleton of part of the arm of man, showing how the radius and ulna twist on each other in pronation (on the left) and in supination (on the right), x 1/5.

are no longer there. In other cases there has been fusion of bones, which can be recognized in ontogeny. The fore-limb of a tadpole or young frog, for example, shows radius and ulna in the forearm as separate bones (Fig. 17.9A), but in the adult frog these have fused together to form a single bone, called a radio-ulna. (Fig. 17.9B). The same sort of thing happens in many mammals, where tibia and fibula may be fused, and in the wrist and ankle of birds (Figs. 6.5 to 6.8).

Reduction in the number of carpals or tarsals is usually partly by loss and partly by fusion.

In formal lay-out, though not in detail, the arm of man (Fig. 17.10) is of a quite primitive type, a fact which illustrates the importance and persistence of the general plan. In other tetrapods adaptive radiation has taken place along many lines, but only seldom has there been much deviation from the plan. This makes it convenient to study the limbs not class by class, but functionally, in accordance with the use to which the limb has been put.

So long as the limb is used only for walking it undergoes little change except for the alterations in the joints that enable it to be straightened,

FIG. 17.11   Right humerus of
Pareiasaurus baini, seen from
above, x 1/16.

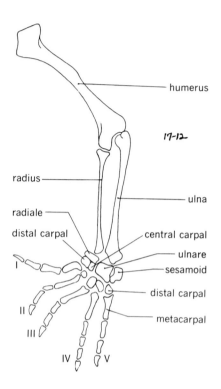

FIG. 17.12   Skeleton of the left fore-limb
of a lizard, *Varanus niloticus*, anterior, x 1/2.

and for an increase in the ratio of length to breadth of the three main
bones (usually known as the long bones). The humerus of *Pareiasaurus*
(Fig. 17.11) was about one-quarter as deep as it was long, while the
width of the bone from front to back, measured along the axis of the
body, was almost as great as its length. By contrast, the humerus of a
running animal is almost cylindrical in section, and some ratios of mini-
mum breadth at mid-point to length are: the lizard *Varanus* 1:10 to 1:12,
depending on size; mouse 1:15; rabbit 1:13; cat (Fig. 17.13) 1:13. As animals become bigger the ratio increases again for mechanical reasons, and is
1:8 in a pony. Generally, the proximal segment is slightly shorter than the
next, but in very heavy animals, which are called graviportal, the humerus
and femur are the longest bones in the body, so that the ratio has fallen
again in the elephant to 1:10 (Figs. 17.14 and 17.26).

One of the most remarkable functions to which the limbs have been put
is that of flying, and the skeleton of the fore-limb has been modified in

three different ways for this purpose. The wing of a bird is shown in Fig.
6.6. There is relatively little specialization but much reduction. Only three
digits are present, and all are reduced in the number of their phalanges,
two of them being very much so. This is connected with the development
of feathers as the structures that impart the necessary force to the air. All
that they need is a firm basis to which to be attached and the necessary
joints for partial rotation of the wing in flapping. These the bird has.

The peculiar feature of the skeleton of the birds is the fused carpometacarpus. This has been mentioned in Chapter 6, where it has been pointed
out that no explanation in terms of flight seems possible, but that it may
be a concomitant of the similar fused tarsometatarsus, which could be a

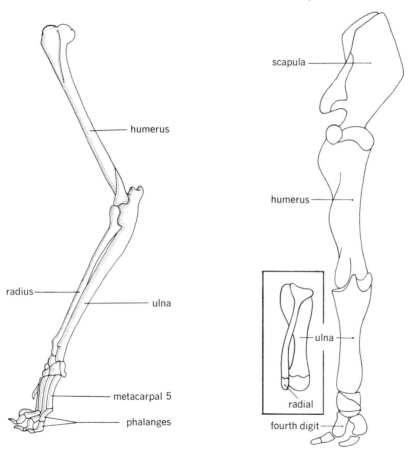

FIG. 17.13   (Right) Skeleton of the left fore-limb of a cat, x 1/2.

FIG. 17.14   (Left) Skeleton of the left fore-limb of an elephant, *Elephas
indicus*, x 1/24. The fifth and fourth digits only are visible. *Inset:* Radius
and ulna in anterior view.

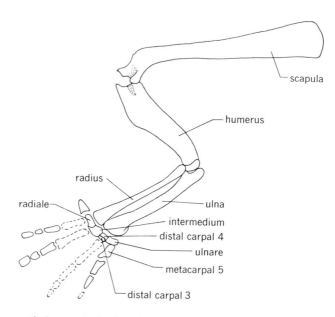

FIG. 17.15   Skeleton of the left fore-limb of *Iguanodon atherfieldiensis* (Ornithischia), Jurassic, x 1/10. The dotted phalanges have been restored from other species of *Iguanodon*. According to Hooley, the bone labeled radiale includes the first distal carpal and the first metacarpal, and the bone labeled ulnare includes the fifth distal carpal.

help in bipedal gait. Some slight support for this view is given by the skeleton of the bipedal dinosaurs (Figs. 17.15, 17.16). In many of these there was clearly little movement in the tarsus or carpus, and the bones of the distal row are often reduced and sometimes apparently missing. They may have been cartilaginous, or they could equally well be fused with the metapodials as in birds. In many Ornithischia the proximal tarsals (tibiale and fibulare) were fused with the corresponding long bone, tibia or fibula, so foreshadowing the tibiotarsus of birds. All this adds support to the suggestion that it was the hind-limb that led the way, and that the origin of the carpometacarpus of birds had nothing to do with flight. The loss of the tarsal joint may have been connected with the digitigrade stance of the dinosaurs. These fused bones were probably present in *Archaeopteryx* (p. 103).

The pterodactyls (Fig. 17.17) were very different. The radius and ulna were fused and the metacarpals elongated and sometimes fused, but otherwise there was little peculiarity in the proximal portions of the fore-limb. The special feature was a greatly extended fourth finger, which has four long phalanges, each about the same length as the humerus or

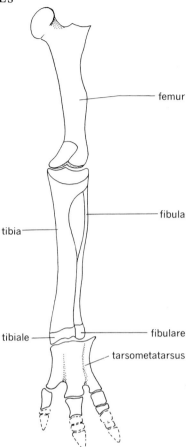

FIG. 17.16 Skeleton of the left hind-limb of *Iguanodon atherfieldiensis*, x 1/12. The dotted phalanges have been restored from other species.

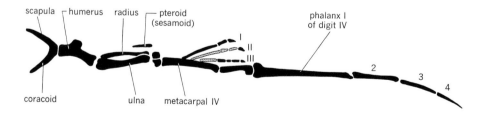

FIG. 17.17 Skeleton of the wing of a pterodactyl, *Pteranadon* sp, x 1/12. The dotted bones are reconstructed.

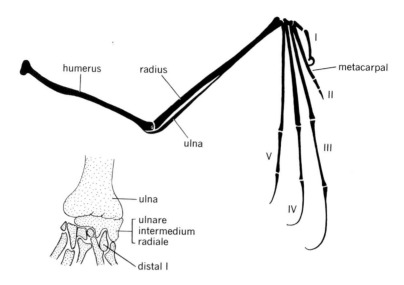

FIG. 17.18   Skeleton of the wing of a bat, *Pteropus* sp., x 1/2. Inset: detail of the carpus, x 2; there is one large fused proximal carpal, no centrale, and five separate distal carpals.

radio-ulna, or in some species even longer. There were also three short hooked digits which look as if they might have been used, as a bat uses its hind-limb, for the animal to hang by when at rest. Some species also show what looks like an extra free metacarpal arising from the wrist at an angle from the others. This is usually said to support a flap of skin between the forearm and shoulder, but it bears a remarkable similarity in position to the first digit in the wing of a bird. This, as discussed in Chapter 6, bears a small tuft of feathers, the bastard wing, which in spite of its insignificant size is of great aerodynamic importance in slow flight. Since it seems that many pterodactyls lived on cliffs, and so must have had a slow stalling speed, it is possible that this little bone also supported a detached flap which served the same purpose.

The wing of a bat (Fig. 17.18), like that of a pterodactyl, is membranous, and the skeleton shows both similarities and differences. The radius and ulna are fused, but at the same time the ulna is reduced, only its proximal third being present, and even that contributes very little to the elbow joint. It looks as if there was no advantage in retaining two separate parallel bones in this part of the wing, and in this respect both bats and pterodactyls are more advanced than birds. There is a short, clawed, first digit, which the bat uses in climbing, some of the large fruit-bats being especially active in this way. The other four fingers are elongated and spread out fan-wise to support the wing, which is also supported by the humerus and radius, by the femur and tibia (the fibula is nearly always reduced or absent), and by the tail. Four clawed toes are free, and used for hanging upside down.

Bats in general can fly every bit as well as birds, but by incorporating most of the hind-limbs in the wing they have greatly diminished their power of movement on land. Pterodactyls appear to have had much weaker flight-muscles, and the hind-limbs, though free, were so placed behind the center of gravity that they would seem to have been of little use for walking. The single line of skeletal support, along one finger, would mean also that the membrane would be much more liable to damage by tearing. Altogether, although they could probably soar well, they appear to have been rather poor fliers, and perhaps for this reason became extinct when the modern birds appeared to compete with them.

The other type of extreme specialization in the pentadactyl limb is found in those amniotes that have returned to the water. No amniote is fully aquatic in the sense of living all its time beneath the surface and breathing dissolved oxygen, but two living groups, the Sirenia and the whales or Cetacea among mammals, never leave the water, and the same was true of the Ichthyosauria of the Trias and Cretaceous among reptiles. The evidence of this statement about the ichthyosaurs is that fossils have been found with the skeletons of several young ones inside an adult. These are evidently pregnant females about to give birth to swimming young viviparously. Other groups, notably the reptilian plesiosaurs (Sauropterygia) contemporaneous with the ichthyosaurs, the penguins among birds, and the seals among mammals, spend or spent almost all their life in the water, coming to land for little but copulation and the birth of young and the laying of eggs.

Both limbs of the ichthyosaurs were mere paddles (Fig. 17.19), the hind-limb being much smaller than the fore-limb. The humerus and femur are reduced in length and the radius and ulna or tibia and fibula are hardly recognizable as such, being mere polygonal lumps, distinguishable from the more distal bones only by their slightly greater size. Beyond these may be, in the fore-limb, as many as about two hundred small bones tightly packed together. Proximally they are more or less polyhedral or cuboid, but distally and on the edges of the limb they are nearly spherical. The hind-limb is similar, but with fewer bones. This condition is usually said to be 'hyperdactyly' and 'hyperphalangy,' meaning that there are more digits and more phalanges than normal, but this description is misleading, since there is rather an indiscriminate filling-up of the whole area of the limb with bones, and proximally, where alone any regularity can be traced, the normal five digits are present. Whatever the condition is called, the resemblance to the skeleton of a fish's fin is obvious. If one can imagine a succession of photographs of the limbs of ancestral ichthyosaurs run as a cinematograph film, one would see the pentadactyl limb changing into

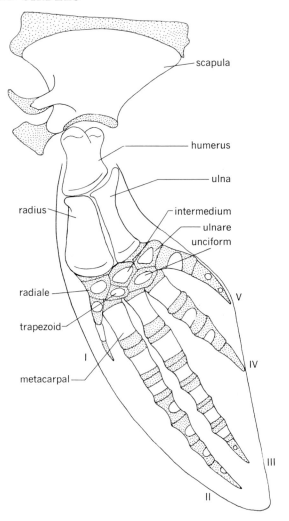

FIG. 17.20 Shoulder girdle and skeleton of the left fore-limb of a porpoise, *Phocaena phocaena*, x 1/2. Cartilage is dotted, and the outline of the fin is shown.

FIG. 17.21 Cartilaginous femur of a blue whale, *Balaenoptera musculus*, x 1/2 The animal is about 100 feet long.

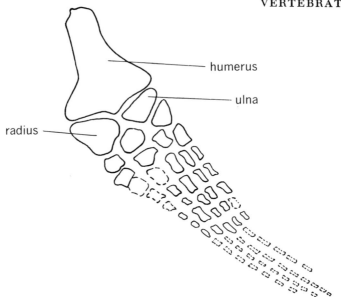

FIG. 17.22   Skeleton of the left fore-limb of a plesiosaur, *Cryptocleidus oxoniensis*, x 1/8. Broken lines indicate phalanges missing from this specimen.

Although the fore-limb of the Sirenia is a flipper with no separate fingers, its skeleton is little modified, with neither hyperdactyly nor hyperphalangy. There are no hind-limbs.

The ichthyosaurs, like fishes and whales, swam by means of their tails, their limbs being presumably used only for the same sort of purposes as the fins of fish; but the plesiosaurs had limbs with joints that gave them good movement, so that they were probably used like those of a swimming turtle or penguin. The humerus and femur were relatively long (Fig. 17.22), but distally there was concentration of bones, and five digits with up to fourteen phalanges.

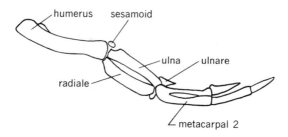

FIG. 17.23   Skeleton of the left fore-limb of a penguin, *Aptenodytes pennanti*, x 1/3.

The penguins, though they have a fore-limb that is useless for anything but swimming, have changed its skeleton remarkably little (Fig. 17.23). The only modification from the normal flying wing is that all the bones are flattened. This shows that, whatever their advantages, hyperdactyly and hyperphalangy are not necessary for an efficient swimming fin.

In the seals also there is little modification of the skeleton of the fore-limb beyond a shortening of the proximal segments and a flattening of the distal ones. The hind-limbs have lost their normal position, and are directed backward, with their morphologically ventral surfaces touching, so that the two limbs together act like a single caudal fin for swimming. The first and fifth digits are long, the others small and almost functionless. The eared seals and walruses have less modification, with the toes of equal length, and can turn their feet out for walking.

We have already seen that whales have lost their hind-limbs, and various other tetrapods have lost both limbs. These include the Apoda among amphibians, and the snakes and many lizards among reptiles. In some snakes, such as the python, there are vestiges of the hind-limb in the shape of a pair of claws, no larger than the animal's scales, beside the anus. In the lizards known as skinks, steps toward the loss of limbs may be seen, for many have useless limbs only a few millimeters long on a body of several centimeters. There are no limbless birds, but some have lost the power of flight, and use their wings, so far as is known, for nothing at all. It is surprising, therefore, that they are as large and well-developed as they are, for most have either a normal skeleton, or, as in the emus, cassowaries, and kiwis, the digits are reduced to one. On account of the different structures of the feet and other characters, most zoologists now think that flightlessness has been evolved several times over, and that such birds as the American rheas, the African ostriches, and the Australian emus are not closely related, but have independently lost their wings. So far as is known the Cretaceous *Hesperornis* had no bones in the wing except a very thin humerus; it is usually reconstructed as having no external wing at all, but this is not necessarily correct. The moas, large birds which became extinct in New Zealand probably only a few hundred years ago, had no bones of the fore-limb, and some did not even have a shoulder girdle.

All mammals apart from the swimming forms already mentioned, the bats, and a few sloths which can only live upside down in trees, have limbs which enable them to move on land. Within this generalization there are many variations, showing adaptive radiation in connection with different modes of life. Something has been said about this in the account of the mammalian orders in Chapter 7, but we may here make some generalizations about the structure of the limb skeleton and the mode of movement.

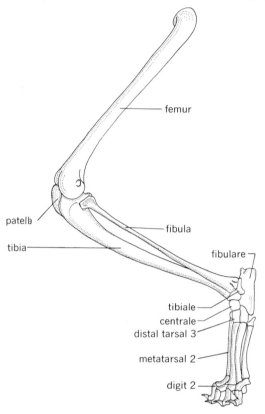

femur

patella

tibia

fibula

fibulare

tibiale
centrale
distal tarsal 3

metatarsal 2

digit 2

FIG. 17.24.   Skeleton of the left hind-limb of a cat, x 1/2.

The central type is more or less reptilian, with separate bones in the second segment, a nearly full set of wrist and ankle bones, and five digits on each foot. This is seen in many insectivores and rodents. Usually the whole foot is placed on the ground and the animal is plantigrade. With increased speed of movement the limb lengthens and the number of digits tends to be reduced. A carnivore such as a dog or cat (Fig. 17.24) shows this elongation, and the raising of the metapodials off the ground to make the animal digitigrade, while the general pattern and number of the bones remain primitive. The artiodactyls and perissodactyls (Fig. 17.25) show further lengthening, raising of the foot so that the animal walks on its nails, and reduction of the digits to two or one. There is also a greater or lesser degree of reduction of the fibula and ulna, showing that when the use of the limb is confined, as it is in these fast-running creatures, to backward and forward movement in locomotion and no other purpose, one bone is all that is needed. The carnivores, though they may be as fast as the ungulates, use their fore-limbs to some extent for holding food, and retain a large ulna; the fibula is somewhat reduced.

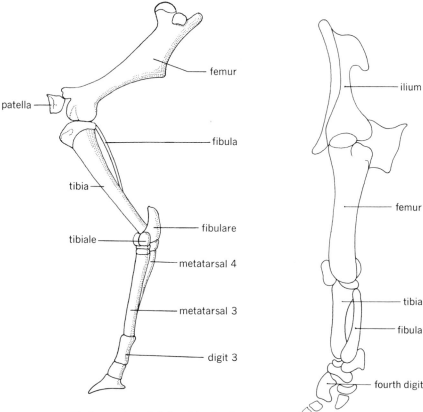

FIG. 17.25   Skeleton of the left hind-limb of a
horse, *Equus caballus*, x 1/8.

FIG. 17.26   Skeleton of the left hind-limb of an elephant, *Elephas
indicus*, x 1/24. The fifth and fourth digits only are visible.

Man shows the same sort of development in his hind-limbs, with great
reduction of the fibula, but he remains five-toed and plantigrade.

Perhaps surprisingly the same type of modification is found in the hind-
limbs of those mammals which have achieved speed not by running but
by jumping. An even greater share of the increased length of limb is made
up of the metatarsals. In the jerboas (rodents, *Dipus*) there is a single
metatarsal which shows by two grooves that it is made of three bones
fused together. There are three toes, and so three condyles at the distal
end of the metatarsus, which thus has a close resemblance to the tarsometatarsus of a bird. The kangaroos (Fig. 17.27) have a single fourth
metatarsal and toe, and vestiges, more or less functionless, of numbers

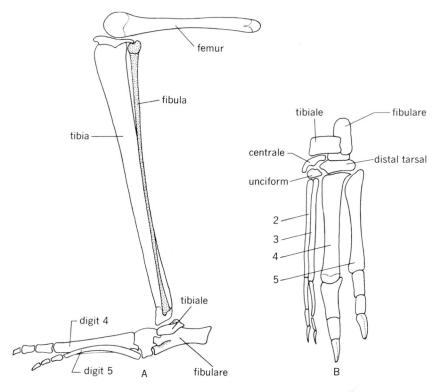

FIG. 17.27   (A) Skeleton of the left hind-limb of a kangaroo, *Macropus rufus*, x 1/6. (B) Skeleton of the left foot of a tree kangaroo, *Dendrolagus inustus*, dorsal aspect, x 1/2.

two, three, and five. The second and third are enclosed in a common membrane, a phenomenon called syndactylism. The explanation of this peculiarity is found in the foot of the tree-climbing opossums, in which the first digit is opposable to the fourth and fifth, especially to the former, so that when a branch of a tree is grasped digits two and three are functionless and tend to be squeezed out of existence. When the arboreal ancestors of the kangaroos took to the ground only the fourth and fifth toes were available to be elongated for speed. The weight of the body was presumably placed on an axis running through the fourth, which was thus the one to be chosen.

Lesser radiations have taken place in various orders. Opposability of the thumb for grasping occurs in the primates, and in most of these the big toe also is opposable. Fore-limbs turned backward for digging, with greatly widened palms, are found in several sorts of insectivore (Fig. 17.28). Man (Fig. 17.10) has a versatile arm, which can be moved in almost any direction and is capable of considerable twisting. This depends on the reten-

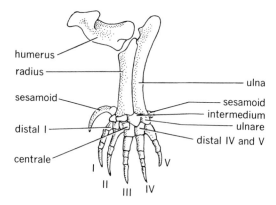

FIG. 17.28 Skeleton of the left fore-limb of a burrowing insectivore, the mole, *Telpa europaea*, dorsal aspect, x 1. The humerus is broad in proportion to its length, as in primitive reptiles (compare Fig. 17.11).

tion of the ulna as a separate bone, and linking of the wrist to the distal end of the radius. When this rotates on the head of the humerus it turns the hand through nearly 180°, from the primitive position of supination (the palm facing ventrally) to pronation (the palm facing dorsally). Further twisting of the hand, through a total of about 220°, is brought about by rotation of the humerus.

Except for those cases where the limb is much modified, each of the major limb bones has a characteristic form throughout the tetrapods. Thus the femur has a head which seldom departs far from a hemisphere in shape, while the humerus generally has a flatter head, and a more deeply grooved pulley-like surface, or trochlea, at the distal end. This makes it fairly easy to learn to place any major bone in its correct position in the limb. Within this general similarity there are differences which are characteristic of the Class, and further differences which distinguish Orders within a Class. The fact that a series of femurs, for example, from a number of different mammals are so obviously variations on one theme is one of the strongest arguments for a common origin for the whole group.

Girdles

The skeleton of the limbs, with which we have so far dealt in this chapter, is for the most part outside the outlines of the trunk, and only occasionally, as in some fish, birds, and mammals, partly enclosed within it. The upper segment, humerus or femur in the tetrapods, one or more basals in fish, articulates with a special part of the appendicular skeleton called a girdle, shoulder or pectoral for the fore-limb, hip or pelvic for the hind-limb.

In the elasmobranchs there are relatively simple bars or hoops of cartilage, as we have seen them in *Squalus* (Figs. 4.5, 4.6). The names applied
to the parts of the girdle are derived from the separate bones of tetrapods,
but there is no well-established homology. The girdles do not make contact with any other part of the skeleton, and have a rather flat surface on
which the fin can move. Each side chondrifies from its own center, and
the two parts grow until they meet and fuse in the mid-ventral line. In
the peculiar Permian sharks such as *Pleuracanthus* which had archiptery-
gial fins, the two sides of the shoulder girdle remained separate. We know
nothing more primitive than this. The usual explanation of the origin of
the girdles is that they were formed by the sinking into the body and
fusion of some of the proximal cartilages of the fin, their place in turn
being taken by other more distal ones. Something like this has clearly
happened in the teleosts, where the basals are, as described above, within
the trunk. (Fig. 17.3).

Perhaps partly because of this secondary position of the basals, the
bones of the two sides of the girdle in teleosts are small and do not touch
each other. There is however, a new and much more important shoulder
girdle of dermal bones, which make a half-loop behind the opening of the
operculum. This is not only the real support for the fins, but an important
link holding the body together. The concentration of the gill slits so that
they are separated only by thin bars, instead of the broad fleshy ones of
the dogfish, means that there is in effect a great gash in the side of the
trunk, running almost from mid-dorsal to mid-ventral line. Behind this
runs the dermal shoulder girdle. Its most dorsal piece is joined to the parietal region of the skull, its ventral piece runs right forward and meets
its fellow in the floor of the mouth. By it, more than by the vertebral column, the trunk is attached to the head.

The link between skull and girdle is the posttemporal, which in fish
seems to belong rather to the girdle than the skull. Since the dermal bones
of the two structures have a similar origin, assignment of it to one or the
other is arbitrary. Below this is a large cleithrum, but one or more supra-
cleithra are sometimes interposed. A backwardly projecting postcleithrum
is of less importance. The more primitive bony fish, such as the Crossopterygii, sturgeons, and *Polypterus,* have a more ventral bone also, the clavicle, which generally meets its fellow. In the teleosts this is generally lost,
and is functionally replaced by a long ventral extension of the cleithrum.

The cartilage bones of the girdles are much more important in tetrapods
than in fish. Both pectoral and pelvic girdle can be reduced to a common
pattern, of one dorsal and two ventral elements meeting in a circular depression, the glenoid cavity in which articulates the head of the humerus,
or the acetabulum for the femur (Fig. 17.29). The dorsal element of the
shoulder girdle is the scapula, the ventral elements are coracoid and procoracoid. ('Pro' in this word is a Greek prefix, and means 'in front of,'

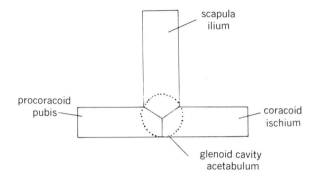

FIG. 17.29   Diagram of the vertebrate limb girdles. Names of the parts of the shoulder girdle are given in the upper line and of the hip girdle in the lower line.

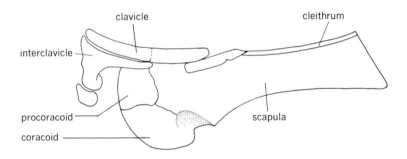

FIG. 17.30   Shoulder girdle of *Pareiasaurus baini*, x 1/8.

not, as it does in Latin, 'instead of.') The dorsal element of the pelvic girdle is the ilium (to be distinguished in spelling from the part of the alimentary canal called the ileum), the ventral elements are a posterior ischium and an anterior pubis. This arrangement is retained in the pelvic girdle, with only slight modifications, throughout all the classes right up to the mammals and birds. It can be clearly seen in the pectoral girdle only in some early reptiles, including the cotylosaurs and therapsids (Fig. 17.30). In others, one of the ventral elements is missing. We shall return to this point below.

The early Amphibia had also a dermal girdle which was very similar to that of the crossopterygians (Figs. 17.31, 17.32). There was a posttemporal connection to the skull, and a large cleithrum and clavicle, with a conspicuous and characteristic T-shaped median interclavicle. The endochondrial bone appears to have been a single scapulocoracoid, as in fishes, so that its homology with the bones in reptiles is difficult to decide.

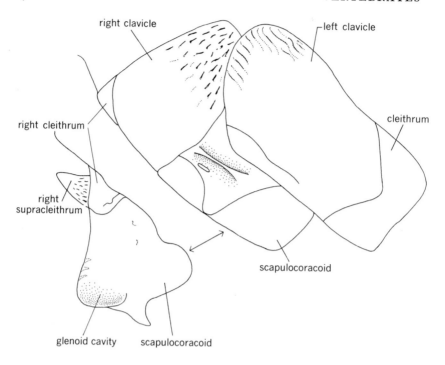

FIG. 17.31 Shoulder girdle of *Eogyrinus attheyi*, drawn from the type specimen, x 1/3. This is a ventral view, and the points indicated by arrows were probably in contact in life. The fossil is now in two pieces, as shown. Compare Fig. 17.32.

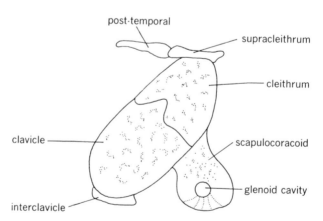

FIG. 17.32 Shoulder girdle of *Eogyrinus attheyi*, lateral view, a reconstruction based on that of Watson. The interclavicle, the supracleithrum, and especially the post-temporal, are somewhat conjectural.

The cleithrum quickly became reduced, but was present in some cotylo-saurs and therapsids (Fig. 17.30). Unless it is represented by a few ves-tiges that have been claimed to be homologous with it in anurans and marsupials, it is present in no modern tetrapods. The clavicle is generally present, but the interclavicle often disappears. The form of the girdle can sometimes be related to mode of life or locomotion, but there appear also to have been trends of no obvious adaptive importance in different groups.

Modern amphibia have peculiar girdles. Urodeles have no dermal girdle, and although scapula, coracoid, and procoracoid are usually described as being present, they remain mostly cartilaginous, ossifying only round the glenoid cavity from one or at most two centers. The dorsal cartilaginous part of the scapula is sometimes given the unnecessary name of supra-scapula. The two coracoids overlap ventrally, instead of meeting edge to edge as is more usual. Since the Stegocephalia, so far as is known, had only one center of ossification in the girdle, it seems impossible to decide whether the ventral element of urodeles, when present, should strictly be called a coracoid or a procoracoid; the first name is simpler.

Anurans have a more complicated shoulder girdle (Fig. 15.13). There is a slender clavicle, which meets the sternum, and on the posterior edge of this a thin line of cartilage usually called procoracoid. A large gap, the coracoid fenestra, separates this from a stout ossified coracoid. There is a bony scapula with a large cartilaginous part or suprascapula above it. The ossification at the base of this cartilaginous part is separated from the main part of the scapula by a thin line of cartilage, and is regarded by some as a cleithrum. Each half-girdle starts as a single rudiment and buds off scapular and coracoid portions, the latter then dividing into procoracoid and coracoid portions. The strip of cartilage called epicoracoid comes from the coracoid. In some anurans, such as the toads (*Bufo*), the coracoids overlap ventrally, as they do in urodeles, but in the more active forms (e.g. *Rana*) they meet and fuse. This change has apparently taken place independently in several families.

While some cotylosaurs have only one ventral element, other contempo-rary genera had two. The argument from serial homology and the almost universal presence of three bones in the amniote pelvic girdle would sug-gest that the shoulder girdle also primitively had two ventral elements. Another view is that since only one ossification was present in Stegoce-phalia (mostly contemporary, it must be remembered, with the cotylo-saurs), the reptiles first added a second bone, and then only some of them added a third. However this may be, the interpretation of the girdle of modern reptiles, birds and mammals is as follows. The sauropsidan (or diapsid) line is descended from reptilian ancestors with only one ventral element, the therapsid (or synapsid) line from those with two. The ma-jority of zoologists think that the single ventral element of the former corresponds to the anterior one of the latter. Hence it should be called pro-coracoid, not coracoid.

The general plan in modern reptiles, and in the majority of later fossils, is that there are a scapula and a procoracoid, together forming the glenoid cavity, and a clavicle and interclavicle; this may be illustrated by the liz-ards (Fig. 15.14). The clavicle and interclavicle may be lost, as in the large dinosaurs such as *Brontosaurus* and in the crocodiles, but otherwise the chief variations are in the shape of the bones. In the chelonians, where the dermal girdle is associated with the shell, the scapula has two prongs, so that the girdle has a characteristic triradiate appearance. Snakes have lost the girdle completely, and it is more or less reduced in legless lizards.

Birds have a shoulder girdle which is reptilian in plan but highly spe-cialized in form (Fig. 15.15). The two slender clavicles meet in a flat interclavicle to form the well-known wishbone or furcula. The procora-coids are very stout bones, and meet the sternum ventrally in a strong suture. The scapulae are elongated; they are generally described as sword-shaped, but their shape is more nearly that of an Eastern scimitar than of any sword used in Western warfare or in fencing. They lie back along the dorsal surface of the ribs, so that they help to anchor the sternum to the backbone.

In adult placental mammals there is only one endochondrial bone in the shoulder girdle (Fig. 17.33). It is the scapula, and it lies against the ribs in much the same position as that of birds. Its peculiar and characteristic shape is shown in the drawing. There is usually also a clavicle, but no interclavicle, unless this is represented by the anterior piece of the ster-num, as some zoologists have thought. The presence and degree of devel-opment of the clavicle are related to the use of the fore-limb. Where, as in man, the arm can be moved inward, the clavicle or collarbone is large. If it were not present, contraction of the breast muscles, instead of rotating the humerus round the glenoid cavity, would simply pull the whole shoul-der inward. Where there is no such use of the fore-limb, the clavicle is more or less reduced, and in some, such as the whales, perissodactyls, and artiodactyls, it has been completely lost.

Curving around the front part of the head of the humerus, and so form-ing part of the glenoid cavity, is a short process from the scapula. The early anatomists thought that in man this resembled the head of a crow, so they called it the coracoid process, from the Greek name for that bird. In embryos it is a separate cartilage, and in man it does not unite with the scapula until about the time of puberty. In some animals (e.g. the rabbit) ossification may begin before fusion, and in a few edentates the coracoid does not fuse with the scapula. It represents the large separate coracoid bone of reptiles.

The pectoral girdle of marsupials is similar to that of placentals, but that of the monotremes is much more reptilian (Fig. 17.34). The scapula is of

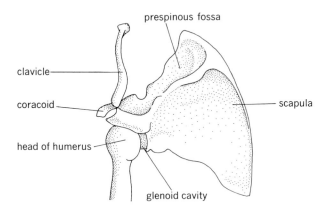

FIG. 17.33   Left human shoulder girdle, from the side and slightly
from in front, x 1/4.

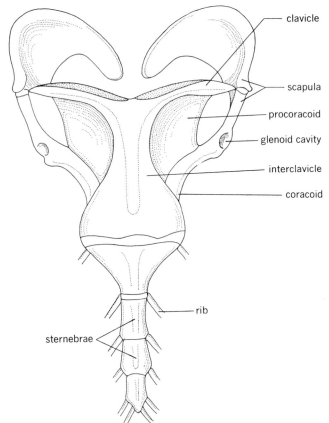

FIG. 17.34   Shoulder girdle and breastbone of *Ornithorhynchus paradoxus*,
ventral, x 3/2.

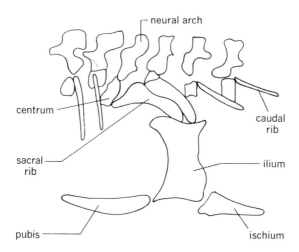

FIG. 17.35   Hip girdle and sacrum of *Paracyclotosaurus davidi* (Stegocephalia), Triassic, x 1/6.

the usual mammalian form, but there are large clavicles and a T-shaped interclavicle quite like that of a therapsid. There are also two ventral elements, a coracoid which is ankylosed with the scapula, and in front of this a smaller procoracoid, which overlaps its fellow as the coracoids do in urodeles.

After the complexities of procoracoid and coracoid, the pelvic girdle of tetrapods is relatively simple, the variations being for the most part functional ones connected fairly obviously with different modes of locomotion.

In the fishes the pelvic girdle is free from the backbone, but in the tetrapods it very early acquired a connection with it. This was at first a mere touching junction between the ilium and the ribs, perhaps held in place by ligament (Fig. 17.35), but it soon became a suture with the transverse processes, and later a fusion with the whole centra into a solid bony mass to make a sacrum. In strict usage the sacral vertebrae are those which actually touch the girdle, and there are seldom more than two or three, but functionally others may be added to the sacrum fore and aft by becoming fused onto it without themselves touching the ilium. The sacrum may be in front of, immediately above, or behind the acetabulum.

In urodeles the pelvic girdle is mostly cartilaginous, but there are usually, as in *Necturus*, ossifications in the ischium and ilium. In anurans too, the pubis is usually unossified (it is bony in *Xenopus*), but it makes a clear third of the acetabulum. The ilium is greatly elongated, and runs forward beside the urostyle to make a fairly firm suture with the transverse process of the last vertebra, usually the ninth. This extreme preacetabular sacrum is presumably associated with the habit of jumping.

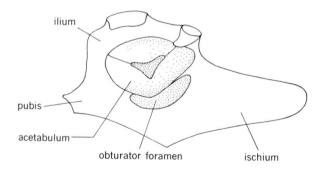

FIG. 17.36   Pelvic girdle of *Cynognathus crateronotus* (Therapsida),
Triassic, x 1/3.

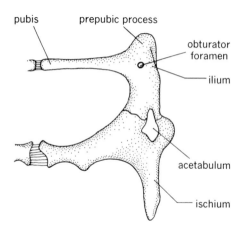

FIG. 17.37   Left half of the pelvic girdle of a lizard, *Uromastix*, sp, ventral,
x 2/3.

All three elements are firmly fused to their fellows as well as to each
other, so that the girdle as a whole is a single structure of considerable
strength.

The primitive reptiles had a pelvic girdle (Fig. 17.36) similar to that of
the primitive amphibians, and in modern forms the chief difference is the
development of a space, the ischiopubic fenestra, between ischium and
pubis, as these become thinner and meet only in short ventral lengths of
cartilage or fiber, as in lizards (Fig. 17.37). The pubis retains a small
obturator foramen through which passes the obturator nerve. The sacrum

is often markedly postacetabular. There are often conspicuous anteriorly directed prepubic processes.

In the pterodactyls and the crocodiles the pubis is small, and does not enter into the acetabulum. The most marked deviations from the normal are found in the Ornithischia and the birds. In both of these the ilium is greatly expanded and the pubis is directed backward beneath the ischium (Fig. 6.8). At the same time there is a reduction in the ventral symphyses; in the Ornithischia only the ischia may unite, while in modern birds both ischia and pubes are widely separate, only the ratites having a fusion at their posterior end, which may be secondary, since in ostriches it is pubic, in rheas it is ischiadic. *Archaeopteryx* had a pubic symphysis, but the pubes were already rotated to point backward. This separation of the bones in the mid-ventral line is usually said to be connected with the laying of large eggs, which would otherwise not be able to escape from the cloaca. Mammals, however, which produce young which are relatively much larger than the eggs of birds, retain the symphyses.

Whatever may be the reason for the loss of the ventral symphysis, it is made possible only by the strengthening of the dorsal part of the girdle, and especially of the sacrum. The ischium of birds is usually completely fused to the ilium, and that to one, two, or three sacral vertebrae, with which a variable number of lumbar and caudal vertebrae are fused fore and aft. The whole solid bony structure, combining the girdle bones of both sides and several vertebrae, is called a synsacrum.

A small pectineal process pointing forward just below the acetabulum has had its homology much disputed. Since in carinates it is formed from the ilium, and in ratites and *Apteryx* partly from this and partly from the pubis, it is probably a variable new formation called into existence for the attachment of muscle when the pubis was bent backward.

The mammals also have achieved a strong fused pelvic girdle, but it is not so firmly fixed to the backbone as is that of birds. The three fused bones of one side are known to anatomists as the os innominatum (Fig. 17.38). The ilia are the largest, and join the sacrum a little in front of the acetabulum. Pubis and ischium are largely separated by a space, which appears to be an enlargement of the obturator foramen, and so derived differently from that of lizards. The ventral symphyses, though short, are usually firm. In most, both pubes and ischia join, but some insectivores, bats, and primates have a pubic symphysis only. In some insectivores (*Sorex, Talpa*) and in some bats there is no symphysis at all.

In the Sirenia there are only two bones, probably ilium and ischium, of which the former is connected by ligament to the transverse process of a vertebra. The pelvic girdle of whales has undergone a further reduction, being represented only by a single bone on each side, whose chief or only function is to serve as an attachment for the fibers of the penis or clitoris.

Marsupials and monotremes have a pelvis of the normal form, but run-

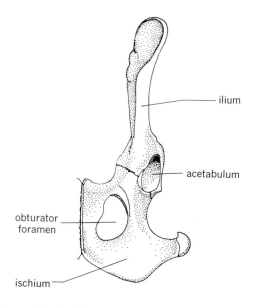

ilium

acetabulum

obturator
foramen

ischium

FIG. 17.38   Pelvic girdle of a dog, x 2/3.

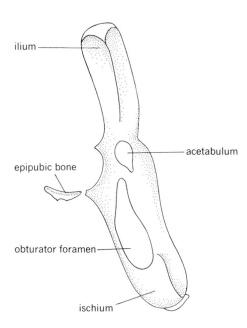

ilium

acetabulum

epipubic bone

obturator foramen

ischium

FIG. 17.39   Pelvic girdle of a dog, ventral, x 2/3.

ning forward from each pubis is a prepubic or epipubic or marsupial bone (Fig. 17.39). These are presumably developed in connection with the pouch that both these groups of mammals possess, but how they really support this, since they run in the abdominal wall, is obscure. They are present in males as well as females, but are very much reduced in the active *Thylacinus*, where one would expect them to be most important. There is some evidence for similar bones in the cynodonts.

18

Exoskeleton and Skin

ONE OF THE characteristic features of vertebrates is a thick epidermis, of many layers of cells of which the outer often secrete the protein keratin. As we have seen, the earliest known vertebrates had in addition to this (or perhaps instead of it) a thick covering of bone, which was complete in the ostracoderms, nearly so in the placoderms. Sometimes, as in the cephalaspids and the Antiarchi, it consisted in part of large plates, sometimes, as in the pteraspids and acanthodians, there were only small overlapping scales. The dermal bones of the skull, jaws, and shoulder girdle are presumably derived from plates of this sort which have sunk slightly into the body. It is impossible to say whether scales or plates are the more primitive. It would seem simpler to start from the small scales and imagine them fusing together to form the large plates, but there is no evidence. It has been argued that a creature with the fused armor of an ostracoderm could not grow, and that therefore the young forms must have had soft joints between smaller plates, which grew as their possessor grew. There is evidence that as the anaspid *Birkenia* increased in size the number of its scales remained at least approximately constant, but that they grew in size. There is no evidence that any vertebrate undergoes an ecdysis comparable to that of arthropods, but the sloughing of the horny layer of the skin in Amphibia and Squamata should make one careful of denying its possibility.

Sections of the scales of these early forms show that on their inner part they consist of a softer lamellar bone, while on the outer side was a harder material without blood vessels, which closely resembled dentine, the material of which the major part of a vertebrate tooth is made. On the exposed outer surface were often points or denticles of a harder material still. If this was enamel, the ostracoderm scale had a close resemblance to the placoid scale of a dogfish, with its dentine running into a bony base and tip of enamel (Fig. 18.1A). (This surface layer is sometimes called vitrodentine. It appears to be physically similar to the enamel of mammalian teeth, which is mostly calcium hydroxyapatite, but whether it is chemically similar seems to be unknown.)

It appears therefore as if the modern elasmobranchs derived their scales by reduction in size and increase in number from whatever agnathan ancestors they had. The modern cyclostomes, by contrast, have lost all trace

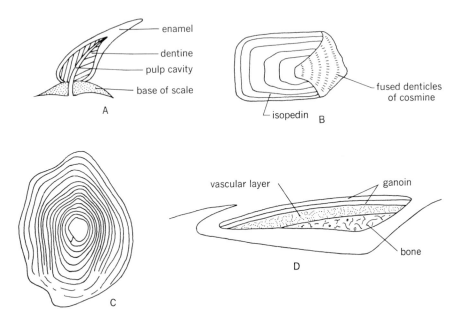

FIG. 18.1   (A) Diagrammatic vertical section of a placoid scale (B) Surface view of a cosmoid scale of *Latimeria chalumnae*, x 1. (C) Surface view of a cycloid scale of a salmon, *Salmo salar*, x 2. (D) Diagrammatic vertical section of a ganoid scale of *Polypterus*, x 10.

of scaly exoskeleton. As has been said in Chapter 4, the teeth of elasmo-branchs are simply specialized scales, and form a continuous series with them over the lips. In some sharks the teeth are secondarily enlarged, and in some they appear to be compound, the bases of several scales having fused.

The early Choanichthyes had scales which were rather similar, but the bone was divided into two different types; the outer layer was much like dentine, but had branching instead of simple tubules, and is by most au-thors called cosmine, while the inner, or more normal bone, is called iso-pedin. Between them was something of a pulp cavity with bone cells, and on the surface was a hard layer which may have been enamel. Such a cos-moid scale is present on the modern coelacanth *Latimeria* (Fig. 18.1B), where the cosmine appears only in the part of the scale which is exposed, the isopedin being elsewhere covered by overlapping adjacent scales.

Presumably from this the teleosts and modern dipnoans have independ-ently evolved a type of scale called cycloid (Fig. 18.1C). It is simply a thin plate of bone, which remains covered by a thin layer of dermis, so that the pigment cells which this contains are outside the scales. Perhaps because of this arrangement, with the overlapping scales making a firm smooth coat so near the surface, the epidermis of teleosts contains no keratin. The growth of the teleost scale goes on intermittently throughout life, so that it shows annual rings like the trunk of a tree. In some fish the posterior edge of the cycloid scale is produced into a row of teeth, when it is known as ctenoid; in others there is an outwardly-projecting spine which has a pulp cavity.

The last major type of fish scale is the ganoid (Fig. 18.1D). This does not seem to differ fundamentally from the cosmoid, but the hard outer layer, called ganoin, is different from the enamel of the cosmoid scale, and the scale grows on its surface as well as its edges. It is found in primitive fish, such as *Polypterus*, *Lepidosteus*, and the sturgeons. It is possibly the ancestor of the cycloid scale.

The more specialized armor of fishes usually or always consists of specialization of the appropriate type of scale. Thus the spines in front of the dorsal fins of *Squalus* are enlarged placoid scales, those of the porcupine fishes (*Diodon*), which are teleosts, are bony projections from the middle of cycloid scales.

The unpaired fins of some teleosts are so thin that their supporting rays almost constitute an exoskeleton. These are of bone, as described in Chapter 15, and have no homologues in the tetrapods.

The exoskeleton of the tetrapods is always based on the protein keratin, which is a tough substance made by the epidermal cells. They lay it down on the inside of their cytoplasmic surface, so that as more of it is produced and the wall made of it becomes thicker, the volume of living protoplasm decreases, until in the end the cells kill themselves. In this way a layer of dead material, which may be several cells thick, is formed on the surface of the body (Fig. 2.8). Keratin is one of a class of fibrous proteins, of which the elastin of yellow fibers is another, which are difficult to break down by enzymes, or by any but the most drastic means. (The indigestibility of ligaments and leather illustrates this.) Its primary function was probably not so much to act as a skeleton as to resist the passage of water, so that the emerging terrestrial vertebrates did not dry up. It does this reasonably well, in spite of the fact that it easily takes up water, a fact which is illustrated by the softening of human hair and fingernails after a bath. The cells that can make keratin seem to be a special family, called epitheliocytes, which have a number of other properties in common, such as the facility for sticking to each other, or experimentally to anything else, such as a glass surface, so that they readily form sheets or membranes. They produce keratin when their growth is slowed down. Keratinization is favored by lack of vitamin A, and under these conditions cells which would normally be ciliated or mucus-producing may become hard, dead, and thick, like epidermis.

If living tetrapods are considered, there is a general increase in the thickness of the superficial layer of keratin from Amphibia to reptiles to birds to mammals. Frogs and newts have only a very thin layer, while the thickness of that in mammals may be illustrated by the fact that pins can be pushed tangentially through the keratinized layer of the human finger without drawing blood and without stimulating any nerve endings. At intermediate points there are some animals with thick skins, but size for size the rule is broadly true. A chicken, for example, has a thinner skin than a rat. This may be taken to indicate a gradual increase in adaptation to life on land.

It is possible, and indeed probable, that the more terrestrial early amphibians had thick skins comparable with those of early reptiles. The thin keratinized layer of the skin of frogs and newts is likely to be connected with their largely aquatic mode of life.

Not only do modern amphibians have a thin layer, but it is uniform and generally unspecialized. From time to time, under the stimulus of secretions of the thyroid and pituitary glands, the keratin is shed in a more or less continuous sheet, the scarf skin, which the animal usually eats.

Reptiles characteristically fuse the keratin from many cells to form a scale, the series being generally arranged, like those of teleosts, to overlap one another, like the tiles or slates on the roof of a house, a condition known as imbricate. Beneath the keratinized part of the scale is a thickened portion of the dermis, and in this in many lizards and snakes a small plate of bone is formed. The outer horny layer is shed from time to time, usually in small pieces, but snakes break the layer on the snout, partly by swelling the head by constricting the internal jugular vein so that blood cannot leave it, and partly by rubbing against a stone. They then crawl out of the scarf skin, pulling it inside out as they do so, so that a complete reversed horny skin is left on the ground.

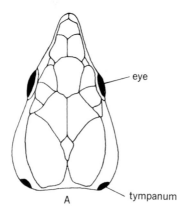

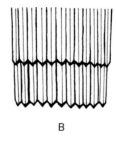

FIG. 18.2 (A) Head of a lizard, *Lacerta viridis*, dorsal, to show the pattern of the scales, x 2. (B) Two rows of scales in the tail of *Lacerta viridis*, x 2.

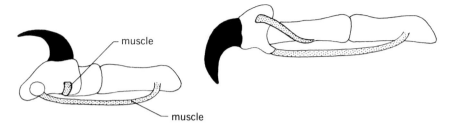

FIG. 18.3   Claw of a tiger, *Felis tigris:* retracted (above), and extended, x 3/4.

Reptilian scales may be small, as in most lizards (Fig. 18.2) or large, as in crocodiles. Their surface may be extended into spines of various sorts and shapes, as in the desert lizard *Moloch*. Impressions in the rocks show that various extinct reptiles bore scales, and this was presumably general.

Scales which do not differ in any important way from those of reptiles are present on the legs of birds, and more rarely in mammals, as on the tails of tree shrews (Tupaiidae) and rats. Claws, found in almost all reptiles, birds, and mammals, are also essentially enlarged scales, situated at the end of a digit or in some other place where they can project from the surface and be used as hooks (Fig. 18.3). The flat nails of the primates, including man, are a simple modification, and so are the hooves of cattle and horses. Claws, nails, and hooves are not shed, but under natural conditions the keratin is worn away distally and replaced at the same rate by the activity of the cells within.

The horns of artiodactyls are slightly more specialized, in that the multicellular mass of keratin, instead of being solid, is hollow, so that when it continues to grow at the base a tapering cone, sometimes nearly a cylinder, is formed (Fig. 18.4). There is usually some degree of uneven growth round the circular base, so that the horn is twisted, often in a very regular spiral; this is tightly wound around a straight or nearly straight axis in many antelopes, in wide open curves in sheep. The horny layer is not shed except in the prong buck (*Antelocapra americana*) of the western plains of North America. In many species the horns are a secondary sexual character, being found only in the male, and in some domestic breeds of cattle genetic hornlessness has been produced. The general function of horns is in combat, whether in defense of the herd against large carnivores, or between rival males.

The feathers of birds, like scales, are specializations of the epidermis, and derive the materials necessary for their development from the blood vessels in the underlying dermis, but their geometrical relationships are different and highly peculiar. A typical fully formed feather (Fig. 18.6) has a cylindrical base, the calamus or quill, beyond which is a solid rib, the rhachis, on which are branches or barbs. At the base of the calamus is

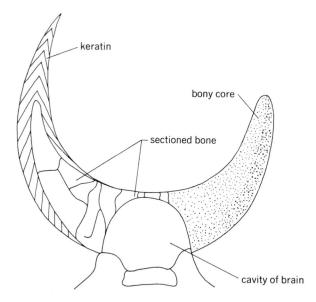

FIG. 18.4   Diagrammatic transverse section through the head of a cow. On the left of the drawing the keratin and bone are in section, on the right the horn has been removed, and the bony core is shown in solid. The sinuses in the sectioned bone are continuous with those of the frontal.

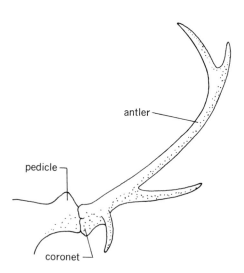

FIG. 18.5   Antler of a young red deer stag (*Cervus elephas*), x 1/10. In an older stag there is a third tine on the beam of the antler, and three or more 'on top.'

FIG. 18.6   Structure of a feather. On the
right, the main parts of a typical quill; on
the left, a small part of the vane, x 100.

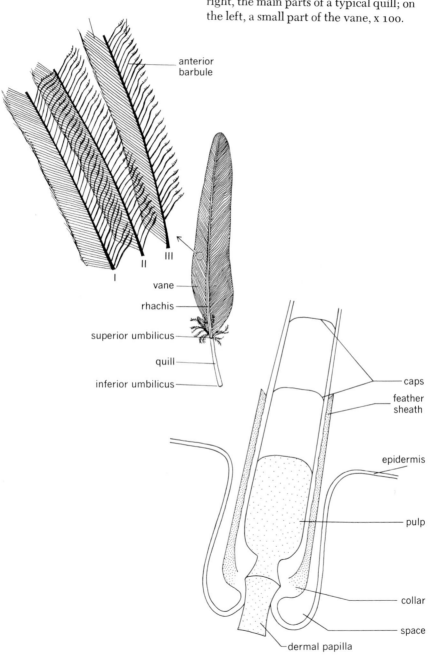

anterior
barbule

III

II

I

vane

rhachis

superior umbilicus

quill

inferior umbilicus

caps

feather
sheath

epidermis

pulp

collar

space

dermal papilla

FIG. 18.7   Diagram of a longitudinal section of the base of a feather, to show
its mode of formation.

a hole, the inferior umbilicus; where the calamus changes to rhachis is another, the superior umbilicus. A feather begins with an initial thickening of the epidermis, after which there is a sinking-in, so that a small pit or follicle is formed, from the bottom of which there projects upward a papilla of dermis (which is mesoderm) surrounded by epidermis (which is ectoderm) (Fig. 18.7). The dermal papilla produces pulp, which afterwards breaks down, so that it does not appreciably contribute to the fully formed feather. The epidermal part of the papilla becomes a dome, the collar, which elongates, its cells forming keratin, so that it is converted to a hollow cylinder. On this cylinder appear ridges which are going to become the barbs, but how the conversion is made is not entirely clear. According to what seems the most probable account the cylinder splits between the ridges, and then along its length down what is called the ventral side of the cylinder. The barbs then fold outward, so that we have a solid axis (the rhachis) which is derived from the dorsal strip of the collar, and two series of barbs branching from this on opposite sides. In the proximal region of the cylinder the split edges of the ridges do not form barbs, but roll in to meet each other and so form a new cylinder, which is the calamus. In this way a second feather, which is a mirror image of the first, can be formed. This is normally a short aftershaft, but in a few birds, notably cassowaries and emus, the shaft and aftershaft are equal in size, so that the feather appears double (Fig. 18.8). The hollow space between the two umbilici contains only a series of transverse shelves, which are ectodermal caps that at various stages have covered the pulp. When a feather is plucked, or when it is shed naturally in the seasonal molt (largely initiated by the thyroid hormone), the epidermal portion breaks away from the top of the papilla. Ectoderm then grows over the exposed dermis from the dorsal to the ventral direction, and a new collar is formed which will expand to a new feather. In this way a single papilla can form several feathers in the life of the bird.

The typical feather (Fig. 18.9A) has the two rows of barbs of slightly unequal length, the one which is anterior on the body being the shorter. Each barb has anterior and posterior barbules, the former with hooks or hamuli and the latter with ridges, so that the flat surface or vane of the feather is firmly locked together on exactly the principle of a zipper. When the hooks become deranged the bird is able to put them in place again by preening with its beak. Other types of feather have variants on this general plan. The flight feathers have the anterior barbs much shorter than the posterior, so giving a firm leading edge, and their tips may be emarginated to reduce the length of the anterior barbs still further; the value of this is to give a slotted-wing effect when the wings are spread, and so reduce the stalling speed. The general contour feathers of the body have few barbules, especially on the proximal barbs, so that the feathers are more fluffy, and in the silky mutant of the domestic fowl there are no barbules

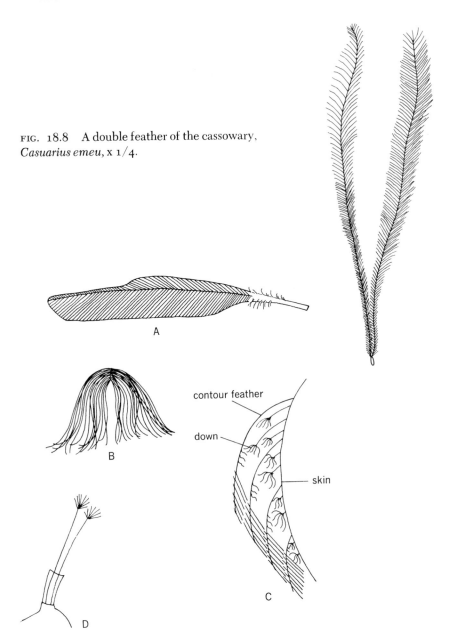

FIG. 18.8 A double feather of the cassowary, *Casuarius emeu*, x 1/4.

contour feather

down

skin

A

B

C

D

FIG. 18.9 (A) Emarginated primary feather of a chaffinch, *Fringilla coelebs*, x 1. (B) Down feather of a swan, *Cygnus olor*, x 2/3. (C) Diagrammatic section through the breast feathers of a swan. The contour feathers have a normal vane distally and plumaceous unhooked barbs proximally, so trapping a large amount of air. (D) Filoplume of an eagle, *Aquilla chrysaetos*, x 2/3.

at all. Between the contour feathers are small filoplumes (Fig. 18.9D), which have only a tuft of barbs at the upper end of the rhachis, and down feathers (Fig. 18.9B), which consist of a tuft of barbs with a short calamus but no rhachis.

The first feathers of chicks are somewhat different from any in the adult, but closely resemble down feathers and filoplumes. The fossils of *Archaeopteryx* show in the rock impressions of feathers that appear to be exactly similar to the contour and flight feathers of present-day birds; in one specimen even barbules have been discerned. Nothing therefore is known of the history of feathers.

The hairs of mammals are formed in a somewhat similar way to feathers, and, like them, are basically cylindrical. There is no primary papilla, but the surface sinks in to form a follicle, from the base of which grows up a dermal papilla with an ectodermal cap or matrix, from which is formed a tube of keratin, containing a core of softer material, that is the hair (Fig. 18.10). When a hair is shed replacement takes place from the papilla, as with a feather. If the cylinder grows evenly all round, the hair is straight; if it is uneven, the hair is flat in section and curly.

The spines of the spiny anteater, the hedgehog, and the porcupine are enlarged and stiffened hairs. The horns of the rhinoceros and the scales

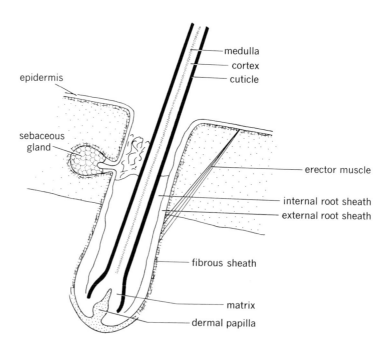

FIG. 18.10   Diagram of a longitudinal section of the base of a hair, to show its mode of formation.

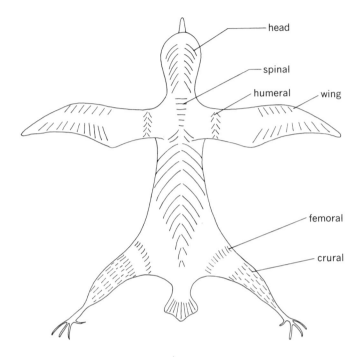

FIG. 18.11   Feather tracts of a young thrush, *Turdus philomelos*, diagrammatic, dorsal. The names of the tracts are given.

of the pangolin (*Manis*) are formed from masses of hair which grow together.

In addition to their cylindrical structure, feathers and hairs have two important biological features in common. First, their distribution on the body is not uniform, but takes place in a pattern that is usually highly characteristic of the species. Contour feathers do not cover the body of a bird uniformly but are found only in patches or pterylae, separated by bare areas, or apteria, which are especially large on the ventral surface (Figs. 18.11, 18.12). The length of the feathers, however, is such that the bare areas are not visible without careful examination. The pattern of hair is not so much in the distribution of the hairs, though this is important in the primates, which may have bare patches on chest or buttocks, as in the direction of growth (Fig. 18.13). This is sometimes said to have adaptive significance in throwing off rain.

Secondly, both feathers and hair may be colored in a way which often indicates specific characteristics, sometimes sexual differences, and occasionally perhaps relationship within a family. The commonest pigment in both hair and feathers is melanin, which according to its density imparts

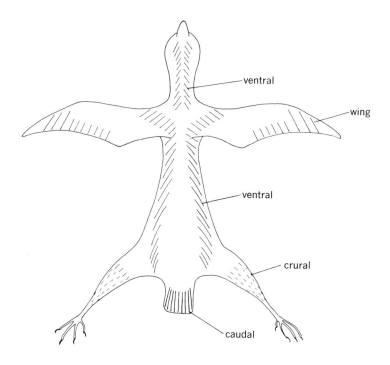

FIG. 18.12   Feather tracts of a young thrush, *Turdus philomelos*, ventral, diagrammatic. The names of the tracts are given.

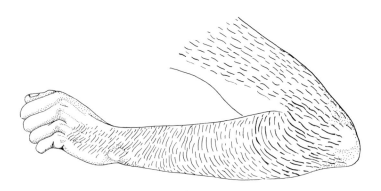

FIG. 18.13   Hair pattern on the arm of a man. Note that the hairs point toward the elbow; this may have had a value to our ancestors in directing the rain off the head when the arms are held up to cover it.

a brown, gray, or black color. The brighter yellow and red colors of feathers are due to lipochromes or carotenoids. The birds can only synthesize these if related carotenoids are present in the food, so that canaries deprived of the plant carotenoid xanthophyll lose their color. There is no blue pigment, blues being due either to diffraction at the surface, as in the magpie (*Pica*), or to Tyndall scattering (dispersion) of light of short wave-length within the feather, as in the blue jay (*Cyanocitta*) and the European kingfisher (*Alcedo*). The latter blue is produced in the same way as the blue of the skies and of human eyes.

In addition to having scales, feathers, and hairs (or their derivatives), which are characteristic of reptiles, birds, and mammals respectively, scattered groups of reptiles and mammals have undergone what may be called rearmament. Many dinosaurs, especially the Stegosauria, had an exoskeleton of dermal bone. In many these bones were quite small, but in others they were large upstanding plates, apparently projecting freely from the

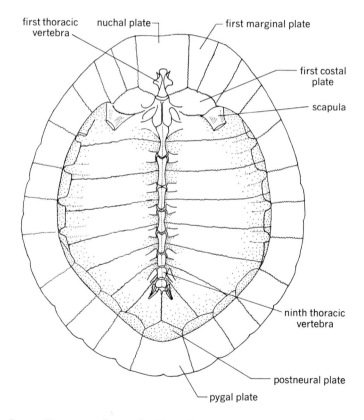

FIG. 18.14 Carapace of a turtle, *Testudo* sp., inner (= ventral) aspect, x 1/2. The horny plates, which overlap and alternate with the marginal bony plates, are not shown.

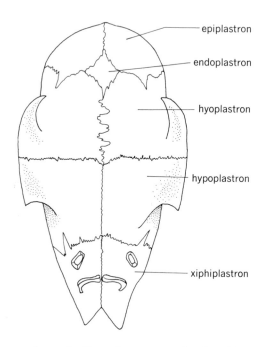

FIG. 18.15   Plastron of a turtle, *Testudo* sp., inner (= dorsal) aspect, x 2/3.

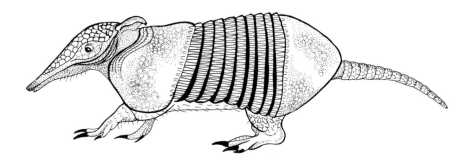

FIG. 18.16   An armadillo, *Dasypus novemcinctus*, x 1/7.

body. *Stegosaurus* itself has been restored in various ways, but it appears to have had two rows of ten or eleven plates each, alternating along the back. The animal was twenty-five to thirty feet long, and the plates were up to thirty inches high. Their surface suggests that in life they were covered with horn. They are said to be defensive, presumably against other dinosaurs.

The shell of the Chelonia is noteworthy for its association of exoskeleton with endoskeleton. The dorsal carapace and ventral plastron (Figs. 18.14 and 18.15) are made of enlarged scales fused together. Each consists of an outer layer of keratin (tortoise-shell) bonded below to a dermal bone, the whole being sutured so as to form a closed box, with holes for head, tail, and limbs. The bones are mostly new dermal formations, but the dermal shoulder girdle is included. All of them are fused to underlying cartilage bones, such as ribs and vertebrae, of the endoskeleton. The plates of tortoise-shell on the whole alternate with those of dermal bone.

The armor of the armadilloes (*Dasypus*), which are mammals, is rather similar to that of the turtles in that there are horny plates with dermal bones beneath them (Fig. 18.16); but there are soft patches between the horn, so that the body can be bent, and in some species rolled into a ball. The extinct related glyptodonts had a fused carapace even more like that of a turtle.

Many artiodactyls have bony projections on the skull. In the giraffe they are short and covered with skin and hair, and are not shed. The antlers of deer are bony outgrowths from the frontals, formed seasonally in the male only, except in caribou and reindeer (*Rangifer*) (Fig. 18.5). They grow very rapidly and are at first covered with soft skin known as velvet. This is later rubbed off. The chief use of the antlers is for combat between rival males, and after the breeding season their blood supply is constricted and they die and drop off. Each year they grow bigger and with more branches (technically known as points), so that the age of a stag can be told approximately from his antlers.

19

The Head

IN A GENERAL way everyone knows what is meant by a head, but to frame a definition that will be anatomically accurate and reasonably descriptive, and that will cover the head of a dogfish as well as that of man, is not easy. It may be, as we shall see later, that it is impossible. For many zoological purposes it is better to think not so much of presence or absence of a head as of the degree to which a head is developed, or, to use a single word, of degree of cephalization; in doing so we must remember that the marks of a head are that it has a concentration of nerve cells and synapses and connector neurons, that it bears some or all of the chief sense organs, and that it bears the mouth with associated feeding apparatus. No protochordate has any distinct part of the body that can reasonably be called a head, but amphioxus has a small degree of cephalization, shown by the oral cirri and the slight expansion of the nerve cord. From something like this we may suppose cephalization to have increased as the vertebrates evolved, until we reach the birds and mammals, with their large brains, and highly specialized and concentrated distance receptors contained in a part of the body that is topographically easily distinguished from the rest of the body. Man himself, with a head that is one-fourteenth the volume of the whole body, is near the top of the tree in this respect.

Vertebrates are not alone in having some degree of cephalization, or even in having a well-developed head. With one exception, all the groups of animals with much cephalization are segmented, and in the insects and spiders, the invertebrate groups with the best-developed heads, these are formed of an invariable number of segments. Since the vertebrates also are segmented, one might expect this to apply to them also. In fact it is obvious that the vertebrate head loses its segmentation even more completely than does the rest of the body. Segments can, however, be found in it, and the number that make up the front part of the head is constant. In the posterior part there is more variability, but within a small taxon, or at least within a species, there is constancy throughout.

The one unsegmented phylum with a fair degree of cephalization is the Mollusca, where both gastropods and cephalopods show it. The cephalopods are the exception to the rule that the head is the anterior end, for it is approximately in the middle of the body. The usual evolutionary explanation of the origin of the head is that it becomes specialized because

443

it is the part that is in front when the animal moves, and so is first to come
into contact with new or changing parts of the outside world. This is not
true of a cuttlefish, whether it is moving slowly forward (in the morphological sense) or rapidly backward.

If one considers a dogfish (or almost any other fish) one finds a well-
marked head. There is a mouth, with teeth which are specialized scales;
eyes and labyrinth, and more lateral line organs than elsewhere; and internally a brain. There are also the gill slits; but respiratory organs, if one
considers the animal kingdom in general, are no essential part of the head.
Associated with all these are specializations in the skeleton, shown by a
fuller disappearance of the notochord than elsewhere and the presence of
the skull and visceral arches. Notably there is an almost complete lack of
visible segmentation.

An early embryo is quite different from this, and shows a series of myotomes and dorsal and ventral nerve roots continuous with those of the
trunk and running almost to the front end of the body; in fact as far forward as the notochord goes, or to the level of the future hypophysis. This
is shown diagrammatically in Fig. 19.1, which shows the dorsal roots going
behind the myotomes (Fig. 19.2) and the ventral roots going to them.
There are eight pairs of somites in what will be the future head, each
often at first hollow with its own portion of celom. The first is in front of
the mouth and is called pre-oral, and from it are formed most of the eyeball muscles. The second is level with the cartilages that are going to form
the jaws; it forms the superior oblique muscle of the eyeball. The third is

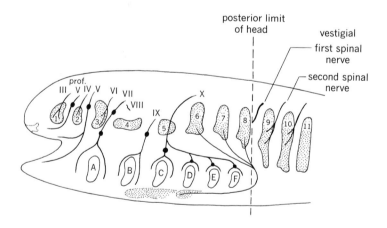

FIG. 19.1   Diagrammatic longitudinal section of a dogfish embryo. 1–6, the
myotomes; III to X, the cranial nerves; A–F, the gill slits.

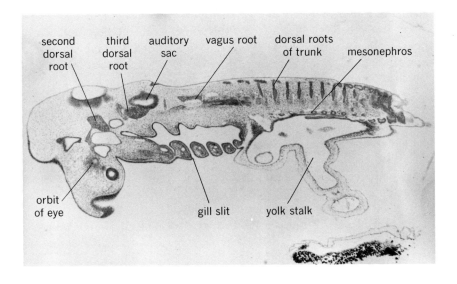

second dorsal root | third dorsal root | auditory sac | vagus root | dorsal roots of trunk | mesonephros

orbit of eye | gill slit | yolk stalk

FIG. 19.2 A longitudinal section of the head of a dogfish (*Scyliorhinus caniculus*), to show the myotomes and the dorsal roots, x 20.

more or less above the hyoid arch and forms the posterior rectus muscle. The motor nerves that supply these three groups of muscle are the oculomotor, pathetic, and abducent respectively, and these are clearly the ventral nerves of the first three segments. The position of the profundus branch of the fifth nerve shows that it is the first dorsal root, while the main portion of the trigeminal and the facial are those of the second and third segments. Each of these divides, the former into maxillary and mandibular branches above and below the mouth, the latter into a pre- and a postspiracular branch in front of and behind the spiracle. This division is repeated in the following dorsal nerves that go to the region of the gill slits, each having a pretrematic and posttrematic branch. Hence it appears a neat assumption that the mouth represents two anterior gill slits that have fused ventrally. There is however, no paleontological evidence for this, and there are some difficulties in the hypothesis.

The fourth somite has only a brief life, and is obliterated by the growth of the labyrinth and auditory capsule, which also eliminate much of the fifth myotome. The remaining segments contribute to the branchial musculature. The dorsal roots persist, and are represented by the glossopharyngeal which goes fore and aft of the first functional gill slit, and the vagus which is a multiple nerve going similarly to the remaining slits. In some sharks there are more segments in the head behind the ear, giving a maximum of ten altogether in *Heptanchus,* with its seven gill slits.

Very few other vertebrates show this dorsal segmentation of the myotomes as clearly as do the elasmobranchs. It is complete in the ammocoete larva of lampreys, but there is hardly a trace of it in most teleosts, in birds, or in many mammals. Some signs of it can be seen in some mammals, such as the opossum, the cat, and man. In view of the wide scatter of its occurrence one can hardly doubt that it is the fundamental pattern of vertebrate development, and that its absence elsewhere is secondary. In the Amphibia and amniotes the first three segments, when they can be seen, correspond to those of the dogfish. The remainder (called metotic, because they are behind the ear) are reduced in number, usually to three. In correspondence with this, the gill slits, when present or visible as transients in the embryos, are not more than three.

The ventral part of the head is less easy to explain. Superficially it is more obviously segmented, with the mouth, spiracle, and gill slits dividing the body wall into successive blocks, the gill arches, which in cyclostomes and selachians may have transient celomic spaces, but the whole picture is obscured by the fact that anything that looks like a myotome breaks down to mesenchyme. (Where no segmentation is recognizable in the muscles, as in the tadpole, this is general throughout the head.) The visceral arches are segmental in position, and look as if they ought to be formed from sclerotomes corresponding to the myotomes. In fact they are not, for they are formed from cells of the neural crest which migrate downward and form mesenchyme, from which the cartilage afterwards condenses. So far from being formed from the somites, they are, so far as this means anything, epiblastic in origin.

Most of the blood vessels in the head are connected with the gills, and so can be associated with the segments. The development of the Amphibia and amniotes shows that the internal carotid is derived largely from the third arch, the systemic from the fourth, and the pulmonary from the sixth; the fifth is usually lost.

The dorsal skull or cranium is the most difficult of all to fit into a segmental scheme, but attempts have been made to do this. In the head of an early embryo the first cartilages to appear, alongside and in front of the notochord, are roughly segmental in arrangement (Fig. 19.3A). Posteriorly a series of sclerotomes continue those of the trunk that are going to form the vertebrae. They will later on contribute to the occipital region of the skull, and in so doing lose all trace of a segmental arrangement. In front of them are a pair of parachordals, a pair of polar cartilages (often missing), and a pair of trabeculae. These are less obviously segmental, but their relationship to the fifth and seventh cranial nerves suggests that they

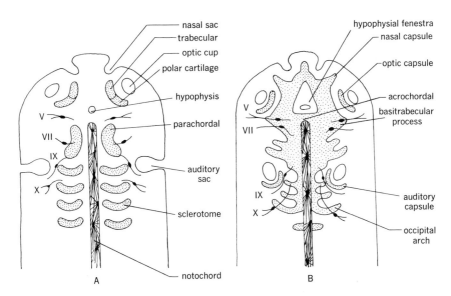

FIG. 19.3   (A) Diagram of a gnathostome embryo, in dorsal view, to show the origin of the chondrocranium. (B) Later stage of the same. Cartilage is dotted. V to X, cranial nerves. (Based on Goodrich's diagrams)

too may continue the segmental series. In amphibians the anterior end of the trabecula, like the visceral arches, is formed from cells derived from the neural crest.

At a slightly later stage all trace of segmentation is obscured (Fig. 19.3B). All the cartilages have met and fused into a single plate, with one large ventral space, the hypophysial fenestra. The plate soon begins to grow up round the brain. Independent lateral pairs of cartilages, the nasal, optic, and auditory capsules, are formed around the sense organs, and the first and last of these soon fuse on to the growing skull. Further growth and change in form gives the chondrocranium as it is seen in the dogfish or in many embryos.

The formation of these cartilages, at least in amphibians, which are the easiest experimental material, is induced by the brain and the appropriate sense organs; transplantation of these causes the formation of the appropriate skeleton elsewhere. Since the central nervous system shows no signs of segmentation, it is a little difficult to see how the skeleton induced by it can be, in any fundamental sense, segmental. Nevertheless, for those who like a neat solution, it is possible to represent almost the whole of the head, other than the brain, as being segmentally arranged in its early stages, as the following table shows:

The segmentation of the vertebrate head. The retractor bulbi is the muscle which in reptiles and mammals withdraws the eyeball; the quadratus and pyramidalis move the nictitating membrane in birds.

SEGMENT	MYOTOME	SKELETON	NERVE		ARTERY	GILL SLIT
			Ventral	*Dorsal*		
1. Premandibular 1st pro-otic	Rectus superior Rectus inferior Rectus anterior Obliquus inferior	Trabecula in embryo	Oculomotor	Deep ophthalmic	Ophthalmic	
2. Mandibular 2nd pro-otic	Obliquus superior	Polar cartilage in embryo Palatoquadrate Meckel's cartilage	Pathetic	Trigeminal	Mandibular or Spiracular	Mouth
3. Hyoid 3rd pro-otic	Rectus externus (Rectractor bulbi) (Quadratus and pyramidalis)	Parachordal in embryo Hyoid	Abducent	Facial and auditory	1st branchial (internal cartoid)	Spiracle
4. 1st metotic	None	Parachordal in embryo 1st branchial arch	None	Glosso-pharyngeal	2nd branchial (systemic)	1st gill slit
5. 2nd metotic	Vestigial	2nd branchial arch	Vestigial	Vagus	3rd branchial	2nd gill slit
6-8. 3rd-5th metotics	Epi- and hypo-branchial muscles	Occipital region of skull 3rd-5th branchial arches	Hypoglossal	Vagus Spinal accessory	4th to 6th branchials (4 = pulmonary)	3rd gill slit 4th-5th gill slits

We may now return to the problem of possible definitions of the head, which may be approached in three ways, from the points of view of segmentation, of cephalization, or of topography. We could say that the head of *Squalus* consists of the first eight segments; we could say that it is the anterior part of the body bearing mouth, eyes, ears, and gills; or, looking at the body of the fish lying on the dissecting board, and considering where to place the knife if we were going to cut the head from the body, we might say that the head is everything in front of the shoulder girdle.

The first of these definitions is not general, since, as we have seen, the number of segments in the head varies, even in the elasmobranchs. The second and third apply pretty well to all fish. In teleosts, where the cleithrum joins the skull, the topographical definition is very clear except for the obviously secondary ventral extension of the clavicles into the floor of the mouth.

Difficulties arise with tetrapods. The segments are reduced and the gills have disappeared. The fate of the branchial arches, which, as we have seen, become in part in mammals the cricoid and arytenoid cartilages on the larynx, show that the part of the body to which they belong is now outside the head, a fact which is confirmed by the occasional persistence of an open gill slit in the throat. There has, in fact, in amniotes been a development of a new part of the body, the neck. Dorsally, with its vertebrae, this is part of the trunk; ventrally, with its cartilages, it is part of the head. What was the head in fish, then, has become head plus a large part of the neck in amniotes. Some small part of the fish's head has moved even further back, making the pulmonary and systemic arteries in the thorax. It seems that no accurate and satisfactory definition of the head, that will apply to all vertebrate classes, is possible. The most accurate is perhaps the topographical one—the part of the body in front of the shoulder girdle. This applies pretty well to fish of all sorts, and to amphibians, but breaks down for amniotes since it would include in the head the cervical vertebrae which belong more closely to the trunk. One is left with the necessity of defining the head functionally for each group of vertebrates, and abandoning all attempts at complete homology.

20

Endocrine Organs

SOME FORM of co-ordination or transmission of information is needed
even in the smallest animals; it is useless for an amoeba to form
pseudopodia at one end of its body unless protoplasm is withdrawn to an
equal extent at the other, and the cilia of an animal such as *Paramecium*
must even more obviously beat in a co-ordinated rhythm if the creature is
to move forward. Very little is known of how co-ordination is brought
about in these one-celled animals, but, as we have seen in Chapter 13, in
all the Metazoa there is a specialized conducting or nervous system. In the
Crustacea, Insecta, and Vertebrata (and more doubtfully in the Annelida
and Mollusca) there is also another type of co-ordination, depending
solely on the release and transmission of chemical substances, without (so
far as is known) the electrical changes so characteristic of the nervous impulse. In this, the endocrine system, there is clearly a similarity to the way
in which the nerve fibers release chemical transmitters (or neurohumors)
at synapses and at their effectors; but while the types of substance produced by the nerves are limited to two in vertebrates and a few more in
arthropods, the substances called hormones produced by the endocrine
system are many and varied.

The endocrine organs are clearly glands because they have as their chief
or sole function the manufacture of material which is to be passed out of
their cells. But unlike most glands, they eliminate their secretion not
through ducts but by diffusion, and especially by diffusion into the blood
system, and so are called glands of internal secretion, or ductless glands.
They do not form a uniform system, either morphologically or histologically, and their treatment together is a matter of convenience only. They
are best known in the mammals, on account of their medical importance,
and our knowledge of them in other classes is often fragmentary. In this
chapter we shall therefore reverse our usual order of treatment, describing
the glands first in mammals, and then trying to trace them back through
other groups.

It is sometimes said that the system of chemical co-ordination is more
primitive than that of the nervous system. In one sense this may be true,
in that the simplest way in which information could be conveyed from one
end of a cell to another would seem to be by diffusion of a simple chemical substance, and this may well be what happens in Protozoa; but there

is no evidence that the elaborated endocrine system of vertebrates was evolved before their nervous system, and there is some that it was not. When one looks at the endocrine glands as a whole it appears probable that they are derived from tissue which already had the power of external secretion. The simplest explanation of the origin of the system is that the animal took advantage of this power, and used some of the substances that the tissue could make to influence distant tissues.

The endocrine organs of mammals have three types of embryological origin: from the wall of the gut; from the nervous system and neural crest; and from the gonads and adjacent parts of the celomic wall. The hormones produced by glands which are derivatives of the gut are proteins (as are the digestive enzymes), while those produced by derivatives of the celomic wall are steroids. The hormones derived from nervous tissue are more varied, but include one, adrenaline, which is closely similar to the sympathin produced at nerve endings.

A number of endocrine glands are derived from the wall of the pharynx. Largest of them is the thyroid, which begins as a median furrow on its floor; this closes and forms a mass of glandular tissue which comes to lie as two lobes, one on each side of the trachea, across which they are joined

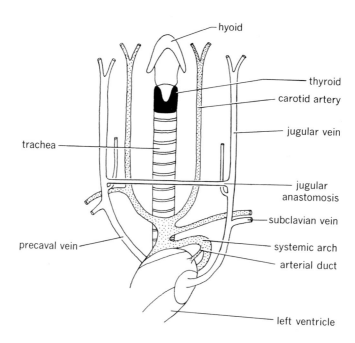

FIG. 20.1   Dissection of the neck of a rabbit, *Oryctolagus cuniculus*, to show the position of the thyroid gland, x 1.

by a neck (Fig. 20.1). In many mammals the neck is broken, so that the gland has two separate parts. In section it has a very characteristic appearance (Fig. 20.2), with follicles containing the secretion, their walls consisting of characteristic cubical cells with large nuclei. It produces two hormones, thyroxin in large quantities and smaller amounts of tri-iodothyronine. These are closely similar chemically, consisting of two

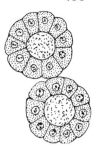

FIG. 20.2   Section of two vesicles of the thyroid gland of a guinea pig, *Cavia porcellus*, x 600. In most mammals the vesicles have a much wider lumen.

benzene rings with substituted iodine, and a side chain with an amino and a carboxy group. When present in the blood both are bound to proteins of the plasma. They have similar effects, and in general stimulate metabolism and oxygen consumption. They are liberated under the action of a hormone from the pituitary (p. 459), but the quantity in the blood varies little from moment to moment. Individual differences in man are very marked. Thus an active thyroid is associated with restlessness and continual activity, and a thin body with slightly prominent eyes, while the opposite features of lethargy, overweight, and sunken eyes, suggest an inadequate thyroid. It is interesting that the guinea pig, which, relative to most mammals, has all these latter characters, has very small thyroid follicles.

A thyroid gland, of similar origin to that of mammals, can be recognized in all classes of vertebrate. In birds it is double and in a similar position to that of mammals though a little distance from the trachea (Fig. 20.3). In lizards it is a single body lying on the trachea, but it is double in some reptiles and in amphibia (Fig. 20.4). In elasmobranchs it is a single pear-shaped structure easily seen in dissection of *Scyliorhinus* at the anterior bifurcation of the ventral aorta.

In teleosts it is much more diffuse, extending along the ventral aorta and sometimes on to the afferent branchial vessels or to greater distances (Fig. 20.5).

Rows of vesicles below the pharynx in the lamprey have a similar appearance to the thyroid and can be traced back to an origin in the epithelium of the endostyle, which we have seen in Chapter 9 to be a remnant of the ciliary feeding apparatus of the first vertebrates. It is not the glandular tracts of the endostyle that become the thyroid, but its unspecialized wall. If the endostyle of the cyclostomes can be homologized with that of amphioxus and the tunicates, the first beginnings of the thyroid can be seen in the protochordates.

The physiological role of the thyroid in birds seems to be much the same as in mammals, but in addition it has some control over molting, so that

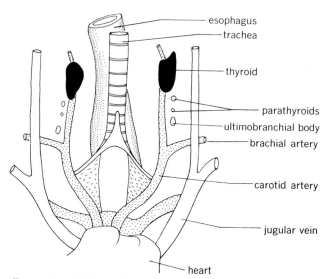

FIG. 20.3   Dissection of the neck of a fowl, to show the position of the thyroid and parathyroid glands and of the ultimobranchial body, XI. (Redrawn from Adams and Eddy, *Comparative Anatomy*, John Wiley, 1949)

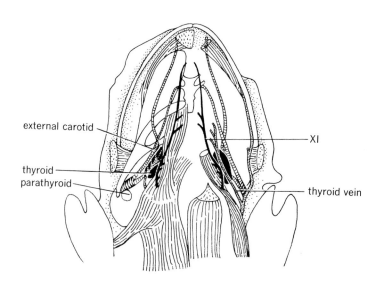

FIG. 20.4   Dissection of a salamander, *Salamandra maculosa*, to show the position of the thyroid and parathyroid glands, x 2. (Redrawn from Francis, *The Anatomy of the Salamander*, Clarendon Press, 1934)

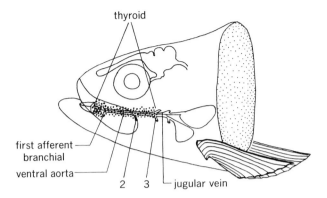

FIG. 20.5   Head of a herring, *Clupea harengus,* to show the position of the thyroid gland. (Redrawn from Buchmann, *Zool. Jahrb, Abt. Anat.* 66, 1940, 191)

there must be a seasonal variation in the production of the hormone. It is concerned with the sloughing of the skin in lizards and snakes, but in Amphibia the chief function of thyroxin is to stimulate the metamorphosis of the larva. There is no certainty that thyroxin increases oxygen consumption in cold-blooded vertebrates, so that its function seems to have changed as the vertebrates evolved, a phenomenon that we shall see again in other hormones. Its relation to oxygen consumption in birds and mammals is perhaps connected with their homeothermy, since when a mammal is placed in a cold chamber the release of hormone from the gland increases.

The thyroid glands of all vertebrates take up iodine from the blood, and this happens also in the non-glandular parts of the endostyle of the ammocoete larva, of amphioxus, and of tunicates. The manufacture of iodine-containing compounds seems to be the fundamental function of the tissue, but what they are used for in the protochordates, or even the fishes, is unknown.

The parathyroid glands, or epithelial bodies, get their usual name from the fact that they lie on or in the thyroids. They are histologically distinct, consisting of solid masses of cells with no follicles, even when, as in the rat, they are embedded in the thyroid. Usually in mammals there are two pairs, and they produce a substance called parathormone, which has a molecular weight of about 9500 and controls the concentration of calcium in the blood. It possibly has other effects also.

Similar glands are found in similar situations in birds, reptiles, and amphibians, but they are unknown in fish. This is not surprising in view of their embryological origin, which is from the epithelium of the gill pouches. In the fish this is presumably too much occupied in forming the gills, so that there is an apparent exception to the rule that the endocrine glands are derived from tissue that had a previous secretory activity. We have seen in Chapter 9, however, that the gills of teleosts are concerned with the salt balance of the body, of which the calcium balance is a special case.

The homology of the parathyroids, like that of so much else in the vertebrate body, is not segmental. Those of mammals, birds, and amphibians are generally formed from the third and fourth pouches, though one pair may atrophy, as in rats; while in lizards development begins in pouches three, four, and five, but only the tissue from the third pouch survives.

Little is known of the function of the parathyroids except in mammals, but in birds its secretion has a relation, not yet clear, to the absorption of calcium, which in some species may be important in connection with egg-laying.

Behind the last pair of gill slits in many embryos there is a pair of small outpushings from the pharynx called ultimobranchial bodies, which look as if they were serially homologous with the slits. Tissue derived from them is associated with the thyroid in mammals. They have no known function, but there are some slight indications that in teleosts they may be associated with the regulation of calcium. If this is confirmed, they could be regarded as serially homologous with the parathyroids.

The rudimentary gill tissue of the spiracle, which in dogfish forms a gill-like pseudobranch, persists in teleosts (where the spiracle is closed) as a structure which looks glandular in its cellular form. Its removal causes dispersion of melanophore pigment, and so darkening, in several species, so that it possibly produces a hormone which concentrates the pigment. Some experiments have provided independent evidence for the existence of such a hormone, but many workers have denied its existence.

The thymus of mammals consists of two masses in the space, the mediastinum, in front of the heart. It is the largest of the structures so far dealt with in this chapter, and is easily seen in dissection, especially in a young animal, for it is at its largest before sexual maturity is reached. In spite of its large size, and its apparently clear connection with growth and development, no certain endocrine action can be ascribed to it and no hormone has so far been extracted from it. Its histological structure is that known as lymphoid (like the spleen and lymph nodes) and it produces immunologically reactive lymphocytes. In the dogfish there are small masses above all the gill slits; in the frog a gland behind and above the angle of the jaw on each side; and in birds in various positions in the neck. The interest of the thymus here is that it, like the parathyroids, is formed from the epithelium of the gill pouches; the third and fourth in mammals, first and third in birds, and a variable number in amphibians and reptiles. Similar derivatives are found in all vertebrates. Since the dorsal part of the pouches of sauropsids forms the thymus, and the ventral part forms the parathyroids, while in mammals it is the other way around, its homology is confused.

Much of the co-ordination of the secretion of digestive enzymes by mammals is carried out by hormones, which are secreted by the glandular wall of the gut without elaboration into specialized organs. The exact number of such hormones is uncertain. The best known of them is secretin, which is secreted by the wall of the duodenum and causes the pancreas to secrete bicarbonate. It is liberated when acid from the stomach comes into the intestine, and, since the bicarbonate neutralizes the acid, there is automatic control of the hydrogen ion concentration. Pancreozymin, liberated by the duodenal mucosa when soluble proteins come in contact with it, stimulates the pancreas to secrete enzymes. Protein in the stomach causes the cells of the pylorus to liberate gastrin, which stimulates the gastric glands to produce acid. All three actions are associated with nervous control through the autonomic system.

Even in mammals the role played by hormones in digestion is not clear, and even less is known of their presence or activity in other vertebrates. What does seem clear is that, as the vertebrates have evolved, their digestive mechanism has become more complicated, both in itself and in its control by both nervous system and hormones.

The chief digestive gland of mammals, the pancreas, arises, as we have seen in Chapter 9, as an outgrowth from the mid-gut. From the wall of its duct masses of cells are separated off, and come to lie as distinct entities among the general glandular tissue. They are called the islets of Langerhans (or now often simply the islets, or islet tissue), and are unconnected with the pancreatic duct, or connected with its branches only by solid strands. Their number is known to range from 15,000 in some guinea pigs to over 2,000,000 in man. (Fig. 20.6.) At least two types of cell, called A

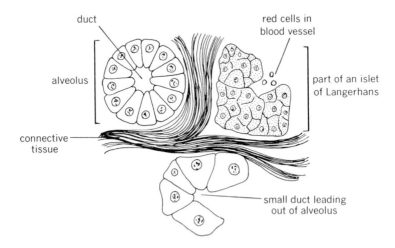

FIG. 20.6   Semi-diagrammatic section of a small portion of the pancreas of a guinea pig, *Cavia porcellus*, x 400.

and B, can be recognized in them, which fits the fact that the gland produces two hormones. The best known of these, insulin, is almost certainly produced by the B cells. It reduces the concentration of glucose in the blood. The other hormone, glucagon, has the reverse effect, and is presumably made by the A cells. Both insulin and glucagon are proteins of low molecular weight—about 6000 for insulin, and rather more than half this for glucagon.

Comparable islet tissue is present in or near the pancreas in all gnathostomes, but in teleosts it is mostly concentrated into a single mass, or it may be scattered near the gall-bladder, spleen, pyloric ceca, and small intestine. In elasmobranchs and birds, and rather more doubtfully in teleosts, amphibians, and reptiles, A and B cells have been recognized. In all these groups the gland has been shown to have some effect on blood sugar, since its removal generally causes hyperglycemia (excessive glucose in the blood), just as it does in mammals, but there are differences in detail and the nature of the hormones concerned is unknown. Birds have few B cells, and correspondingly produce much glucagon, but are insensitive to insulin.

Cyclostomes have no pancreas, but near the intestinal cecum, which could be the forerunner of this gland, there is a compact mass of cells, which is derived from follicles which arise from the wall of the intestine near the bile duct in the larva. Similar tissue is formed from the bile duct itself and lies on the liver. All these cells have some resemblance to those of the islets, but there is no evidence that they secrete hormones. The general picture of the evolution of the islets would be that sometime before the gnathostomes arose, or at the very base of their stock, cells which were originally concerned with the secretion of digestive enzymes (themselves simple proteins) became diverted to produce hormones which, instead of simply breaking down carbohydrates in the gut, affected their metabolism in the liver and elsewhere. Eventually two such hormones were evolved, of complimentary effects, one, insulin, becoming more important in the theropsidan line, the other, glucagon, in the sauropsidan.

The last endocrine gland derived from the gut is a bridge to the second group, those derived from nervous tissue. The pituitary gland of mammals has long been known to have a double origin, an upgrowth from the roof of the buccal cavity meeting a downgrowth from the floor of the thalamencephalon. The old division of this organ into anterior and posterior lobes corresponds neither to its development nor to its endocrine functions, and a more rational nomenclature is shown in Fig. 20.7. The part formed from the buccal cavity is now usually called the adenohypophysis, that from the brain the neurohypophysis.

The pituitary is a complex gland, each of its parts producing its own hormones; many of these act not directly on the part of the body which they are ultimately going to affect, but on other endocrine organs, espe-

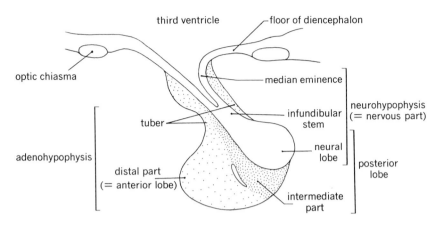

FIG. 20.7   Diagram of a sagittal section of the pituitary gland of mammal, to show the nomenclature of the parts.

cially the thyroid and the gonads, so that removal or disease of the pituitary has far-reaching effects. A bare list of the actions of the mammalian pituitary is this: The distal part (the anterior lobe of the old nomenclature) produces certainly six hormones, and possibly more: growth hormone promotes increase in size, especially of limbs and jaws; thyrotropin stimulates the thyroid to liberate thyroxin; corticotropin similarly stimulates the adrenal cortex (pp. 461-2); follicle-stimulating hormone (FSH) causes the ripening of the Graafian follicles of the ovary, while interstitial cell stimulating hormone (ICSH) or luteinizing hormone (LH) causes the follicle from which an egg has been discharged to change into a corpus luteum, and causes a corresponding development of the interstitial cells of the testis in the male (pp. 463-4); prolactin initiates milk secretion. FSH, ICSH, and prolactin are known collectively as gonadotropins. All six hormones are proteins, with molecular weights between 20,000 and 100,000. There is some evidence that each is produced by a different type of cell.

Neither the tuber nor the intermediate part is known to produce any hormones in mammals.

The neural (or posterior) lobe produces two hormones, which are closely related proteins. Oxytocin causes the contraction of some smooth muscles, especially of the uterus and the milk glands, so that it is concerned in birth and milk ejection. Vasopressin causes chiefly the contraction of other smooth muscles, so that it leads to a rise in blood pressure and a retention of urine. Each hormone, however, produces in a slight degree the effects of the other. Two different vasopressins with slightly different amino acid sequences are present in different mammals.

It is obvious that if the pituitary is to do its work successfully many of its hormones, especially the gonadotropins, must vary seasonally in their production, and there is good evidence that they do. Moreover, it is clear from much experimental work, as well as general observations of animals in nature, that the seasonal cycle is initiated by external factors of the environment, especially light and temperature. These are received as stimuli by the sense organs and nervous system, and there must thereafter be some link between the nerves and the pituitary. This link is of two sorts. The adenohypophysis receives a double blood supply: directly from the internal carotid artery, and indirectly from the same artery after it has supplied the floor of the thalamencephalon in the region of the median eminence, and has broken up into capillaries there. There is therefore a hypophysial portal system, and there is now little doubt that the production of gonadotropins depends on the receipt, through this, of hormones produced in the hypothalamus as a result of the stimuli of light or temperature perceived through the eyes or skin.

The adenohypophysis probably has no nerve supply. By contrast, the neurohypophysis is innervated by many fibers from various points in the thalamencephalon, and these fibers have been shown to contain material comparable to that of the neural lobe. It seems now to be generally agreed that the lobe itself is not a gland, but merely a storage organ, and that vasopressin and oxytocin are in fact produced by nerve cells of the hypothalamus that have acquired a glandular nature, and that these substances are then passed slowly down the nerve fibers into the neural lobe.

The pituitary gland of birds is very similar to that of mammals, in its general structure, in its blood supply, and in the action of its hormones. Prolactin, for example, which in view of its connection with the mammary glands one might expect to be a peculiarly mammalian hormone, is responsible for the development of the bare brood patches in incubating birds (males included, in some species), and even induces the development of the peculiar crop glands of pigeons, which produce the milk on which the nestlings are fed.

In other vertebrates the pituitary develops in the same general way, but there are some peculiarities and simplifications. In most teleosts the adenohypophysis develops as a solid mass, but this is presumably secondary, since a hollow is present in elasmobranchs, and in *Protopterus* a hollow forms after development has begun. The saccus vasculosus which grows out of the dorsal wall of the neurohypophysis in fishes is not glandular and has no known function. A hypophysial portal system comparable to that of mammals and birds does not seem to be established in fish.

There is in amphioxus a hollow, Hatschek's pit, on the roof of the mouth. It comes partly from the pre-oral pit, which has a connection with the left pre-oral celomic space. If its asymmetry is explained as being a secondary feature due to the general asymmetry of the larva, it is in the right position to be the forerunner of Rathke's pouch, the hollow which in elasmobranchs and some others develops into the adenohypophysis. The relationship is supported by the fact that in the electric ray *Torpedo*, Rathke's pouch communicates with the premandibular somites.

The infundibular organ of amphioxus, a group of flagellate cells on the floor of the cerebral vesicle, has been suggested as the forerunner of the neurohypophysis, but as it appears to be sensory rather than glandular the connection is dubious.

Whatever may have been the origin of the pituitary, its function has changed with time. There is evidence that corticotropin is present and active in elasmobranchs and teleosts, as well as in tetrapods, but although all vertebrates have gonadotropins, and all except perhaps elasmobranchs have vasopressin and oxytocin, or related substances, their effects, which are only partly known, do not agree with those in mammals. Oxytocin, for example, is important in amphibians in regulating the water balance, especially through the skin, and there is a close connection with the habitat, aquatic forms such as *Necturus* and *Xenopus* showing much greater response than the more terrestrial frogs and toads.

In amphibians, and in some fish and reptiles, the darkening of the skin is caused by the dispersion of pigment in chromatophores, which is induced by a hormone called intermedin produced by the intermediate part of the gland. This substance can be extracted from the pituitary of birds and mammals, but has no known function in them. According to some authors a hormone with the reverse effect—concentration of pigment and so lightening of the skin—is produced by the tuber of amphibians and some fish. If it really exists, it is the only hormone known to be produced in this part of the gland.

The pineal body, originally a dorsal eye (p. 248), is possibly an endocrine gland. It plays some part in the color change of sockeye Salmon (*Oncorhynchus nerka*) and of ammocoete larvae of lampreys, possibly by the liberation of a hormone, for its removal causes darkening. A substance called melatonin, which is a simple derivative of the common aromatic amino acid tryptophan, has been extracted from mammalian pineals. It has an intense concentrating action on the melanophores of amphibians.

With the adrenal gland we come to another compound structure, which makes a bridge from the endocrine glands derived from nervous tissue to those derived from celomic epithelium. Each gland in a mammal lies near the kidney (Fig. 12.15), and in section (Fig. 20.8) shows an inner medulla and an outer cortex. The former gives an intense color with chromic acid and its derivatives, and so is called chromaffin tissue; since the corresponding tissue in other vertebrates is not in a medullary or central position this term is preferred for general use. Although 'cortex,' which means an outer layer, is equally inappropriate outside the mammals, no more suitable term has been invented; for 'adrenocortical tissue,' which is often used, is merely 'adrenal cortex' increased in length by 50 per cent.

The cells of the medulla have many resemblances to nerve cells and, like the cells of the sympathetic ganglia, are derived from the neural crest. They appear, in fact, to be nerve cells that have been deflected to a gland-ular function. They produce adrenaline (on which the chromaffin reaction depends), which has a number of effects which are almost, but not quite, the same as those produced by the sympathin (or noradrenaline) liberated by sympathetic nerves. In general it causes the contraction of smooth muscle and the activity of glands.

The cortex is derived from mesoderm of the celomic wall near to that which produces the mesonephros. It makes several hormones, all of which

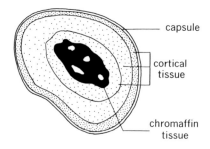

FIG. 20.8   Diagram of a section of the adrenal of a rat, *Rattus norvegicus*, x 15. The spaces in the chromaffin tissue are venous sinuses.

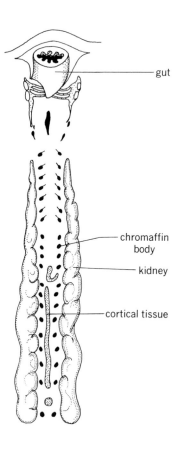

FIG. 20.9   Adrenal tissues of a dogfish, *Mustelus canis*, XI. (Redrawn from Harman and Brownell, *The Adrenal Gland*, Lea and Febiger, 1949)

are steroids, based on a seventeen-carbon atom nucleus arranged in four rings. Different substances are produced by different cells, but their effects have not yet been fully sorted out. In general, they increase the formation of carbohydate from protein and fat, and cause secretion of sodium. They have also some effects on the sexual cycle.

Chromaffin tissue can be recognized in all vertebrates. In amphibians, reptiles, and birds it is distributed among the cortical tissue in various patterns, the resulting compound gland being reasonably compact. In teleosts both chromaffin tissue and cortex are scattered along the cardinal veins, with some intermingling and much specific variation. The cyclostomes are probably similar. In elasmobranchs the chromaffin tissue is in segmental blocks along the cardinal sinus, while the cortex is a fairly compact mass between the kidneys (Fig. 20.9).

The chromaffin reaction shows that adrenaline (or noradrenaline) is present in all the vertebrate classes, but its natural function in many of these is doubtful, since its action when injected into them is very slow. Some authors have suggested that it only becomes important in warm-blooded animals, where it can act more quickly, but it seems unlikely that it would be so universal if it had no function.

Very little is known of the cortex in lower vertebrates. Some at least of the cortical steroids are present in all classes, and it seems likely that they have the same general effect in all. The excretion of sodium by the gills of teleosts and by the nasal glands of birds can both be increased by the injection of mammalian steroids.

We have seen in Chapter 12 that the gonads of both sexes of mammal contain, in addition to the actual sexual cells and their supporting tissue, what are known as interstitial cells, for which Leydig cells is an alternative name. These cells produce hormones, called collectively androgens (of which testosterone is the chief) in the male and estrogens (of which estradiol is the chief) in the female. They are all steroids, closely related in chemical nature to the hormones produced by the adrenal cortex. Their functions are many, but in general it can be said that androgens are concerned with the development of maleness, including the secondary sexual characters and probably the behavior characteristic of the sex, while estrogens are concerned with femaleness. Small quantities of androgens are produced by females and small quantities of estrogens by males, and the development of the original indeterminate duct system of the embryo is largely dependent on the balance between the two types of hormone; in general androgens suppress the development of the Müllerian duct and stimulate that of the Wolffian duct, the reverse situation (which is that of the female) being the neutral condition.

In most mammals there is an annual cycle of development of the interstitial tissue, which leads to the annual cycle of reproductive activity. The cause of the renewed activity of the tissue is the receipt of interstitial cell stimulating hormone from the pituitary, which, as we have seen above, is itself dependent on external factors such as light and temperature.

The cycle in the female is more complicated, for added to the annual cycle is the shorter one of estrus. This too depends on the pituitary, but also on the structure called the corpus luteum, which is formed after an ovary has been discharged from a Graafian follicle. The follicle stimulating hormone causes the corpus luteum to develop and produce another set of steroids, called progestins (of which progesterone is the chief) which prepares the uterus for the attachment of the embryo and produces other characteristic changes in the reproductive organs and mammary glands. Progestins suppress estrus, but if there is no fetus present the corpus luteum degenerates and estrus can occur again under the influence of the pituitary. The estrous cycle is thus established. If pregnancy occurs the corpus luteum persists, and estrus cannot occur again. In some mammals, however, the function of the corpus luteum in maintaining pregnancy and suppressing estrus is taken over by the placenta itself, which must therefor rank as an endocrine gland.

Interstitial tissue, or cells corresponding to it, has been described in the gonads of most vertebrates, and various sexual hormones have been found here and there. Only in birds is much known about their production and action, and once again they show a remarkable parallelism to, as well as striking differences from, mammals. The testes produce androgens which probably control the male characters in the usual way, but although estrogens and progestins are present in the female, the former are produced by the follicles and the latter by the interstitial cells, the exact opposite of the case in mammals. Moreover, some of their effects are different, for estrogens are necessary for the development of the Müllerian ducts in the female. It is tempting to connect this with the fact that in birds the male is the sex with the regularly paired sex chromosomes, while in mammals it is the female. There is much interspecific variation in the action of the hormones, for while they determine the color of the plumage in some birds that have sexual dimorphism, in others this is under genetic control. As with most of the other endocrine organs, it seems that the establishment of their activity has been gradual, and has reached full development only in the mammals.

21

Muscles

WE HAVE left to the last the organ system which is the bulkiest in the body, that of the muscles; it includes the flesh as it is seen and felt as the tissue occupying most of the space between the skin and the bones, as well as important parts of the alimentary, excretory, reproductive, and vascular systems. In spite of its quantitative importance, and the very detailed analysis to which it has been subjected in human anatomy, it is extremely difficult to treat from a comparative point of view. This is largely because it shows opportunism to an even greater degree than does the vascular system. Whenever tension has been needed, it seems that muscles have been formed; this is in accordance with the general observation that to make growing muscles bigger the best way is to use them, and with the fact that in tissue culture muscle cells tend to arrange themselves along lines of stress. If the way in which a limb, for example, is moved, has changed in the course of evolution, the muscles have changed so as to correspond, dividing, joining together, or appearing as new structures. When to this lability is added the fact that many muscles in most vertebrates are formed from a liquid mesenchyme, it is obvious that the assignment of homologies will always be difficult and may be impossible.

Muscles are based histologically on the fiber, which is of three main types. In one, called skeletal, somatic, striated, striped, or voluntary, the fiber is a syncytium (Fig. 21.1), varying much in size but with an average length of about 2.5 cm., and diameter 0.05 mm. On the outside a sheath, the sarcolemma, encloses a liquid sarcoplasm in which lie many nuclei and several parallel myofibrils running the length of the fibers. Each myofibril is made up of narrow rods of the protein actin and thicker rods of another protein, myosin, arranged in a regular hexagonal pattern. The rods are not continuous, but overlap as shown in Fig. 21.2. This fine structure, which has been found out by electron microscopy, corresponds to the visible structure (from which the names striped and striated for this sort of muscle are derived) shown diagrammatically in Fig. 21.2. The light and dark bands have long been known by the letters of the alphabet shown, and all of these except the Z band clearly correspond to appearances given by the protein structure. In contraction the actin rods slide into the spaces between those of myosin, probably with the formation of a complex protein

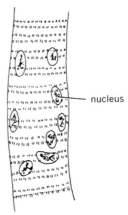

FIG. 21.1   A portion of a striped muscle fiber of a mammal, x 300.

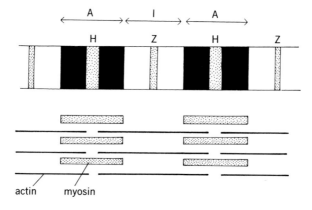

FIG. 21.2   Diagrams of the structure of a striped muscle fiber, as shown by the electron microscope. *Above:* the dark and light bands and the letters by which they are known. *Below:* the rods of actin and myosin that correspond to the bands. (Redrawn from Yapp, *Borradaile's Manual of Elementary Zoology,* Oxford University Press, 1963)

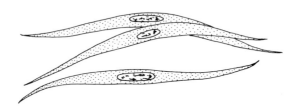

FIG. 21.3   Smooth muscle fibers, x 140.

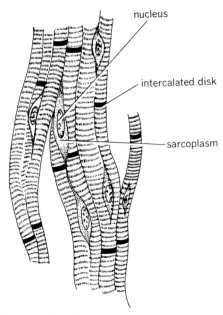

nucleus

intercalated disk

sarcoplasm

FIG. 21.4 A small piece of cardiac muscle, x 250.

actomyosin, so that the A and Z bands decrease in length; this also agrees with what has long been known from studies with the light microscope.

Visceral, smooth, plain, or involuntary muscle fibers are usually not more than half a millimeter long, and each is a single cell, with one nucleus (Fig. 21.3). No cross striations are visible, and the electron microscope has failed to show any regular pattern of actin and myosin. Nevertheless, the mode of contraction of smooth muscle, though different in detail, seems to be fundamentally similar to that of striped muscle.

The muscle of the heart, or cardiac muscle, is unique in that the fibers branch and join one another (Fig. 21.4). Nuclei, cross striations, and myofibrils can be seen, and there are also occasional cross walls, which correspond in number to the nuclei. Opinions differ as to whether these are cell walls or not, but whatever they are, there is no doubt that the whole heart behaves, as described in Chapter 10, as a functional syncytium.

The muscular system contains more than the muscle fibers that give it its characteristic appearance. The fibers are more or less surrounded by areolar connective tissue, which in places may appear as sheets of white fibers, which are the chief cause of toughness in meat. Blood vessels run among the fibers, and they are well supplied with nerves. In skeletal muscle these include motor nerves, which end in motor end plates beneath the sarcolemma (Fig. 13.2), and the sensory fibers which are attached to the sensory muscle spindles (p. 282). Visceral muscle is supplied by the autonomic system, and has nerve cell bodies as well as fibers present in it (p. 269). Cardiac muscle also has an autonomic supply, but differs from the other two sorts in that it contracts and maintains its rhythm independently of any nerve supply.

The morphological classification of the muscular system corresponds closely, but not entirely, to the three types of fiber. Cardiac muscle is found only in the heart, and no more will be said of it here. The typical striped muscles are those of the general body and limbs, and are derived from the myotomes of the somites, or from the mesenchyme which replaces them in many tetrapods, and to a small extent from the somatopleure of the lateral plate. Smooth fibers, on the other hand, are mostly derived from the splanchnopleure, and so make up the muscular parts of the gut. The splanchnopleure in front of the heart, however, forms largely muscle fibers which are striated, and appear as the muscles of the gill arches and jaws. The splanchnopleure is innervated by the dorsal roots of the spinal nerves, the myotomes by ventral roots, and this explains the complicated innervation of such an organ as the tongue of mammals. The muscles in it that belong to the pharyngeal arches are derived from splanchnopleure and are innervated by cranial nerves V, VII, IX, and X, while its chief bulk, consisting of the intrinsic muscles, is derived by migration from the myotomes of the occipital region of the head, and is innervated by nerve XII. An exception in the other direction is that the smooth fibers which make up much of the walls of the arteries, and rather less of those of veins, are derived from whatever mesoblastic tissue—splanchnopleure, somatopleure, or mesenchyme—may be appropriate to their position. The smooth muscles found in the dermis, for example those by which the hairs are raised, are also derived from the somatopleure. Finally, a few muscles, such as those of the iris, are not formed from mesoderm at all, but from neural crest or neural tissue.

No entirely satisfactory classification of the muscular system is therefore possible. Cardiac muscle, and the smooth or visceral muscles of the gut, the vascular system, and the urinary and genital systems and the skin, appear as constituent parts of the organs to which they belong, and have been dealt with elsewhere in this book. Important general structural features of them are that they are never attached to the skeleton (though the attachment of dermal muscles at the base of hairs may be regarded as an incipient exception to this), and that they tend to form sheets, tubes, or rings, rather than to be arranged with parallel fibers so as to produce a straight pull (the erector muscles of the hairs are again an exception). This clearly accords with the function of making for contraction in tubes, as in the gut, arteries, and urogenital ducts, or in sacs, as in the urinary bladder, lungs and swim bladder. Ring-like muscles, or sphincters, are especially common in the alimentary canal, where they restrict the flow of its contents from one section to the next.

The contraction of a muscle is an active process, in which energy is released by the hydrolysis of adenosine triphosphate (ATP), a reaction in which the myosin probably itself takes part as an enzyme. The supply of adenosine triphosphate is limited, and it is continually being reformed, the energy for this, and so for the muscular contraction, coming ultimately from the oxidation of carbohydrate. This is quite different from the contraction of a stretched spring or piece of rubber, in which the energy has been supplied from outside, possibly long before the contraction takes place. The muscle fiber has only a very small elasticity (probably lying mainly in the sarcolemma), so that after contraction it does not of itself return to its resting length, but does so only if it is pulled by some outside force. This accounts for the arrangement of nearly all muscles as pairs of antagonists, which act in opposite directions. (The distinction sometimes made between an agonist and an antagonist is not only etymologically wrong but logically impossible, since if the actions of the antagonists were not equal and opposite there would be continual movement in one direction.) In the gut the circular and longitudinal muscles are antagonistic; in the limbs there may be a fairly simple pairing of skeletal muscles, but more often a large number of muscles pull in different directions on a bone, so that at rest the vector total of the forces that they exert is zero.

The main part of the somatic muscular system is sometimes called axial, and is divided into the upper epi-axonic and lower hypo-axonic systems, which in fish are separated by the horizontal septum (p. 337). Both systems in fish are derived from the myotomes, which grow ventralward so as almost to meet. The segmental arrangement is maintained, but the muscles of each segment become folded so as to make a Σ with the points forward (Fig. 1.3). The result of this is that in a transverse section of the body several muscles are cut (Fig. 21.5). For the most part they are not attached to the bones or cartilage, but to the fibrous myocommata that separate successive myomeres (p. 126).

The effect of this arrangement is that contraction of the trunk muscles causes lateral bending, the muscles of the two sides being antagonistic to one another. In short fishes, such as many teleosts, the relative thickness of the body is such that only a single shallow curve can be produced. Contraction of the muscles of the right side, for example, has the effect of shortening that side, so bringing head and tail closer together; when the muscles of the right side relax and those of the left contract, the body of the fish first straightens and then bends in the opposite direction. The tail is more flexible, so that it moves more than the head, but the deflection of the head from side to side as the fish swims is very noticeable (Fig. 21.6A). In a longer and thinner fish, such as a dogfish (Fig. 4.2), there is a marked wave-like progression of the contraction of the muscles of one side from head to tail; the result is that at least two curves are produced, the anterior part of the body being, for example, concave to the right,

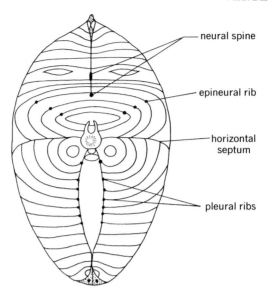

FIG. 21.5   A thick transverse section, or steak, through the trunk of a salmon, *Salmo salar*, x 1/2.

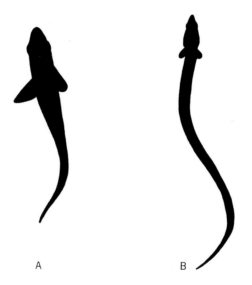

FIG. 21.6   (A) A short fish, the whiting, *Gadus merlangus*, swimming, seen from above. Little more than half a wave is present in the body at one time. (B) A long thin fish, the eel, *Anguilla vulgaris*, swimming, seen from above. Rather more than one full wave is present in the body. (Redrawn from Gray *J. Exp. Biol.* 10, 1933)

while the tail is concave to the left. In a long fish such as an eel (*Anguilla*) several such curves may be present at once (Fig. 21.6B). In these cases the head swings much less out of the straight path than it does in the short fishes.

Whether there is one curve or many, the locomotion is produced by the oblique lateral movement of the body, especially of the caudal fin. The force produced on the water is vertical to the direction of movement of the body, and can be resolved into two components at right angles, one along the fish's axis, one transverse to this. Since the body moves from side to side alternate transverse forces cancel each other out, and only the force along the axis is effective. The equal and opposite force produced, in accordance with Newton's first law of motion, by the water on the fish, drives the animal forward.

Relatively few fish have departed far from this basic pattern. In *Amia* and the electric eel *Gymnarchus* the general myotomic muscles seem not to be used for locomotion, but an elongated dorsal fin is thrown into transverse waves by muscles at its base presumably derived from the epi-axonic system. The forces are similar to those in normal swimming, but the axis of the body is unbent and there is no deflection of the head from side to side. The sea horse (Fig. 4.33) uses its dorsal fin in a similar way for vertical movement, and the myotomic muscles of the tail contract in such a way as to make this prehensile.

The muscles of the limbs, or appendicular system, may be regarded as derived from those of the trunk. In the elasmobranchs they can be seen to develop from the myotomes (Fig. 21.7). For the most part, from each myotome which is going to contribute to the fin two buds arise. Each of these later separates from its myotome and divides into a dorsal and a ventral part with a radial cartilage between them. At its simplest, the musculature of the adult fin consists of a dorsal and a ventral mass derived from the associated buds, so that the only movement possible is a simple raising and lowering round the basal joint.

The condition in other fish is somewhat similar, but is rather more complicated in association with the much greater freedom of movement of many of their fins. The paired fins of *Cladoselache* (Fig. 17.2), with their parallel radial cartilages, may well have had a simpler condition, in which the radial muscles, derived from separate myotomes, remained distinct. In the skates and rays the dorsal and ventral fibers of the pectoral fin run parallel with the axis of the body, so that their antagonistic contraction throws the fin into vertical waves. (Fig. 4.19.) This is in marked contrast to the lateral bending of nearly all other fish.

The somatic muscular system of tetrapods is very different from that of fish. It comes mostly from mesenchyme, and segmentation can be recognized only with difficulty. Bundles of fibers are arranged as discrete muscles, sometimes forming a series down the body, sometimes appearing as

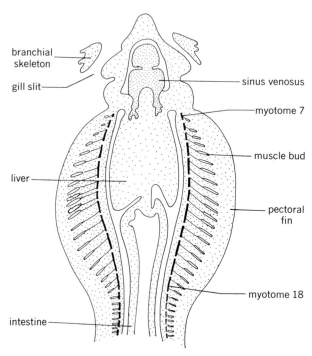

branchial skeleton

gill slit

liver

intestine

sinus venosus

myotome 7

muscle bud

pectoral fin

myotome 18

FIG. 21.7 A semi-diagrammatic frontal section of a dogfish embryo to show the formation of the fin. Except at the anterior end, where there is only one, two buds from each myotome from no. 7 to no. 18 grow into the fin. (Based on Goodrich, *Structure and development of Vertebrates*, Macmillan, 1930)

unique pairs. Generally each end of the muscle is attached to a piece of the skeleton, but this is a slightly misleading way of putting it. What happens is that the white fibers of the connective tissue in the muscle are continuous with those of the bone; the muscle and bone cannot therefore be separated without cutting these fibers. Contraction of the muscle must pull the two parts of the skeleton to which it is attached closer together. Usually one part moves much more than the other; the relatively immovable point, which is usually the proximal one, is called the origin, the more movable one the insertion. Sometimes, before entering the insertion, the white fibers run together, without any muscle fibers, for a shorter or longer distance; they then make a tendon. A similar tendon less often occurs at the origin; occasionally there is one in the middle of a muscle, when the latter is said to have two bellies, or to be digastric. A broad tendon is called an aponeurosis. Occasionally a muscle has its origin not on a bone but on a flat tendinous sheet or fascia.

The skeletal muscles, and especially those of the limbs, apply their forces on the principle of the lever. These may be of any of the three orders recognized in mechanics (Fig. 21.8). By far the commonest are those of the third order, and this means that the mechanical advantage, which is the ratio of the distance between the point of application of the force and the fulcrum to that between the point of application of the load and the fulcrum, is less than one. It follows from this that the distance through which the insertion of the muscle moves when it contracts is less than that through which the load moves. Since it is a well-known principle of mechanics that

$$\frac{\text{Distance moved by the pulling agent}}{\text{Distance moved by the load}} = \frac{\text{Load}}{\text{Force}}$$

it follows that the magnitude of the force produced by the muscle has to be much greater than that of the load it lifts; usually it is about ten times as big. This result may seem surprising, and may suggest that animals have not done so well for themselves as man's machines, in which the ratio is the other way round. This is not, however, so, for a low mechanical advantage

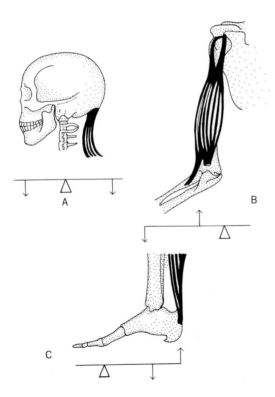

FIG. 21.8   Diagrams of the orders of levers, with examples from the human body. (A) the head and the semispinal muscle; (B) the arm and the biceps muscle; (C) the foot and the gastrocenemius muscle.

means much quicker action (an automobile cannot travel as fast in a low gear as in a high), and speed is often very important to an animal.

Levers of the first order are uncommon in the body, and constitute an exception to the necessity for muscles to be antagonistic. In the example shown in Fig. 21.8 the center of gravity of the head is in front of the fulcrum, and is balanced chiefly by the nuchal ligament, which is not muscular but consists of elastic fibers. When contraction of the muscle is over, the weight of the head will stretch it again.

The trunk muscles of urodeles and of anuran tadpoles have more resemblance to the muscles of fish than have those of any other tetrapods. This is in accordance with the fact that these amphibians live the same sort of life as fish do, and swim in much the same way, with lateral bending of the tail. We cannot however, be sure that their muscles retain a primitive structure, since, as has been discussed in the chapter on the heart, present-day amphibians are much more aquatic than many early types, and there may have been a retention of larval characters (in the urodeles) or a return to the water with new characters to suit the environment. It does, however, seem likely that the larvae of the ancestors of existing amphibians had not diverged far from the muscular system of a fish, or the present pattern would not have been recoverable.

A skinned mud puppy in lateral view (Fig. 21.9) shows three main series of muscles. The epi-axonic musculature, above the lateral line, consists of a series of short dorsal trunk muscles running from one vertebra to the next. The hypo-axonic musculature consists of two series, oblique above and longitudinal (rectus abdominis) below, making the ventral wall of the body. Both oblique and longitudinal muscles are divided by myocommata which mark the segments. The oblique muscles slope down from head to tail. When they are removed another internal oblique set can be seen, running up from head to tail. Within and above the longitudinal abdominal muscles are fibers running transversely across the wall of the abdomen.

Contraction of the longitudinal abdominal and dorsal muscles, and to some extent of the oblique muscles, will cause the lateral bending of the body by which the animal swims. This bending is helped also by the contraction of subvertebral muscles lying below the transverse processes of the vertebrae and derived from the hypo-axonic series. The transverse muscles, and to some extent the oblique muscles, will tighten the abdominal wall when they contract. Their chief function is probably to sling the viscera when the animal is on the land.

In adult anurans the epi-axonic muscles are concentrated dorsally; there is a series connecting successive vertebrae, but the main muscle is a long dorsal (longissimus dorsi) which runs the length of the trunk from the skull to the sacral vertebra and urostyle. The subvertebral muscles are similarly concentrated ventrally. Contraction of all these muscles will

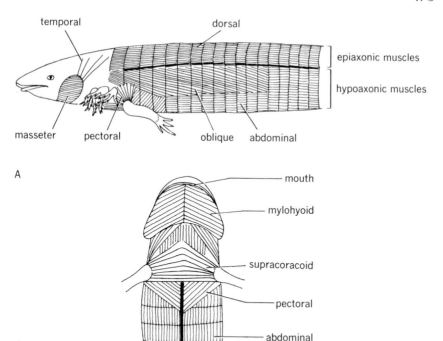

temporal — dorsal

epiaxonic muscles

hypoaxonic muscles

masseter — pectoral — oblique — abdominal

A

mouth

mylohyoid

supracoracoid

pectoral

abdominal

B

FIG. 21.9 Skinned *Necturus* to show the musculature, x 1/2. (A) Lateral. (B) Ventral.

bend the body not laterally but in a dorsoventral plane. The hypo-axonic musculature has only three series, the longitudinal abdominal, external oblique, and transverse. They are no longer concerned in locomotion. Myocommata are no longer visible.

Most reptiles have trunk muscles recognizably similar to those of anurans, but there are complications because of the presence of ribs, which break up the oblique muscles into an involved series of intercostals and other short muscles. Many early amphibians, as well as reptiles, had long ribs, and some had them even in the abdominal region and in the tail (Fig. 17.35). The simple condition of the hypo-axonic musculature of anurans (which have no ribs) and of urodeles (which have very short ones) is therefore likely not to be primitive.

The crocodiles have retained enough of the primitive position of the dorsal and subvertebral muscles to be able to use them for lateral bending of the tail, by means of which they swim. The same was presumably true of the ichthyosaurs.

The change from water to land life is very largely, as we have seen in the history of the limbs, a change from swimming to running, and the muscles become more complex and more important as the limbs become longer and move to the position beneath the body which they have in mammals (p. 83). But in the fast-running mammal much of the propulsive effort comes from a bending and straightening of the back in a vertical plane, especially in the lumbar region. The bending is produced chiefly by the longitudinal abdominal muscles which now run only from the sternum and last pair of ribs to the pubis; their contraction brings the two ends of the vertebral column, and so the fore- and hind-limbs, nearer together. This is a relatively passive movement, not done against much resistance. The reverse movement, which is strongly active and thrusts the animal forward by the resistance of the hind-limbs against the ground, is produced mainly by contraction of the series of long dorsal muscles (longissimus dorsi), which run from the ilium to the transverse processes and metapophyses of the vertebrae and to the ribs. Other fibers, which may be considered as part of the same muscle, run from the posterior to the anterior neural spines. These vertical movements of the backbone are well seen in a running grayhound, and propulsive effort in straightening the back is well known in rowing, although here the fixed point is the arms which hold the oars in the water, and the legs, in the boat, move forward.

The emphasis on vertical instead of lateral bending of the backbone is found in marsupials as well as placentals, which suggests that it was already present in the therapsid reptiles. The general dog-like appearance of many of these supports this deduction. It is therefore not surprising that the two groups of mammals which have become completely aquatic (Sirenia and Cetacea) have retained vertical flexion. They have developed tail fins which are externally very similar to those of fish, but they extend horizontally instead of vertically, and the tail moves up and down in the water not from side to side.

Various small muscles attached to the transverse and other processes of the vertebrae of mammals bring about some lateral bending and also some twisting of the backbone, especially in the neck and tail; the degree of this varies widely. A few mammals, such as American monkeys, the carnivore *Potos* (the kinkajou) and some rodents, have tails which are fully prehensile.

The body of birds is much more rigid than that of mammals, and in accordance with this the muscles of the trunk are smaller and much less important. The thorax is relatively larger and the abdomen shorter; all four series of ventral muscles are present, but the abdominal wall is thin. In the neck, the muscles attached to the vertebrae are very complicated, as would be expected from its great flexibility (p. 332).

In bony fish, the shoulder girdle is rigidly attached to the skull, and there is no interruption of the flank muscles right up to the head. It is possible that the earliest land vertebrates had a similar fixed shoulder girdle (p. 416), but in most, and in all modern forms, it is free from the skull.

Further, it is not, like the hip girdle, articulated with or fused to the back-bone, and in many mammals the two halves of the girdle do not meet the sternum or each other ventrally. Nevertheless, since the girdle is the base for the attachment of the fore-limbs, it must have some rigidity. This is achieved by a special development of the oblique muscles to attach the scapula to other bones. A series of serrate muscles runs upward from the ribs to the scapula, and a rhomboid (sometimes clearly divided into an anterior minor and a posterior major portion) runs downward from the neural spines of the cervical and thoracic vertebrae to the scapula.

These, and some others, sling the shoulder girdle in such a way that, though fairly firm, it can undergo some movement. This is probably important in the bounding gallop of many mammals which land on their fore-feet with what must be a considerable shock. A slightly movable base will be less easily damaged than a rigid one. In man the scapula is capable of some voluntary movement.

In the anterior part of the body, which is never much concerned with locomotion, the form of both epi-axonic and hypo-axonic muscles is different. We have noted in Chapter 19 how the first three head somites give rise to the eyeball muscles. Although they sometimes come from mesenchyme, these muscles are remarkably constant throughout the vertebrates.

In the thorax and neck of fish the ventral muscles are specialized as the hypobranchial musculature. This is well seen in the dissection of the afferent blood system of the dogfish as the large coracomandibular and coracohyoid muscles which run forward from the coracoid to the lower jaw and hyoid respectively, and in the coracobranchial muscles which run between the afferent branchial arteries from the coracoid to the gill arches. In tetrapods similar but much smaller muscles run from the sternum or shoulder girdle to the hyoid and to the cartilages of the larynx, which are all that is left of the branchial skeleton. Some hypobranchial muscles are also incorporated in the tongue. The innervation of all these muscles from the ninth and tenth cranial nerves is witness to their derivation from the posterior somites of the head.

The muscles of the diaphragm of mammals are entirely new in position, but they may represent part of the ventral abdominal system. Since the phrenic nerve which innervates them is a spinal nerve from the neck, it is possible that they originated much further forward and moved back to keep place with the lungs, which also begin anteriorly in the pharynx, and move backward.

In some tetrapods the appendicular muscles arise, as in fishes, from the myotomes, but in others they are formed as condensations in mesenchyme. Whenever, in both fishes and tetrapods, the segmental arrangement is clear, the number of spinal nerves that go into the limb to form the brachial plexus (p. 260) corresponds. Where, therefore, the muscles of the limb show no obvious segmentation, we may take it that the number of nerves contributing to the plexus indicates the number of segments notionally involved. Sometimes a few myotomes and nerves at the anterior and posterior edge of the limb begin to take part in its formation, and then withdraw.

In the embryos of tetrapods the limb muscles appear, like those of fish, as a dorsal series above the skeleton, and a ventral series below, but in the adult this simple relationship is lost. This is partly because the muscles become split into a very complicated arrangement, so that they completely envelop at least the more proximal parts of the skeleton, and partly because, with rotation of the limb to come beneath the body, the simple dorsal and ventral distinctions are no longer appropriate. In general, the dorsal muscles are represented by those that straighten the limb, which are called extensors, the ventral ones by those that bend it, called flexors.

The number of separate muscles in each tetrapod limb is high, but since authors sometimes differ in deciding whether a complex muscle is one that is partly divided, or two that are associated together, exact numbers cannot be given. In the leg of a frog there are twenty to thirty, of a bird about forty, and man about sixty. The corresponding approximate numbers for the fore-limb are twelve, fifty, and sixty. There is much variation within a class, and sometimes within quite small taxonomic divisions, so that it is not surprising that homologies are difficult. Even muscles that have been given the same name, because of their obvious similarities in position and function, may not be considered homologous by those who have studied them closely. This is so, for instance, of the calf muscle or gastrocnemius. In spite of this, it is possible to trace something of a functional evolution of the limb muscles throughout the tetrapods, and especially in the amniotes.

The shoulder of a mud puppy, skinned and seen from the side, shows a fan of six muscles running from the shoulder girdle and dorsal fascia to the humerus (Fig. 21.9A). Contraction of these in turn will obviously lift the limb, draw it forward, and then backward again, which is the way the animal walks. The humerus is pulled downward by two muscles, the supracoracoid and the pectoral, running from the sternum to the lower surface of the humerus (Fig. 21.9B).

In anurans and amniotes the simple fan-shaped arrangement of the dorsal muscles is lost, but the last spoke of the fan is perhaps represented by the lateral dorsal (latissisus dorsi), a broad muscle in frogs, reptiles, birds, and mammals. In reptiles it has its origin not from the skeleton but from the tendinous fascia covering the back. In mammals it arises from the neural spines of thoracic and lumbar vertebrae and from the fascia, and in birds from the cervical and thoracic vertebrae and sometimes from the ribs. Other muscles, whose relationship to the urodele condition is obscure, run from the scapula to the humerus. In a tetrapod, with its limbs beneath the body, all they have to do is swing the fore-leg backward and forward.

The largest of the ventral muscles, the pectoral, has had an interesting history. In primitive four-footed animals it is one of the chief muscles of locomotion, its contraction pulling the fore-limb downward, and usually somewhat backward. In the typical mammals, which have brought the limbs to a position below the body, the pectoral muscle is divided into several parts, most of which pull the limb backward in walking (or, what comes to the same thing, pull the body forward on the limb, the foot remaining fixed in contact with the ground). In the cat the smallest and most anterior of its five parts pulls the humerus inward, so that the animal can strike in this direction with its paw. In man it is a large muscle running out from the sternum to the humerus. Its lower border runs just posterior to the nipple, and then makes the anterior border of the armpit. Its normal contraction pulls the arm inward and to the front, the socket of the humerus being prevented from moving by the clavicle; if the arm is raised above the head, contraction of the pectoral will pull it down again, a motion similar to that of the fore-limb of an ordinary mammal in walking.

In birds the pectoral is a very large muscle, the two together making in some hummingbirds as much as one-third of the weight of the whole body. It pulls the wing downward, thus giving it its effective stroke, but also slightly forward. Its large size has necessitated the development of the high ridge or carina on the sternum (p. 344) for its origin.

Comparable functional changes have taken place in the evolution of the hind limb. In reptiles a large part of the propulsive movement of the leg comes from two caudofemoral muscles, which have their origin on the caudal vertebrae and insert on the femur, so that they pull the limb backward when they contract. These muscles are present but much reduced in some mammals (in the cat they run from the second and third caudal vertebrae to insert on the patella), and they are absent from others, such as man and rabbit. They are functionally replaced in all mammals by the large gluteal muscles, running from the ilium to the femur. These may be a development of the much smaller iliofemorals of reptiles, or they may be a new evolution. In man the propulsive thrust comes mainly from muscles lower down the limb, especially those of the calf, which tend to straighten the ankle and so push forward with the foot. The gluteal muscles are, however, proportionately larger than ever, and make the buttocks. Their function now is largely to hold the legs straight so that the man does not fall over.

In birds also, which have only a few caudal vertebrae, the caudofemoral muscles are reduced and may be absent. There are several muscles called gluteals, but their homology with those of mammals is not certain. They may be developments of the iliofemorals of reptiles.

In the limbs the tendons, especially those at the insertion, are more important than in the trunk. This enables the active part of the muscle to be placed at a distance from the part which it moves, so that it can pull on a distal bone just as the showman pulls the strings of his puppets to manipulate their limbs. The extreme is perhaps shown by the ambiens, a muscle present in many birds (but not the song birds, woodpeckers, and some others), but otherwise known only, doubtfully, in crocodiles. Its origin is the pectineal process of the pelvic girdle, and it runs down the inside front edge of the thigh to the knee, where its tendon begins, and then runs round the outside of the leg to a position behind the tibia (Fig. 21.10). Here the white fibers of the tendon become once more sur- rounded with muscle fibers, which make up what are generally considered

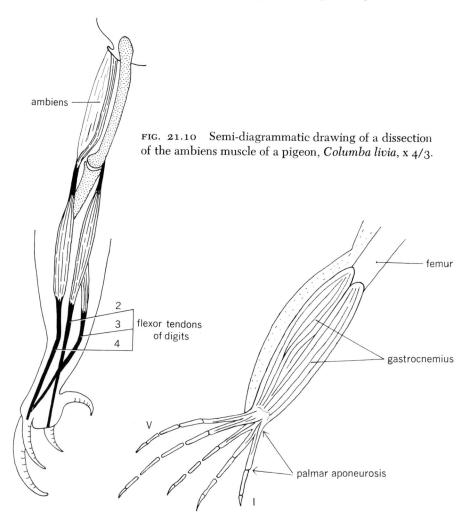

FIG. 21.10 Semi-diagrammatic drawing of a dissection of the ambiens muscle of a pigeon, *Columba livia*, x 4/3.

FIG. 21.11 Gastrocnemius muscle of a lizard, *Lacerta viridis*, x 3/2. Digits have been turned so that their ventral surface is shown.

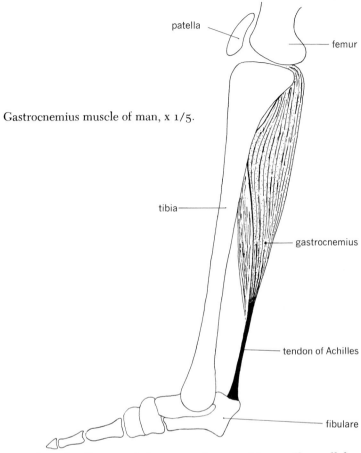

patella

femur

FIG. 21.12   Gastrocnemius muscle of man, x 1/5.

tibia

gastrocnemius

tendon of Achilles

fibulare

as separate muscles, the flexors of the toes; they could equally well be considered as distal parts of the ambiens, which would then be a digastric muscle. However that may be, their tendons run round the heel to be inserted on the phalanges of the digits in such a way that their contraction bends the toes. But contraction of the ambiens must also do this, so that the activity of a muscle which is attached to the pelvic girdle here moves the extreme distal end of the limb.

The tendons of the limb muscles of birds are in general long, so that there is little flesh on the radius and ulna or on the tibiotarsus, presumably because it is advantageous for a flying animal to have its weight concentrated. Those of mammals are not so long, but are more marked than those of reptiles or amphibians. An interesting difference between the system in mammals and reptiles is shown by the gastrocnemius. That of a lizard (Fig. 21.11) ends distally in a flat aponeurosis which inserts on the toes. That of mammals (Fig. 21.12) has a single long tendon which inserts on the projecting fibulare or heel. (The name "tendon of Achilles"

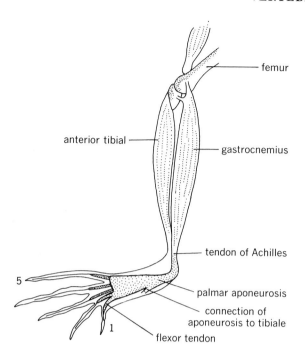

FIG. 21.13   Gastrocnemius muscle of a frog, *Rana temporaria*, x 1. Digits have been turned so that their ventral surface is shown.

for this structure, which is very prominent in man, comes from the story that Achilles' mother Thetis, believing that her son would never die if he was dipped in the river Styx, immersed him, but held him by this tendon so as not to wet her hand; he was afterward wounded in the heel at the Siege of Troy, and died). The frog, with its peculiar way of moving by jumping, has also evolved a strong Achilles' tendon and a prominent heel (Fig. 21.13).

We have already seen that the visceral muscles in the branchial region are unusual in being striped. They differ also from other visceral muscles in being attached to the skeleton, though it is perhaps notable that the gill elements which they join are themselves different from other cartilages in being derived from epiblast (the neural crest) and not from mesoblast.

The muscles of the functional gill arches, better developed in elasmobranchs than in teleosts (Fig. 21.14), assist in breathing by moving the separate elements of the skeleton on each other like a trellis-work or lazy-tongs. They are mostly absent from tetrapods, but have perhaps given rise to some muscles of the shoulder and neck, including the trapezius, which runs (in mammals) from the occiput and anterior vertebrae to the clavicle and the spine of the scapula, and is used in shrugging the shoulders.

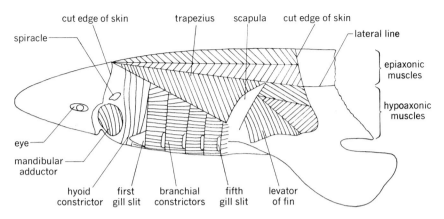

FIG. 21.14 Slightly diagrammatic drawing of a superficial dissection of the branchial muscles of *Squalus acanthias*, x 2/3.

The large superficial constrictor of the hyoid, which in sharks runs down from the dorsal to the ventral elements of the arch just beneath the skin (although most of the muscle fibers do not reach the cartilages) (Fig. 21.14), is represented by two types of muscle in tetrapods. In reptiles there is a muscle, badly called the sphincter of the neck, in much the same position (Fig. 21.15), but in mammals the fibers have moved forward to become the series of superficial muscles by which the lips, cheeks, and other parts of the face can be moved.

Another element of the hyoid musculature of fishes becomes the posterior belly of the digastric muscle of tetrapods (Fig. 21.16), which is in much the same position as the hyomandibular cartilage where it slings the jaw of sharks. Most of the jaw muscles of tetrapods may be presumed to have come from those of the mandibular arch of fishes, but they are more

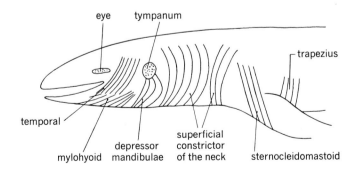

FIG. 21.15 Slightly diagrammatic drawing of a superficial dissection of the head of a lizard, *Lacerta viridis*, to show the muscles, x 2.

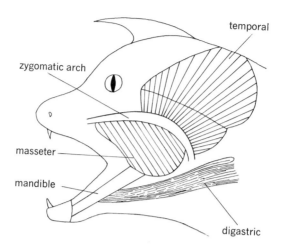

temporal

zygomatic arch

masseter

mandible

digastric

FIG. 21.16 Slightly diagrammatic drawing of a dissection of the main jaw muscles of a cat, x 2/3.

varied and better developed. We have already seen their importance in connection with the evolution of the skull of reptiles. The simple adductor muscle of fishes becomes the temporal and pterygoid muscle of reptiles, and in mammals the former is divided into the temporal in the strict sense and the masseter, which has its origin on the zygomatic arch, all that is left of the outer wall of the skull of reptiles. The masseter is especially large in rodents, where it is the chief agent in the gnawing action of the jaw.

Electric Organs

Electric organs are found in a number of fishes, and are best developed in *Torpedo ocellata* (the torpedo or electric ray) (Fig. 21.17), *Gymnotus* (= *Electrophorus*) *electricus* (the electric eel), and *Malopterurus electricus* (the electric catfish). In the last the organs are modified skin glands, but in all the other fish that have been examined they are derived from striped muscle, and so may conveniently be dealt with here. In most, the electric organs are derived from the muscle fibers, but in *Torpedo* and in the smaller organs of species of *Raia* they are probably derived from the motor end plates. Most of the electric fish are not closely related to each other, so that the organs must have evolved several times. In all cases the principle is the same; blocks or discs of tissue, called electroplaxes, are so arranged that small voltages (which may be regarded as no different from the potential differences across the membranes of other organs, especially nerve and muscle) are summed, like those of electric batteries, in series. By this means voltages sometimes as high as three hundred can be produced.

The function of electric organs is not very clear. In some species they may be defensive (*Gymnotus*, for example, gives out strong intermittent shocks when it is handled), but in others, especially those which produce only low voltages, they seem to be used to enable the fish to determine the position of conductors, including the bodies of other fish, which distort its electric field. In *Gymnarchus* from West Africa those distortions are apparently picked up by specially modified lateral line organs. It is misleading to speak of this type of detection as radar, which depends on the reflection of electromagnetic waves.

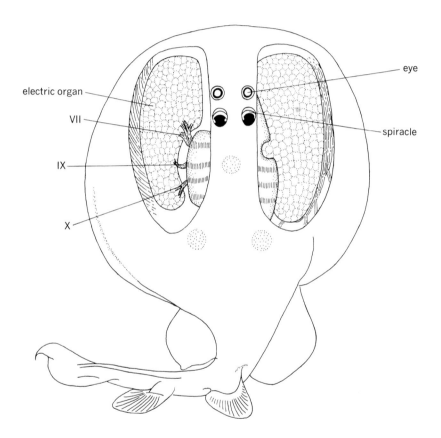

FIG. 21.17 Superficial dissection of the electric ray, *Torpedo ocellata*, to show the electric organs, x 1/2. VII to X, cranial nerves.

Glossary

UNTIL the seventeenth century almost all scientific books were written in Latin, and even in the second half of the eighteenth century, some, such as the classifications of Linnaeus, were in that language. The early anatomists described many of the bones, nerves, and other parts of the body, and their Latin names have survived until the present day. Although Latin in form, they are often derived from the Greek, and so a little understanding of both languages is helpful to the biologist.

Latin, like German, is an inflected language; the function of a noun in a sentence is not shown, as it is in English, by its position, but by its ending, which indicates what is called its case. Fortunately the biologist need not worry about most of these cases, but he should be able to recognize the nominative singular (the ordinary form of the word), the nominative plural, and the genitive (or possessive) of both singular and plural. There are five main systems of case endings, or declensions, complicated by three genders (masculine, feminine, and neuter, but having little to do with sex) and many irregular forms. The nominative singular is often shorter than the other cases, and it is usually from these longer forms that the corresponding adjective is formed in English: for example, cervical, to do with the neck, from *cervicis*, genitive singular of *cervix*, a neck.

In general, first declension nouns are feminine and end in -*a* in the nominative singular. The four forms we are interested in may be illustrated by: nominative singular *vena*, a vein; genitive singular, *venae*; nominative plural, *venae*; genitive plural, *venarum*.

Most second declension nouns are masculine and end in -*us*. Our four forms are shown by: *musculus*, a muscle[1]; *musculi*; *musculi*; *musculorum*. Neuter nouns, ending in -*um*, are different in the nominative plural: *atrium*, a courtyard; *atrii*; *atria*; *atriorum*.

The third declension is more complicated, and has several sub-systems, most of which involve a lengthening of the word from the nominative singular. Examples are: MASCULINE, *pes*, a foot; *pedis*; *pedes*; *pedum*—FEMININE, *cervix*, a neck; *cervicis*; *cervices*; *cervicum*—NEUTER, *vas*, a vessel; *vasis*; *vasa*; *vasorum*.

---

[1] This meaning of the word is not found in classical Latin.

The fourth declension is the most confusing to students, because many of its nouns end in *-us*, like those of the second; in the nominative plural they change their pronunciation but not their spelling, the *u* becoming long and pronounced *oo*. For example, *ductus*, a duct; *ductus; ductus; ductum.* Neuter nouns of this declension end in *-u:* for example, *cornu*, a horn; *cornus; cornua; cornuum.*

Fifth declension nouns are mostly feminine and end in *-es*. The chief point about them is that the nominative plural is the same as the nominative singular. An example is *species; speciei; species; specierum.*

Adjectives are declined like nouns of the first and second declensions, and must agree with their nouns in gender as well as case: *vas deferens* becomes in the plural *vasa deferentia; vena cava* becomes *venae cavae.*

Many of the early anatomical terms consisted of a noun followed by an adjective. This is especially true of muscles, as in *musculus pectoralis*, the pectoral muscle. It applies also to many bones: *os coracoideum*, the coracoid bone. It is now customary to use many of these adjectives by themselves, as if they were nouns. Thus we may speak of the coracoid without ambiguity.

For some structures there were alternative names, as *scapula*, or *os scapulare*. When this was so, there are usually two forms in English, one for the noun and another for the adjective: scapula, the shoulder blade; scapular cartilage.

Blood vessels usually retain the double form, partly by custom, as in *sinus venosus*, and partly because it is necessary to distinguish between arteries and veins, for example, subclavian artery; subclavian vein.

The names of arteries and veins are generally anglicized, those of bones sometimes are, those of muscles and nerves are more often left in the Latin forms. In this book, wherever possible, the names of all parts of the body have been anglicized, but sometimes there is no recognized English form and the Latin has been retained, e.g. *sinus venosus.*

Some difficulty arises through the transliteration of Greek, which had a slightly different alphabet from ours. When the Greek gamma ($\gamma = g$) came before another gamma, or before a consonant of the same type of sound (kappa, $\kappa = k$; chi, $\chi = ch$; xi, $\xi = x$;) it had the same pronunciation as the *n* in English *ng* or *nk*, and so is transliterated as *n*, e.g. ganglion, pharynx. Greek kappa ($\kappa = k$) always appears in Latin (whose alphabet had no *k*) as *c;* in English words it is most often represented by *c*, but sometimes by *k*, or both spellings may co-exist, e.g. leucocyte, leukocyte(but never leukokyte, although the second element of the word also comes from a Greek word with kappa).

The Greek rho ($\rho = r$) at the beginning of a word was always aspirated, and is shown as *rh*. When a word of this form appeared as the second half of a compound word, the Greeks doubled the *rho*. The early scientists who took over such words in a Latin or an English form followed this custom, but unfortunately inserted an unnecessary and unpronounced *h*, giving such ugly spellings as platyrrhine.

The sounds of *ch, dz, ks, ph* (= f), *ps*, and *th* are represented by single letters in the Greek alphabet. The *dz* sound is written in English as *z, ks* as *x*, but otherwise the double letters are used.

Long and short *e* and long and short *o* have different symbols in Greek. In the glossary the long forms are indicated by a bar above the letter ($\bar{e}$, $\bar{o}$), the short forms being unmarked. The Greek upsilon (v) is written in the glossary as *u*, but in Latin words, and those derived from the Latin, or of Latinized form, it usually appears as *y*, e.g. pterodactyl.

Diphthongs need special care. Greek *ai* becomes Latin *ae*, e.g. haemorrhagia, and English *e*, e.g. hemorrhage. In British usage *ae* tends to be retained in the English spelling of the more recently introduced words.

Greek *ei* generally becomes *i* in Latin, and this spelling is used also in English. Some authors, however, have retained the Greek spelling in made-up words, even though they are of Latin form. Thus cheiroptergyium (from Gk. *cheir*, a hand and *pterugion*, a wing or fin) and chiropterygium are both used, but since the word is intended to be Latin the second form is to be preferred. Greek *eidos*, like, when used as a suffix becomes -*oid*, e.g. sesamoid. This is because the word was used as a suffix in Greek, and an *o* was usually inserted between the main part of the word and the termination.

In general Greek *oi* becomes Latin *oe*, and when the word is fully assimilated into English it is written *e*. E.g. *Coelacanthus*, (a fish with a hollow spine), and English heterocelous (applied to a vertebra hollow in two directions). British usage retains *oe* more often than American. Greek *ou* becomes *u* in Latin. English words that come direct from the Greek, or through French, retain the diphthong, e.g. acoustic. When a Latin form is used the correct spelling has *u*, e.g. acousticolateral, but acusticolateralis.

The derivations of words can be found in any good dictionary. The glossary that follows is intended to help the student to recognize the most frequently used roots, so that he can understand new combinations when he meets them. Prefixes and suffixes are especially important. Some biological words are taken direct from the Latin (*vena*, a vein); others are Latin words used in a new sense (*musculus*, which in classical Latin meant a little mouse, was first used in its present sense in 1533). Still others are Greek words used in a Latinized form (*pterygium*, for Greek *pterugion*, a wing). Most are compound inventions from one or more roots, sometimes learned, sometimes barbarous (gene, presumably from Greek *genein*, to produce). The glossary contains chiefly these roots and words whose meaning is not obvious. Words taken directly from the Latin, with the same spelling and meaning, are not listed. The genitive singular as well as the nominative is given when it helps to explain the root. One or

two examples of words in which the prefixes or combining forms are used
are generally given.

a-   Gk., without (acelous, hollow; asymmetry)

ab-   L., from (abducent, leading away from)

acetabulum   L., a cup for holding vinegar (cf. acetic acid)

acro-   Gk. *akros,* highest (acrodont)

actino-   Gk. *actis,* a ray (Actinopterygii)

acoustic   Gk. *akoustikos,* having to do with hearing

ad-   L., to (adductor, drawing one thing (e.g. a limb) toward another (e.g.
      the body). Before a consonant the *d* may be dropped and the initial con-
      sonant doubled, e.g. afferent, carrying toward.

amphi-   Gk., on both sides (amphicelous)

an-, ana-   Gk., up, back, again (anapophysis)

an-   Gk. *a,* without, before a vowel (Anura)

andro-   Gk. *anēr, andros,* man as opposed to woman (androgen)

apo-   Gk., off, away (zygapopophysis. 'Aponeurosis' means 'a changing into a
      tendon', and so is applied to the flat sheet of connective tissue at the
      end of many muscles)

-apsid   Gk. *apsis,* the mesh of a net, an arch (diapsid)

arch- or **archi-**   Gk., chief (Archosauria). It has also been barbarously used to
      mean primitive, e.g. archenteron, archinephros. The correct Greek prefix
      for this would be *archaio,* which becomes *archaeo-* or *archeo-,* as in
      Archaeopteryx, literally the first wing, and so the first bird.

arti-   L. *articulus,* a little joint (articular)

atlas   The first cervical vertebra, because this holds the head as Atlas was
      supposed to hold the world on his shoulders

atrium   L., the courtyard of a house, and so in anatomy the space into which
      vessels or ducts open

auricle   L. *auriculum,* a little ear. The auricle of the heart is so called because
      of its fancied resemblance to the ear flap or pinna.

auto-   Gk. *autos,* self (autonomic nervous system)

basi-   An English prefix derived from the noun base. Its meaning in compound
      words is not always obvious.   (basibranchial, the most ventral of the
      cartilages of the branchial skeleton; basidorsal, the usually most im-
      portant dorsal cartilaginous element of the vertebra; basipterygium, the
      proximal element of the fin skeleton)

bi-   L., prefix having the sense of two, or twice (biceps, a muscle with two
      heads). The corresponding Greek prefix, which should be used for words
      of Greek origin, is *di-.*

blast-, -blast   Gk. *blastos,* a sprout or sucker (of a plant); hence an embryo (of
      animals). In zoology the prefix and suffix always have reference to a type
      of embryo or embryonic structure (blastula, literally a little embryo;
      blastocele, epiblast).

brachial L. *brachium,* the arm and especially forearm. Used of anything, such as a nerve or artery, that runs from or to the forelimb.

brachy- Gk. *brachus,* short (brachydont)

branchi- Gk. *braggion,* a gill (*Branchiostoma*)

buccal L. *bucca.* This word is usually translated 'cheek,' but from the examples given in Lewis and Short's Latin Dictionary it appears to have been the exact equivalent of what zoologists call the buccal cavity, for which there is no single unambiguous English word.

bulbus L., a bulb; hence anything bulb-shaped (bulbus arteriosus)

bulla L., a bubble; hence anything more or less spherical in shape, especially when the shape is achieved by the expansion of something previously flat (tympanic bulla)

bursa Late L., a purse, from a Greek word of the same form meaning the hide of an animal, and so something made of leather. In zoology it is used for anything purse-shaped (bursa of Fabricius).

calamus Gk. *kalamos,* a reed. The stem of a feather, so called because, like that of a reed, it is hollow but partly filled with a dead pith.

callous L. *callus,* the thick layer of skin, the horny layer of the epidermis; hence anything resembling this (callous body, or corpus callosum)

canine L. *canis,* a dog

capillary L. *capilla,* a hair

capitulum L. diminutive of *caput,* a head

cardiac Gk. *kardia,* the heart

cardinal L. *cardo,* a hinge; hence something important

carina L., the keel of a ship

carn- L. *carnem,* flesh (carnassial, carnivorous)

carotid Gk. *karoun,* to stupefy. Hence carotid arteries, because compression of them causes stupor. (There are no carotid veins.)

carpo- Gk. *karpos,* wrist

cata- Gk. *kata,* down; opposite of *ana-* (catarrhine, descriptive of Primates which have the nostrils directed downward)

caudal L. *cauda,* tail

cav- L. *cavus,* hollow (caval)

cecum L. *caecum,* the neuter form of the adjective meaning blind. Originally intestinum caecum, the blind gut of man, and then any comparable opening from the alimentary canal of other animals.

celiac Gk. *koilia,* belly (celiac artery)

celo-, -cele Gk. *koilos,* hollow (celom, nephrocele)

cephalic Gk. *kephalē,* head

cerato- Gk. *keras,* horn (ceratobranchial)

-cercal Gk. *kerkos,* a tail (strictly of a mammal) (diphycercal)

cerebrum L., brain

cerebellum L. dim. of *cerebrum*

cervical L. *cervix*, neck. It is used also of neck-like parts of organs (the cervix of the uterus).

cheiro- or **chiro-** Gk. *cheir*, a hand (chiropterygium)

chiasma Anything shaped like the Greek letter chi (X) (especially optic chiasma)

chondr· Gk. *chondros*, cartilage (chondrocranium)

chorda- Gk. *chordē* and L. *chorda*. Both these words originally meant the guts of an animal, especially as used for food (tripe), but also for pieces of gut used for other purposes, for example, the string of a musical instrument. From this latter usage we get the English word *cord*. The *ch* is retained in compound words derived from the Greek, e.g. notochord. As a prefix, *chorda-* generally implies something to do with the notochord (chordamesoderm).

choroid From the Greek *chorion*, the membrane that encloses the fetus in the womb. Used of any membrane that, like the chorion, is highly vascular.

chromato- -chrome Gk. *chrōma*, color (chromatophore, lipochrome)

cilium, ciliary L. *cilium*, an eyelid; taken also to mean an eyelash

clavicle L. *clavicula*, a little key; hence the collar bone

cleidoic Gk. *kleis*, a bolt or key for closing a door; hence cleidoic=shut off

cleithrum Gk. *kleithron*, a bar for closing a door (a variant of the last); hence a bar-shaped bone. The Latin spelling should be *clithrum*.

cloaca L., a sewer

coccyx L., a cuckoo. The terminal vertebrae in man were so called because they were thought to resemble the bill of that bird.

cochlea L. *cochlea*, a snail. *Coclea* is the more usual spelling in Latin.

collagen Gk. *kolla*, glue

-comma Gk. *komma*, pl. *kommata*, a separated piece of something, or the division between pieces (myocomma)

conus L., a cone; hence anything cone-shaped (conus arteriosus)

copro- Gk. *kopros*, dung (coprodeum)

coracoid Gk. *korax*, a crow or raven. The coracoid process of the human shoulder girdle was so called because of its fancied resemblance to the head of that bird; hence coracoid bone

coronoid Gk. *korōnē*, a crow. It seems to be impossible to distinguish clearly between the meanings of this word and the last. Coronoid, like coracoid, was originally applied to a process resembling the head of a bird, but now refers especially to the uppermost of the three processes at the posterior end of the mammalian lower jaw, and to the bones corresponding to it in position, but not homology, in other vertebrates.

corpus, pl. corpora L., body (corpus callosum, corpora lutea)

cosmine Gk. *kosmein*, to adorn

costal L. *costa*, a rib

cranial Gk. *kranion*, the skull

cribri- L. *cribrum*, a sieve (cribriform)

cricoid Gk. *krikos*, a ring

crista L., a crest or cock's comb; hence a ridge

cten- Gk. *kteis*, a comb (ctenoid scale)

cupule L. *cupula*, a little cask; hence a cup

cuneiform L. *cuneus*, a wedge

cyclo- Gk. *kuklos*, a ring or circle (cyclostome)

cyno- Gk. *kuōn, kunos*, a dog (cynodont)

-dactyl Gk. *dactulos*, a finger (pentadactyl)

dendr- Gk. *dendron*, a tree (dendron, dendrite)

dent- L. *dens*, a tooth (dentition)

derm-, -dermis Gk. *derma*, skin (dermatome, epidermis)

di- Gk., prefix having the sense of two or twice (diapsid)

dia- Gk., through (diastema, a space between)

diplo- Gk., double (*Diplodocus*)

diphy- Gk., double (diphycercal)

-dont See -odont

ductus L., a leading, hence a tube or pipe carrying liquid (ductus arteriosus)

dura Feminine of L. *durus*, hard (dura mater, the harder of two coverings of the brain)

e- See **ex-** of which it is a shortened form

ecto- Gk., outside (ectoderm)

elasmo- Gk. *elasma*, a sheet of metal beaten thin; hence a flat plate (elasmobranch)

endo- ⎱
ento- ⎰ Gk., within (endodermis, entocuneiform)

epi- Gk., upon or above (epi-axonic)

erythro- Gk. *eruthros*, red (erythrocyte)

estro- Gk. *oistros*, a gadfly or its sting, and hence frenzy and the period of female sexual desire. In compounds it is used for anything connected with this. (Estrogen)

ethm- Gk. *ēthmos*, a sieve (ethmoid)

eu- Gk. adverb, well. In compounds it generally implies the more nearly perfect of two sets of things (Eutheria).

eury- Gk., wide (Euryapsida)

ex- L., out of; hence without. Before consonants the *x* is usually dropped, but the initial consonant of the next element may be doubled (efferent, carrying away).

exo- Gk., outside (exoskeleton) *Exo*=*ecto*.

extra- L., on the outside (extracellular)

fascia L. *fascia*, a strap or bandage; hence a flat sheet of fibrous tissue

fenestra L. *fenestra*, a window (both words originally meant a mere opening in a wall, without glass)

-fer-, -fer L. *ferre*, to carry (afferent, carrying to)

fibula   L., a brooch

follicle   L. *folliculus,* a small bag

fontanelle   Fr., a little fountain

foramen   L., a hole

-form   L. *forma,* form or shape (caniniform)

fossa   L., a ditch; hence fossa, a channel in a skull, fossil, fossorial

fovea   L., a pit

frontal   L. *frons,* the forehead

fundus   L., bottom

ganglion   Gk., originally a tumor under the skin, but used by Galen (c. A.D. 150) in its present sense

gan-   Gk. *ganos,* brightness (ganoid scales, from their appearance)

gastr-   Gk. *gastēr,* the belly (gastrula)

gen- and **-gen**   Gk. *genea,* race or family, or L. *generare,* to beget (genital, androgen)

geo-   Gk. *gē,* the earth

glen-   Gk. *glēnē,* the eyeball, but used by Galen for the socket of a joint (glenoid cavity, originally applied to any shallow socket, but now exclusively for that which takes the head of the humerus)

gli- -glia   Gk. *glia,* glue (glial, neuroglia)

glom-   L. *glomus,* ball (glomerulus)

glosso-, -glossal, -glottis   Gk. *glōssa* or *glōtta,* tongue (glossopharyngeal, hypoglossal, epiglottis)

gluc-   Gk. *glukus,* sweet (glucose)

gnatho-   Gk. *gnathos,* the jaw, usually the upper jaw (gnathostome)

gon-, -gon   Gk. *gonē,* offspring (gonad, glucagon)

-grade   L. *gradi,* to walk (plantigrade)

gul-   L. *gula,* the throat (gular)

gymn-   Gk. *gumnos,* naked (Gymnophiona)

hamate   L. *hama,* hook

helico-   Gk. *helix,* twisted or spiral (helicotrema)

hem-   Gk. *haima,* blood (hemal)

hemi-   Gk. *hēmi-,* half (hemibranch)

hepato-   Gk. *hēpar,* the liver (hepatoenteric)

hetero-   Gk. *heteros,* the other, one of two, and hence as a prefix, odd, uneven, different, the opposite of *homo-* (heterocelous)

holo-   Gk. *holos,* whole (holonephric)

homeo-   Gk. *homoios,* similar (homeothermal)

homo-   Gk. *homos,* the same (homocercal)

hyo-   Gk. *huo-eides,* shaped like the letter upsilon (*v*) (the hyoid bone, from its shape)

hyper-   Gk. *huper,* over, above (hyperdactyly)

hypo- Gk. *hupo,* under, beneath (hypoblast)

hypso- Gk. *hupsi,* on high, aloft (hypsodont)

ichthy- Gk. *ichthus,* a fish (ichthyopterygium)

il- L. *ilia,* nearly always used in this plural form (of which the singular was *ile,* or *ilium,* and later *ileum*), meant the flanks, or sides of the body below the ribs, and so by transference the entrails that are between these. Confusingly, the spelling with *i* has come to be applied to a bone of the pelvic girdle (ilium, adjectival prefix *ilio-*) and that with *e* to a part of the small intestine (ileum, adjectival prefix *ileo-*).

in- L., not (innominate, unnamed)

incus L. *incus,* an anvil

infra- L. *infra,* below (infraorbital)

inter- L. *inter,* between (interdorsal)

intero- L., interior, inner (interoceptive)

iso- Gk. *isos,* equal to (isocercal)

iter L., a way (*iter a tertio ad quartum ventriculum,* the passage or way from the third to the fourth ventricle of the brain)

jugal L. *jugum,* a crossbeam

jugular L. *jugulum,* the collar bone; by transference the throat above this

keratin Gk. *keras,* horn

kinetism Gk. *kinēsis,* movement

lab- L. *labium,* a lip (labial)

lacrimal L. *lacrima,* a tear (often incorrectly spelled lacrymal or lachrymal)

lagena L., a large flask

-lemma Gk. *lemma,* a skin or husk (neurilemma)

leuco- or **leuko-** Gk. *leukos,* white (leukocyte)

levator L., one who lifts; applied to muscles which raise something

lieno- L. *lien,* the spleen (lienogastric)

ling- L. *lingua,* tongue (lingual)

lipo- Gk. *lipos,* fat (lipochrome)

lith- Gk. *lithos,* stone (otolith)

lopho- Gk. *lophos,* a crest or ridge (lophodont)

lumbar L. *lumbus,* loin

lumen L., light, and hence an opening

lut- L. *luteus,* yellow (corpora lutea)

lymph L. *lympha,* clear water

macro- Gk. *makros,* large (*Macropus*)

macula L., a spot

magnus, -a, -um L., large

malar L. *mala,* the upper jaw

malleus L., a hammer

maxilla   L., originally the lower jaw, then both jaws, now the bone of the upper jaw

marsup-   Gk. *marsupion*, L. *marsupium*, a pouch

meatus   L., a way (external auditory meatus)

mediastinum   L. *mediastinus* (mod. L. neuter of med. L. *mediastinus*, medial after cl. L. *mediastinus*, inferior servant

medulla   L., the marrow of bones or the pith of plants

meg-   Gk. *megas*, great (megamere)

melan-   Gk. *melas, melanos*, black (melanocyte)

ment-   L. *mentum*, the chin (mentomeckelian)

-mere   Gk. *meros*, a part (myomere)

mes-, meso-   Gk. *mesos*, middle (mesonephros)

meta-   Gk. *meta*, between or after (metanephros)

micro-   Gk. *mikros*, small (microcyte)

monimo-   Gk. *monimos*, steady or stationary (monimostyly)

mon, mono-   Gk. *monos*, alone, only, single (monophyodonty)

morpho-   Gk. *morphē*, form or shape (morphogenesis)

morula   L. dim. of *morum*, a mulberry

motor   L., a mover

multi-   L. *multus*, many (Multituberculata)

muscle   L. *musculus*, a little mouse. The resemblance is somewhat fanciful.

myel-   Gk. *muelos*, marrow (myelencephalon)

myo-   Gk. *mus*, a mouse; hence a muscle (myomere)

neo-   Gk. *neos*, new (neopallium)

nephr-   Gk. *nephros*, a kidney (nephrotome). Nephridium is a little kidney.

neur-   From the Greek *neuron*. This word meant a nerve, and most of the English words derived from it have to do with nerves or nervous tissue (neuron, neuroblast, neural, epineurium). It also meant a tendon, since the Greeks did not distinguish between these two rather similar-looking structures, and this sense is retained in aponeurosis.

-nomic   Gk. *nomos*, law (autonomic)

noto-   Gk. *nōton*, the back of a man or animal (notochord)

nuchal   From the Arabic; originally applied to the spinal cord and then to the nape of the neck

ob- o-   L., against. Before a consonant the *b* may be dropped and the consonant doubled. (occiput, literally against the head)

oculo-   L. *oculus*, eye (oculomotor)

odont-, -odont   Gk. *odous, odontos*, a tooth (odontoid, lophodont)

-oid   Gk. *eidos*, like

omni-   L. *omnis*, all (omnivore)

omo-   Gk. *omos*, the shoulder, including the upper arm (omosternum)

onto- Gk. *ontos*, being (participle). Generally implies the self or individual as opposed to the race or group, for example, ontogeny

oo- Gk. *ōon*, egg. It is pronounced as two syllables (oocyte).

ophthalm- Gk. *ophthalmos*, the eye (superficial ophthalmic nerve)

opisth- Gk. *opisthios*, hind, belonging to the rear part (opisthonephros)

or- L. *os, oris*, the mouth (oral)

ornith- Gk. *ornis, ornithos*, bird (Ornithischia)

ortho- Gk. *orthos*, straight, right (orthosympathetic)

ossicle L. *ossiculus*, dim. of *os*, bone

ost- Gk. *osteon*, bone (Osteichthyes)

ostario- Gk. dim. of *osteon* (Ostariophysi)

ostraco- Gk. *ostrakon*, an earthen vessel; hence the shell of a snail or tortoise (ostracoderm)

oto- Gk. *ous, ōtos*, ear (otolith)

paleo- Gk. *palaios*, old (paleopallium)

pallium L., a cloak (paleopallium)

para- Gk. *para*, beside. The sense in English compounds is not always clear; usually it means no more than something of much the same sort as the structure indicated by the rest of the word, for example, parathyroid.

parietal L. *paries, parietis*, a wall

pectineal L. *pecten, pectinis*, a comb

pectoral L. *pectus, pectoris*, the breast

penta- Gk. *pente*, five (pentadactyl)

peri- Gk. *peri*, around (pericardium)

perisso- Gk. *perissos*, extraordinary, and so in arithmetic of an odd number (perissodactyl)

-phore Gk. *phoreus*, a bearer or carrier (chromatophore)

phrenic Gk. *phrēn*, the diaphragm

-physis Gk. *phuein*, to produce or grow. The suffix usually implies an outgrowth from something. (hypophysis)

physo- Gk. *phusa*, a bladder (physoclistous)

pia feminine of L. *pius*, dutiful, hence tender (pia mater, the softer of the two coverings of the brain)

plac- Gk. *plax, plakos*, anything flat (placoid)

plant- L. *planta*, the sole of the foot (plantar)

plasmo-, -plasm Gk. *plasma*, something formed or molded (sarcoplasm)

platy- Gk. *platus*, wide (platybasic)

pleur- Gk. *pleuron*, a rib, but generally used in the plural (*pleura*) to mean the side of the body (pleurocentrum). Confusion is caused because pleura has come to mean in anatomy not the sides of the body but the membranes that enclose the lungs.

plexus L., a plaiting

-pod   Gk. *pous, podos*, foot (tetrapod)

portal   L. *porta*, a gate (anterior intestinal portal). The part of the liver where the vein from the intestine enters was called the porta, and this vein was called hepatic portal. By analogy the vein running from the kidney to the liver was called renal portal.

post-   L., behind or after (postfrontal)

pre-   L. *prae*, in front or before (prefrontal)

pro-   Gk., in front or before (procoracoid)

procto-, -proct   Gk. *prōktos*, the anus (proctodeum)

profundus   L., deep

proto-   Gk. *protos*, first or foremost (protocercal)

psalterium   L., a stringed instrument; hence the Book of Psalms. (The psalterium of artiodactyls has leaves like a book.)

pter-, ptero-   Gk. *pteron*, feather, *pterux*, wing (pterodactyl, pterotic, pterygium)

quad-   L. *quadrus*, square, from *quattuor*, four (quadrate)

radi-   L. *radius*, a rod, spoke, or ray (radial)

ramus   L., a branch (ramus communicans)

re-   L., implying again or backward

recept-   L., from the participle of *recipere*, to receive (receptor)

rectum   Neuter of L. *rectus*, straight (The full name of the last part of the alimentary canal is intestinum rectum.)

reticulum   L., a little net

rhabd-   Gk. *rhabdos*, a rod (Rhabdopleura)

rhachis   Gk., the backbone

rheo-   Gk. *rhein*, to flow (rheotaxis)

rhino-, -rhine   Gk. *rhis, rhinos*, the nose (Rhinoceros, platyrrhine)

rhod-   Gk. *rhodon*, a rose (rhodopsin, because of its color)

rhyncho-   Gk. *rhugchos*, the muzzle of a mammal or beak of a bird (Rhynchocephalia)

saccus   L., a sack

sacrum   Neuter of L. *sacer*, sacred (Os sacrum, the sacred bone, so called because of its shape in man)

sagittal   L. *sagitta*, an arrow

salt-   L. *saltare*, to dance; hence, from a style of dancing, to jump (saltatorial)

sarco-   Gk. *sarx, sarkos*, flesh or muscle (sarcolemma)

saur-, -saur   Gk. *sauros*, a lizard (sauropsidan, cotylosaur)

scala   L., a flight of steps, a ladder (scala media)

scler-   Gk. *sklēros*, hard (sclerotome)

sect-, -sect   L., From the participle of L. *secare*, to cut (section)

seleno-   Gk. *selēnē*, the moon (selenodont)

ser-, sero-   L. *serum*, whey; hence a watery liquid

sinus L., a curve or bay; hence used of a large (venous) blood vessel

soma, somato- Gk. *soma, somatos,* the body (somite, somatopleure)

sphen- Gk. *sphen,* a wedge (the sphenoid bone)

splanchno- Gk. *splangchna,* the inward parts of the body, especially the heart, lungs, liver, and kidneys (splanchnopleure)

splenial L. *splenium,* a patch

squamo- L. *squama,* a scale (squamous)

stapes L., a stirrup

stato- Gk. *statos,* standing (statolith)

stego-, -stegial Gk. *stege,* a roof (Stegocephalia)

stereo- Gk. *stereos,* firm or solid (stereocilia, steroid)

sternum Gk. *sternon,* the chest

stomo-, -stome Gk. *stoma, stomatos,* the mouth (stomodeum)

striate L. *stria,* a channel or furrow

sub- (su-, suc-, sup-, sus-) L., under (submucosa)

supra- L., above (supraoccipital)

sym-, syn- Gk. *sun,* with (symphysis, synapse)

tarso- Gk. *tarsos,* the flat of the foot. In anatomy tarsus has come to mean the ankle.

tect-, -tect L. *tectum,* roof (tectorial membrane)

tegument- L. *tegumentum,* a cover (tegumental membrane)

tel-, tele- Gk. *tēle,* far off (telencephalon)

tetra- Shortened form of Greek *tettares,* four (tetrapod)

thalam- Gk. *thalamos,* an inner room (thalamencephalon)

theco- Gk. *thēcē,* a box (thecodont)

ther- Gk. *thēr,* a wild beast. Used in zoology in the sense of a mammal. (Theromorpha)

thyr- Gk. *thureos,* a shield. The thyroid gland was given its name because of its shape in man.

-tome Gk. *tomē,* a cut (sclerotome)

trabecula L., a small beam

trans- L., across

tri- L. and Gk., three (trigeminal)

-trichia Gk. *thrix, trichos,* hair (dermotrichia)

triplo- Gk. *triploos,* triple (triploblastic)

trochlea L., a pulley

tropy- Gk. *tropē,* a turn (tropybasic)

-ula, or -ulus A Latin diminutive (*alula,* a little wing, from *ala,* a wing)

ultimo- L. *ultimus,* furthest, last (ultimobranchial)

unc- L. *uncus,* a hook (unciform)

unguli- L. *unguis,* a fingernail or toenail (unguligrade)

-ural, uro-   Gk. *oura,* tail (hypural, Urochordata)

ur-, uro-   Gk. *ouron,* urine (urogenital)

vagus   L., wandering

vas   L., a vessel or dish

velum   L., a veil

ventr-   L. *venter,* the belly. Ventricle, which was originally a diminutive of this word and was used for the stomach, has come to mean in zoology a hollow space.

vertebra   L., a joint

vesic-   L. *vesica,* the bladder (vesical)

vitell-   L. *vitellus,* yolk (vitelline)

vomer   L., a plowshare

-vore, -vorous   L. *vorare,* to eat (carnivore)

xiphi-   Gk. *xiphos,* a sword (xiphisternum)

zyg-   Gk. *zugon,* anything that joins two things together (zygapophysis)

Classification of the Chordates

TAXONOMY is for experts, but one cannot read far in the literature without learning that the experts almost always disagree on many points. There is no perfect classification, and the general zoologist must choose what seems to him the best for his purpose. The scheme that follows has been used as the framework for this book and is offered to the student as a guide. Most of its divisions are now generally agreed upon, but some modifications from current practice have been introduced where they seem helpful. I do not consider that there is enough evidence to associate the protochordates and vertebrates in a single phylum (they have much less resemblance, for example, than the annelids and the molluscs), but those who wish to follow the common custom of doing so may rename the two vertebrate subphyla (Agnatha and Gnathostomata) as superclasses.

Numbered classificatory divisions (taxa) are the total of those generally recognized; unnumbered taxa are examples only. The examples of genera are those which are mentioned to illustrate particular points in the text, and are not necessarily those most characteristic of the group. Where no genus is mentioned in the text one well-known name is given.

An asterisk (°) before the name of a taxon indicates that it is believed to be wholly extinct.

Phylum Protochordata

Subphylum 1 Cephalochordata

Genera:

Branchiostoma, Asymmetron

Subphylum 2 Hemichordata

Balanoglossus, Dolichoglossus, Rhabdopleura

Subphylum 3 Urochordata

Ciona, °*Ainiktozoon*

Phylum Vertebrata

Subphylum 1 Agnatha
    Class 1 Cyclostomata

Genera:

Bdellostoma, Myxine,
Lampetra, Petromyzon

    Class 2 °Osteostraci

°*Cephalaspis*

    Class 3 °Anaspida

°*Birkenia, ?*°*Jamoytius,*
°*Lasanius*

    Class 4 °Heterostraci

°*Pteraspis*

    Class 5 °Coelolepida

°*Lanarkia*

Subphylum 2 Gnathostomata
    Class 1 °Placodermi (= Aphetohyoidea)
        Order °Acanthodii

°*Climatius,* °*Mesacanthus*

        Order °Antiarchi

°*Bothriolepis*

    Class 2 Elasmobranchii (= Chondrichthyes)
        Subclass 1 Selachii
            Order °Cladoselachii

°*Cladoselache*

            Order °Pleuracanthodii

°*Pleuracanthus*

            Order Euselachii

Cetorhinus, Heptanchus, Raia,
Scyliorhinus, Sphyrna, Squalus,
Torpedo

        Subclass 2 Bradyodonti
            Order Holocephali

Chimaera

    Class 3 Crossopterygii
        Order 1 Rhipidistia

°*Coelacanthus,* °*Coccoderma,*
°*Ectosteorhachis,* °*Eusthenop-*
teron, Latimeria, °*Osteolepis,*
°*Rhabdoderma*

        Order 2 Dipnoi

°*Dipterus,* °*Ceratodus,*
Epiceratodus, Lepidosiren,
Protopterus

Class 4 Actinopterygii (= Osteichthyes)
  Superorder 1 Chondrostei
    Order Palaeoniscoidei

Polypterus

    Order Acipenseroidei

Acipenser, Polyodon

  Superorder 2 Holostei

Amia, Lepidosteus

  Superorder 3 Teleostei
    Order Anguilliformes (= Apodes)

Anguilla

    Order Clupeiformes (= Isospondyli)

Clupea, Cyclosthone, Esox, Oncorhynchus, Salmo, Salvelinus

    Order Cypriniformes (= Ostariophysi)

Ameiurus, Cyprinus, Electrophorus, Erythrynus, Malopterurus, Phoxinus, Rhodeus, Rutilus

    Order Gadiformes

Gadus

    Order Gasterosteiformes

Hippocampus

    Order Mormyriformes

Gymnarchus

    Order Perciformes

(Families Serranidae, Sparidae)
Anabas, Anarrichas, Fierasfer, Periophthalmus, Thynnus, Trigla

    Order Pleuronectiformes

Pleuronectes, Scophthalmus

    Order Tetraodontiformes

Diodon

Class 5 Amphibia
  Subclass 1 *Stegocephalia
    Order *Labyrinthodontia
      Suborder *Embolomeri

?*Diplovertebron, *Eogyrinus*

      Suborder *Rhachitomi

**Eryops*

      Suborder *Stereospondyli

**Paracyclotosaurus*

    ? Order *Seymouriamorpha

?*Seymouria*

  Subclass 2 Urodela

Amblystoma, Necturus, Salamandra, Triton

Subclass 3 Anura
    Order *Proanura
                   *Protobatrachus
    Order Arcifera
                   Alytes, Bufo, Chiroleptes, Hyla
    Order Firmisternia
                   Rana, Rhinoderma
    Order Aglossa
                   Hymenochirus, Pipa, Xenopus
Subclass 4 Apoda (= Gymnophiona = Caecilia)
                   Hypogeophis, Ichthyophis

Class 6 Reptilia
    Subclass 1 Anapsida
        Order 1 *Cotylosauria
                   *Pareiasaurus, ?*Seymouria*
        Order 2 Chelonia
                   Chelone, Lepidochelys, Testudo
        Order 3 *Millerosauria
                   Milleretta
    Subclass 2 *Synaptosauria (= Euryapsida)
        Order 1 *Protorosauria
                   Araeoscelis
        Order 2 *Sauropterygia (= Plesiosauria)
                   *Cryptocleidus, *Macroplata*
    Subclass 3 *Ichthyopterygia
        Order 1 *Ichthyosauria
                   Ichthyosaurus
    Subclass 4 Lepidosauria
        Order 1 *Eosuchia
                   *Prolacerta, *Youngina*
        Order 2 Rhynchocephalia
                   Sphenodon
        Order 3 Squamata
                   Anguis, Crotalus, Lacerta,
                   Moloch, Naia, Sceloporus,
                   Vipera
    Subclass 5 Archosauria
        Order 1 *Pseudosuchia (= Thecodontia)
                   Euparkeria
        Order 2 *Phytosauria
                   Belodon
        Order 3 Crocodilia
                   Alligator, Crocodilus,
                   Geosaurus
        Order 4 *Saurischia
                   *Brontosaurus, *Diplodocus,*
                   Tyrannosaurus

Order 5 *Ornithischia
*Iguanodon
Order 6 *Pterosauria (= Pterodactyla)
*Pteranodon
Subclass 6 Synapsida
Order 1 *Pelycosauria (= Theromorpha)
*Edaphosaurus
Order 2 *Mesosauria (= Proganosauria)
*Mesosaurus
Order 3 *Therapsida
*Bauria, *Cynognathus

Class 7 Aves
Subclass 1 *Archaeornithes
*Archaeopteryx

Subclass 2 Neornithes
Superorder 1 *Odontognathae
*Hesperornis

Superorder 2 Impennes
Order 1 Sphenisciformes
Aptenodytes, Pygoscelis

Superorder 3 Neognathae
Order Anseriformes
Cygnus

Order Apodiformes
Apus, Collocalia

Order Apterygiformes
Apteryx

Order Caprimulgiformes
Steatornis

Order Casuariiformes
Casuarius

Order Charadriiformes
(Family Scolopacidae)
Rhyncops

Order Columbiformes
Columba

Order Coraciiformes
Alcedo

Order Galliformes
Gallus

Order Passeriformes
Suborder Oscines
Cyanocitta, Delichon, Emberiza,
Fringilla, Pica, Troglodytes,
Turdus

Order Piciformes
Jynx, Picus

Order Psittaciformes

Ara, Psittacus

Order Struthioniformes

Struthio

Class 8 Mammalia
　Subclass 1 *Ictidosauria

Diarthrognathus

　Subclass 2 *Allotheria (= Multituberculata)

Plagiaulax

　Subclass 3 *Symmetrodonta

Spalacotherium

　Subclass 4 Prototheria (= Monotremata)

Echidna, Ornithorhynchus

　Subclass 5 *Docodonta (= Eotheria)

Docodon

　Subclass 6 *Triconodonta

Triconodon

　Subclass 7 *Pantotheria (= Eupantotheria = Trituberculata)

Amphitherium

　Subclass 8 Metatheria (= Marsupialia)

Dasyurus, Dendrolagus,
Hypsiprimnus, Macropus,
Perameles, Thylacinus

　Subclass 9 Eutheria (= Placentalia)
　　Order Insectivora

(Families Macroscelidae,
Tupaiidae)
Chrysochloris, Erinaceus,
Myogale, Neomys, Potomogale,
Sorex, Talpa

　　Order Chiroptera

Megaderma, Myotis

　　Order Dermoptera

Cynocephalus
(= *Galeopithecus*)

　　Order Edentata

Bradypus, Choloepus, Dasypus

　　Order Pholidota

Manis

　　Order Tubulidentata

Orycteropus

　　Order Primates
　　　Suborder 1 Prosimii (= Lemuroidea)

Lemur, Tarsius

　　　Suborder 2 Anthropoidea

(Superfamily 1 Platyrrhini
(= Ceboidea))

Cebus
(Superfamily 2 Catarrhini
(= *Cercopithecoidea*))
Macaca, Homo

Order Carnivora
  Suborder 1 *Creodonta

                              Arctocyon

  Suborder 2 Fissipedia

                              Canis, Felis, Mustelus, Potos

  Suborder 3 Pinnipedia

                              Phoca

Order Artiodactyla

                              Antelocapra, Bos, Cervus,
                              Dama, Giraffa, Hippopotamus,
                              Odocoileus, Ovis, Rangifer

Order Perrissodactyla

                              Equus, Rhinoceros, Tapir

Order Proboscidea

                              Elephas

Order Sirenia

                              Dugong (= *Halicore*), *Manatus*

Order Cetacea

                              Delphinus, Monodon, Phocaena

Order Lagomorpha

                              Oryctolagus, Sylvilagus

Order Rodentia

                              Arctomys, Castor, Dipodomys,
                              Dipus, Marmota, Neomys,
                              Sciurus

Index

The first page only of an account is shown, and references to taxonomic groups in the chapters on the organ systems are not indexed, since they will be found in their logical place under the structure concerned; generic names are fully indexed.

Italic type for page references indicates an important reference, bold face type, an illustration. Arteries, bones, cartilages, nerves, and veins are collected together under those words. Animals and structures are sometimes indexed in the singular even though the text form is plural.

DATE DUE